# Biomaterials:
# The Intersection of Biology and Materials Science

## Second Edition

J. S. Temenoff

*Wallace H. Coulter Department of Biomedical Engineering*
*Georgia Tech and Emory University, Atlanta, GA*

A. G. Mikos

*Departments of Bioengineering and Chemical and Biomolecular Engineering*
*Rice University, Houston, TX*

 Pearson

Content Management: Dawn Murrin, Erin Ault
Content Production: Rajinder Singh
Product Management: Holly Stark
Product Marketing: Krista Clark
Rights and Permissions: Rimpy Sharma

Please contact https://support.pearson.com/getsupport/s/ with any queries on this content.

Cover Image by Jacqueline Mahannah.

Library of Congress Cataloging-in-Publication Data
Names: Temenoff, J. S., author. | Mikos, Antonios G., author.
Title: Biomaterials : the intersection of biology and materials science /
    J.S. Temenoff, Wallace H. Coulter Department of Biomedical Engineering,
    Georgia Tech and Emory University, Atlanta, GA, A.G. Mikos, Departments
    of Bioengineering and Chemical and Biomolecular Engineering, Rice
    University, Houston, TX.
Description: Second edition. | Hoboken, NJ : Pearson, [2023] | Includes index.
Identifiers: LCCN 2021043673 | ISBN 9780134605456 | ISBN 9780137625932
Subjects: LCSH: Biomedical materials.
Classification: LCC R857.M3 T46 2023 | DDC 610.28/4—dc23
LC record available at https://lccn.loc.gov/2021043673

1 2022

Rental:
ISBN-10:      0-13-460545-4
ISBN-13: 978-0-13-460545-6

# Dedications

To my mother, who encouraged me to ask "Why?"
and my father, who encouraged me to ask "How?"
(JST)


To Mary, Georgios, and Lydia
(AGM)

# Contents

Foreword from the First Edition    xix
Preface to the Second Edition    xxi
What's New in the Second Edition    xxii
Acknowledgments    xxiii
Pearson's Commitment to Diversity, Equity, and Inclusion    xxiv

## 1

## Materials for Biomedical Applications    1

1.1     Introduction to Biomaterials    1
        1.1.1    Important Definitions    1
        1.1.2    History and Current Status of the Field    2
        1.1.3    Future Directions    6
1.2     Biological Response to Biomaterials    7
1.3     Biomaterial Product Testing and Regulatory Approval    8
        1.3.1    Device Regulation    9
        1.3.2    Drug/Biologics Regulation    9
1.4     Types of Biomaterials    9
        1.4.1    Metals    10
        1.4.2    Ceramics    10
        1.4.3    Polymers    10
        1.4.4    Naturally Derived versus Synthetic Polymers    12
1.5     Processing of Biomaterials    13
1.6     Important Properties of Biomaterials    13
        1.6.1    Degradative Properties of Biomaterials    13
        1.6.2    Surface Properties of Biomaterials    14
        1.6.3    Bulk Properties of Biomaterials    15
        1.6.4    Characterization Techniques    15
1.7     Principles of Chemistry    16
        1.7.1    Atomic Structure    16
        1.7.2    Atomic Models    16
                 1.7.2.1    Bohr Model    17
                 1.7.2.2    Wave-Mechanical Model    17
        1.7.3    Atomic Orbitals    18
                 1.7.3.1    Shapes of Subshells (Orbitals)    18
                 1.7.3.2    Order of Subshells and the Aufbau Principle    18
        1.7.4    Valence Electrons and the Periodic Table    20
        1.7.5    Ionic Bonding    22
                 1.7.5.1    Bonding and Force-Distance Curves    22
                 1.7.5.2    Characteristics of the Ionic Bond    23
        1.7.6    Covalent Bonding    24
                 1.7.6.1    Atomic Orbitals and Hybridization    24
                 1.7.6.2    Molecular Orbitals    27
                 1.7.6.3    Mixed Bonds    27

1.7.7   Metallic Bonding    28
1.7.8   Secondary Forces    29
Summary    30
Problems    31
References    32
Additional Reading    33


# 2

## Chemical Structure of Biomaterials    34

2.1   Introduction: Bonding and the Structure of Biomaterials    34
2.2   Structure of Metals    35
   2.2.1   Crystal Structures    35
      2.2.1.1   Face-Centered Cubic Structure    35
      2.2.1.2   Body-Centered Cubic Structure    37
   2.2.2   Crystal Systems    38
   2.2.3   Defects in Crystal Structures    43
      2.2.3.1   Point Defects    43
      2.2.3.2   Impurities    44
   2.2.4   Solid State Diffusion    45
      2.2.4.1   Diffusion Mechanisms    46
      2.2.4.2   Modeling of Diffusion    46
2.3   Structure of Ceramics    49
   2.3.1   Crystal Structures    49
      2.3.1.1   AX Crystal Structures    50
      2.3.1.2   $A_mX_p$ Crystal Structures    52
      2.3.1.3   Carbon-Based Materials    53
   2.3.2   Defects in Crystal Structures    55
      2.3.2.1   Point Defects    55
      2.3.2.2   Impurities    56
2.4   Structure of Polymers    57
   2.4.1   General Structure    57
      2.4.1.1   Repeat Units    57
      2.4.1.2   Molecular Weight Determination    59
      2.4.1.3   Mer Configuration    63
      2.4.1.4   Polymer Structure    65
   2.4.2   Polymer Synthesis    67
      2.4.2.1   Addition Polymerization    67
      2.4.2.2   Condensation Polymerization    68
      2.4.2.3   Polymer Production Via Genetic Engineering    68
   2.4.3   Copolymers    69
   2.4.4   Methods of Polymerization    70
   2.4.5   Crystal Structures and Defects    72
      2.4.5.1   Crystal Structures    72
      2.4.5.2   Point Defects and Impurities    72
   2.4.6   Hydrogels    72
2.5   Techniques: Introduction to Material Characterization    74
   2.5.1   X-Ray Diffraction    75
      2.5.1.1   Basic Principles    75
      2.5.1.2   Instrumentation    77
      2.5.1.3   Information Provided    79

2.5.2　Ultraviolet and Visible (UV-VIS) Light Spectroscopy　79
　　2.5.2.1　Basic Principles　79
　　2.5.2.2　Instrumentation　81
　　2.5.2.3　Information Provided　82
2.5.3　Infrared (IR) Spectroscopy　83
　　2.5.3.1　Basic Principles　83
　　2.5.3.2　Instrumentation　85
　　2.5.3.3　Information Provided　86
2.5.4　Nuclear Magnetic Resonance Spectroscopy (NMR)　89
　　2.5.4.1　Basic Principles　89
　　2.5.4.2　Instrumentation　90
　　2.5.4.3　Information Provided　92
2.5.5　Mass Spectrometry　92
　　2.5.5.1　Basic Principles　92
　　2.5.5.2　Instrumentation　94
　　2.5.5.3　Information Provided　95
2.5.6　High-Performance Liquid Chromatography (HPLC): Size-Exclusion Chromatography　96
　　2.5.6.1　Basic Principles　96
　　2.5.6.2　Instrumentation　97
　　2.5.6.3　Information Provided　99
Summary　100
Problems　101
References　104
Additional Reading　105

# 3

## Physical Properties of Biomaterials　106

3.1　Introduction: From Atomic Groupings to Bulk Materials　106
3.2　Crystallinity and Linear Defects　107
　　3.2.1　Dislocations　107
　　　　3.2.1.1　Edge Dislocations　107
　　　　3.2.1.2　Screw and Mixed Dislocations　108
　　　　3.2.1.3　Characteristics of Dislocations　110
　　3.2.2　Deformation　110
3.3　Crystallinity and Planar Defects　113
　　3.3.1　External Surface　113
　　3.3.2　Grain Boundaries　114
3.4　Crystallinity and Volume Defects　116
3.5　Crystallinity and Polymeric Materials　117
　　3.5.1　Percent Crystallinity　117
　　3.5.2　Chain-Folded Model of Crystallinity　119
　　3.5.3　Defects in Polymer Crystals　120
　　　　3.5.3.1　Linear Defects　120
　　　　3.5.3.2　Planar and Volume Defects　122
3.6　Thermal Transitions of Crystalline and NonCrystalline Materials　122
　　3.6.1　Viscous Flow　122
　　3.6.2　Thermal Transitions　122
　　　　3.6.2.1　Metals and Crystalline Ceramics　122
　　　　3.6.2.2　Amorphous Ceramics (Glasses)　123
　　　　3.6.2.3　Polymers　123

3.7    Techniques: Introduction to Thermal Analysis    128
    3.7.1    Differential Scanning Calorimetry    128
        3.7.1.1    Basic Principles    128
        3.7.1.2    Instrumentation    128
        3.7.1.3    Information Provided    130
    Summary    132
    Problems    133
    References    134
    Additional Reading    134

# 4

## Mechanical Properties of Biomaterials    135

4.1    Introduction: Types of Mechanical Properties    135
4.2    Mechanical Testing Methods, Results, and Calculations    136
    4.2.1    Tensile and Shear Properties    137
        4.2.1.1    Calculations for Tensile and Shear Tests    137
        4.2.1.2    Stress-Strain Curves and Elastic Deformation    139
        4.2.1.3    Molecular Causes of Elastic Deformation    141
        4.2.1.4    Stress-Strain Curves and Plastic Deformation    141
        4.2.1.5    Molecular Causes of Plastic Deformation    148
        4.2.1.6    Causes of Plastic Deformation—Metals and Crystalline Ceramics    148
        4.2.1.7    Causes of Plastic Deformation—Amorphous Polymers and Ceramics (Glasses)    150
        4.2.1.8    Causes of Plastic Deformation—Polymers (General)    151
        4.2.1.9    Causes of Plastic Deformation—Semi-Crystalline Polymers and Elastomers    152
    4.2.2    Bending Properties    155
    4.2.3    Time-Dependent Properties    157
        4.2.3.1    Creep    157
        4.2.3.2    Molecular Causes of Creep—Metals    159
        4.2.3.3    Molecular Causes of Creep—Ceramics    159
        4.2.3.4    Molecular Causes of Creep—Polymers    160
        4.2.3.5    Stress Relaxation and its Causes    160
        4.2.3.6    Mathematical Models of Viscoelastic Behavior    161
        4.2.3.7    Viscoelastic Behavior—Maxwell Model    162
        4.2.3.8    Viscoelastic Behavior—Voigt Model    163
    4.2.4    Influence of Porosity and Degradation on Mechanical Properties    166
4.3    Fracture and Failure    167
    4.3.1    Ductile and Brittle Fracture    167
    4.3.2    Polymer Crazing    168
    4.3.3    Stress Concentrators    169
4.4    Fatigue and Fatigue Testing    170
    4.4.1    Fatigue    170
    4.4.2    Fatigue Testing    171
    4.4.3    Factors that Affect Fatigue Life    172
4.5    Methods to Improve Mechanical Properties    173

4.6    Techniques: Introduction to Mechanical Analysis    175
       4.6.1    Mechanical Testing    175
                4.6.1.1    Basic Principles    175
                4.6.1.2    Instrumentation    175
                4.6.1.3    Information Provided    176
       Summary    176
       Problems    178
       References    180
       Additional Reading    180

# 5

## Biomaterial Degradation    181

5.1    Introduction: Degradation in the Biological Environment    181
5.2    Corrosion/Degradation of Metals and Ceramics    182
       5.2.1    Fundamentals of Corrosion    183
                5.2.1.1    Oxidation-Reduction Reactions    183
                5.2.1.2    Half-Cell Potentials    184
                5.2.1.3    Nernst Equation    185
                5.2.1.4    Galvanic Corrosion    188
       5.2.2    Pourbaix Diagrams and Passivation    188
       5.2.3    Contribution of Processing Parameters    190
                5.2.3.1    Crevice Corrosion    190
                5.2.3.2    Pitting Corrosion    191
                5.2.3.3    Intergranular Corrosion    191
       5.2.4    Contribution of the Mechanical Environment    192
                5.2.4.1    Stress and Galvanic Corrosion    192
                5.2.4.2    Stress Corrosion Cracking    192
                5.2.4.3    Fatigue Corrosion    193
                5.2.4.4    Fretting Corrosion    193
       5.2.5    Contribution of the Biological Environment    193
       5.2.6    Means of Corrosion Control    194
       5.2.7    Ceramic Degradation    194
5.3    Degradation of Polymers    194
       5.3.1    Primary Means of Polymer Degradation    195
       5.3.2    Chain Scission by Hydrolysis    195
       5.3.3    Chain Scission by Oxidation    195
       5.3.4    Other Means of Degradation    198
                5.3.4.1    Environmental Stress Cracking    198
                5.3.4.2    Enzyme-Catalyzed Degradation    199
       5.3.5    Effects of Porosity    199
5.4    Biodegradable Materials    199
       5.4.1    Biodegradable Ceramics    200
                5.4.1.1    Erosion Mechanisms    200
                5.4.1.2    Factors that Influence Degradation Rate    201
       5.4.2    Biodegradable Polymers    201
                5.4.2.1    Introduction to Biodegradable Polymers and
                           Definitions    201
                5.4.2.2    Degradation Mechanisms    204
                5.4.2.3    Factors That Influence Degradation Rate    204
5.5    Techniques: Assays for Extent of Degradation    205

Summary    206
Problems    207
References    207
Additional Reading    208


6

Biomaterial Processing    209
6.1    Introduction: Importance of Biomaterials Processing    209
6.2    Processing to Improve Bulk Properties    209
        6.2.1    Metals    210
                6.2.1.1    Alloying    210
                6.2.1.2    Strain Hardening    211
                6.2.1.3    Grain Size Refinement    211
                6.2.1.4    Annealing    211
                6.2.1.5    Precipitation Hardening    213
        6.2.2    Ceramics    213
        6.2.3    Polymers    213
6.3    Processing to Form Desired Shapes    214
6.4    Processing of Metals    214
        6.4.1    Forming Metals    214
                6.4.1.1    Forging Metals    215
                6.4.1.2    Rolling Metals    215
                6.4.1.3    Extrusion of Metals    215
                6.4.1.4    Drawing Metals    215
        6.4.2    Casting Metals    216
                6.4.2.1    Sand Casting of Metals    216
                6.4.2.2    Investment Casting of Metals    216
        6.4.3    Powder Processing of Metals    216
        6.4.4    Rapid Manufacturing of Metals    218
        6.4.5    Welding Metals    218
        6.4.6    Machining of Metals    219
6.5    Processing of Ceramics    219
        6.5.1    Glass Forming Techniques    219
        6.5.2    Casting and Firing of Ceramics    220
                6.5.2.1    Casting Ceramics    220
                6.5.2.2    Firing Ceramics    220
        6.5.3    Powder Processing of Ceramics    221
        6.5.4    Rapid Manufacturing of Ceramics    221
6.6    Processing of Polymers    223
        6.6.1    Thermoplasts versus Thermosets    223
        6.6.2    Forming Polymers    223
                6.6.2.1    Extrusion of Polymers    223
                6.6.2.2    Fiber Spinning of Polymers    224
        6.6.3    Casting Polymers    225
                6.6.3.1    Compression Molding of Polymers    225
                6.6.3.2    Injection Molding of Polymers    226
                6.6.3.3    Blow Molding of Polymers    226
        6.6.4    Rapid Manufacturing of Polymers    226
6.7    Processing to Improve Biocompatibility    228

6.7.1   Sterilization    228
    6.7.1.1   Steam Sterilization    229
    6.7.1.2   Ethylene Oxide Sterilization    229
    6.7.1.3   Radiation Sterilization    229
6.7.2   Fixation of Natural Materials    230
Summary    231
Problems    232
References    233
Additional Reading    233

# 7

## Surface Properties of Biomaterials    234

7.1   Introduction: Concepts in Surface Chemistry and Biology    234
  7.1.1   Protein Adsorption and Biocompatibility    235
  7.1.2   Surface Properties Governing Protein Adsorption    235
7.2   Physicochemical Surface Modification Techniques    237
  7.2.1   Introduction to Surface Modification Techniques    237
  7.2.2   Chemical Surface Modification: Covalent Interactions    237
    7.2.2.1   Plasma Treatment    239
    7.2.2.2   Chemical Vapor Deposition    241
    7.2.2.3   Physical Vapor Deposition    241
    7.2.2.4   Radiation Grafting/Photografting    242
    7.2.2.5   Self-Assembled Monolayers    243
  7.2.3   Chemical Surface Modification: Non-Covalent Interactions    244
    7.2.3.1   Solution Coatings    245
    7.2.3.2   Langmuir-Blodgett Films    245
    7.2.3.3   Layer-by-Layer Coatings    246
    7.2.3.4   Surface-Modifying Additives    247
    7.2.3.5   Ion Beam Implantation    247
    7.2.3.6   Plasma Treatment    249
    7.2.3.7   Conversion Coatings    249
    7.2.3.8   Bioactive Glasses    249
  7.2.4   Laser Methods for Surface Modification    249
7.3   Biological Surface Modification Techniques    250
  7.3.1   Covalent Biological Coatings    251
  7.3.2   Non-Covalent Biological Coatings    253
  7.3.3   Immobilized Enzymes    253
7.4   Surface Properties and Degradation    254
7.5   Patterning Techniques for Surfaces    254
7.6   Techniques: Introduction to Surface Characterization    258
  7.6.1   Contact Angle Analysis    259
    7.6.1.1   Basic Principles    259
    7.6.1.2   Instrumentation    261
    7.6.1.3   Information Provided    262
  7.6.2   Light Microscopy    262
    7.6.2.1   Basic Principles    262
    7.6.2.2   Instrumentation    263
    7.6.2.3   Information Provided    265

7.6.3   Electron Spectroscopy for Chemical Analysis (ESCA) or X-ray
Photoelectron Spectroscopy (XPS)   265
    7.6.3.1   Basic Principles   265
    7.6.3.2   Instrumentation   266
    7.6.3.3   Information Provided   268
7.6.4   Attenuated Total Internal Reflectance-Fourier Transform Infrared
Spectroscopy (ATR-FTIR)   268
    7.6.4.1   Basic Principles   268
    7.6.4.2   Instrumentation   269
    7.6.4.3   Information Provided   270
7.6.5   Secondary Ion Mass Spectrometry (SIMS)   270
    7.6.5.1   Basic Principles   270
    7.6.5.2   Instrumentation   271
    7.6.5.3   Information Provided   272
7.6.6   Electron Microscopy: Transmission Electron Microscopy (TEM) and
Scanning Electron Microscopy (SEM)   272
    7.6.6.1   Basic Principles   272
    7.6.6.2   Instrumentation   275
    7.6.6.3   Information Provided   275
7.6.7   Scanning Probe Microscopy (SPM): Atomic Force Microscopy
(AFM)   276
    7.6.7.1   Basic Principles   276
    7.6.7.2   Instrumentation   277
    7.6.7.3   Information Provided   279
Summary   280
Problems   281
References   285
Additional Reading   286

# 8

## Protein Interactions with Biomaterials   288

8.1   Introduction: Thermodynamics of Protein Adsorption   288
    8.1.1   Gibbs Free Energy and Protein Adsorption   289
    8.1.2   System Properties Governing Protein Adsorption   290
8.2   Protein Structure   293
    8.2.1   Amino Acid Chemistry   293
    8.2.2   Primary Structure   293
    8.2.3   Secondary Structure   293
    8.2.4   Tertiary Structure   300
    8.2.5   Quaternary Structure   301
8.3   Protein Transport and Adsorption Kinetics   302
    8.3.1   Transport to the Surface   302
    8.3.2   Adsorption Kinetics   304
8.4   Reversibility of Protein Adsorption   305
    8.4.1   Reversible and Irreversible Binding   305
    8.4.2   Desorption and Exchange   306
8.5   Techniques: Assays for Protein Type and Amount   309
    8.5.1   High-Performance Liquid Chromatography (HPLC): Affinity
Chromatography   310

8.5.1.1    Basic Principles    310
8.5.1.2    Instrumentation    310
8.5.1.3    Information Provided    310
8.5.2    Colorimetric Assays    314
8.5.2.1    Basic Principles and Instrumentation    315
8.5.3    Fluorescent Assays    316
8.5.3.1    Basic Principles    316
8.5.3.2    Instrumentation    316
8.5.3.3    Information Provided    317
8.5.4    Enzyme-Linked Immunosorbent Assay (ELISA)    317
8.5.5    Western Blotting    318
Summary    320
Problems    321
References    323
Additional Reading    323

9

# Cell Interactions with Biomaterials    324

9.1    Introduction: Cell-Surface Interactions and Cellular Functions    324
9.2    Cellular Structure    325
9.2.1    Cell Membrane    325
9.2.2    Cytoskeleton    327
9.2.3    Mitochondria    328
9.2.4    Nucleus    328
9.2.4.1    Structure and Function of the Nucleus    328
9.2.4.2    Structure of DNA    328
9.2.4.3    Structure of RNA    332
9.2.5    Endoplasmic Reticulum    334
9.2.6    Vesicles    334
9.2.7    Membrane Receptors and Cell Contacts    335
9.2.7.1    Types of Cell Contacts    335
9.2.7.2    Types of Membrane Receptors and Ligands    336
9.3    Extracellular Environment    338
9.3.1    Collagen    338
9.3.2    Elastin    340
9.3.3    Proteoglycans    341
9.3.4    Glycoproteins    341
9.3.5    Other ECM Components    343
9.3.6    Matrix Remodeling    345
9.3.7    ECM Molecules as Biomaterials    346
9.4    Cell–Environment Interactions That Affect Cellular Functions    347
9.4.1    Cell Survival    347
9.4.2    Cell Proliferation    347
9.4.2.1    Cell Cycle: Interphase    348
9.4.2.2    Cell Cycle: Mitosis    348
9.4.3    Cell Differentiation    350
9.4.4    Protein Synthesis    352
9.4.4.1    Collagen Synthesis: Transcription    352
9.4.4.2    Collagen Synthesis: Translation and Post-Translational Modification    353

9.5     Models of Adhesion, Spreading, and Migration    358
    9.5.1   Basic Adhesion Models: DLVO Theory    358
    9.5.2   DLVO Theory Limitations and Further Models    359
    9.5.3   Models of Cell Spreading and Migration    360
        9.5.3.1   Cell Spreading    360
        9.5.3.2   Cell Migration    360
9.6     Techniques: Assays to Determine Effects of Cell–Material Interactions    364
    9.6.1   Cytotoxicity Assays    365
        9.6.1.1   Direct Contact Assay    365
        9.6.1.2   Indirect Contact Assays    366
        9.6.1.3   Elution Assay    366
        9.6.1.4   Colony-Forming Assays    367
    9.6.2   Adhesion/Spreading Assays    367
    9.6.3   Migration Assays    368
    9.6.4   DNA and RNA Assays    370
        9.6.4.1   Polymerase Chain Reaction (PCR) and Reverse-Transcription Polymerase Chain Reaction (RT-PCR)    370
        9.6.4.2   DNA Microarrays    373
        9.6.4.3   DNA/RNA Sequencing (Next-Generation Sequencing)    373
        9.6.4.4   Chromatin Immunoprecipitation (ChIP)    375
        9.6.4.5   Single-Cell Analysis    376
    9.6.5   Protein Production Assays    377
        9.6.5.1   Proteomics    377
        9.6.5.2   Immunostaining    377
    9.6.6   Laser Confocal Scanning Microscropy    378
        9.6.6.1   Basic Principles    378
        9.6.6.2   Instrumentation    379
        9.6.6.3   Information Provided    380
Summary    381
Problems    383
References    387
Additional Reading    388

# 10

# Biomaterial Implantation and Acute Inflammation    390

10.1    Introduction: Overview of Innate and Acquired Immunity    390
    10.1.1   Characteristics of Leukocytes    392
        10.1.1.1   Leukocyte Types    392
        10.1.1.2   Leukocyte Formation    392
        10.1.1.3   Life Span of Leukocytes    392
    10.1.2   Sources of Innate Immunity    392
10.2    Clinical Signs of Inflammation and Their Causes    393
10.3    Role of Tissue Macrophages and Neutrophils    394
    10.3.1   Migration of Neutrophils    394
    10.3.2   Actions of Neutrophils    395
        10.3.2.1   Phagocytosis    396
        10.3.2.2   Respiratory Burst    396
        10.3.2.3   Secretion of Chemical Mediators    396

10.4    Role of Other Leukocytes    397
    10.4.1 Monocytes/Macrophages    397
    10.4.2 Actions of Macrophages    397
        10.4.2.1 Phagocytosis and Biomaterials    398
        10.4.2.2 Secretion of Chemical Mediators    398
        10.4.2.3 Role as Antigen-Presenting Cells    399
    10.4.3 Macrophage Subtypes    399
    10.4.4 Other Granulocytes    400
10.5    Termination of Acute Inflammation    400
10.6    Techniques: *In Vitro* Assays for Inflammatory Response    401
    10.6.1 Leukocyte Assays    401
    10.6.2 Other Assays    402
    Summary    404
    Problems    405
    References    407
    Additional Reading    407

# 11

## Wound Healing and the Presence of Biomaterials    408

11.1    Introduction: Formation of Granulation Tissue    408
11.2    Foreign Body Reaction    410
11.3    Fibrous Encapsulation    411
11.4    Chronic Inflammation    412
11.5    Four Types of Resolution    413
11.6    Repair versus Regeneration: Wound Healing in Skin    414
    11.6.1 Skin Repair    414
    11.6.2 Skin Regeneration    415
11.7    Techniques: *In Vivo* Assays for Inflammatory Response    416
    11.7.1 Considerations in Development of Animal Models    417
        11.7.1.1 Choice of Animal    417
        11.7.1.2 Choice of Implant Site    418
        11.7.1.3 Length of Study    419
        11.7.1.4 Biomaterial Considerations: Dose and
                Administration    419
        11.7.1.5 Inclusion of Proper Controls    420
    11.7.2 Methods of Assessment    420
        11.7.2.1 Histology/Immunohistochemistry    421
        11.7.2.2 Electron Microscopy    421
        11.7.2.3 Biochemical Assays    422
        11.7.2.4 Mechanical Testing    422
    Summary    424
    Problems    425
    References    426
    Additional Reading    427

## 12

# Immune Response to Biomaterials    428

12.1   Introduction: Overview of Acquired Immunity    428
12.2   Antigen Presentation and Lymphocyte Maturation    429
    12.2.1  Major Histocompatibility Complex
        (MHC) Molecules    429
        12.2.1.1  MHC Class I    430
        12.2.1.2  MHC Class II    430
        12.2.1.3  MHC Molecule Variation and
                Tissue Typing    430
        12.2.1.4  Intracellular Complexation with
                MHC Molecules    432
    12.2.2  Maturation of Lymphocytes    433
    12.2.3  Activation and Formation of Clonal Populations    433
12.3   B Cells and Antibodies    434
    12.3.1  Types of B Cells    434
    12.3.2  Characteristics of Antibodies    435
        12.3.2.1  Structure of Antibodies    435
        12.3.2.2  Classes of Antibodies    435
        12.3.2.3  Mechanisms of Antibody Action    437
12.4   T Cells    437
    12.4.1  T Cells and NK cells    437
    12.4.2  Helper T Cells ($T_h$)    438
    12.4.3  Cytotoxic T Cells ($T_c$)    440
    12.4.4  Natural Killer Cells (NK Cells)    440
12.5   The Complement System    440
    12.5.1  Classical Pathway    440
    12.5.2  Alternative Pathway    443
    12.5.3  Membrane Attack Complex    444
    12.5.4  Regulation of the Complement System    444
    12.5.5  Effects of the Complement System    445
12.6   Undesired Immune Responses to Biomaterials    445
    12.6.1  Innate versus Acquired Responses
        to Biomaterials    445
    12.6.2  Hypersensitivity    446
        12.6.2.1  Type I: IgE Mediated    446
        12.6.2.2  Type II: Antibody Mediated    447
        12.6.2.3  Type III: Immune Complex Mediated    447
        12.6.2.4  Type IV: T Cell Mediated    447
        12.6.2.5  Hypersensitivity and the Classes
                of Biomaterials    448
12.7   Techniques: Assays for Immune Response    449
    12.7.1  *In Vitro* Assays    449
    12.7.2  *In Vivo* Assays    451
    Summary    452
    Problems    454
    References    455
    Additional Reading    455

# 13

## Biomaterials and Thrombosis    457

13.1    Introduction: Overview of Hemostasis    457
13.2    Role of Platelets    458
    13.2.1 Platelet Characteristics and Functions    458
    13.2.2 Platelet Activation    458
        13.2.2.1 Means of Activation    458
        13.2.2.2 Sequelae of Activation    458
13.3    Coagulation Cascade    459
    13.3.1 Intrinsic Pathway    459
    13.3.2 Extrinsic Pathway    460
    13.3.3 Common Pathway    461
13.4    Means of Limiting Clot Formation    463
13.5    Role of the Endothelium    464
13.6    Tests for Hemocompatibility    465
    13.6.1 General Testing Concerns    465
    13.6.2 *In Vitro* Assessment    466
    13.6.3 *In Vivo* Assessment    468
    Summary    469
    Problems    470
    References    472
    Additional Reading    472

# 14

## Infection, Tumorigenesis, and Calcification of Biomaterials    473

14.1    Introduction: Overview of Other Potential Problems with Biomaterial Implantation    473
14.2    Infection    474
    14.2.1 Common Pathogens and Categories of Infection    474
    14.2.2 Steps to Infection    475
    14.2.3 Characteristics of the Bacterial Surface, the Biomaterial Surface, and the Media    476
        14.2.3.1 Bacterial Surface Properties: Gram-Positive versus Gram-Negative Bacteria    476
        14.2.3.2 Bacterial Surface Properties: Cell Capsule and Biofilm    476
        14.2.3.3 Biomaterial Surface Properties    479
        14.2.3.4 Media Properties    479
    14.2.4 Specific and Nonspecific Interactions Involved in Bacterial Adhesion    479
    14.2.5 Summary and Techniques to Reduce Implant-Associated Infections    480
14.3    Techniques for Infection Experiments    481
    14.3.1 Characterizing Bacterial Surfaces    481
        14.3.1.1 Surface Hydrophobicity    481
        14.3.1.2 Surface Charge    482

14.3.2 *In Vitro* and *In Vivo* Models of Infection    482
    14.3.2.1 *In Vitro*: Bacterial Adhesion and Killing    483
    14.3.2.2 *Ex Vivo* and *In Vivo* Infection Models    485
14.4 Tumorigenesis    486
  14.4.1 Definitions and Steps of Tumorigenesis    486
  14.4.2 Chemical versus Foreign Body Carcinogenesis    486
  14.4.3 Timeline for Foreign Body Tumorigenesis    487
    14.4.3.1 Foreign Body Tumorigenesis with Large Implants    487
    14.4.3.2 Foreign Body Tumorigenesis with Nanomaterials    487
  14.4.4 Summary of Biomaterial-Related Tumorigenesis    488
14.5 Techniques for Tumorigenesis Experiments    489
  14.5.1 *In Vitro* Models    489
  14.5.2 *In Vivo* Models    491
14.6 Pathologic Calcification    491
  14.6.1 Introduction to Pathologic Calcification    491
  14.6.2 Mechanism of Pathologic Calcification    492
  14.6.3 Summary and Techniques to Reduce Pathologic Calcification    493
14.7 Techniques for Pathologic Calcification Experiments    493
  14.7.1 *In Vitro* Models of Calcification    493
  14.7.2 *In Vivo* Models of Calcification    494
  14.7.3 Sample Assessment    494
Summary    497
Problems    499
References    502
Additional Reading    503

Appendix I    List of Abbreviations and Symbols    504

Index    508

# Foreword from the First Edition

Biomaterials have received considerable attention over the last thirty years as a means of treating diseases and easing suffering. The focus of treatment is no longer in conventional passive devices but rather a combination of device-integrated biomaterials and the necessary therapeutic treatment. Biomaterials have found applications in approximately 8,000 various kinds of medical devices that have been used in repairing skeletal systems, returning cardiovascular functionality, replacing organs, and repairing or returning senses. Even though biomaterials have had a pronounced impact in medical treatment, a need still exists to be able to design and develop better polymer, ceramic, and metal systems along with the ability to characterize and test their properties. This book is the first in a long time to point out such need and to give students a clear picture of how to approach such subjects.

The two authors take a fresh approach to the problem. They focus on a thorough materials analysis that does not take shortcomings on mechanical properties, structure or molecular analysis, but at the same time offers a thorough presentation of biological considerations in a succinct way.

Polymeric biomaterials originated as off-the-shelf materials that clinicians were able to use in solving a problem—dialysis tubing was originally made of cellulose acetate, vascular grafts were fabricated from Dacron, and artificial hearts were molded from polyurethanes. However, these materials did not possess the chemical, physical, and biological properties necessary to prevent further complications. Thus, recent advances in synthetic techniques have allowed these properties to be imparted on biomaterials that help to alleviate the accompanying biocompatibility issues. This becomes so clear in this book!

Much consideration is given to the design of a material for a specific application. Certain properties of the material must be controlled so as to perform the necessary function and elicit the appropriate response. These properties can be tailored to the specific need by carefully controlling the structural characteristics, modifying the surface properties, and employing biomimetic characteristics in the material design. Biomimetic principles are gaining widespread acceptance in the development of biomaterials, especially for drug delivery, regenerative medicine, and nanotechnology. The use of protein moieties and protein-like components on the surface or in the bulk of synthetic materials contacting biological systems has certain advantage over traditional systems. The authors are to be congratulated for pointing this out.

This book will be a successful text because it recognizes that biomaterials are first and foremost *materials!* The authors provide a refreshing approach to the medical aspects of biomaterials. It has exceptionally lucid chapters on Cell/Materials and Protein/Materials interactions. The students will finally understand immunology when they read Chapter 12. And thrombosis, one of the most important problems of biomaterials, is simply expertly presented in Chapter 13.

This textbook is a comprehensive fundamental text that will undoubtedly become a staple in biomaterials education. It addresses the right amount of knowledge and will fill a major gap in the field of biomaterials science. Professors Temenoff and Mikos have made a great service to the field.

Nicholas A. Peppas, Sc.D.
Fletcher S. Pratt Chair of Chemical Engineering,
Biomedical Engineering, and Pharmacy
*University of Texas at Austin*

# Preface to the Second Edition

*Intersect:* to share a common area (*Merriam-Webster Dictionary*)

As in the first edition of this book, we continue to believe that the field of biomaterials has evolved over approximately the past 60+ years from the intersection of multiple disparate viewpoints, including materials science, biology, engineering, and clinical, business, and regulatory perspectives. With this history, the multidisciplinary nature of biomaterials is inescapable. As educators in this field, we understand the challenges of preparing students with a broad range of backgrounds to address the complex issues associated with designing and implementing new biomedical devices.

With this in mind, we originally set out to write a balanced and cohesive textbook that would introduce fundamental concepts of biomaterials to undergraduate engineering majors in their second year of study or later. Given this target audience, like the first edition, this text assumes basic knowledge of chemistry and physics, but does not require in-depth exposure to more complex mathematical concepts such as partial differential equations, or any knowledge of cell biology or biochemistry.

After an overview of the scope of the biomaterials field, Chapter 1 reviews basic chemical principles required to understand the forces underlying the material structures introduced in Chapter 2. Chapters 3 and 4 provide more information about physical and mechanical properties of the main classes of biomaterials (metals, ceramics, and polymers). Throughout these sections, material classes are compared and contrasted to further student knowledge of how each may be optimal for different applications. After discussion of how materials are "built up" from their subunits, in Chapters 5 and 6, we turn to how these materials are "torn down" (degraded) in the body and how processing parameters affect key material properties, such as degradation and mechanical strength.

Chapters 7 and 8 are both the physical and intellectual centers of this text as they represent contact between the materials science and the biological concepts in the book. Topics covered in these chapters include surface modification techniques and their effects on protein adsorption. Chapter 9 relates how cells react to these adsorbed proteins in general, before leading into a discussion of particular cell responses (acute inflammation and wound healing) in Chapters 10 and 11. No depiction of biological response to implanted materials would be complete without a discussion of immune response and hypersensitivity (Chapter 12); thrombosis (Chapter 13); and infection, tumorigenesis, and pathologic calcification (Chapter 14).

To maintain a balanced discussion, the 14 chapters in this book were purposefully divided into seven chapters on materials science, and seven chapters on the biological response. Continuing the spirit of "intersection," characterization methods and regulatory issues were not written as insular sections, but rather included throughout book as appropriate. We believe that integrating ever more complex biological knowledge into the design of improved materials is essential to produce the next generation of biomaterials, and hope that this book provides a first step for many future biomaterialists in discovering vital intersections of their own.

# What's New in the Second Edition

As the field of biomaterials has evolved and expanded over the ~15 years since the first edition, we felt that a new edition of the book was needed to cover new and evolving topics in both materials science (such as rapid manufacturing) and state-of-art biological techniques ('omics and others). Many of the changes included in the second edition of this book were in response to feedback from instructors from around the world who have adopted this textbook in their classrooms, and we thank them for all of the constructive suggestions. In addition, comments from students in introductory biomaterials classes at both Rice University and Georgia Institute of Technology over the past decade have guided additions and clarifications.

In particular, changes to this edition include the following:

- Addition of color images for increased clarity (particularly of histological images).

- All new end-of-chapter problems.

- We conducted an external review of the text's content to determine how it could be improved to address issues related to diversity, equity, and inclusion. The results of that review informed the revision.

- Additional example problems in many chapters, particularly problems that demonstrate the utility of the various assays described in each chapter.

- Expanded section in Chapter 1 on steps to U.S. regulatory approval for devices and therapies using biomaterials.

- Expanded sections in Chapter 6 on rapid manufacturing of biomaterials.

- Reorganized and expanded sections in Chapter 7 on spatial patterning of biomaterial surfaces.

- New sections in Chapter 9 to summarize new and emerging biological characterization techniques, such as various types of omics analysis, single-cell characterization techniques, and confocal microscopy.

- New text and figures in Chapters 10 and 12 to summarize state-of-the-art knowledge about the subtypes of cells involved in the innate and acquired immune response.

- Expanded section in Chapter 14 on required tests for mutagenesis.

# Resources for Instructors

All instructor resources are available for download at www.pearson.com. If you are in need of a login and password for this site, please contact your local Pearson representative.

# Instructor's Solutions Manual

Available to adopters of this textbook, it contains the solutions to the homework problems. The Solutions Manual is available in PDF format.

# PowerPoint Slides

A complete set of all the figures and tables from the textbook are available in PowerPoint format.

# Acknowledgments

The development and production of a textbook such as this is an ambitious undertaking that requires the contributions of a myriad of talented and dedicated individuals. Accordingly, we would like to acknowledge the several individuals and institutions whose assistance and perseverance made the completion of this text possible. In particular, Kurt Kasper, Ph.D. (Rice University), was indispensable in the preparation of the first edition of this book, and much of his work remains in the new edition. Liane Tellier, Ph.D. (Georgia Tech/Emory), and Elda Trevino, Ph.D. (Georgia Tech/Emory), provided select content and example problems in the second half of the book. Jason Guo, Ph.D. (Rice University), drew all chemical structures, contributed select figures, and updated end-of-chapter references. Mollie Smoak, Ph.D. (Rice University), together with Jason Guo compiled the market data for medical devices, and Sean Bittner, Ph.D. (Rice University), updated the information for rapid manufacturing techniques.

We would also like to acknowledge several individuals who played vital roles in the evaluation and development of the revised text. Particularly, we thank Krishnendu Roy, Ph.D. (Georgia Tech), for helping to test this version of the book in the classroom. We appreciate the students in the Georgia Tech Introduction to Biomaterials class (BMED/MSE 4751) in the Summer Semester of 2019 for their patience during the classroom testing of this textbook. We also thank the trainees in the laboratory of Johnna Temenoff, Ph.D. at Georgia Tech/Emory University (namely, Brandon Philbrick) and the laboratory of Antonios Mikos, Ph.D. at Rice University (namely, Letitia Chim and Gerry Koons), for their diligence in helping edit drafts of the second edition of this book. Finally, we acknowledge the artistic talent of Jacqueline Mahannah, who prepared the dynamic and engaging art work appearing on the cover of this book.

J. S. Temenoff
A. G. Mikos

# Pearson's Commitment to Diversity, Equity, and Inclusion

**Pearson is dedicated to creating bias-free content that reflects the diversity, depth, and breadth of all learners' lived experiences.**

We embrace the many dimensions of diversity, including but not limited to race, ethnicity, gender, sex, sexual orientation, socioeconomic status, ability, age, and religious or political beliefs.

Education is a powerful force for equity and change in our world. It has the potential to deliver opportunities that improve lives and enable economic mobility. As we work with authors to create content for every product and service, we acknowledge our responsibility to demonstrate inclusivity and incorporate diverse scholarship so that everyone can achieve their potential through learning. As the world's leading learning company, we have a duty to help drive change and live up to our purpose to help more people create a better life for themselves and to create a better world.

**Our ambition is to purposefully contribute to a world where:**

- Everyone has an equitable and lifelong opportunity to succeed through learning.

- Our educational content accurately reflects the histories and lived experiences of the learners we serve.

- Our educational products and services are inclusive and represent the rich diversity of learners.

- Our educational content prompts deeper discussions with students and motivates them to expand their own learning (and worldview).

## Accessibility

We are also committed to providing products that are fully accessible to all learners. As per Pearson's guidelines for accessible educational Web media, we test and retest the capabilities of our products against the highest standards for every release, following the WCAG guidelines in developing new products for copyright year 2022 and beyond.

 You can learn more about Pearson's commitment to accessibility at
**https://www.pearson.com/us/accessibility.html**

## Contact Us

While we work hard to present unbiased, fully accessible content, we want to hear from you about any concerns or needs with this Pearson product so that we can investigate and address them.

 Please contact us with concerns about any potential bias at
**https://www.pearson.com/report-bias.html**

 For accessibility-related issues, such as using assistive technology with Pearson products, alternative text requests, or accessibility documentation, email the Pearson Disability Support team at **disability.support@pearson.com**

# Materials for Biomedical Applications

**Main Objective**

To understand what the field of biomaterials encompasses, to appreciate the general concerns of a biomaterialist, and to review principles from general chemistry as needed.

**Specific Objectives**

1. To understand the breadth of the field and important consensus definitions relating to biomaterials.
2. To be able to compare/contrast natural and synthetic materials.
3. To be able to compare/contrast surface and bulk properties and understand that design criteria depend on the final application.
4. To understand that the material induces a biological response which can, in turn, affect the material performance.
5. To understand that the form of the material can influence its properties and the biological response to its implantation.
6. To understand how electron structure contributes to various types of bonding.

## 1.1 Introduction to Biomaterials

This chapter is designed to provide an overview of the breadth of the field of biomaterials science and discuss briefly all the aspects of this discipline, which will be explored more fully in later chapters. In addition, it provides important basic definitions and background information for the remainder of the book. The chapter begins with a discussion of the scope and history of biomaterials science and the role of the biomaterialist. In later sections, degradative, surface, and bulk properties of materials are related to the choices incumbent upon biomaterialists, as they design/select the optimal material for particular applications. Finally, a review of basic chemical principles underlying important material properties is presented.

### 1.1.1 Important Definitions

Biomaterials is a wide-ranging field, encompassing aspects of basic biology, medicine, engineering, and materials science, that has developed to its current form primarily since World War II. Because of the breadth of the field, confusion often exists about what a biomaterial is, and, in particular, the role of the biomaterialist in modern medicine. Therefore, we begin our discussion of biomaterials science with key definitions to better characterize the discipline.

According to a consensus decision by a panel of experts, a **biomaterial** is:

> A material intended to interface with biological systems to evaluate, treat, augment, or replace any tissue, organ, or function of the body [1].

Therefore, **biomaterials science** is the study of biomaterials and their interactions with the biological environment [2]. This discipline includes subjects relating to materials science, such as mechanical properties of materials or surface modification of implants, as well as biological topics such as immunology, toxicology, and wound healing processes.

Regardless of which aspect of biomaterials science is addressed, the "bio" of "biomaterial" cannot be forgotten. Because the overall goal of the field is to develop materials that will be implanted in humans, one of the most important concepts in biomaterials science is that of *biocompatibility*. According to another consensus definition, **biocompatibility** is

> The ability of a material to perform with an appropriate host response in a specific application [1].

Thus, a **biomaterialist**, as a practitioner of biomaterials science, is responsible for alterations to the composition of a biomaterial and/or its fabrication process in order to control the biological response and produce an implant with maximal biocompatibility. As these definitions indicate, a biomaterialist must consider both the material properties and the biological reaction to ensure that the chosen material is appropriate for the given application. Therefore, this book will address both the materials science (Chapters 1–7) and the biological (Chapters 8–14) aspects of biomaterials, with the goal of introducing principles to guide future biomaterialists in the selection and development of optimal materials for a wide variety of applications and implantation sites.

## EXAMPLE PROBLEM 1.1

Are the following items biomaterials? Why or why not?

(a) Contact lens
(b) Splinter
(c) Vascular graft
(d) Crutches

Solution: "A biomaterial is a material intended to interface with biological systems to evaluate, treat, augment, or replace any tissue, organ or function of the body [1]." (a) and (c) are biomaterials according to this definition. (a) interfaces with the ocular environment to augment the light-focusing function of the eye for vision. Similarly, (c) interfaces with the vascular environment to replace vascular (venous/arterial) function. (b) is neither intended to interface with the biological environment nor to serve a biological function. (d) could be viewed either as a biomaterial or not by the given definition. It depends upon the justification of the terms "augment," "replace," and "interface." ∎

## 1.1.2 History and Current Status of the Field

Although we consider biomaterials a relatively young field, its origins date back thousands of years. Archaeologists have uncovered remains of humans containing metal dental implants from as early as 200 A.D., and it is known that linen was used as a suture material by the Egyptians. However, the development of the biomaterials field significantly increased after World War II with the widespread availability of synthetic materials that were originally designed for use in the war [3].

For example, implantation of plastics (synthetic polymers) in humans was first reported in the 1940s. Many of these first attempts centered around poly(methyl methacrylate), which had been previously employed as a material for aircraft, and nylon, a common parachute material. However, the field progressed quickly from these first materials to encompass a wide range of material types. The two decades after World War II saw the advent, among others, of the first successful artificial hip (metallic biomaterials), kidney dialysis machines (originally using a natural polymer derivative, cellulose), and vascular grafts (another naturally derived polymer, silk) [3].

The long-term success of these devices was due, in addition to the advancement in materials, to better surgical techniques, including proper sterilization, and patient monitoring. Also, a greater knowledge of biology, particularly as it related to biocompatibility, had a significant impact on the field of biomaterials. Although in the first few decades after World War II any material could be placed in a patient in an emergency situation, the need for biomaterial regulation was soon recognized, and national and international standards requiring rigorous testing before implantation were developed [3].

Today, biomaterials represent a significant portion of the health-care industry, with an estimated market size of over $38 billion per year in North America (see Table 1.1). Replacement heart valves, vascular grafts, hip and knee replacements, and orthopedic fixation plates and screws comprise a large portion of the biomaterials market. With health-care expenditures in 2020 reaching an estimated $3.8 trillion in the United States alone, research and development (R&D) into better medical devices has become a priority. Over $194 billion was invested into medical-related R&D in the United States in 2018.

In the cardiovascular area, approximately $1.6 billion was spent on replacement heart valves and $2.2 billion on vascular grafts in the United States in 2020. Figure 1.1 depicts one typical design of a heart valve, while synthetic vascular grafts are shown in Figure 1.2. After insertion, both of these devices can restore proper blood flow and thus greatly improve the patient's ability to function normally. However, a number of problems can occur. For replacement heart valves, the most

**Figure 1.1**
Image of a bileaflet heart valve prosthesis.

### TABLE 1.1

| Biomaterials in the U.S. Healthcare Market | | |
|---|---|---|
| Medical Device | Biomaterials Used | Market (US$) |
| Orthopedics (2020) [4] | | $ 20,800,000,000 |
| Joint replacement (hip, knee, extremity) (2020) [5] | Titanium, stainless steel, poly(ethylene) | $ 10,700,000,000 |
| Bone cement (2020) [6] | Poly(methyl methacrylate) | $ 638,000,000 |
| Fixation plates and screws (2020) [7] | Titanium, stainless steel, poly(lactic acid) | $2,360,000,000 |
| Cardiovascular (2020) [8] | | $ 20,700,000,000 |
| Vascular graft (2020) [9] | Dacron, expanded titanium | $ 2,200,000,000 |
| Heart valve (2020) [8] | Dacron, carbon metal | $ 1,600,000,000 |
| Stent (2020) [10] | Stainless steel, poly(lactic acid) | $ 3,100,000,000 |
| Other | | |
| Sutures (2020) [11] | Poly(lactic acid), poly (dioxanone), poly(propylene) | $ 1,380,000,000 |
| Breast implants (2019) [12] | Silicone, human/porcine dermis | $ 714,510,000 |
| Wound dressings (2020) [13] | Polyurethane, hydrogels, human dermis | $ 2,800,000,000 |
| Hemodialysis (2020) [14] | Poly(sulfone), silicone | $25,000,000,000 |
| Total U.S. healthcare expenditures (2020) [15] | | $ 3,800,000,000,000 |
| Total U.S. health R&D (2018) [16] | | $ 194,200,000,000 |
| Total U.S. medical device market (2020)[17] | | $ 168,760,000,000 |
| North America biomaterials market (2020) [18] | | $ 38,464,000,000 |

**Figure 1.2**
Image of vascular grafts constructed of expanded poly(tetrafluoroethylene). (Reprinted with permission from [23].)

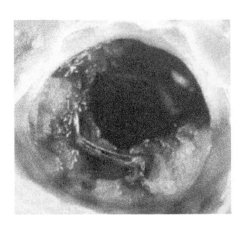

**Figure 1.3**
Image of blood clots on a bileaflet heart valve. (Reprinted with permission from [24].)

common complications include blood clotting, mechanical failure, and infection (see Fig. 1.3). In vascular grafts, blood clotting or overgrowth of tissue, which blocks the interior of the vessel and prevents blood flow, can be causes for device failure.

An estimated $10.7 billion was spent on artificial joint replacements, such as the knee or hip, in the United States in 2020. An example of an artificial hip is shown in Figure 1.4. Such replacements restore the ability to walk, or even engage in moderate athletic activity, and thus greatly improve the patient's quality of life. Over time, however, these prostheses can loosen, leading to tissue damage and creating the need for a second surgery to repair or replace the implant.

Heart-lung machines, like the one seen in Figure 1.5, are used daily in operating rooms worldwide to recirculate blood externally, allowing a patient's heart to be stopped so that surgery can be performed on it. Although the development of such devices was crucial to the field of cardiac surgery and saves the lives of many patients each year, certain problems remain. Due in part to the limitations of the current biomaterial filters, the heart-lung machine is unable to attain the efficiency of the native lung for blood oxygenation. This, in turn, requires higher pumping pressures than are normally exerted by the heart, which can lead to blood cell lysis (breakage). In addition, anticoagulants are required to prevent blood clotting during circulation through the machine, thereby increasing the risk of uncontrolled bleeding after surgery.

**Figure 1.4**
An orthopedic hip implant, exhibiting the use of all three classes of biomaterials: metals, ceramics and polymers. In this case, the stem, which is implanted in the femur (upper bone of the leg), is made with a metallic biomaterial. The implant may be coated with a ceramic to improve attachment to the bone, or a polymeric cement (not shown) can be used to hold the stem in place. At the top of the hip stem is a ball (metal or ceramic) that works in conjunction with the corresponding socket to facilitate motion in the joint. The corresponding inner socket is made out of either a polymer (for a metallic ball) or ceramic (for a ceramic ball), and attached to the pelvis by a metallic outer socket.

(Axelbueckert/123RF.)

Metallic outer socket

Metallic or ceramic ball

Polymeric or ceramic inner socket

Ceramic coating

Metallic hip stem

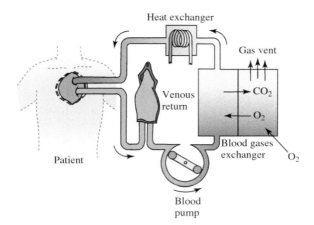

**Figure 1.5**
Schematic of a heart-lung machine setup. (Reprinted with permission from [19].)

Approximately \$25 billion was spent on hemodialysis in the United States in 2020. Patients with compromised kidney function must receive renal dialysis three times per week [19] to remove waste from the blood in order to maintain life. In this procedure, the blood is pumped across a dialysis membrane, which allows waste products of certain sizes to flow out of the blood (see Fig. 1.6). However, this device suffers from problems similar to those described for the heart-lung machine, including blood cell lysis, and the potential for infection or undesired activation of a portion of the body's immune response (the complement system, discussed in Chapter 12).

### 1.1.3 Future Directions

Over the course of the past 50 years, several stages in biomaterials development can be identified. Starting in the 1960s–1970s, the first generation of biomaterials was designed to be **inert**, or not reactive with the body, thereby decreasing the potential for negative immune response to the implant. In the 1990s, this concept was gradually replaced with a second generation of materials designed to be **bioactive**, interacting in a positive manner with the body to promote localized healing.

Because biomaterials science occupies a unique niche at the intersection of several disciplines, advances in disparate subjects have propelled the field to its current status. Experiments providing detailed knowledge of cell and molecular biology and genetics have led to the development of these "smart" or "instructive" materials, which can help guide the biological response in the implant area. Advances in surgical techniques like minimally invasive surgery have promoted the design of

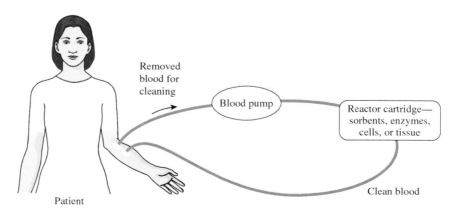

**Figure 1.6**
Schematic of kidney dialysis setup.

injectable materials that can be applied locally and with minimal pain to the patient. New developments in materials science, such as composites involving nanoscale objects as reinforcing agents, have inspired the creation of a new set of nanostructured biomaterials. Advances in three-dimensional printing have allowed for fabrication of cell-material constructs with spatial control over placement of cells for *in vitro* replication of key aspects of organ structure and function.

Further advances in all of these fields are expected to have a great impact on the future of biomaterials. Thus, a new generation of biomaterials is emerging—those that are designed to become completely integrated and cause the full reproduction of damaged tissue, as exemplified in current research in biomaterials for tissue-engineering/regenerative medicine applications. The perpetual evolution of new processes and materials makes the field of biomaterials very dynamic. This book is therefore designed to relate basic principles in biology and materials science to both currently used materials and as potential design parameters for the next generation of biomaterials.

## 1.2 Biological Response to Biomaterials

One of the major concerns of the biomaterialist is the biological response to the chosen material, which determines its biocompatibility. Immediately after implantation, inflammation usually occurs. Clinically, this is characterized by redness, swelling, warmth, and pain around the implant site. However, this phenomenon is usually temporary and may be resolved in a number of ways, including complete integration of the material into the surrounding tissue or isolation of the implant with fibrous encapsulation.

Depending on the implant site and the nature of the material, other reactions may also ensue, such as activation of the immune system, localized blood clotting, infection, tumor formation, or implant calcification. Although many of these responses are not desirable, certain reactions may be acceptable, depending on the application. For example, calcification of an implant used to support bone tissue may be necessary to ensure good integration between the biomaterial and the surrounding bone.

Factors such as the type of material, the shape of the implant, material degradation characteristics, surface chemical properties, and bulk chemical and mechanical properties have been identified as important to the overall biocompatibility of a biomaterial and to its suitability for specific applications. Therefore, the biomaterialist must select the material type and processing method to obtain optimal degradative, surface, and bulk characteristics, keeping in mind the final location and application of the implant.

At the most basic level, it is the protein and cellular response to the material that determines the overall success of the implant. Therefore, characterization of these responses is necessary. Experiments assessing both cell/protein interactions with biomaterials and overall biocompatibility can be carried out either *in vitro* or *in vivo*. **In vitro** (literally "in glass" [1]) tests take place in a well-controlled laboratory environment, while **in vivo** experiments require biomaterial implantation in a living system, such as an animal model [1].

EXAMPLE PROBLEM 1.2

The biological response to a material is of utmost concern to a biomaterialist. The response must be appropriate for the desired application. For example, calcification of implant materials for bone applications is often sought for proper integration of the implant with the surrounding bone tissue. Would calcification of an artificial heart valve composed of decellularized porcine (pig) pericardium be a favorable biological response? Why or why not?

**Solution:** No. Heart valves serve to ensure proper fluid flow patterns in the heart, so that blood can be pumped to perfuse the periphery. Consequently, heart valves must be flexible and durable to properly open and closely cyclically. Calcification leads to undesired stiffness of the material in this case that will impede the function of the valve (opening/closing) and decrease the efficiency of cardiac output. ▪

## 1.3 Biomaterial Product Testing and Regulatory Approval

The ultimate *in vivo* event takes place upon final device implantation in humans. However, due to ethical concerns, before this can occur, many *in vitro* and *in vivo* biocompatibility tests must be performed. These are dictated by and analyzed in accordance with standards compiled by agencies such as the ASTM International (ASTM) and the International Organization for Standardization (ISO).[1] These agencies are responsible for the development of technical standards for materials, products, systems, and services. More specifics on these guidelines are found in later sections of this book.

In the United States, the U.S. Food and Drug Administration (FDA) is the federal agency tasked with regulating medical products in order to ensure safety and efficacy of the treatments. Currently, the part of the FDA that oversees medical products is divided into three branches, based on the type of product:

1. Center for Devices and Radiological Health (CDRH): regulates medical devices/equipment
2. Center for Biologics Evaluation and Research (CBER): regulates products such as proteins/antibodies, human cells or tissues for transplantation, gene therapy products, etc.
3. Center for Drug Evaluation and Research (CDER): regulates agents to diagnose or treat disease

A fourth type of product, called a **combination product**, also falls under FDA oversight. These products combine at least two of the types listed and therefore cannot easily be regulated by a single branch of the FDA. Some examples are protein or drug coatings on an implant (e.g., drug-eluting cardiovascular stent or anti-microbial coating on an orthopedic implant), a cell-seeded scaffold (e.g., skin substitute), or a prefilled device (e.g., insulin injector pen). Regulation of these products occurs by first determining the primary mode of action, or the believed main mechanism of the therapy. The center that oversees that mode of action then becomes the primary point of oversight for that product, with consultation to the other appropriate FDA centers as needed.

In terms of new products, each center has developed its own application process tailored to the type of products it regulates. A brief summary is provided below, but, since these regulations are constantly evolving, please see the government website for the most current information (www.fda.gov).

---

[1]*ASTM International* was originally the *American Society for Testing and Materials*. Also, *ISO* is derived from the Greek word "isos" due to variations in the translation of *International Organization for Standardization*.

## 1.3.1 Device Regulation

Generally, for devices, designations are given based on their potential risk to the patient. The three classifications are as follows:

**Class I** devices present minimal potential for harm to the patient and are, thereby, the least regulated (e.g., bandages and examination gloves).
**Class II** devices are not generally considered to pose substantial risk to the patient (e.g., powered wheelchairs and infusion pumps).
**Class III** devices are the most stringently regulated medical devices. These devices often support or sustain human life (e.g., heart valves), or present a potentially large risk of illness or injury (e.g., silicone gel-filled breast implants).

If a device can be shown to be "substantially equivalent" to a Class I or II device already on the market, a **Premarket Notification** 510(k) procedure may be followed. In this case, the company only has to produce evidence that the device is similar to one already available. However, for Class III devices that are not substantially equivalent to previous devices, a **Premarket Approval** (PMA) process is required before they are allowed to be marketed. A PMA typically requires extensive data on both safety and effectiveness, including human clinical trials. It is important to note here that the FDA approves devices, not materials, so currently, specific biomaterials can only be used in the context of approved final devices.

## 1.3.2 Drug/Biologics Regulation

While a different approval process is followed for drugs and many biologics, like devices, clinical trials are required to show safety and efficacy. For a new drug, an Investigational New Drug (IND) application must be submitted to CDER before clinical trials can begin. Clinical trials leading to FDA approval generally have three phases:

**Phase I:** Smaller study (up to 100 patients or healthy volunteers) to determine safety and dosage
**Phase II:** Larger study (up to several hundred patients) to determine efficacy and side effects
**Phase III:** Large study (300–3000 patients) to determine efficacy and monitor adverse reactions

After clinical trials, the investigators can then submit a New Drug Application (NDA) using the data from the trials to obtain full approval from the FDA for commercial marketing. Many biologics are regulated in a similar manner to drugs, but the NDA and IND applications must be submitted to CBER. However, as mentioned earlier, regardless of the center involved, prior to proceeding to clinical trials, the FDA generally requires substantial *in vitro* and *in vivo* (in animals) data demonstrating safety and efficacy of the device. Specific *in vitro* and *in vivo* assays often requested by the FDA to demonstrate safety will be covered in Chapters 9–14.

# 1.4 Types of Biomaterials

One of the primary roles of the biomaterialist is to choose the appropriate type of material for a specific application. In general, materials are classified as **organic** if they contain carbon or **inorganic** if they do not. More specifically, biomaterials fall into one of three categories of materials: metals, ceramics, or polymers.

**TABLE 1.2**

| Metals Commonly Used in Biomedical Applications | |
| --- | --- |
| Metal | Applications |
| Cobalt-chromium alloys | Artificial heart valves, dental prostheses, orthopedic fixation plates, artificial joint components, vascular stents |
| Gold and platinum | Dental fillings, electrodes for cochlear implants |
| Silver-tin-copper alloys | Dental amalgams |
| Stainless steel | Dental prostheses, orthopedic fixation plates, vascular stents |
| Titanium alloys | Artificial heart valves, dental implants, artificial joint components, orthopedic screws, pacemaker cases, vascular stents |

## 1.4.1 Metals

**Metals** are inorganic materials possessing nondirectional metallic bonds with highly mobile electrons (see Section 1.7 for more about bond types). A list of metals and alloys (combinations of multiple elemental metals) commonly used in biomedical applications is found in Table 1.2. In addition to their ability to conduct electricity, metals are strong and relatively easily formed into complex shapes. This makes metals a suitable material for orthopedic (hip and knee) replacements (Fig. 1.4), for dental fillings and implants for craniofacial restoration, and for cardiovascular applications such as stents and pacemaker leads.

## 1.4.2 Ceramics

**Ceramics** are inorganic materials composed of nondirectional ionic bonds between electron-donating and electron-accepting elements. Ceramic materials most often employed as biomaterials are listed in Table 1.3. Ceramics may contain crystals or may be noncrystalline (amorphous) **glasses**. Ceramics are very hard and are more resistant to degradation in many environments compared to metals. However, they are quite brittle because of the nature of ionic bonds. Due to the similarity between the chemistry of ceramics and that of native bone, ceramics are most often used as a part of orthopedic implants or as dental materials (Fig. 1.4). Because of their brittle nature, they are commonly employed in applications requiring small loads.

## 1.4.3 Polymers

Unlike the other two classes of biomaterials, **polymers** are organic materials possessing long chains that are held together by directional covalent bonds (Fig. 1.7).

**TABLE 1.3**

| Ceramics Commonly Used in Biomedical Applications | |
| --- | --- |
| Ceramic | Applications |
| Aluminum oxides | Orthopedic joint replacement components, orthopedic load-bearing implants, implant coatings, dental implants |
| Bioactive glasses | Orthopedic and dental implant coatings, dental implants, facial reconstruction components, bone graft substitute materials |
| Calcium phosphates | Orthopedic and dental implant coatings, dental implant materials, bone graft substitute materials, bone cements |

**Figure 1.7**
Chemical structure of poly(methyl methacrylate), a polymer commonly used as a bone cement. (a) shows a section of the polymer chain, with the dotted lines indicating the repeating unit, which is also shown in (b).

(a)          (b)

Polymers are widely used in biomedical applications due to the range of physical and chemical properties possible with these materials [20]. Examples of some of the synthetic polymers that are often used as biomaterials are found in Table 1.4. Alternatively, polymers that are derived from natural sources, such as proteins commonly found in the body, have been widely explored as biomaterials. Common uses for these types of polymers are also listed in Table 1.4.

Regardless of the origin of the polymer, there are several polymer sub-classes that are useful to the biomaterialist in that each may be particularly suited to certain tissue types. For example, **elastomers** can sustain substantial deformation at low

**TABLE 1.4**

| Synthetic and Naturally Derived Polymers Commonly Used in Biomedical Applications | |
|---|---|
| Polymer | Applications |
| **Synthetic** | |
| Poly(2-hydroxyethyl methacrylate) | Contact lenses |
| Poly(dimethyl siloxane) | Breast implants, contact lenses, knuckle replacements |
| Poly(ethylene) | Orthopedic joint implants |
| Poly(ethylene glycol) | Pharmaceutical fillers, wound dressings |
| Poly(ethylene terephthalate) | Vascular grafts, sutures |
| Poly($\varepsilon$-caprolactone) | Drug delivery devices, sutures |
| Poly(lactic-co-glycolic acid) | Resorbable meshes and sutures |
| Poly(methyl methacrylate) | Bone cements, diagnostic contact lenses |
| Poly(tetrafluoroethylene) | Vascular grafts, sutures |
| Poly(isoprene) | Gloves |
| Poly(propylene) | Sutures |
| **Naturally derived** | |
| Alginate | Wound dressings |
| Chitosan | Wound dressings |
| Collagen | Orthopedic repair matrices, nerve repair matrices, tissue-engineering matrices |
| Elastin | Skin repair matrices |
| Fibrin | Hemostatic products, tissue sealants |
| Glycosaminoglycan | Orthopedic repair matrices |
| Hyaluronic acid | Orthopedic repair matrices |

stresses and return rapidly to their initial dimensions upon release of the stress [1], suggesting that they may be suitable for cardiovascular applications, where tissue elasticity is an important property. Another category of polymers called **hydrogels** exhibit the ability to swell in water and to retain a significant fraction of water within their structures without completely dissolving [1]. Due to their high water content, hydrogels have been explored for a variety of soft tissue applications.

It is also possible to form **composite** materials to improve bulk or surface properties of biomaterials. Composites are materials consisting of two or more chemically distinct components, one of which is often a polymer [21]. Composites are often created to optimize mechanical properties. For example, a fiber-reinforcing material (usually carbon) can be dispersed throughout a polymer. Although a detailed discussion of composite materials is beyond the scope of this text, it is interesting to note that many consider the structure of human tissues to resemble a fiber-reinforced composite.

### 1.4.4 Naturally Derived versus Synthetic Polymers

Naturally based polymers can be derived from sources within the body (collagen, fibrin, or hyaluronic acid) or outside the body (chitosan, alginate). One of the most common natural biomaterials found in the human body is the protein **collagen**. Many different types of collagen exist in various tissues, and several of these, particularly types I and II, have been explored as biomaterials. Another protein-based material, **fibrin**, results from the combination of the blood clotting factors fibrinogen and thrombin. Both collagen and fibrin have been used in tissue-engineering attempts to repair cartilage defects and in other orthopedic applications.

In addition to proteins, naturally based polymers may be derived from sugars (carbohydrates). **Hyaluronic acid** is an example of a carbohydrate molecule occurring in human tissues that is often employed as a biomaterial. However, the source of other carbohydrate-derived materials may be nonhuman. Chitosan, a sugar-based substance found in arthropod exoskeletons, agarose, which is formed by algae, and alginate, derived from seaweed, are all currently being investigated as biomaterials for a variety of applications. For example, a combination of chitosan and alginate has been examined for wound dressings.

There are advantages and disadvantages to both natural and synthetic polymers, and particular materials may lend themselves to certain applications over others. In many cases, naturally derived polymers have chemical compositions similar to the tissues they are replacing. Therefore, they may be more fully integrated into the surrounding tissue over time or more easily altered (remodeled) in response to changes in tissue needs. However, concerns exist about the feasibility of finding large amounts of some of these materials for clinical applications, their relatively low mechanical properties, and the assurance of pathogen removal. In addition, regions of these molecules may be recognized as "foreign" by the body's immune system, leading to a type of material "rejection." Further potential problems arise when the biomaterial is based on not a single naturally occurring polymer, but decellularized tissue. Here, unwanted calcification leading to device failure (discussed in Chapter 14) is a particular concern.

In contrast, synthetic polymers can be easily mass-produced and sterilized, so supply issues are less of a problem. Additionally, their physical, chemical, mechanical, and degradative properties can be tailored for specific applications. However, unless specifically treated, most synthetic materials do not interact with tissues in an active manner and therefore cannot direct or aid in healing around the implant site. Also, few synthetic polymers have been approved by regulatory agencies for use in humans in specific applications.

Regardless of source, all of the materials described in this section are polymeric, so they have a number of key properties in common and can all be modified or processed using similar techniques. Therefore, in the following chapters, the term "polymer" will be used to refer, for the most part, to both naturally derived and synthetic materials.

## EXAMPLE PROBLEM 1.3

Which of the following classes of biomaterials would be most appropriate for use to fabricate an artificial tendon, a tissue that must sustain substantial deformation at low forces and return rapidly to its original dimensions upon release of the stress? Why?

(a) Metals
(b) Ceramics
(c) Polymers

**Solution:**   (c) Because of the wide range of mechanical properties attainable with polymeric materials, elastomeric polymers are easily found. Metals and ceramics, however, typically allow for little tensile deformation before failure, and they typically require large stresses for small elongations in tension.   ∎

## 1.5   Processing of Biomaterials

In addition to the material type, the processing method is another important choice for the biomaterialist. Processing can affect bulk properties such as strength, as well as surface properties of materials. In fact, many processing techniques have been developed to alter only the surface physical or chemical properties without affecting the rest of the material. These include spraying a ceramic coating on a metal hip implant to improve integration with the surrounding bone or coating a catheter with antibiotics to prevent infection (see Chapter 7 for more on these methods).

Processing is also necessary to form materials into specified shapes. The shape of the material alters the surface area available, which, in turn, can affect the degradative properties and the biological response. Implant geometry is often dictated by the characteristics of the tissue to be replaced. For instance, biomaterials may be fabricated into sheets for skin applications, cylinders for vascular grafts, or a ball-and-cup combination for hip replacement.

## 1.6   Important Properties of Biomaterials

The selection of the biomaterial and appropriate processing techniques for a given application is determined primarily by the degradative, surface, and bulk properties of the material. As explained next, each of these characteristics directly affects the biological response; thus, these are the most important aspects to consider when designing an optimal biomaterial for a given implant type.

### 1.6.1 Degradative Properties of Biomaterials

The shape and size of the implant, its location in the body, and the chemical, physical, and mechanical bulk and surface properties of the biomaterial affect its degradation *in vivo*. Although the temperature and pH of body fluids are relatively mild, during inflammation, cells may be recruited to the area and produce active substances to transform the region into a harsh environment, thus promoting material degradation.

Degradation can be an undesired side effect of implantation, or it may be designed into the chemical nature of the biomaterial. Such biodegradable materials are currently under investigation as carriers for cells and bioactive factors for tissue-engineering applications. For both desired and undesired degradation, the time before failure (environmental stability) is crucial to implant design. In addition, the biocompatibility of degradation by-products must be examined along with the biocompatibility of the intact material. Because the nature and amount of degradation depends strongly on the chemistry and mechanical demands of the implant site, *in vivo* testing is often required to accurately assess biomaterial degradation time and any possible inflammatory response.

## 1.6.2 Surface Properties of Biomaterials

On a mechanistic level, the biological response to a material is highly affected by the proteins that attach (adsorb) to its surface. Biomaterial surface properties determine protein adsorption, and thus are a key consideration for the biomaterialist. The **surface** of a material is defined to be the few atomic layers on the exterior of the object. Surface properties can be different than those in the rest of the material (the **bulk**) due to special processing schemes that alter only the outermost layers of the material, or as a result of interactions with cells and proteins in the body.

Surface properties include both chemical and physical characteristics. An example of a surface chemical property is hydrophobicity. A **hydrophobic** material (literally, "water-fearing") contains many chemical moieties that do not interact favorably with water [1]. In contrast, **hydrophilic** ("water-loving") materials have an affinity for water [1]. Hydrophobicity is one of the most important parameters affecting the adsorption of proteins to a biomaterial in an aqueous environment, such as that found *in vivo*.

Surface physical properties, such as surface roughness, also impact the protein and cellular response to a biomaterial. A rough topography, which may be caused by a combination of chemistry and processing techniques, can act to physically trap biological constituents at the implant surface, thereby altering the interactions between the biomaterial and the surrounding tissue.

## EXAMPLE PROBLEM 1.4

Would a hydrophobic or hydrophilic polymer be a more appropriate choice for a contact lens application? Why? Would a melting temperature ($T_m$) of the polymer above 37°C or below 37°C be more appropriate for this application? Why?

**Solution:** A hydrophilic polymer would be more appropriate to interface with the aqueous environment of the eye. Additionally, a melting temperature above 37°C would be more appropriate, as one would not want the polymer to be molten at body temperature (37°C) in this application. ∎

## EXAMPLE PROBLEM 1.5

A 1 mL droplet of distilled water is dropped onto each material A and B as shown. Which material is more hydrophilic? Justify your answer.

**Solution:** Material A is more hydrophilic. For a given volume of water, the surface area of interaction is greatest for A. Thus, it is more hydrophilic—that is, it has a greater affinity for water than B. ∎

### 1.6.3 Bulk Properties of Biomaterials

Overall biocompatibility depends also in part on the properties of the bulk material. In addition, this is often the most important parameter in determining the suitability of certain materials for specific applications. Bulk properties may play a smaller role than surface characteristics in determining the initial inflammatory response. However, they have a large long-term impact, since a biomaterial with inappropriate bulk properties will very likely lead to device failure.

Bulk characteristics of biomaterials include mechanical properties, physical properties and chemical composition. **Mechanical properties**, such as strength and stiffness, are extremely important in that they should match, as much as possible, the properties of the tissue to be replaced. Specifically, tissues may exhibit distinctly different mechanical properties in different directions (**anisotropy**). This is due to the unique function of many tissues. For example, a long bone in the leg can support more load along its length than in other directions, since this is where most of the force is exerted during walking or standing. Therefore, although mechanical requirements in a given location can be complex, they must be taken into consideration when selecting a suitable replacement. Additionally, fatigue properties are crucial because many implants will need to withstand repeated loading to reproduce the desired function in the body. For example, heart valves open over 40 million times per year in the average human, making material fatigue properties a key selection parameter when designing artificial heart valves.

Mechanical properties of materials are highly affected by their physical and chemical characteristics. Bulk **physical properties** include crystallinity and thermal transitions, such as melting point. Crystallinity is important because it alters a material's mechanical properties and its water uptake, both of which can impact the degradative properties of the biomaterial, as well as its interactions with surrounding cells and proteins. Transition points, such as melting temperature, are also crucial, since the biomaterial must be stable over a long period of time at body temperature.

The **chemical composition** of a biomaterial dictates the other bulk properties, just as the chemistry at the surface determines many of the surface properties. As with the surface, one of the major chemical characteristics of the bulk material is its degree of hydrophobicity. Many chemical properties are, at the most basic level, a result of the type of bonds present in the material (discussed in Section 1.7).

### 1.6.4 Characterization Techniques

In order to better understand how degradative, surface, and bulk properties affect the biological response to a biomaterial, it is important first to measure them. A plethora of techniques, both quantitative and qualitative, have been developed to examine material properties and are discussed in more detail throughout the text. **Quantitative** procedures produce a numerical measure of a property (in absolute or relative units), whereas **qualitative** experiments give a general overview of the property of interest, without supplying a numerical value. For example, the act of observing a material under a microscope is qualitative, while the techniques discussed in the following text are more quantitative.

Quantitative characterization of degradative and bulk properties often involves a form of spectroscopy, chromatography, or mechanical testing. **Spectroscopy** measures how compounds absorb different types of energy, while **chromatography** uses various means to physically separate molecules on the basis of chemical characteristics such as charge or size. Mechanical assessment of materials is performed with a mechanical testing frame that allows for controlled loading of the sample by pulling, pushing, or bending it at a preset rate.

Because surfaces are chemically active, many surface analysis techniques require special preparation procedures or equipment to prevent contamination. However, despite these limitations, a wide range of surface characterization methods has been developed. Many methods involve modifications of techniques described previously for bulk properties, such as spectroscopy. In addition, more qualitative methods, such as various types of microscopy, can provide valuable information on the structure and topography of the biomaterial surface.

## EXAMPLE PROBLEM 1.6

For each of the following methods for the determination of the degradation profile of a hydrogel, indicate whether it is quantitative or qualitative:

(a) Visual inspection at each time point
(b) Hydrogel mass measurements at each time point

**Solution:** (a) is a qualitative measure, whereas (b) is a quantitative measure. ∎

# 1.7 Principles of Chemistry

Generally, when designing or selecting a biomaterial that is most appropriate for a specific application, one is, in essence, considering the chemical constitution of the material, since this dictates all the other important characteristics. Therefore, in this section, we review basic chemical principles as an introduction to understanding why each class of materials exhibits certain distinctive properties. The relation of chemical structure to macroscopic properties, a key aspect of materials science, will be revisited in later chapters.

## 1.7.1 Atomic Structure

Although many subatomic species have been discovered, in this text we will use the simplified model that divides an atom into a nucleus and orbiting electrons (Fig. 1.8). The nucleus contains protons and neutrons, which are much larger than the orbiting electrons. The number of protons (each having a positive charge of $1.67 \times 10^{-19}$ Coulombs (C)) is the atom's **atomic number** ($Z$). In an electrically neutral atom, this positive charge is balanced by an equal number of electrons, each of which has a negative charge equal in magnitude to that of a proton. Neutrons are electrically neutral but do contribute significantly to the **atomic mass**.

Atomic mass is usually measured in **atomic mass units** (amu). One amu is roughly equivalent to the mass of a proton or neutron ($1.66 \times 10^{-24}$ g). For example, carbon has six protons and six neutrons, giving an atomic mass of 12 amu.[2] Atomic weight of an element can be reported in amu, or in mass per mole. One **mole** of material contains $6.023 \times 10^{23}$ (Avogadro's number) molecules of that element.

## 1.7.2 Atomic Models

Over the past century, a detailed theory based on **quantum mechanics** has been developed that explains that electrons moving around a nucleus have both wave-like and particle-like qualities. Although an in-depth treatment of this subject is beyond

---

[2]Atomic weights reported on the periodic table (Fig. 1.14), are actually weighted averages of the masses of different isotopes of an element. **Isotopes** have the same number of protons and electrons, but differ in the number of neutrons in the nucleus.

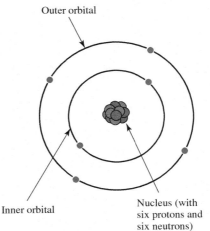

Outer orbital

Inner orbital

Nucleus (with six protons and six neutrons)

**Figure 1.8**
The Bohr atomic model, which separates the atom into a nucleus (containing protons and neutrons) and orbiting electrons. For an electrically neutral atom, the positive charge of the nucleus is balanced by an equal number of electrons. In this model, electrons are depicted as orbiting the nucleus in discrete energy states, or orbitals, which are separated by a finite amount of energy [25].

the scope of this book, an examination of simple models depicting both of these qualities is presented. Both models are correct, and both will be used to describe material phenomena in later chapters, depending on which provides the clearest explanation.

### 1.7.2.1 Bohr Model

One of the first (and simplest) models developed based on quantum mechanical principles was the **Bohr model** of the atom (Fig. 1.8). Here, electrons are thought to orbit the nucleus in discrete energy states, or orbitals. Orbitals are separated by a finite amount of energy, so to move from one orbital to another, an electron would have to gain or lose a set amount of energy. If an atom is exposed to energy of a certain frequency, it may gain a discrete amount of this energy and promote one of its electrons to a higher orbital (see Fig. 1.9). After this occurs, the electron will often return to its normal orbital (ground state), emitting a photon of energy equal to the difference in energy between the original orbital and the excited-state orbital. These photon emissions are the basis of a number of materials characterization techniques, as discussed in Chapter 2.

### 1.7.2.2 Wave-Mechanical Model

The Bohr model failed to explain several phenomena involving electrons, which led to the development of the **wave-mechanical model** of the atom. In this model, electrons, instead of being treated as small particles, are considered to have wave-like characteristics and are described by equations for wave motion. Here, orbitals are thought of as the probability that

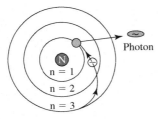

Photon

n = 1
n = 2
n = 3

**Figure 1.9**
If exposed to energy of a certain frequency, atoms may enter an excited state and promote one or more electrons to a higher orbital. After this occurs, the electron will often return to its normal orbital (ground state), emitting a photon of energy equal to the difference in energy between the original orbital and the excited-state orbital [26].

**Figure 1.10**
The distribution of the hydrogen electron as depicted by both the (a) Bohr and (b) wave-mechanical atomic models. Orbitals have discrete energy levels in both the Bohr and wave-mechanical models. However, in the wave-mechanical model, orbitals are thought of as the probability that an electron will occupy a certain space around the nucleus, and they are characterized by probability functions (electron clouds) [22].

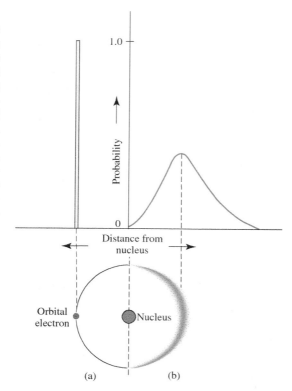

an electron will occupy a certain space around the nucleus and are characterized by probability functions (electron clouds). Figure 1.10 compares the probability of finding the hydrogen electron at a given distance from the nucleus as depicted by both the Bohr and wave-mechanical atomic models.

### 1.7.3 Atomic Orbitals

**1.7.3.1 Shapes of Subshells (Orbitals)**   Per the wave-mechanical model, three of four parameters called **quantum numbers** dictate the size, shape, and orientation of the electron probability functions. More specifically, this model terms the discrete Bohr energy states as *electron shells*, which can further be divided into *subshells* (often called orbitals). Subshells are designated by lowercase letters *s, p, d* or *f*. Each subshell can have several energy states that are specified by the third quantum number. For example, there are five states for a *d* subshell, three states for a *p* subshell, and only one for an *s* subshell. Plotting the wave functions in three dimensions reveals that each type of subshell has only one characteristic shape. The different energy states are then depicted by identical subshells oriented in different directions (usually *x, y,* and *z* for the *p*-subshell; see Fig. 1.11). Thus, the Bohr model was further refined by the wave-mechanical model, which divides the shells into subshells, each of which has its associated energy value.

**1.7.3.2 Order of Subshells and the Aufbau Principle**   Solutions to wave equations using all possible quantum numbers give the set of shells and subshells for all elements (Fig. 1.12). It is important to note that, in this system, the lower the shell number, the lower the energy (energy associated with 1*s* orbital is less than for 2*s*, etc.). Additionally, the energy of the subshells in each shell increases from *s* to *f*. However, energy states can overlap between shells—this is especially true of *d* and *f* subshells. For example, the energy associated with the 3*d* subshell is greater than that for the 4*s*.

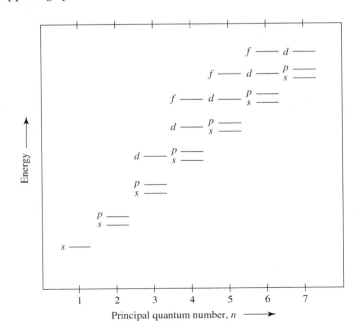

**Figure 1.11**
Depiction of the energy states for the $2p$ subshell. Because each subshell has a characteristic shape as determined by the electron probability functions (dumbbell-shaped for $p$ subshells), the different energy states are represented by identical subshells oriented along different axes ($x$, $y$, and $z$) [27].

Following these general rules of energy states, it would seem logical that electrons would prefer to be in the lowest energy state possible and therefore would fill the shells and subshells in order of increasing energy. This, combined with another quantum-mechanical theory, the **Pauli exclusion principle**, which requires that each state can hold no more than two electrons (with opposite spin), provides the groundwork to predict the **electron configuration** of an atom. To sequentially add electrons to energy states is called the **Aufbau principle** and is governed by the following set of rules:

1. Lower energy states are filled before higher ones.

2. No energy state may be occupied by more than two electrons (Pauli exclusion principle) and each of these electrons must have a different orientation to their intrinsic angular momentum (spin). An electron's spin has two possible orientations and is designated with an up- or down-facing arrow (Fig. 1.13). The energy state is filled when it contains two electrons with opposite spin. Therefore, $s$ subshells contain a maximum of 2 electrons, $p$ can contain 6, and $d$ can contain 10.

3. **Hund's rule** dictates that in subshells with more than one energy state (such as the three $p$ subshells), each subshell will first be filled with one electron. Subsequently, a second electron with opposing spin will be added to each subshell.

**Figure 1.12**
The relative energies of shells and subshells for all elements. Note that the lower the shell number, the lower the energy (e.g., energy associated with $1s$ is less than for $2s$). Additionally, the energy of the subshells in each shell increases from $s$ to $f$. However, energy states can overlap between shells (e.g., energy of the $3d$ subshell is greater than that of the $4s$) [22].

**Figure 1.13**
Stable electron configurations for carbon (C), nitrogen (N), oxygen (O), and fluorine (F). The Pauli exclusion principle states that each energy state may be occupied by at most two electrons possessing different orientation to their intrinsic angular momentum (indicated by an up- or down-facing arrow). Therefore, *s* subshells contain a maximum of 2 electrons, *p* can contain 6, *d* can contain 10, and so on. In these four examples, the *s* subshells are full, whereas the *p* subshells (which consist of two electrons in the *p* subshells for carbon and up to five for fluorine) are not [27].

Electron configuration is usually noted by a superscript with the number of electrons in that shell-subshell combination. For hydrogen, this would be $1s^1$, while carbon is designated $1s^2 2s^2 2p^2$. Table 1.5 gives the electron configurations for selected common elements. There are actually a variety of electron configurations; the one that can be predicted following the rules described in the preceding text is considered the **ground state** for that atom. However, through a variety of means, atoms can enter an **excited state** where one or more electrons are found at higher energy levels. Atomic excitation is the basis of a number of spectroscopic techniques discussed later in this text.

### 1.7.4 Valence Electrons and the Periodic Table

Following the Aufbau principle, some atoms are found to have completely filled orbitals (called a **closed-shell configuration**). These elements are more stable and thus do not participate in most chemical reactions. Other elements have partially filled orbitals (**open-shell configuration**).

**Valence electrons** are those that occupy the outermost shell (here, we are most concerned with the *s* and *p* subshells). If these subshells of the valence shell are not filled, an element may share or exchange valence electrons with other elements to become more stable. This is the basis of formation of primary bonds, which will be discussed in the following sections.

The **periodic table** organizes elements with increasing atomic number based on number of valence electrons (Fig. 1.14). The elements are placed in the seven horizontal rows (periods) so that all elements in a column (group) have similar properties, usually related to the number of valence electrons present. Those with closed-shell configurations are found in Group 18. In general, those toward the left of the chart have one or two electrons more than are needed for a full valence shell and, thus, are willing to give up electrons to become positively charged ions. These elements are termed **electropositive**. In contrast, those elements toward the right are **electronegative** since they willingly accept electrons to form a negative ion with a full valence shell. Figure 1.14 shows the electronegativity values for all the elements. As will be discussed later, the difference in electronegativity between two atoms helps determine the type of bond formed between them.

**TABLE 1.5**

| Ground State Electron Configurations for Selected Common Elements | | | |
|---|---|---|---|
| Element | Symbol | Atomic Number | Electron Configuration |
| Hydrogen | H | 1 | $1s^1$ |
| Helium | He | 2 | $1s^2$ |
| Lithium | Li | 3 | $1s^2 2s^1$ |
| Beryllium | Be | 4 | $1s^2 2s^2$ |
| Boron | B | 5 | $1s^2 2s^2 2p^1$ |
| Carbon | C | 6 | $1s^2 2s^2 2p^2$ |
| Nitrogen | N | 7 | $1s^2 2s^2 2p^3$ |
| Oxygen | O | 8 | $1s^2 2s^2 2p^4$ |
| Fluorine | F | 9 | $1s^2 2s^2 2p^5$ |
| Neon | Ne | 10 | $1s^2 2s^2 2p^6$ |
| Sodium | Na | 11 | $1s^2 2s^2 2p^6 3s^1$ |
| Magnesium | Mg | 12 | $1s^2 2s^2 2p^6 3s^2$ |
| Aluminum | Al | 13 | $1s^2 2s^2 2p^6 3s^2 3p^1$ |
| Silicon | Si | 14 | $1s^2 2s^2 2p^6 3s^2 3p^2$ |
| Phosphorus | P | 15 | $1s^2 2s^2 2p^6 3s^2 3p^3$ |
| Sulfur | S | 16 | $1s^2 2s^2 2p^6 3s^2 3p^4$ |
| Chlorine | Cl | 17 | $1s^2 2s^2 2p^6 3s^2 3p^5$ |
| Argon | Ar | 18 | $1s^2 2s^2 2p^6 3s^2 3p^6$ |
| Potassium | K | 19 | $1s^2 2s^2 2p^6 3s^2 3p^6 4s^1$ |
| Calcium | Ca | 20 | $1s^2 2s^2 2p^6 3s^2 3p^6 4s^2$ |
| Scandium | Sc | 21 | $1s^2 2s^2 2p^6 3s^2 3p^6 3d^1 4s^2$ |
| Titanium | Ti | 22 | $1s^2 2s^2 2p^6 3s^2 3p^6 3d^2 4s^2$ |
| Vanadium | V | 23 | $1s^2 2s^2 2p^6 3s^2 3p^6 3d^3 4s^2$ |
| Chromium | Cr | 24 | $1s^2 2s^2 2p^6 3s^2 3p^6 3d^5 4s^1$ |
| Manganese | Mn | 25 | $1s^2 2s^2 2p^6 3s^2 3p^6 3d^5 4s^2$ |
| Iron | Fe | 26 | $1s^2 2s^2 2p^6 3s^2 3p^6 3d^6 4s^2$ |
| Cobalt | Co | 27 | $1s^2 2s^2 2p^6 3s^2 3p^6 3d^7 4s^2$ |
| Nickel | Ni | 28 | $1s^2 2s^2 2p^6 3s^2 3p^6 3d^8 4s^2$ |
| Copper | Cu | 29 | $1s^2 2s^2 2p^6 3s^2 3p^6 3d^{10} 4s^1$ |
| Zinc | Zn | 30 | $1s^2 2s^2 2p^6 3s^2 3p^6 3d^{10} 4s^2$ |
| Gallium | Ga | 31 | $1s^2 2s^2 2p^6 3s^2 3p^6 3d^{10} 4s^2 4p^1$ |
| Germanium | Ge | 32 | $1s^2 2s^2 2p^6 3s^2 3p^6 3d^{10} 4s^2 4p^2$ |
| Arsenic | As | 33 | $1s^2 2s^2 2p^6 3s^2 3p^6 3d^{10} 4s^2 4p^3$ |
| Selenium | Se | 34 | $1s^2 2s^2 2p^6 3s^2 3p^6 3d^{10} 4s^2 4p^4$ |
| Bromine | Br | 35 | $1s^2 2s^2 2p^6 3s^2 3p^6 3d^{10} 4s^2 4p^5$ |
| Krypton | Kr | 36 | $1s^2 2s^2 2p^6 3s^2 3p^6 3d^{10} 4s^2 4p^6$ |

[22]

**Figure 1.14**

The periodic table of elements organizes elements with increasing atomic number based on number of valence electrons. Elements with closed-shell configurations are found in Group 18 or 8A.

(Lars Poyansky/Shutterstock.)

### 1.7.5 Ionic Bonding

**1.7.5.1 Bonding and Force-Distance Curves**   **Primary bonds** involve the sharing or transfer of valence electrons and are stronger than secondary bonds, which will be discussed later in this chapter. Equations describing primary bonding can best be visualized by considering what would happen as two atoms are slowly brought together over a large distance (Fig. 1.15). At first, there will be no interaction since the atoms are too far apart. However, as they move closer, they will begin to exert both attractive and repulsive forces on each other. The strength of these forces depends on the distance between the atoms. The cause of the attractive force varies depending on the type of bonding, but this force governs the interaction between the atoms at intermediate distances. At very close distances, there is a strong repulsive force that results from the overlap of the core and valence electron shells from the two atoms.

The total force ($F_{total}$) between the two atoms at any given separation distance ($r$) is the sum of the attractive ($F_A$) and repulsive ($F_R$) forces:

$$F_{total}(r) = F_A(r) + F_R(r)$$

(1.1)

As shown in Fig. 1.15, at a certain separation distance, $r_0$, an equilibrium is reached where there is no total force:

$$F_A(r_0) + F_R(r_0) = 0$$

(1.2)

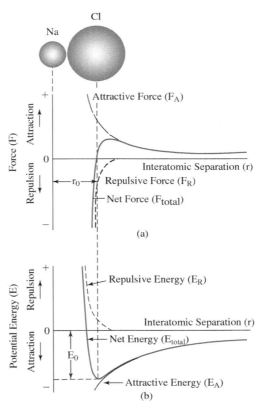

**Figure 1.15**
(a) Attractive, repulsive and total forces between two atoms as a function of separation distance. The strength of the attractive and repulsive forces depends on the distance, with repulsive forces predominating at small separation lengths due to the overlap of the core and valence electron shells from the two atoms. (b) Attractive, repulsive and total energies between two atoms as a function of separation distance. Note that, at $r_0$, there is a minimum in the total energy curve—the corresponding energy $E_0$ is considered the bonding energy for the pair of atoms [22, 25].

Because there is no total force at this distance, atoms prefer to remain at this spacing and will resist attempts to force movement closer or further apart. The distance $r_0$ is measured from the center of one atom to the center of the other and is considered to be the **bond length** between the two atoms.

Since energy $(E)$ is defined as force $(F)$ over a distance $(r)$, the above equation can be converted from terms of force to terms of energy through integration over an infinite separation distance:

$$E_{total}(r) = \int_{\infty}^{r} F_{total}(r')dr' = \int_{\infty}^{r} F_A(r')dr' + \int_{\infty}^{r} F_R(r')dr' = E_A(r) + E_R(r) \quad (1.3)$$

Figure 1.15(b) depicts the attractive $(E_A)$, repulsive $(E_R)$, and total energies $(E_{total})$ based on separation distance $(r)$. Like the force curves (Fig. 1.15(a)), the total energy curve is the sum of the contributions of the attractive and repulsive energies. Also in correspondence to the force curve, at $r_0$, there is a minimum in the total energy curve. This is the **bonding energy** for the two atoms, and represents the amount of energy that would be required to separate them to an infinite distance.

**1.7.5.2 Characteristics of the Ionic Bond**  There are three types of primary bonds: ionic, covalent, and metallic. The concepts of bond energy and separation distance detailed earlier in the text are valid for all types of primary bonds, although the magnitude and shape of the energy versus distance curves may differ. We begin our discussion with ionic bonding, since this type follows the models for bond force and energy most directly.

Ionic bonds occur between atoms that have large differences in electronegativity, for example, between elements in Group 1 and Group 16 or 17. A common molecule demonstrating ionic bonding is NaCl. In this case, the single electron in the valence shell of Na $(1s^2 2s^2 2p^6 3s^1)$ is transferred to the highly electronegative Cl, which is one electron short of a full valence shell $(1s^2 2s^2 2p^6 3s^2 3p^5)$. Through this transfer, a positive ion (**cation**) of Na ($Na^+$) and negative ion (**anion**) of Cl ($Cl^-$) is formed, with both ions having full valence shells. This generates an electrostatic attraction between the two ions, which is the source of the attractive force in the force-separation distance curves for ionic bonds. The magnitude of this force, the **Coulombic force** ($F_C$), is a function of both the charge of the ions and their separation distance ($r$); that is,

$$F_C(r) = \frac{-K_C}{r^2} \tag{1.4}$$

$$K_C = k_0(Z_1 q)(Z_2 q) \tag{1.5}$$

where $r$ is the separation distance between the centers of ions 1 and 2, $Z_1$ and $Z_2$ are the valence of the charged ions, $k_0$ is a proportionality constant $(9 \times 10^9 \, \text{VmC}^{-1})$, and $q$ is the charge of a single electron. The corresponding equation for the repulsive force ($F_R$) reflects the large increase seen as the ions are forced closer together:

$$F_R(r) = \frac{-K_R}{r^n} \tag{1.6}$$

where $K_R$ and $n$ are constants, with $n > 2$. As previously discussed, these equations can then be integrated to obtain the corresponding attractive and repulsive energies.

Ionic bonds have the same magnitude in all directions and thus are termed nondirectional. To ensure stability, each negative ion must be surrounded in three dimensions by positive ions, and vice versa. This imposes constraints on the structure of ionic crystals. Ionic bonds are most commonly found in ceramic materials. As described previously, ceramics demonstrate characteristic mechanical properties (hardness and brittleness) that can be directly related to this bond type.

### 1.7.6 Covalent Bonding

**Covalent bonds** are formed through the sharing of valence electrons, rather than complete electron transfer, as observed in ionic bonds. In this case, there are electronegative elements but no electropositive ones. Since there is no ion formation with covalent bonds, the attractive force found as a part of the force-separation distance curve is not strictly Coulombic, but attraction does exist between the atomic cores and shared electrons. The corresponding repulsive force is generated when core electrons from the atoms come in proximity to each other. Covalent bonds are found in polymeric biomaterials.

#### 1.7.6.1 Atomic Orbitals and Hybridization    The number of covalent bonds that an atom can form depends on the number of valence electrons present. As mentioned previously, atomic subshells (also called orbitals) have specific shapes and orientations. In order to increase the probability of forming covalent bonds, these orbitals can change energy and shape (**hybridize**). For example, the carbon atom would typically have two valence electrons in the $2s$ and two in the $2p$ orbitals. However, in methane ($CH_4$), the carbon atom has gained enough energy to promote one $2s$ electron to the third $p$ orbital and then all of the valence orbitals are altered to form four $sp^3$ hybrid orbitals. The shape of these hybrid orbitals is depicted in Figure 1.16. Although energy is required for promotion of an electron between orbitals, the newly formed hybrid orbitals have a large lobe that can be directed toward other atoms to promote covalent binding. The energy released as the bond is formed more than compensates for the original energy requirement for hybridization.

Depending on the number of valence electrons, $sp$, $sp^2$, and $sp^3$ hybrid orbitals are possible. The orientation of the large lobes in each case is somewhat different

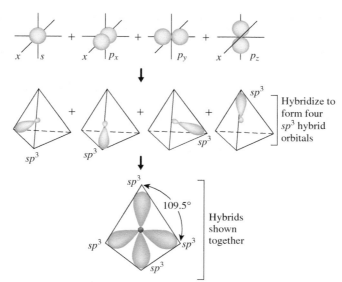

**Figure 1.16**
Formation of four $sp^3$ hybrid orbitals from one valence electron in the 2s and three in the 2p. Each of the newly formed hybrid orbitals have a large lobe that can be directed toward other atoms to promote covalent binding.

and is governed by the idea that, due to electrostatic repulsion between the electrons, the most stable atomic structure will place the lobes as far apart as possible. Spatial orientations of the most common hybrid orbital types are found in Figure 1.17. The spatial orientation of the hybrid orbitals affects where bonding occurs and results in different bond angles for different compounds. These bond angles play an important role in the physical properties of synthetic and naturally derived polymers.

Unlike ionic bonding, covalent bonding is directional because the shared electrons lie between the two atoms. This directionality affects the overall properties of covalently bonded materials. Bonds formed along the internuclear axis of two atoms are called **sigma** ($\sigma$) **bonds**. These are the type of bonds most often associated with covalent bonding. However, in certain cases, such as for double or triple bonds (such as are found in ethylene ($C_2H_4$) or acetylene ($C_2H_2$)—see Fig. 1.18), we must consider a second type of bond, the **pi** ($\pi$) **bond**. In ethylene, instead of hybridizing to $sp^3$ orbitals as happens in $CH_4$, each carbon has three of the valence electrons in $sp^2$ hybrid orbitals and one in a regular $p$ orbital. The $sp^2$ orbitals form $\sigma$ bonds between one carbon, each hydrogen, and the other carbon

| Hybrid orbital Set | Atomic orbital set | Hybridization | Examples |
|---|---|---|---|
| Two $sp$ | $s,p$ | Linear<br>180° | $BeF_2$, $HgCl_2$ |
| Three $sp^2$ | $s,p,p$ | Trigonal planar<br>120° | $BF_3$, $HO_3$ |
| Three $sp^3$ | $s,p,p,p$ | Tetrahedral<br>109.5° | $CH_4$, $NH_3$, $H_2O$, $NH_4^+$ |

**Figure 1.17**
Spatial orientations of the most common hybrid orbital types. The spatial orientation of the hybrid orbitals affects where bonding occurs and results in different bond angles for different compounds.

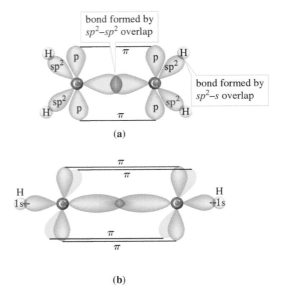

**Figure 1.18**

$\pi$ bonds in ethylene and acetylene molecules. (a) Bonds found in the ethylene molecule. $\sigma$ bonds are formed along the internuclear axis between two atoms, such as the $sp^2$ orbital between carbon and each hydrogen and the $sp^2$ orbital between the two carbon atoms. This leaves two electrons in the unhybridized $p$ orbitals, which can then interact in a sideways fashion to complete the valence shell of each carbon, thus forming a $\pi$ bond parallel to the internuclear axis. (b) Bonds found in the acetylene molecule. A second $\pi$ bond is formed in a similar manner to ethylene. $\pi$ bonds are not as strong as $\sigma$ bonds, but their presence can affect the properties and activity of proteins and synthetic polymers.

(Fig. 1.18(a)). This leaves two electrons in the unhybridized $p$ orbitals, one associated with each carbon. These $p$ orbitals can then interact in a sideways fashion to complete the valence shell of each carbon, thus forming a $\pi$ bond perpendicular to the internuclear axis.

A second $\pi$ bond is formed in a similar manner in the acetylene molecule (C–C triple bond, see Fig. 1.18(b)). $\pi$ bonds are not as strong as $\sigma$ bonds, but can affect rigidity of materials because they constrain certain parts of molecules in planar orientations. Therefore, the presence of such bonds has an impact on the properties and activity of proteins and synthetic polymers.

## EXAMPLE PROBLEM 1.7

Determine the orbital structures of the backbones of the following polymers:

(a)

(b)

(c)

Solution:

(a) A $\sigma$ bond is formed between the two carbons in the backbone of poly(ethylene) by the overlap of two $sp^3$ hybrid orbitals.
(b) A $\sigma$ bond and a $\pi$ bond are formed between the two carbons in the backbone of poly(acetylene) by the overlap of $sp^2$ hybrid orbitals and $p$ orbitals, respectively.
(c) A $\sigma$ bond and two $\pi$ bonds are formed between the two carbons in the backbone of poly(yne) by the overlap of $sp$ hybrid orbitals and $p$ orbitals, respectively.    ∎

**1.7.6.2 Molecular Orbitals**  Although the concepts of atomic orbitals and hybridization serve to explain many of the properties of the covalent bond, another model involving **molecular orbitals** is needed to more fully describe energy absorption and excited states, which are important to many of the spectroscopic techniques that will be discussed later in this text. Molecular orbitals have many of the same properties as atomic orbitals, but they are associated with an entire molecule. Like atomic orbitals, they have definite energy levels and can hold only two electrons, each with different spins. There are two types of molecular orbitals: bonding and antibonding (Fig. 1.19).

In **bonding molecular orbitals**, the wave functions describing the electrons in atomic orbitals from two different atoms overlap in a reinforcing way and enhance each other. Thus, there is a high probability of finding the electrons in the region along the internuclear axis, where there is a strong attraction to the nuclei. This configuration is very stable, and the electrons are at a lower energy than they were in their respective atomic orbitals. The bonding molecular orbital is the basis for covalent bonds between atoms.

On the other hand, in **antibonding molecular orbitals**, the electrons' wave functions overlap in a destructive way and cancel each other in the region between the nuclei, and the greatest electron density is found on the opposite sides of the nuclei (Fig. 1.19). Since this excludes electrons from the very area where a bond should form, this orbital is less stable (has higher energy) than the corresponding atomic orbitals of the individual atoms.

Like atomic orbitals, there are both $\sigma$ and $\pi$ molecular orbitals (Fig. 1.20). $\sigma$ bonding and antibonding molecular orbitals describe the electron density in the line between two nuclei, while $\pi$ bonding and antibonding molecular orbitals arise from the sideways overlap of atomic orbitals and therefore describe the electron density in spatial orientations other than along the internuclear axis (Fig. 1.20).

**1.7.6.3 Mixed Bonds**  From the descriptions of the bond types discussed in the preceding text, it can be assumed that ionic bonds are formed primarily when there

**Figure 1.19**
The combination of two H $1s$ atomic orbitals to form bonding ($\sigma$) and anti-bonding ($\sigma^*$) molecular orbitals in $H_2$. In bonding molecular orbitals, the wave functions describing the electrons in atomic orbitals from two different atoms overlap in a reinforcing way and enhance each other. This orbital is very stable, and the electrons are at a lower energy than they were in their respective atomic orbitals. On the other hand, in antibonding molecular orbitals, the electrons' wave functions overlap in a destructive way and cancel each other in the region between the nuclei (a node is formed between the nuclei). Since this excludes electrons from the very area where a bond should form, this orbital is less stable (has higher energy) than the corresponding atomic orbitals of the individual atoms [28].

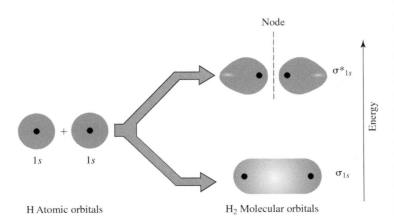

**Figure 1.20**
(a) $\sigma$ molecular orbitals. $\sigma$ bonding and antibonding molecular orbitals describe the electron density in the line between two nuclei. (b–c) $\pi$ molecular orbitals. $\pi$ bonding and antibonding molecular orbitals arise from the sideways overlap of atomic orbitals and therefore describe the electron density in spatial orientations other than that along the internuclear axis.

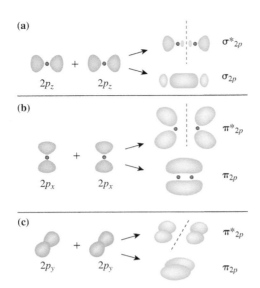

is a large difference in electronegativity between the elements in a compound, and covalent bonds are formed when there is a smaller difference. However, this is a simplified explanation and, in reality, there is a gradual shift between the bond types. Thus, many bonds have characteristics that are partially ionic and partially covalent. Calculations suggest that a difference in electronegativity of approximately 1.7 results in a bond with half-covalent and half-ionic properties. Many ceramics have bonds that display mixed characteristics. As expected, the extent to which a material's bonds exhibit ionic or covalent characteristics will affect its general physical properties.

### 1.7.7 Metallic Bonding

Metallic bonds are generally formed in materials containing elements that are electropositive. Because there are no electronegative elements to accept the valence electrons, the electrons are donated to the entire structure. This creates a "cloud" or "sea" of electrons that are mobile and surround a core of cations (Fig. 1.21). Metallic bonds do involve electron sharing, similar to covalent bonds, but are nondirectional, like ionic bonds. Here, the valence electrons are considered to be delocalized and

**Figure 1.21**
Schematic of metallic bonding. Because there are no electronegative elements to accept the valence electrons, the electrons are donated to the entire structure. This creates a "cloud" or "sea" of electrons that are mobile and surround cation cores [22].

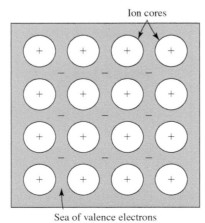

Ion cores

Sea of valence electrons

have equal probability of being associated with any of the ion cores. The mobility of electrons in metals is what leads to their high electrical conductivity.

In metallic bonds, the attractive force seen as part of the force-separation distance curve is caused by the electrostatic attraction between the positively charged ion cores and the negatively charged electron clouds. Similar to the other bond types, a repulsive force is generated when the filled shells of the ion cores start to overlap.

## 1.7.8 Secondary Forces

Although the type of primary bonds a material possesses dictates many of its properties, **secondary bonds** (or **van der Waals bonds**) can play a large role as well. Secondary bonds involve attraction between atoms that require neither electron transfer nor electron sharing. Thus, they are substantially weaker than primary bonds. In general, this attraction occurs between molecules that, for various reasons, have a portion that is slightly positively charged and a portion that is slightly negatively charged (a **molecular dipole**). The positive end of one molecule then associates with the negative end of another via Coulombic attraction, forming a three-dimensional network.

Although it is possible to have temporary (fluctuating) dipole molecules, which give rise to van der Waals forces, the strongest type of secondary bonding occurs with molecules considered to be permanent dipoles. These are called **polar molecules** and include water ($H_2O$). In water, the electronegative oxygen draws electrons away from the hydrogen nuclei. This, in combination with the extra, unbonded electrons in the oxygen atom, causes the oxygen portion of the molecule to carry a partial negative charge (Fig. 1.22). The hydrogen atoms can then interact with the negative (oxygen) end of another water molecule, forming a **hydrogen bond**. These bonds are important in explaining certain properties of water, such as its high heat capacity and the fact that it expands as it moves from a liquid to solid state (freezes). As discussed in later chapters, hydrogen bonding is also essential to the structure (and thus function) of both synthetic polymers and naturally formed materials such as proteins.

**Figure 1.22**
(a) Hydrogen bond between water molecules. The electronegative oxygen draws electrons away from the hydrogen nucleus, which, in combination with the extra, unbonded electrons in the oxygen atom, causes the oxygen portion of the molecule to carry a partial negative charge. The hydrogen atoms can then interact with the negative (oxygen) end of another water molecule to form the hydrogen bond. (b) An illustration of a three-dimensional lattice of hydrogen bonds in water [29].

## Summary

- Biomaterials science is a broad field that involves the development, characterization, and application of materials to interface with biological systems in the evaluation, treatment, or augmentation of biological functions while invoking an appropriate host response.
- The field of biomaterials has evolved from the use of industrial materials in the 1940s to the advent of more "designer" materials for a wide range of applications, such as prosthetic heart valves, hip replacements, and kidney dialysis membranes.
- In the United States, the Food and Drug Administration (FDA) is responsible for oversight of medical products. Regulation is carried out by one of three divisions within the FDA (CDRH, CBER, and CDER).
- The biological response to a biomaterial is influenced largely by the properties of the material, including the shape, degradation characteristics, surface chemistry, bulk material chemistry, and mechanical properties. In turn, this biological response can have an effect on the material itself.
- The three general categories of biomaterials are metals, ceramics, and polymers.
- Polymeric materials can be either synthetic or naturally derived. Naturally derived polymers originate from biological sources and may closely mimic tissues targeted for replacement and integrate well into the surrounding tissue, but they are often of limited supply, have low mechanical properties, and pose the potential for pathogen transmission. Synthetic polymers, on the other hand, can be produced and sterilized in large quantities with properties tailored for specific applications, but they are usually not capable of interacting with surrounding tissue in an active manner.
- The envisioned final application of a biomaterial dictates the properties and design criteria required of the biomaterial. Surface properties, such as surface roughness and degree of hydrophobicity, are defined by the outermost few atomic layers of the material and highly influence interaction with the surrounding biological environment, especially in the short term. The bulk properties of the material include mechanical properties, physical properties, and chemical composition, which strongly affect the overall performance and long-term stability of the implant.
- The method in which a biomaterial is processed imparts that material with a certain form or geometry. The form of the biomaterial can influence the properties of the material and the biological response to the material. For example, thin sheets are well suited for skin replacements, and flexible, hollow cylinders are appropriate for vascular grafts.
- One of the primary considerations for selection of a biomaterial is the chemical composition of the material. Basic models of molecular chemistry state that an atom is composed of a core nucleus of protons and neutrons orbited by a number of electrons equal to the number of protons. The exact location of the electrons in orbit can be described in terms of discrete energy states (Bohr model) or in terms of space-occupying probabilities (wave-mechanical model). The Aufbau principle, the Pauli exclusion principle, and Hund's rule work in concert to provide a mechanism for predicting the electron configuration of an atom. Atoms with different electron configurations can interact in different ways in various forms of bonding, including ionic bonding (electron transfer), covalent bonding (electron sharing), metallic bonding (nondirectional electron sharing), and bonding through secondary forces, such as hydrogen bonding.

# Problems

1.1  An artery is a flexible blood vessel that withstands various pressures from the flow of blood. A common application of biomaterials is in the fabrication of a vascular stent to prevent reclosure of arteries after angioplasty (removal of plaques that impede blood flow). In many of these products, metals are used and formed into a "chain link" type architecture, as shown in the following figure.

   (a) What specific bulk and surface material properties would be required for this application?

   (b) Explain why this material type and architecture were chosen in terms of the properties you have listed in (a).

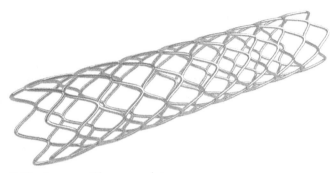

(Mile Atanasov/Shutterstock.)

1.2  A current area of biomaterials research is in developing a tissue-engineered bone replacement to be placed in large bone defects. In general, this approach involves seeding bone cells on a scaffolding material with the idea that the entire construct would be implanted into the site of injury to replace lost bone.

   (a) Would a natural or synthetic material be best for the scaffold? Justify your answer in terms of the expected response of the body to your construct and why that material class may be better for the chosen application.

   (b) What FDA regulatory pathway would likely be involved in approval of this product?

1.3  Whether or not the biological response to a material is acceptable depends on the specific application (see definition of biocompatibility, Section 1.1). Assume a new material shows activation of the immune system *in vivo*. Discuss whether or not this result would be acceptable for the following applications and explain your reasoning:

   (a) Stem of hip implant
   (b) Tissue-engineered vascular graft
   (c) Carrier for vaccine delivery
   (d) Coating for implanted electrode
   (e) Nanoparticle for cancer therapy

1.4  Fluorine (F) is more electronegative than oxygen (O).

   (a) If you replace O with F in a compound, which of the three major classes of primary bonds would it affect the most? Explain why you chose this class.

   (b) How would this replacement affect secondary bonding?

# References

1. D. F. Williams, *The Williams Dictionary of Biomaterials*. Liverpool: Liverpool University Press, 1999.

2. B. D. Ratner, A. S. Hoffman, F. J. Schoen, and J. E. Lemons, "Biomaterials science: a multidisciplinary endeavor," in *Biomaterials science: an introduction to materials and medicine*, 2nd ed., B. D. Ratner, A. S. Hoffman, F. J. Schoen, and J. E. Lemons, Eds. San Diego: Elsevier Academic Press, 2004, pp. 1–9.

3. B. D. Ratner, "A history of biomaterials," in *Biomaterials science: an introduction to materials and medicine*, 2nd ed., B. D. Ratner, A. S. Hoffman, F. J. Schoen, and J. E. Lemons, Eds. San Diego: Elsevier Academic Press, 2004, pp. 10–19.

4. "Orthopedic Devices Market Size By Product, Industry Analysis Report, Regional Outlook, Application Potential, Price Trends, Competitive Market Share & Forecast, 2021 – 2027," *Global Market Insights*, 2021. [Online]. Available: https://www.gminsights.com/industry-analysis/orthopedic-devices-market.

5. "Joint Replacement Market Size, Share & Trends Analysis Report By Product (Knees, Hips, Extremities), By Fixation Type, By End-use (Hospitals, Orthopedic Clinics), By Procedure, By Region, And Segment Forecasts, 2021 - 2028," *Grand View Research*, 2021. [Online]. Available: https://www.grandviewresearch.com/industry-analysis/joint-replacement-market-report.

6. "Bone Cement Market in the US 2021-2025," *Research and Markets*, 2021. [Online]. Available: https://www.researchandmarkets.com/reports/5354537/bone-cement-market-in-the-us-2021-2025.

7. "North America Trauma Fixation Devices Market Research Report," *Market Data Forecast*, 2021. [Online]. Available: https://www.marketdataforecast.com/market-reports/north-america-trauma-fixation-devices-market.

8. "Size of the Cardiovascular Devices Market in the U.S. in 2007, 2014, and 2021, by Category," *Statista*, 2021. [Online]. Available: https://www.statista.com/statistics/648833/cardiovascular-devices-market-united-states-by-category.

9. "Vascular Graft Market Size, Competitive Market Share & Forecast, 2021 – 2027," *Global Market Insights*, 2021. [Online]. Available: https://www.gminsights.com/industry-analysis/vascular-graft-market.

10. "North America Coronary Stent Market Research Report," *Market Data Forecast*, 2021. [Online]. Available: https://www.marketdataforecast.com/market-reports/north-america-coronary-stent-market.

11. "North America Surgical Sutures Market Research Report," *Market Data Forecast*, 2021. [Online]. Available: https://www.marketdataforecast.com/market-reports/north-america-surgical-sutures.

12. "North America Breast Implants Market to 2027," *Research and Markets*, 2020. [Online]. Available: https://www.researchandmarkets.com/reports/5138164/north-america-breast-implants-market-to-2027.

13. "Advanced Wound Dressing Market Size, Share & Trends Analysis Report," *Grand View Research*, 2021. [Online]. Available: https://www.grandviewresearch.com/industry-analysis/advanced-wound-care-dressing-market.

14. "Kidney Dialysis Centers Industry Profile," *Dun and Bradstreet First Research*, 2021. [Online]. Available: http://www.firstresearch.com/Industry-Research/Kidney-Dialysis-Centers.html.

15. "National Health Expenditures," *Centers for Medicare and Medicaid Services*, 2021. [Online]. Available: https://www.cms.gov/Research-Statistics-Data-and-Systems/Statistics-Trends-and-Reports/NationalHealthExpendData/index.html.

16. "U.S. Investments in Medical and Health Research and Development Report, 2013-2018," *Research!America*, 2019. [Online]. Available: https://www.researchamerica.org/polls-publications/us-investments-medical-and-health-research.

17. "Medical Devices Market Size," *Fortune Business Insights*, 2021. [Online]. Available: https://www.fortunebusinessinsights.com/industry-reports/medical-devices-market-100085.

18. "North America Biomaterials Market Research Report," *Market Data Forecast*, 2021. [Online]. Available: https://www.marketdataforecast.com/market-reports/north-america-biomaterials-market.

19. P. S. Malchesky, "Extracorporeal artificial organs," in *Biomaterials science: an introduction to materials and medicine*, 2nd ed., B. D. Ratner, A. S. Hoffman, F. J. Schoen, and J. E. Lemons, Eds. San Diego: Elsevier Academic Press, 2004, pp. 514–526.

20. J. E. Mark, *Physical properties of polymers handbook*. Woodbury, New York: American Institute of Physics, 1996.

21. C. Migliaresi and H. ALexander, "Composites," in *Biomaterials science: an introduction to materials and medicine*, 2nd ed., B. D. Ratner, A. S. Hoffman, F. J. Schoen, and J. E. Lemons, Eds. San Diego: Elsevier Academic Press, 2004, pp. 181–197.

22. J. Callister, *Materials science and engineering: an introduction*, 3rd ed. New York: John Wiley and Sons, 1994.

23. J. B. Park and R. S. Lakes, *Biomaterials: an introduction*, 2nd ed. New York: Plenum Press, 1992.

24. R. F. Padera Jr. and F. J. Schoen, "Cardiovascular medical devices," in *Biomaterials science: an introduction*

*to materials and medicine*, 2nd ed., B. D. Ratner, A. S. Hoffman, F. J. Schoen, and J. E. Lemons, Eds. San Diego: Elsevier Academic Press, 2004, pp. 470–494.

25. J. F. Shackelford, *Introduction to materials science for engineers*, 5th ed. Upper Saddle River: Prentice Hall, 2000.

26. H. W. Pollack, *Materials science and metallurgy*. Reston Pub. Co., 1977.

27. K. P. C. Vollhardt and N. E. Schore, *Organic chemistry*, 2nd ed. New York: W. H. Freeman, 1994.

28. T. L. Brown, J. LeMay, and B. E. Bursten, *Chemistry: the central science*, 6th ed. Englewood Cliffs: Prentice Hall, 1994.

29. B. Alberts, D. Bray, J. Lewis, M. Raff, K. Roberts, and J. Watson, *Molecular biology of the cell*, 3rd ed. New York: Garland Publishing, 1994.

## Additional Reading

V. Bhat, Ed., *Biomaterials*, 2nd ed. Springer Netherlands, 2002.

E. Duncan, "Regulatory Overview for Medical Products Using Biomaterials," in *Biomaterials science: an introduction to materials and medicine*, 3rd ed., B. D. Ratner, A. S. Hoffman, F. J. Schoen, and J. E. Lemons, Eds. San Diego: Academic Press, 2013, pp. 1405–1413.

S. C. Gad and S. Gad-McDonald, *Biomaterials, medical devices, and combination products: biocompatibility testing and safety assessment*. CRC Press, 2015.

P. M. Galletti and C. K. Colton, "Artificial lungs and blood-gas exchange devices," in *The biomedical engineering handbook*, 1st ed., J. D. Bronzino, Ed. CRC Press, 1995, pp. 1879–1897.

N. J. Hallab, J. J. Jacobs, and J. L. Katz, "Orthopedic Applications," in *Biomaterials science: an introduction to materials and medicine*, 2nd ed., B. D. Ratner, A. S. Hoffman, F. J. Schoen, and J. E. Lemons, Eds. San Diego: Elsevier Academic Press, 2004, pp. 526–555.

J. E. Lemons, "Voluntary Consensus Standards," in *Biomaterials science: an introduction to materials and medicine*, 2nd ed., B. D. Ratner, A. S. Hoffman, F. J. Schoen, and J. E. Lemons, Eds. San Diego: Elsevier Academic Press, 2004, pp. 783–788.

F. H. Silver and D. L. Christiansen, *Biomaterials science and biocompatibility*. New York: Springer Science & Business Media, 1999.

J. S. Temenoff, E. S. Steinbis, and A. G. Mikos, "Biodegradable Scaffolds," in *Orthopedic tissue engineering: basic science and practice*, V. M. Goldberg and A. I. Caplan, Eds. Informa Health Care, 2004, pp. 77–103.

D. Voet and J. G. Voet, *Biochemistry*, 3rd ed. Wiley, 2004.

E. A. Vogler, "Role of Water in Biomaterials," in *Biomaterials science: an introduction to materials and medicine*, 2nd ed., B. D. Ratner, A. S. Hoffman, F. J. Schoen, and J. E. Lemons, Eds. San Diego: Elsevier Academic Press, 2004, pp. 59–65.

I. V. Yannas, "Natural Materials," in *Biomaterials science: an introduction to materials and medicine*, 2nd ed., B. D. Ratner, A. S. Hoffman, F. J. Schoen, and J. E. Lemons, Eds. San Diego: Elsevier Academic Press, 2004, pp. 127–137.

D. Williams, *Essential biomaterials science*. Cambridge, UK: Cambridge University Press, 2014.

# 2 Chemical Structure of Biomaterials

## Main Objective

To understand the different types of bonding and how these are organized into material subunits for metals, ceramics, and polymers.

## Specific Objectives

1. To compare and contrast building blocks of metals, ceramics, and polymers.
2. To understand and be able to produce lattice parameters for simple crystal structures in metals and ceramics.
3. To compare and contrast types of defects and impurities in metals and ceramics.
4. To understand and use simple models of diffusion.
5. To understand general methods of polymer synthesis.
6. To understand how the chemical structure of polymers affects their ability to form regular structures (crystals).
7. To understand the theory behind and possible limitations to various chemical composition characterization techniques presented.

## 2.1 Introduction: Bonding and the Structure of Biomaterials

This chapter will focus on how the types of bonds described in Chapter 1 relate in three dimensions to form different classes of biomaterials. In order to more fully appreciate the differences between these material types, the structures of metals, ceramics, and polymers will be compared and contrasted.

For this discussion, it is important to distinguish between crystalline and amorphous materials. In crystalline materials, atoms are arranged in a periodic pattern resulting in long-range order. Amorphous materials lack this systematic atomic arrangement and can be considered to possess a molecular structure much more like that of a liquid. Although metals are typically crystalline, ceramic and polymeric materials can be either crystalline or amorphous, depending on their chemical constituents and processing method.

# 2.2   Structure of Metals

We begin our discussion of chemical structures with metallic biomaterials. These materials have been widely explored for a variety of biomedical applications, but are best known as the basis of joint replacements. Metals are crystalline, and because metallic bonding is nondirectional, there are a wide variety of atomic configurations possible to create a number of crystal structures.

## 2.2.1   Crystal Structures

A number of physical properties depend on the crystal structure of a material. For ease of communication, crystal structures are usually described on the basis of their unit cells. A **unit cell** is the configuration of atoms in a small section of the crystal that is repeated again and again in three dimensions to form the final material. Although the limits of the unit cell are arbitrarily chosen, standard cells are parallelepipeds with corners coinciding with the centers of atoms. Figure 2.1 depicts a diagram of a simple cubic unit cell and its relationship to three-dimensional atomic structure.

When discussing crystal structures, it is convenient to compare them using parameters such as **coordination number** and **atomic packing factor** (**APF**). Each atom in a crystal has a coordination number equal to the number of nearest-neighbor atoms. The APF is based on the **atomic hard-sphere model**, which depicts each atom as a sphere requiring a fixed volume (Fig. 2.2). APF is a means of discussing how much unoccupied space there is in a particular structure and is found using:

$$\text{APF} = \frac{\text{volume of atoms in a unit cell}}{\text{total unit cell volume}}$$

**2.2.1.1   Face-Centered Cubic Structure**   Although a simple cubic unit cell like that shown in Figure 2.1 is easy to visualize, in reality, very few materials of interest adopt this crystal structure. In fact, metals have a variety of crystal structures depending on temperature, processing, and alloying. For many metals, a common crystal structure is **face-centered cubic** (FCC). Aluminum, copper, lead, silver, and gold are some

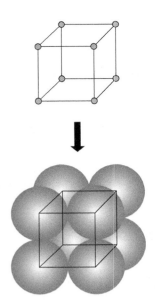

**Figure 2.1**
Schematic of a simple cubic unit cell and its relationship to three-dimensional atomic structure. The corners of the unit cell coincide with the centers of the atoms in the final structure. (Reprinted with permission from [2].)

(a)

(b)

**Figure 2.2**
(a) The atomic hard-sphere model of a face-centered cubic unit cell. The parameter $a$ is the unit cell edge length and $r$ is the atomic radius. In this geometry, there are atoms located at each of the corners as well as the centers of each face. The atomic packing factor for FCC crystals is 0.74, and the coordination number is 12. (b) Relationship of a unit cell to the larger structure of an FCC crystal. Note how atoms (or lattice points) are shared between multiple unit cells (e.g., each corner lattice point is shared between eight unit cells, whereas face-centered atoms are shared between two unit cells) [2, 10].

**TABLE 2.1**

| Crystal Structure for Common Metals | | | | | |
| Metal | Crystal Structure[a] | Atomic Radius[b] (nm) | Metal | Crystal Structure | Atomic Radius (nm) |
| --- | --- | --- | --- | --- | --- |
| Aluminum | FCC | 0.1431 | Molybdenum | BCC | 0.1363 |
| Cadmium | HCP | 0.1490 | Nickel | FCC | 0.1246 |
| Chromium | BCC | 0.1249 | Platinum | FCC | 0.1387 |
| Cobalt | HCP | 0.1253 | Silver | FCC | 0.1445 |
| Copper | FCC | 0.1278 | Tantalum | BCC | 0.1430 |
| Gold | FCC | 0.1442 | Titanium ($\alpha$) | HCP | 0.1445 |
| Iron ($\alpha$) | BCC | 0.1241 | Tungsten | BCC | 0.1371 |
| Lead | FCC | 0.1750 | Zinc | HCP | 0.1332 |

[a]FCC = face-centered cubic; HCP = hexagonal close-packed; BCC = body-centered cubic.

[b]A nanometer (nm) equals $10^{-9}$ m; to convert from nanometers to angstrom units (Å), multiply the nanometer value by 10.

(Reprinted with permission from [1].)

of the metals that exhibit this structure at room temperature (see Table 2.1). In this geometry, atoms are located at each of the corners as well as the centers of each face (Fig. 2.2). Examining the hard sphere model in Figure 2.2, the unit cell edge length ($a$) and the atomic radius ($r$) can be related through the formula

$$a = 2r\sqrt{2} \tag{2.1}$$

In a FCC crystal, the corner atoms are shared by eight unit cells and the face atoms are shared by two. Therefore, $(8 \times \frac{1}{8}) + (6 \times \frac{1}{2})$, or the equivalent of four atoms belong to each unit cell. Using the expressions for volume of a sphere and cube, the calculation for APF results in 0.74. This is the largest fraction obtainable using atoms all having the same radius.

Also shown in Figure 2.2, the coordination number for FCC crystals is 12. As an example, the atom in the center of the front face of the cell has four corner nearest neighbors, four face atoms touching from behind, and another four equivalent neighbor face atoms in the unit cell in front of it, coming out of the page (not shown).

## EXAMPLE PROBLEM 2.1

Consider a FCC crystal, as shown in Figure 2.2.

(a) Show why the relation between $r$ and $a$ is $a = 2r\sqrt{2}$.
(b) Apply this relationship and the knowledge that a FCC crystal has the equivalent of four atoms per unit cell to show that the APF for FCC crystals is 0.74.

Solution:

(a) Consider one side of the FCC crystal as shown:

 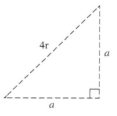

It is apparent that a right triangle can be drawn with two sides equal to $a$ and the hypotenuse equal to $4r$, as the atoms are in contact. Thus, through the use of the Pythagorean theorem, we obtain:

$$a^2 + a^2 = (4r)^2$$
$$2a^2 = 16r^2$$
$$a^2 = 8r^2$$
$$\underline{a = 2r\sqrt{2}}$$

**(b)** The volume of a unit cell is as follows: $V_{unit\ cell} = a^3$.

Substituting the relation from part (a) gives $V_{unit\ cell} = \left(2r\sqrt{2}\right)^3$.
A FCC unit cell contains the equivalent of four atoms; thus, the volume occupied by atoms in the unit cell is as follows:

$$V_{atoms} = 4\left(\tfrac{4}{3}\pi r^3\right)$$

The APF is the ratio of the volume of the unit cell occupied by atoms to the volume of the unit cell, and can be expressed as follows:

$$APF = \frac{V_{atoms}}{V_{unit\ cell}} = \frac{(16/3)\pi r^3}{16r^3\sqrt{2}} = \frac{\pi}{3\sqrt{2}} = \underline{0.74} \qquad \blacksquare$$

**2.2.1.2 Body-Centered Cubic Structure**  Another common crystal structure for metals such as chromium or iron is the **body-centered cubic** (BCC, see Table 2.1). This unit cell is depicted in Figure 2.3. In this structure, there are atoms at all eight corners and a single atom at the center of the cube. From the figure, the unit cell edge length ($a$) and the atomic radius ($r$) are related by the formula

$$a = \frac{4r}{\sqrt{3}} \qquad (2.2)$$

In a BCC crystal, the corner atoms are shared by eight unit cells and the central atom is not shared. Therefore, $\left(8 \times \tfrac{1}{8}\right) + 1$ or the equivalent of two atoms belong to each unit cell. This results in an APF of 0.68, which is less than that for a FCC

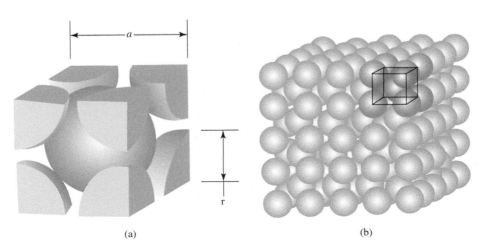

(a)                           (b)

**Figure 2.3**
(a) The atomic hard-sphere model of a body-centered cubic unit cell. The parameter $a$ is the unit cell edge length and $r$ is the atomic radius. In this geometry, there are atoms at all eight corners and a single atom at the center of the cube. The atomic packing factor for BCC crystals is 0.68, and the coordination number is 8. (b) The relationship of a unit cell to the larger structure of a BCC crystal. Note how only the corner atoms are shared among multiple (eight) unit cells [2, 10].

crystal. Similarly, the coordination number of 8 for the BCC structure is lower. This can be seen most easily by taking the atom at the center of the cube, which has the eight corner atoms as nearest neighbors (Fig. 2.3).

Although we have focused on cubic unit cell geometries, metals often have other types of unit cells. Another common type is based on a hexagonal structure. Metals with **hexagonal close-packed** (HCP) unit cells include cobalt and titanium (see Table 2.1). However, detailed descriptions of this and more complicated unit cell geometries are beyond the scope of this text.

## 2.2.2 Crystal Systems

As mentioned earlier, since there are many types of crystal structures, it is typically more convenient to represent these geometries as **lattice structures,** as depicted in Figure 2.4. In this convention, the vertices of the unit cell are called **lattice points**. The unit cell can be completely defined by determining the lengths of the edges of the unit cell ($a$, $b$, and $c$), and the angles between each of the axes ($\alpha, \beta$, and $\gamma$, see Fig. 2.4). These six values are referred to as **lattice parameters**. (Note that in lattice systems, the exact placement of individual atoms in the unit cell is ignored.)

There exist seven unique combinations of lattice parameters, each of which is a **crystal system**. These include the cubic and hexagonal systems mentioned previously, as well as several others shown in Table 2.2. As seen in Figure 2.5, a given crystal system can produce more than one crystal structure. For example, both FCC and BCC crystals belong to the cubic crystal system.

To further expand the utility of the crystal lattice concept, a coordinate system known as **Miller indices** has been developed to indicate the location of points and the orientation of planes in the lattice structure. Due to the complexity of the geometries involved in some crystal systems, we will confine our discussion of this notation to cubic crystals only. In the following example, a FCC crystal is used to demonstrate how Miller indices expedite naming points in such a unit cell (Fig. 2.6).

As shown in Figure 2.6, this notation uses a right-hand Cartesian coordinate system that is aligned with the edges of the unit cell. The coordinates of a certain

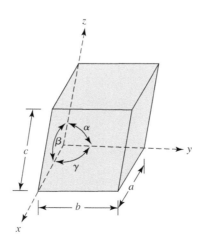

**Figure 2.4**
Generic lattice structure for a unit cell. The unit cell can be defined by the lengths of the edges of the unit cell ($a$, $b$, and $c$) and the angles between each axis ($\alpha$, $\beta$, and $\gamma$) [1].

## TABLE 2.2

| The Seven Main Crystal Systems and Their Corresponding Lattice Parameters and Angles | | |
|---|---|---|
| System | Axial lengths and angles* | Unit cell geometry |
| Cubic | $a = b = c, \alpha = \beta = \gamma = 90°$ | |
| Tetragonal | $a = b \neq c, \alpha = \beta = \gamma = 90°$ | |
| Orthorhombic | $a \neq b \neq c, \alpha = \beta = \gamma = 90°$ | |
| Rhombohedral | $a = b = c, \alpha = \beta = \gamma \neq 90°$ | |
| Hexagonal | $a = b \neq c, \alpha = \beta = 90°, \gamma = 120°$ | |
| Monoclinic | $a \neq b \neq c, \alpha = \gamma = 90° \neq \beta$ | |
| Triclinic | $a \neq b \neq c, \alpha \neq \beta \neq \gamma \neq 90°$ | |

*The lattice parameters $a$, $b$, and $c$ are unit cell edge lengths. The lattice parameters $\alpha$, $\beta$, and $\gamma$ are angles between adjacent unit cell axes, where $\alpha$ is the angle viewed *along* the $a$ axis (i.e., the angle *between* the $b$ and $c$ axes). The inequality sign ($\neq$) means that equality is not required. Accidental equality occasionally occurs in some structures.

(Reprinted with permission from [2].)

atom are written as $h$, $k$, $l$, where the three indices represent fractions of the lattice parameters $a$, $b$, and $c$. Following these guidelines, the atom at B would be indicated by 0,1,0. An atom located at point D would be 1,1,1 and an atom in the center of the face, such as H, would be 1/2,1,1/2.

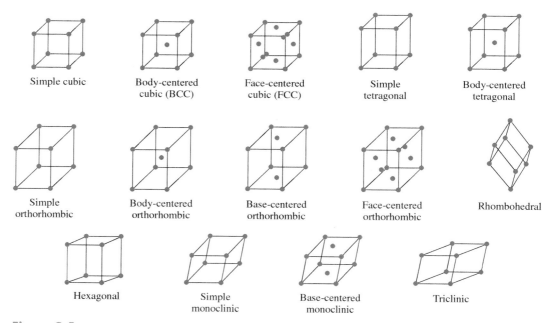

**Figure 2.5**
The crystal structures associated with the cubic, tetragonal, orthorhombic, rhombohedral, hexagonal, monoclinic, and triclinic lattice systems. (Adapted with permission from [2].)

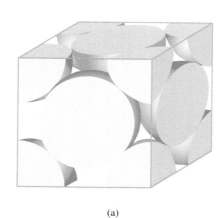

(a)

**Figure 2.6** (a) Hard-sphere model of face-centered cubic unit cell. (b) Corresponding diagram of unit cell with select points depicted using Miller indices. The coordinates of a certain atom are written as $h$, $k$, $l$, where the three indices represent fractions of the lattice parameters $a$, $b$, and $c$. In this figure, the origin has been arbitrarily defined as point O [3].

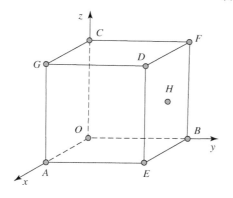

| Position | Coordinate |
|----------|------------|
| $O$ | 0, 0, 0 (Origin) |
| $A$ | 1, 0, 0 |
| $B$ | 0, 1, 0 |
| $C$ | 0, 0, 1 |
| $D$ | 1, 1, 1 |
| $E$ | 1, 1, 0 |
| $F$ | 0, 1, 1 |
| $G$ | 1, 0, 1 |
| $H$ | 1/2, 1, 1/2 |

(b)

Planes in crystal structures are designated similarly using Miller indices. Again, the axes are placed along the edges of the unit cell (Fig. 2.7). The following steps are then performed:

1. Determine the points at which the plane intersects the $x$, $y$, and $z$ axes. If the plane is parallel to an axis, the intercept for that axis is taken to be $\infty$.
2. Take the reciprocal of the intercepts.
3. Multiply/Divide by an integer to clear fractions.
4. Record integer indices in parentheses with no commas ($h\ k\ l$).
5. Negative numbers are indicated by a bar over the integer.

Using this procedure, plane $A$ in Figure 2.7 has intercepts $\infty, \infty, 1$ and, thus, its Miller indices are (0 0 1). Similarly, plane $B$ has intercepts 1,1,1 and indices (1 1 1), while plane $C$ has intercepts $1, \infty, \frac{1}{2}$ and indices (1 0 2).

## EXAMPLE PROBLEM 2.2

Calculate the Miller indices for planes $A$, $B$, and $C$. Note that by convention negative values for indices are denoted with a bar above the number, rather than a negative sign before the number.

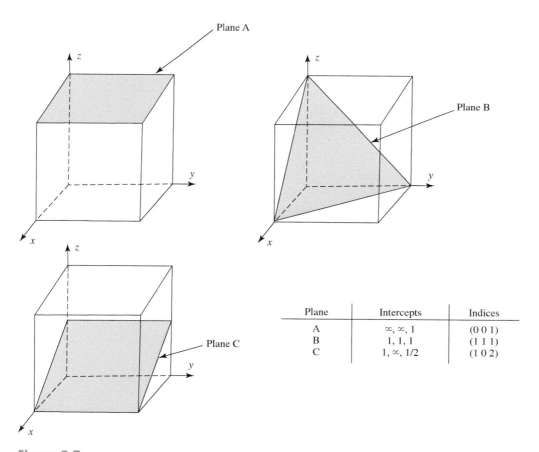

| Plane | Intercepts | Indices |
|-------|------------|---------|
| A | $\infty, \infty, 1$ | (0 0 1) |
| B | 1, 1, 1 | (1 1 1) |
| C | 1, $\infty$, 1/2 | (1 0 2) |

**Figure 2.7**
Three planes and their resulting Miller indices, which indicate the orientation of the plane. Indices are based on the reciprocal of the intercepts [3].

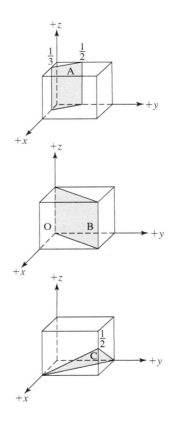

Solution:

For plane A:

|  | $x$ | $y$ | $z$ |
|---|---|---|---|
| Plane A intercepts | 1/3 | 1/2 | $\infty$ |
| reciprocals | 3 | 2 | 0 |
| indices | (3 | 2 | 0) |

For plane B:

Since this particular example goes through the origin (O), the origin must be shifted to the edge of the unit cell as follows:

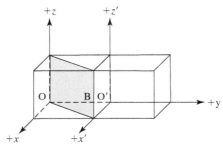

You then use this new origin to determine the intercepts of the plane:

|  | $x$ | $y$ | $z$ |
|---|---|---|---|
| Plane B intercepts | 1 | $-1$ | $\infty$ |
| reciprocals | 1 | $-1$ | 0 |
| indices | (1 | $\bar{1}$ | 0) |

For plane C:

|                    | $x$ | $y$ | $z$ |
| ------------------ | --- | --- | --- |
| Plane C intercepts | 1   | 1   | 1/2 |
| reciprocals        | 1   | 1   | −2  |
| indices            | (1  | 1   | $\bar{2}$) |

■

### 2.2.3 Defects in Crystal Structures

Our discussion in the previous section assumed a perfect structure for all crystals. However, the formation of a perfect crystal is impossible to achieve under normal conditions. Defects in the crystal structure can be either detrimental or beneficial to the physical and mechanical properties of a material, as we will see in the following chapters. There are several different types of defects, and they are often named according to the number of dimensions affected by the imperfection. We will focus in this chapter on **point defects**, which involve only one or two atoms in a crystal.

2.2.3.1 **Point Defects**   The most common types of point defects are vacancies and self-interstitials, both of which are depicted in Figure 2.8. A **vacancy** is found at a lattice site where an atom would normally be present, but is currently missing. A **self-interstitial** occurs when an atom from the crystal is crowded into the interstitial space between two adjacent atoms, occupying a space that would otherwise be empty.

Defects occur as a natural result of the thermodynamics of crystal growth. While an in-depth discussion of crystal formation is beyond the scope of this book, a simplified explanation is that the creation of defects is favorable because they increase the entropy of the system. Following these principles, the number of vacancies ($N_v$) in a crystal can be related to the absolute temperature ($T$) of the system by the formula

$$N_v = N e^{\frac{-Q_v}{kT}} \tag{2.3}$$

where $N$ is the total number of atomic sites (atoms + vacancies), $Q_v$ is the activation energy for formation of a vacancy, and $k$ is Boltzmann's constant ($1.38 \times 10^{-23}$ J/atom-K or $8.62 \times 10^{-5}$ eV/atom-K).

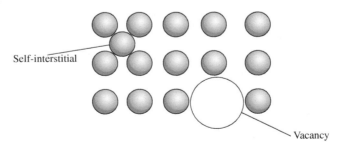

Self-interstitial

Vacancy

**Figure 2.8**
Point defects in crystal structures. A vacancy is found at a lattice site where an atom would normally be present, but is currently missing. A self-interstitial occurs when an atom from the crystal is crowded into the interstitial space between surrounding atoms, occupying a space that would otherwise be empty.

While the formation of defects is thermodynamically favorable, both vacancies and self-interstitials cause strains on the local lattice structure (**lattice strain**). In fact, interstitial defects are uncommon in metals because, in these materials, the atom is so much larger than the interstitial space that it produces large regional distortions in the lattice structure.

**2.2.3.2 Impurities**    In a general sense, the presence of impurities in a material may be considered a type of point defect since they affect the local lattice structure and induce a degree of lattice strain. Impurities can be an artifact of material processing or can be added deliberately to alter the final properties of the material. Like defects, the addition of impurities increases the entropy of the system.

A **solid solution** is formed if the normal crystal structure is maintained upon addition of the impurity atoms. As in a liquid solution, mixing occurs on the atomic level to create a new substance in which each type of atom is homogeneously distributed. In this case, the host material is known as the **solvent**, while the impurity is the **solute**. The solute atoms can either fill spaces between the solvent atoms (**interstitial solution**) or take the place of the solvent atoms (**substitutional solution**) (Fig. 2.9).

While it is not entirely possible to predict when interstitial or substitutional solutions will be formed, interstitial solutions generally occur when the solute atom is smaller than the solvent, allowing for its placement in the interstitial spaces without extreme lattice strain. In the same vein, it has been found that substitutional solutions are favored for a variety of solute/solvent ratios if the following conditions are met:

1. The difference in the size of the atomic radii of the solvent and solute atoms must be less than approximately 15%.
2. The electronegativities of the two atoms must be similar.
3. The valence charges of the two atoms must be similar.
4. The crystal structure of the two atomic species must be identical (important only for solutions in which there is a large fraction of solute).

These are the **Hume-Rothery rules**, named after the person who first suggested them. The first rule is a result of the fact that if the size difference of a solute atom is too great, the solvent atoms will be forced away from their equilibrium bonding positions and there will be a large amount of lattice strain. The second and third conditions assure that the two species will have similar properties such as bond lengths and strengths.

**Figure 2.9**
Impurities in crystal structures. In this case, the host material is termed the solvent, while the impurity is the solute. The solute atoms can either fill spaces between the solvent atoms (interstitial solution) or take the place of the solvent atoms (substitutional solution).

The best-known solid solutions are metal alloys. In **alloys**, the impurity atom has been added in a particular concentration to improve properties of the host material. Alloys are commonly used to increase strength (see Chapter 4), impart corrosion resistance (see Chapter 5), or improve electrical properties of a pure metal. Common interstitial solid solution alloys include steels (alloys of carbon and iron), which form the basis of stainless steel orthopedic implants. Cobalt-chromium alloys, used for similar applications, are examples of substitutional solid solutions. The concentration of the various species in an alloy can be described in terms of **weight percent composition**, which is the weight of a certain element in relation to the total weight of the alloy. Alternatively, **atom percent composition**, the number of moles of a particular element related to the total moles of all the elements in the alloy, can be used.

## EXAMPLE PROBLEM 2.3

The titanium alloy Ti–6Al–4V is a common metal employed in the manufacture of orthopedic implants. This weight percent composition of the alloy is 90% Ti, 6% Al, and 4% V. Determine the following for a Ti–6Al–4V femoral head component of a hip implant (mass of component is 3.0 lbs):

(a)  The mass (in grams) of each element in the implant.
(b)  The number of moles of each element in the implant.
(c)  The atom percent composition of the implant.

Solution:

(a)  $(3.0 \text{ lbs})(0.4536 \text{ kg/lb})(1,000 \text{ g/kg}) = 1,361 \text{ g (mass of implant)}$

$(0.9)(1,361 \text{ g}) = \underline{1,225 \text{ g Ti in the implant}}$

$(0.06)(1,361 \text{ g}) = \underline{82 \text{ g Al in the implant}}$

$(0.04)(1,361 \text{ g}) = \underline{54 \text{ g V in the implant}}$

(b)  $(1,225 \text{ g Ti})(1/47.9 \text{ g/mol Ti}) = \underline{25.6 \text{ mol Ti in the implant}}$

$(82 \text{ g Al})(1/27.0 \text{ g/mol Al}) = \underline{3.0 \text{ mol Al in the implant}}$

$(54 \text{ g V})(1/50.9 \text{ g/mol V}) = \underline{1.1 \text{ mol V in the implant}}$

(c)  Total moles $= 25.6 + 3.0 + 1.1 = 29.7 \text{ mol}$
$(25.6/29.7) = \underline{86.2\% \text{ Ti in the implant (atom percent)}}$

$3.0/29.7 = \underline{10.1\% \text{ Al in the implant (atom percent)}}$

$(1.1/29.7) = \underline{3.7\% \text{ V in the implant (atom percent)}}$   ▪

## 2.2.4 Solid State Diffusion

In the preceding section, we have discussed point defects (and impurities) as if they were fixed in the crystal lattice. In reality, this is not the case—motion of defects and impurities can occur throughout the material. This occurs through **diffusion**, which is the movement of material via atomic motion. Since at room temperature most metals are solids, the type of diffusion that occurs through metals is often referred to as **solid state diffusion**. Diffusion can occur in pure metals, with atoms exchanging positions (**self-diffusion**), or atoms of another type can diffuse into the metal (**interdiffusion or impurity diffusion**). Diffusion of other elements into metals, or diffusion of defects within metals, can have significant effects on their overall physical and mechanical properties.

**2.2.4.1 Diffusion Mechanisms** Diffusion can be seen as a series of atomic jumps from position to position in a crystal. For an atom to make these jumps, there must be an empty adjacent site and the atom must possess enough energy to change position. Since atoms are always vibrating within their bonds, at any given time a certain fraction possesses enough vibrational energy to overcome both the energy barrier associated with breaking bonds and an increase in lattice strain during atomic movement to diffuse to a neighboring site. The fraction possessing the required amount of energy increases as the temperature of the material increases.

Two main types of diffusion occur in metals. The first kind is **vacancy diffusion**. As the name implies, in this type of diffusion an atom jumps to an adjacent vacancy, thereby exchanging the location of the atom and the vacancy (Fig. 2.10(a)). Because of this, the direction of atomic diffusion is opposite to that of vacancy diffusion.

The second type of diffusion found in metals is **interstitial diffusion**. In this case, an atom migrates from one interstitial position to a neighboring position (Fig. 2.10(b)). This usually occurs only with small atoms such as hydrogen, carbon, nitrogen, and oxygen that can easily fit into the interstitial spaces. Because of the small size of the diffusing species and their increased mobility, interstitial diffusion generally occurs more rapidly than vacancy diffusion.

**2.2.4.2 Modeling of Diffusion** Mathematical models involving differential equations have been developed to describe various kinds of diffusion. Many of these are generalized equations that apply to diffusion in gases and liquids as well as solids. We will confine the following discussion to models of **steady-state diffusion**, the case in which the diffusion flux does not change with time.

**Figure 2.10**
(a) Vacancy diffusion in metals. As the name implies, in this type of diffusion an atom jumps to an adjacent vacancy, thereby exchanging the location of the atom and the vacancy. Because of this, the direction of atomic diffusion is opposite to that of vacancy diffusion. (b) Interstitial diffusion in metals. In this case, an atom migrates from one interstitial position to a neighboring position. This usually occurs only with small atoms that can easily fit into the interstitial spaces.

Motion of a host or substitutional atom

(a)

Position of interstitial atoms before diffusion

Position of interstitial atoms after diffusion

(b)

The amount of diffusion that can occur under a certain set of conditions is dependent on several factors. One of these is the time over which the movement of atoms is allowed to occur. One way to express the rate of atom transfer is the **diffusion flux** ($J$), which is the mass (or number of atoms) ($M$) diffusing through a certain cross-sectional area ($A$) per unit time ($t$). This can be written as

$$J = \frac{M}{At} \qquad (2.4)$$

Or, as a differential equation,

$$J = \frac{1}{A}\frac{dM}{dt} \qquad (2.5)$$

where $J$ typically has units of kg/m²-s or atoms/m²-s.

As mentioned earlier, if $J$ does not change with time, this condition is steady-state diffusion. One example of steady-state diffusion is the movement of gas atoms across a thin metal plate, given that the concentrations (partial pressures) of the gas on both sides of the plate are held constant (Fig. 2.11(a)).

If the concentration ($C$) of the gas atoms is plotted against position in the sheet ($x$) as shown in Figure 2.11(b), this graph is called the **concentration profile**. The slope between two positions (e.g., $x_A$ and $x_B$) is the **concentration gradient** between these two points:

$$\text{Concentration gradient} = \frac{dC}{dx} \qquad (2.6)$$

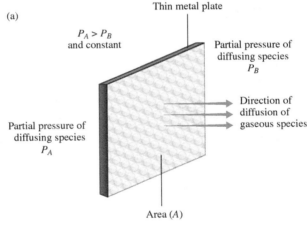

(a)

$P_A > P_B$ and constant

Thin metal plate

Partial pressure of diffusing species $P_B$

Direction of diffusion of gaseous species

Partial pressure of diffusing species $P_A$

Area ($A$)

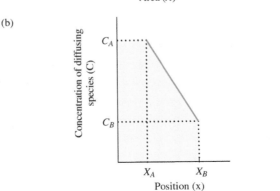

(b)

Concentration of diffusing species ($C$)

$C_A$

$C_B$

$X_A$      $X_B$

Position ($x$)

**Figure 2.11**
(a) Schematic of diffusion across a thin plate, an example of steady-state diffusion. Diffusion flux ($J$) is the mass (or number of atoms) $M$ diffusing through a certain cross-sectional area ($A$) per unit time ($t$). If $J$ does not change with time, this is steady-state diffusion, which occurs here because the partial pressures of gas on each side of the plate are held constant. (b) Concentration profile for the situation shown in (a). The slope between two positions (e.g., $x_A$ and $x_B$) is the concentration gradient between these two points.

As shown in the figure, in this case, the concentration gradient is taken to be linear, so

$$\frac{dC}{dx} = \frac{\Delta C}{\Delta x} = \frac{C_A - C_B}{x_A - x_B} \tag{2.7}$$

For diffusion problems, concentration is usually expressed in terms of mass of diffusing atoms (here, gas atoms) per unit volume of solid ($kg/m^3$ or $g/cm^3$).

For the situation depicted in Figure 2.11(a), the diffusion flux is proportional to the concentration gradient according to

$$J = -D\left(\frac{dC}{dx}\right) \tag{2.8}$$

This expression is often referred to as **Fick's first law** of diffusion. The negative sign indicates that atoms move *down* the concentration gradient (from areas of higher concentration to areas of lower concentration). $D$ (called **diffusivity**) is a proportionality constant with units of $m^2/s$. It depends on parameters of a given system, such as a crystal's interplanar spacing, and is also dependent on temperature. $D$ can be expressed as

$$D = D_0 e^{\frac{-Q}{RT}} \tag{2.9}$$

where $D_0$ is a constant with units of $m^2/s$, $Q$ is the activation energy for diffusion, $R$ is the gas constant (8.314 J/mol-K), and $T$ is the absolute temperature of the system.

## EXAMPLE PROBLEM 2.4

Consider the alloy $TiAl_3$, which readily oxidizes to form a layer of $Al_2O_3$. Assuming that the activation energy of diffusion of oxygen through the $Al_2O_3$ layer is 337.66 kJ/mol and that the frequency factor ($D_0$) is $167.2 \times 10^{-4}$ $m^2/s$, determine the following:

(a) The diffusivity through the $Al_2O_3$ layer at room temperature (25°C).
(b) The diffusivity through the $Al_2O_3$ layer at body temperature (37°C).
(c) The diffusivity through the $Al_2O_3$ layer at the melting temperature of $Al_2O_3$ (2045°C).
(d) The diffusivity through the $Al_2O_3$ layer at the melting temperature of Ti (1662°C).
(e) The diffusivity at absolute zero.
(f) Explain in terms of molecular motion why the diffusivity at the melting temperature of $Al_2O_3$ is many orders of magnitude greater than that at room temperature or even body temperature.

Solution:

(a) The diffusivity ($D$) is calculated from formula 2.9 as follows:

$$D = D_0 e^{\frac{-Q}{RT}}$$

The problem states that $Q = 337.66$ kJ/mol and $D_0 = 167.2 \times 10^{-4}$ $m^2/s$.
The gas constant $R = 8.314$ J/mol-K. Recall that temperatures in C convert to K by $K = °C + 273$.

$$D = 167.2 \times 10^{-4} \, [m^2/2] e^{\frac{-337.66 \times 10^3 \, J/mol}{(8.314 \, J/mol)(298 \, K)}}$$

$$\underline{D = 1.41 \cdot 10^{-61} \, m^2/s}$$

**(b)** $D = 167.2 \cdot 10^{-4}[m^2/s]e^{\frac{-337.66\times10^3\,J/mol}{(8.314\,J/mol)(310\,K)}}$

$\underline{D = 2.18 \cdot 10^{-59}\,m^2/s}$

**(c)** $D = 167.2 \cdot 10^{-4}[m^2/s]e^{\frac{-337.66\times10^3\,J/mol}{(8.314\,J/mol)(2318\,K)}}$

$\underline{D = 4.25 \cdot 10^{-10}\,m^2/s}$

**(d)** $D = 167.2 \cdot 10^{-4}[m^2/s]e^{\frac{-337.66\times10^3\,J/mol}{(8.314\,J/mol)(1935\,K)}}$

$\underline{D = 1.34 \cdot 10^{-11}\,m^2/s}$

(e) Absolute zero is at 0K and represents a complete absence of molecular motion. Without molecular motion, diffusion cannot occur; thus, the diffusivity would be <u>zero</u>.

(f) This problem examines the diffusivity of oxygen through the $Al_2O_3$ layer of $TiAl_3$. As the melting temperature of $Al_2O_3$ is given to be 2,045°C, the aluminum oxide is a solid at the much lower temperatures of 25°C (room temperature) and 37°C (body temperature). In the solid state, molecular motion is very limited due to the lower thermal energy in the material. Thus, diffusion of oxygen through the material is greatly impeded at these temperatures. However, at the melting temperature, the thermal energy has reached a sufficient level to facilitate molecular motion. In this state, diffusion of oxygen can occur much more readily. ∎

## 2.3 Structure of Ceramics

Like metals, ceramic biomaterials have found their primary use in joint replacement applications due to their strength and excellent wear properties. Because the bonds in ceramics are partially to totally ionic in nature, crystal structures in ceramic materials are thought of as being composed of ions rather than atoms. The variety of chemical compositions of ceramic materials results in a wider range of crystal structures than with metals. A few of the most common crystal structures are discussed in the following sections.

### 2.3.1 Crystal Structures

Ceramic crystal structure is affected by two parameters that are not concerns in metallic structures: the magnitude of the electrical charge on the constituent ions and the physical size of these ions. The former is important because the crystal must remain electrically neutral. Thus, the crystal structure of NaCl should allow the pairing of one $Na^+$ ion with one $Cl^-$ ion. However, for $CaF_2$, two $F^-$ ions must be allowed to interact with a single $Ca^{2+}$ ion.

The second characteristic requires the knowledge of the radii of both the cations ($r_c$) and anions ($r_a$) composing a ceramic material (see Table 2.3). Cations are generally smaller than anions because electron-electron repulsion decreases with the loss of electrons from the valence shell and the nucleus is able to pull the remaining electrons closer. For an optimally stable structure, cations should have contact with the maximum allowable number of anions (and vice versa for the anions). In this case, an ion's coordination number refers to the number of nearest neighbors with opposite charge, and it depends on the $r_c/r_a$ ratio. One can see in Figure 2.12 that certain ratios will not allow close contact between cations and anions and thus produce unstable structures.

**TABLE 2.3**

| Radii of Both the Cations ($r_c$) and Anions ($r_a$) Composing a Ceramic Material (for a Coordination Number of 6) | | | |
|---|---|---|---|
| Cation | Ionic Radius (nm) | Anion | Ionic Radius (nm) |
| $Al^{3+}$ | 0.053 | $Br^-$ | 0.196 |
| $Ba^{2+}$ | 0.136 | $Cl^-$ | 0.181 |
| $Ca^{2+}$ | 0.100 | $F^-$ | 0.133 |
| $Cs^+$ | 0.170 | $I^-$ | 0.220 |
| $Fe^{2+}$ | 0.077 | $O^{2-}$ | 0.140 |
| $Fe^{3+}$ | 0.069 | $S^{2-}$ | 0.184 |
| $K^+$ | 0.138 | | |
| $Mg^{2+}$ | 0.072 | | |
| $Mn^{2+}$ | 0.067 | | |
| $Na^+$ | 0.102 | | |
| $Ni^{2+}$ | 0.069 | | |
| $Si^{4+}$ | 0.040 | | |
| $Ti^{4+}$ | 0.061 | | |

(Reprinted with permission from [1].)

Based on this concept, a minimum $r_c/r_a$ ratio that will allow each coordination number has been determined (see Table 2.4). Each coordination number is associated with a certain nearest-neighbor geometry. For example, for a coordination number of 4, the cation is found at the center of a tetrahedron, with anions at each corner (see Table 2.4). The most common coordination numbers for ceramics are 4, 6, and 8.

**2.3.1.1 AX Crystal Structures**   For ceramics in which both the cation and anion have the same charge, an equal number of each is required for a stable crystal structure. These are called AX crystals, with A representing the cation and X representing the anion. The most common AX structure is the **sodium chloride structure**. The coordination number for both cations ($Na^+$) and anions ($Cl^-$) is 6, and the unit cell is depicted in Figure 2.13. As seen in the figure, the structure can be thought of as two interpenetrating FCC-type crystals, one composed of anions and the other of cations. Compounds such as MgO, MnS, LiF, and FeO also follow this structure.

**Figure 2.12**
Examples of stable and unstable coordination in ionic crystals (**yellow circles are cations**). An ion's coordination number refers to the number of nearest neighbors with opposite charge. As shown here, a single coordination number can produce either stable or unstable structures, depending on the relative sizes of the cations and anions.

Stable

Stable

Unstable

Anion

Cation

**TABLE 2.4**

| Critical $r_c / r_a$ Ratios and Associated Nearest-Neighbor Geometries for Each Coordination Number ($r_c$ = cation radius length, $r_a$ = anion radius length) | | | |
|---|---|---|---|
| Coordination Number | Lower Critical ($r_c/r_a$) Value | ($r_c/r_a$) Stability Range | Geometry* |
| 2 | 0 | $0 < r_c/r_a < 0.155$ | Always possible |
| 3 | 0.155 | $0.155 < r_c/r_a < 0.225$ | |
| 4 | 0.225 | $0.225 < r_c/r_a < 0.414$ | |
| 6 | 0.414 | $0.414 < r_c/r_a < 0.732$ | |
| 8 | 0.732 | $0.732 < r_c/r_a < 1$ | |

* In this column, $r = r_c$ and $R = r_a$.

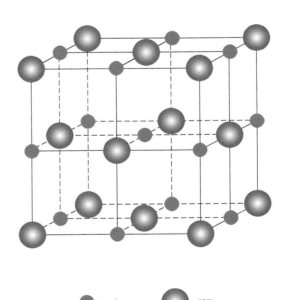

**Figure 2.13**
The unit cell for an ionic crystal having a sodium chloride structure. The coordination number for both cations ($Na^+$) and anions ($Cl^-$) is 6. The structure can be thought of as two interpenetrating FCC-type crystals, one composed of anions and the other of cations [1].

Na$^+$          Cl$^-$

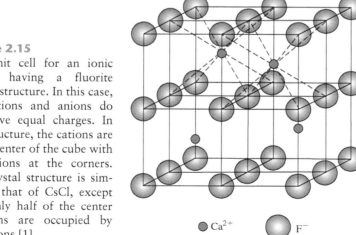

**Figure 2.14**
The unit cell for an ionic crystal having a cesium chloride structure. The coordination number in this case is 8 for both the $Cs^+$ and $Cl^-$ ions. In this unit cell, the anions are located at the vertices of a cube with a single cation at the center. Although it looks similar, this is not a BCC crystal since there are two different atoms (ions) involved [1].

Another prevalent AX crystal has the **cesium chloride structure**. The coordination number in this case is 8 for both the $Cs^+$ and $Cl^-$ ions and the unit cell is shown in Figure 2.14. In this unit cell, the anions are located at the vertices of a cube with a single cation at the center. The locations of anions and cations in the unit cell can be interchanged to produce the same crystal structure. Although it looks similar, this is not a BCC crystal since there are two different atoms (ions) involved.

**2.3.1.2  $A_mX_p$ Crystal Structures**    Ceramic materials are often composed of cations and anions that do not have equal charges, leading to compounds with the formula $A_mX_p$, where $m$ and/or $p \neq 1$. A common example is found in fluorite ($CaF_2$). The coordination number for $Ca^{2+}$ is 8, and the system exhibits a cubic coordination geometry (Fig. 2.15). The cations are at the center of the cube, with the anions at the corners. The crystal structure is similar to that of CsCl (see Fig. 2.14), except that only half of the center positions are occupied by $Ca^{2+}$ ions.

**Figure 2.15**
The unit cell for an ionic crystal having a fluorite ($CaF_2$) structure. In this case, the cations and anions do not have equal charges. In this structure, the cations are at the center of the cube with the anions at the corners. The crystal structure is similar to that of CsCl, except that only half of the center positions are occupied by $Ca^{2+}$ ions [1].

It is also possible for compounds to have more than one type of cation, leading to $A_m B_n X_p$ crystal structures, which are more complicated than those presented here. These and even more complex combinations are commonly found in various ceramic biomaterials. This is mainly due to the fact that most ceramics developed for biomedical applications are mixtures of several ionic species, such as zinc-sulfate-calcium-phosphate (ZSCAP) ceramics, which include $ZnSO_4$, $ZnO$, $CaO$, and $P_2O_5$, or ferric-calcium-phosphorous-oxide (FECAP) ceramics, which include $Fe_2O_3$, $CaO$, and $P_2O_5$.

**2.3.1.3 Carbon-Based Materials** Although carbon-based materials do not neatly fall into any of the classes of materials (metals, ceramics, or polymers), one common form, **graphite**, is sometimes considered a ceramic. Even though it does not possess a standard unit cell, graphite is crystalline. As depicted in Figure 2.16, the structure consists of planes of hexagonally arranged carbon atoms. Within the planes, each carbon atom is bonded covalently to three neighbors, while the fourth valence electron participates in van der Waals interactions with the plane above it. A property of graphite that is important to the biomaterialist is its ability to adsorb gases. This is used in the formation of **pyrolytic carbon,** in which carbon in the gaseous state is deposited onto another material (in this case, graphite). Pyrolytic carbon has been used in a number of cardiovascular devices, including replacement heart valves.

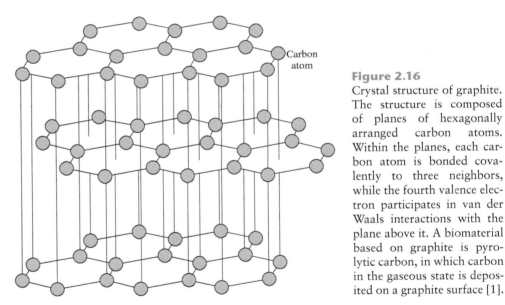

Carbon atom

**Figure 2.16**
Crystal structure of graphite. The structure is composed of planes of hexagonally arranged carbon atoms. Within the planes, each carbon atom is bonded covalently to three neighbors, while the fourth valence electron participates in van der Waals interactions with the plane above it. A biomaterial based on graphite is pyrolytic carbon, in which carbon in the gaseous state is deposited on a graphite surface [1].

An additional synthetic form of carbon can be found in **single-walled nanotubes** (SWNTs) and **multi-walled nanotubes** (MWNTs). A SWNT can be visualized as a single sheet of graphite rolled to form a tube. Similarly, a MWNT can be visualized as a tube rolled from multiple layers of graphite sheets. These carbon nanotubes are generally a few nanometers in diameter and on the order of a micron in length. The SWNT can be characterized by the degree of chirality or "twist" in its structure. A two-dimensional vector, $C_h$ (Fig. 2.17), can be defined to describe the chirality of the SWNT, such that

$$C_h = n\mathbf{a}_1 + m\mathbf{a}_2 \equiv (n, m) \tag{2.10}$$

The structure of a SWNT is defined by the indices $n$ and $m$ of the two basis vectors $\mathbf{a}_1$ and $\mathbf{a}_2$, where $n$ and $m$ must be integers. Tubes for which $n = m$ are termed "armchair" tubes, and tubes for which $m = 0$ are termed "zigzag" tubes. These terms refer to the pattern of carbon atoms that one would see along the vector $C_h$. The tubes for all other integer values of $n$ and $m$ are referred to as "chiral" tubes, as the carbon chains appear to spiral around the tubes in these cases. SWNTs have been explored for use in the mechanical reinforcement of biomaterials for several applications, including the reinforcement of synthetic polymers for orthopedic applications.

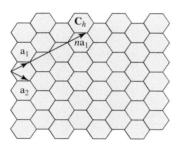

(a)   Zigzag SWNT ($m = 0$)

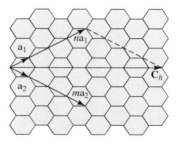

Armchair SWNT ($n = m$)

**Figure 2.17**
The structure of single-walled carbon nanotubes (SWNTs). (a) The sheets of graphite represented in this figure could be visualized to form a SWNT by rolling one side of the sheet in contact with the other. The twist or chirality of the SWNT is defined by a two-dimensional vector, $C_h$. Two special cases of SWNT are the zigzag ($m = 0$) and armchair ($n = m$) conformations. These terms refer to the pattern of carbon atoms that one would see along the $C_h$ vector. (b) The 3D structure of a carbon nanotube.

(b)

## 2.3.2 Defects in Crystal Structures

**2.3.2.1 Point Defects**  As with metals, a number of defect types have been observed in ceramic crystals. Both interstitial and vacancy point defects can occur for either the cation or anion. It is important to note that an additional constraint exists in the formation of defects in ceramic materials as compared with metals. Because ceramics are ionic in nature, the defect should not affect the electroneutrality of the material. Therefore, individual point defects do not occur since that would leave the crystal with a net charge; instead, groups of defects are formed.

One such defect group is called a **Schottky defect**, in which there are vacancies in both cations and anions in the correct ratio to maintain neutrality. This defect is shown for two different AX-type crystals in Figure 2.18. Although the vacancies are shown grouped together spatially in this diagram, in reality, the anion and cation vacancies can occur in areas of the crystal that are far apart. Defects are created in ionic crystals based on the same thermodynamic principles that drive their formation in metals (increased entropy). Thus, a similar expression can be used to relate the number of Schottky defects in an AX material to the absolute temperature ($T$) of the sample:

$$N_{v,cat} = N_{v,an} = Ne^{\frac{-Q_{vp}}{2kT}} \qquad (2.11)$$

Here, $N_{v,cat}$ is the number of cation vacancies, $N_{v,an}$ is the number of anion vacancies, $N$ is the total number of atomic sites (atoms + vacancies), $Q_{vp}$ is

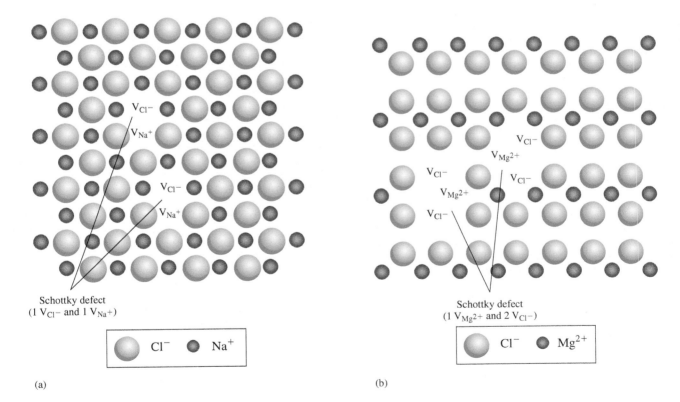

Schottky defect
($1\ V_{Cl^-}$ and $1\ V_{Na^+}$)

| $Cl^-$ | $Na^+$ |

(a)

Schottky defect
($1\ V_{Mg^{2+}}$ and $2\ V_{Cl^-}$)

| $Cl^-$ | $Mg^{2+}$ |

(b)

**Figure 2.18**
(a&b) Schottky defects in ceramic crystals. As shown here for $AX$ (a) and $A_mX_p$ (b) type crystals, there are vacancies in both cations and anions in the correct ratio to maintain electroneutrality. Although the vacancies are shown grouped together spatially in this diagram, in reality, the anion and cation vacancies can occur in areas of the crystal that are quite distant.

the activation energy for the formation of a cation/anion vacancy pair, and $k$ is Boltzmann's constant.

Another common defect cluster in ceramic crystals is the **Frenkel defect**. In this case, a vacancy/interstitial pair is created to maintain electroneutrality. Usually this type of defect only occurs with cations, since anions are too large to reside in the interstitial space of the crystal without a significant amount of lattice strain. A typical Frenkel defect is shown in Figure 2.19. The equation describing the number of Frenkel defects as a function of absolute temperature ($T$) is

$$N_v = N_i = N e^{\frac{-Q_{vi}}{2kT}} \tag{2.12}$$

where $N_v$ is the number of vacancies, $N_i$ is the number of interstitials, $N$ is the total number of atomic sites (atoms + vacancies), $Q_{vi}$ is the activation energy for formation of a vacancy and an interstitial, and $k$ is Boltzmann's constant. The extent of both Schottky and Frenkel defects affect the mechanical properties of ceramic biomaterials as they can act as stress concentrators (see Section 4.3.3).

**2.3.2.2 Impurities** Impurities similar to those in metal crystals are often found in ceramic crystals. Solid solutions can be formed and the same terminology (solvent and solute) applies. Although both substitutional and interstitial solutions exist, solute anions form mainly substitutional solutions since they are too large to fit easily in the interstitial space. Cations, in contrast, readily form both types of solutions (Fig. 2.20).

As with the point defect clusters discussed earlier, the addition of the impurity must not affect the electroneutrality of the host material. For stability, the solute ion must be similar in size and charge to the solvent ion. If this is not the case (for example, if a $Ca^{2+}$ ion substitutes for a $Na^+$ ion in NaCl), the lattice compensates, often through forcing vacancies of host ions (ejection of additional $Na^+$ ion to restore

**Figure 2.19**
Frenkel defects in ceramic crystals. In this case, a vacancy/interstitial pair is created to maintain electroneutrality. Usually this type of defect only occurs with cations, since anions are too large to reside in the interstitial space of the crystal without a significant amount of lattice strain.

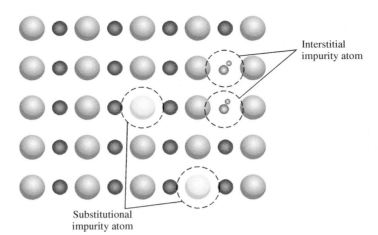

**Figure 2.20**
Impurities found in ceramic crystals. Although both substitutional and interstitial solutions exist, solute anions form mainly substitutional solutions since they are too large to fit easily in the interstitial space. In contrast, cations readily form both types of solutions.

neutrality). These are vacancies that occur in addition to the normal thermal vacancies described by the previous equations.

As in metals, diffusion of point defects and impurities can occur within ionic crystals. The rate of diffusion depends on temperature and can be modeled with the same equations as discussed earlier for diffusion in metals. A main difference is that there must be simultaneous diffusion of at least two species (ions and vacancies) to maintain electroneutrality within the material.

## 2.4 Structure of Polymers

The third major type of biomaterials is polymeric materials. Polymers are also called **macromolecules** because of their size, which can be on the order of $10^5$–$10^6$ g/mol. Many polymers, both naturally derived and synthetic, have hydrogen-carbon covalent bonds as a main constituent. The variety of possible polymers and their corresponding range of physical and mechanical properties have led to their use in applications as diverse as blood vessel replacements and bone cements. Both amorphous and crystalline polymeric materials are used in clinical applications. However, before the crystal structure of polymers can be described, we must first explain their chemical structure, which is significantly more complex than that of metals or ceramics.

### 2.4.1 General Structure

**2.4.1.1 Repeat Units**  The smallest building block of a polymer is called a **mer** ("polymer" literally means "many mers"). A mer is a structural entity composed of a fixed number of atoms in a given structure that is repeated over and over to form the polymer (Fig. 2.21). For this reason, a mer is often called the **repeat unit** of a polymer. A molecule containing only one mer is a **monomer**, while those composed of 2 to ~10 mers are **oligomers**.

As seen in Table 2.5, repeat units for common polymers can be **saturated**, such as those in poly(ethylene)[1] or poly(vinyl chloride), in which each carbon in the mer is bonded to

---

[1]Standard guidelines for polymer nomenclature generally require that polymers be named by prefixing "poly" to the name, offset in parentheses, of the structural repeating unit of the polymer. If the name of the structural repeating unit of the polymer is only one word, then the parentheses are optional. For example, poly(ethylene) can also be written as polyethylene, whereas, the parentheses are required for poly(vinyl chloride).

**Figure 2.21**
Examples of mer units in polymers. A mer is a structural entity composed of a fixed number of atoms in a given structure that is repeated over and over to form the polymer [1].

### TABLE 2.5

| Structure of Common Polymers | |
| --- | --- |
| Polymer | Structure |
| Poly(ethylene) (PE) | |
| Poly(ethylene glycol) (PEG) | |
| Poly(styrene) (PS) | |
| Poly(methyl methacrylate) (PMMA) | |
| Poly(glycolic acid) (PGA) | |
| Poly(lactic acid) (PLA) | |
| Poly(tetrafluoroethylene) (PTFE) | |

four other atoms (two carbons and two other types of atoms). Alternatively, they may be unsaturated, such as those for poly(isoprene), see Figure 2.26 in which two of the carbons in the repeat unit are bonded with double bonds. The presence of unsaturated repeat units can affect the crystallinity and crosslinking of polymers, as discussed in Chapter 3. In addition, while many repeat units, such as those listed in this paragraph, are **bifunctional** (may bond with other mers on both ends), others, such as those in phenolformaldehyde, have three active bonds that can bond with other mers. Such repeat units are termed **trifunctional,** and may result in a polymer network, as described later in this chapter.

**2.4.1.2 Molecular Weight Determination**   A distinctive feature of most polymers is the extreme length of their chains. One way to represent this is the **degree of polymerization** (number of repeat units in a polymer), usually indicated by the letter $n$ in the chemical formula for the polymer.

For example, the notation

$$... CH2—CH2—CH2—CH2—CH2—CH2—CH2—CH2 ...$$

can be abbreviated as

$$-\left[-CH_2 - CH_2 -\right]_n-$$

Alternatively, the polymer's size can be described in terms of the molecular weight of the chain.

## EXAMPLE PROBLEM 2.5

Determine the molecular weight of the following polymers:

(a) Poly(ethylene)[2], a material commonly used in the wearing surface of the acetabular cup component of hip prostheses.

(b) Poly(tetrafluoroethylene), a material commonly employed in the fabrication of vascular grafts.

(c) Poly(methyl methacrylate), a material commonly used as a bone cement in orthopedic procedures.

---

[2]In many of the problems and figures in the remainder of the book, this condensed structural notation, often used by organic chemists, will be used. In this type of notation, carbon-carbon bonds are represented by dark lines, and the writing of "C" and the appropriate number of "H's" to fulfill the valence shell of each carbon is omitted.

(d) This peptide sequence (RGD, or arginine, glycine, aspartic acid), commonly used in the modification of materials to increase cell adhesion to the material.

Solution:

(a) Molecular weight of the repeat unit:
2 carbon atoms and 4 hydrogen atoms per repeat unit

$$\text{Atomic mass of carbon} = 12 \text{ g/mol}$$

$$\text{Atomic mass of hydrogen} = 1 \text{ g/mol}$$

$$2(12 \text{ g/mol}) + 4(1 \text{ g/mol}) = 28 \text{ g/mol/repeat unit}$$

Since there are 14 repeat units in this polymer chain, the molecular weight of the polymer equals 14 times the molecular weight of the repeat unit, plus 2 "end units," one to terminate each end of the polymer chain:

$$\text{end unit: } 1\,C(12 \text{ g/mol}) + 2H(1 \text{ g/mol each}) = 14 \text{ g/mol}$$

Therefore, the total molecular weight is:

$$28 \text{ g/mol/repeat unit} \times 14 \text{ repeat units} + 14 \text{ g/mol/end unit}$$
$$\times\ 2 \text{ end units} = \underline{420 \text{ g/mol}}$$

(b) Molecular weight of the repeat unit:
2 carbon atoms and 4 fluorine atoms per repeat unit

$$\text{Atomic mass of carbon} = 12 \text{ g/mol}$$

$$\text{Atomic mass of fluorine} = 19 \text{ g/mol}$$

$$2(12 \text{ g/mol}) + 4(19 \text{ g/mol}) = 100 \text{ g/mol/repeat unit}$$

Since there are 14 repeat units in this polymer chain, the molecular weight of the polymer equals 14 times the molecular weight of the repeat unit, plus 2 "end units," one to terminate each end of the polymer chain:

$$\text{end unit: } 1\,C(12 \text{ g/mol}) + 2H(1 \text{ g/mol each}) = 14 \text{ g/mol}$$

$$100 \text{ g/mol/repeat unit} \times 14 \text{ repeat units} + 14 \text{ g/mol/end unit}$$

$$\times\ 2 \text{ end units} = \underline{1{,}428 \text{ g/mol}}$$

(c) Molecular weight of the repeat unit:
5 carbon atoms, 8 hydrogen atoms, and 2 oxygen atoms per repeat unit

$$\text{Atomic mass of carbon} = 12 \text{ g/mol}$$

$$\text{Atomic mass of hydrogen} = 1 \text{ g/mol}$$

$$\text{Atomic mass of oxygen} = 16 \text{ g/mol}$$

$$5(12 \text{ g/mol}) + 8(1 \text{ g/mol}) + 2(16 \text{ g/mol}) = 100 \text{ g/mol/repeat unit}$$

Since there are 100 repeat units in this polymer chain, the molecular weight of the polymer equals 100 times the molecular weight of the repeat unit, plus 2 "end units," one to terminate each end of the polymer chain:

$$\text{end unit: } 1\,C(12 \text{ g/mol}) + 2H(1 \text{ g/mol each}) = 14 \text{ g/mol}$$

$$100 \text{ g/mol/repeat unit} \times 100 \text{ repeat units} + 2 \text{ end units}$$

$$\times (14 \text{ g/mol/end unit}) = \underline{10{,}028 \text{ g/mol}}$$

(d) This is a peptide (RGD or arginine, glycine, aspartic acid). There is no repeat unit for this peptide. The elemental composition of the peptide is as follows:

Carbon: 12 atoms
Hydrogen: 24 atoms
Nitrogen: 6 atoms
Oxygen: 6 atoms

Thus, the molecular weight of the peptide is as follows:

$$12(12 \text{ g/mol C}) + 24(1 \text{ g/mol H}) + 6(14 \text{ g/mol N}) + 6(16 \text{ g/mol O})$$

$$= \underline{348 \text{ g/mol}}$$

■

During synthesis, polymers with a distribution of molecular weights are formed. Therefore, an average molecular weight is generally determined. There are two common definitions for average molecular weight, **number-average molecular weight** $(\overline{M}_n)$ and **weight-average molecular weight** $(\overline{M}_w)$. The number-average molecular weight is found by dividing the chains into a series of size ranges and computing the fraction of chains with that size. This can be written as

$$\overline{M}_n = \sum_i x_i M_i \tag{2.13}$$

where

$$x_i = \frac{N_i}{\sum_i N_i} \tag{2.14}$$

$N_i$ is the number of chains with molecular weight $M_i$. $M_i$ represents an average molecular weight for the chosen molecular weight range.

The weight-average molecular weight is calculated using the weight fraction of the chains within the selected size ranges; that is,

$$\overline{M}_w = \sum_i w_i M_i \tag{2.15}$$

where

$$w_i = \frac{W_i}{\sum_i W_i} \tag{2.16}$$

and

$$W_i = N_i M_i \tag{2.17}$$

It should be noted that as the size range chosen to define $N_i$ and $M_i$ becomes smaller and smaller, these expressions approach the averaging of each individual chain. The reason that both types of average molecular weight are calculated is that while $\overline{M}_n$ treats all polymer chains equally, for $\overline{M}_w$, the larger chains make a larger contribution to the final value. In some cases, $\overline{M}_w$ can be correlated more directly with the mechanical and physical properties of the material (Fig. 2.22).

The **polydispersity index** (*PI*) is the ratio of the two molecular weights:

$$PI = \frac{\overline{M}_w}{\overline{M}_n} \tag{2.18}$$

The smallest possible value for the *PI* is 1.00 (all the polymer molecules have the same molecular weight), and it increases as the molecular weight distribution broadens (Fig. 2.23).

**Figure 2.22**
Relationship between molecular weight of poly(lactic acid) and mechanical properties.
*Descriptors of different mechanical properties, discussed in Chapter 4. Data taken from Engleberg et al. Biomaterials, vol. 12, pp. 292–304, 1991.*

**Figure 2.23**
Diagram based on results from a type of size-exclusion chromatography (gel permeation chromatography) of poly(propylene fumarate) (PPF) and different poly(styrene) (PS) standards. In this type of chromatography, the larger molecular weight polymer exits first and is detected at an earlier time.
PPF: $\overline{M}_n$: 3,580
PS standards from left to right: $\overline{M}_n$: 26,600, $\overline{M}_n$: 23,300, $\overline{M}_n$: 10,000, $\overline{M}_n$: 4,620, $\overline{M}_n$: 3,260, $\overline{M}_n$: 1,790, $\overline{M}_n$: 869, $\overline{M}_n$: 423.
Note that the PPF peak is much broader than that of the standards. While the polydispersity of the PPF synthesized in the laboratory is near 2, the PS standards are synthesized in such a manner so their PI is near 1. At lower molecular weights, this is more difficult, so the PI of the lowest standard ($\overline{M}_n$ 423) is 1.22.

## EXAMPLE PROBLEM 2.6

Consider the following polymer size fractions of a given polymer sample:

| Fraction | Molecular Weight | Number of Chains |
|---|---|---|
| 1 | 5,000 | 1,000 |
| 2 | 10,000 | 1,000 |
| 3 | 1,000,000 | 3 |

(a) Calculate the number-average molecular weight of the polymer.
(b) Calculate the weight-average molecular weight of the polymer.

(c) Which average molecular weight determination did the 3 chains of molecular weight 1,000,000 most significantly affect? Why?

(d) Calculate the polydispersity index of the polymer.

Solution:

(a) $\bar{M}_n = \dfrac{\sum_i N_i M_i}{\sum_i N_i}$

In this case,

$$\bar{M}_n = [(1,000 \times 5,000) + (1,000 \times 10,000) + (3 \times 1,000,000)]/(1,000 + 1,000 + 3)$$
$$= \underline{8,987\ \mathrm{Da}}\,[\mathrm{Note:}\ 1\ \mathrm{Da} = 1\ \mathrm{g/mol}]$$

(b) $\bar{M}_w = \dfrac{\sum_i N_i M_i^2}{\sum_i N_i M_i}$

In this case,

$$\bar{M}_w = [1,000 \times (5,000)^2 + 1,000 \times (10,000)^2 + 3 \times (1,000,000)^2]/$$
$$[(1,000 \times 5,000) + (1,000 \times 10,000) + (3 \times 1,000,000)] = \underline{173,611\,\mathrm{Da}}$$

(c) The 3 chains of 1,000,000 molecular weight most significantly affected the weight-average molecular weight, as this quantity considers the molecular weight of each species present in a weighted fashion to give greater influence to the fractions with the higher molecular weight than those with simply the highest number of chains.

(d) $PI = \dfrac{\bar{M}_w}{\bar{M}_n}$

In this case, $PI = (173,611\ \mathrm{Da})/(8,987\ \mathrm{Da}) = \underline{19}$ (note that $PI$ does not carry units). ■

### 2.4.1.3 Mer Configuration

One of the most striking aspects of polymers (and one that distinguishes them from metals and ceramics) is that single macromolecules can take a variety of shapes. This is primarily caused by the rotation of the carbon atoms in the backbone, the way changing the position of individual links in a chain will change the path of the entire chain (Fig. 2.24). Thus, polymers may fold back on themselves or contain a number of bends and kinks (Fig. 2.25). These types of molecular entanglements play a large role in the mechanical properties of polymers, as will be discussed in Chapter 4.

On a molecular level, the bending of polymer molecules is due to the conformation of individual repeat units. The term **conformation** is used to describe the part of the structure of a molecule that can be changed by rotation around single bonds. Repeat unit (and thus polymer) conformation can be highly affected by chemical composition. The presence of bulky side groups (like the benzene ring in poly(styrene)) impairs rotation around the backbone. In a more extreme case, when rigid C–C double bonds are present, no rotation is possible around the backbone and conformation is effectively "frozen."

Polymer conformation is also influenced by the placement of the repeat units. **Configuration** is the part of the structure of a molecule that cannot be changed except by the breaking and reforming of primary bonds. There are several common polymer configurations, as depicted in Figure 2.26. In this figure, "R" represents a generic side group or atom (such as the benzene ring in poly(styrene) or the Cl

**Figure 2.24**
Conformations of polymers. Single macromolecules can take a variety of shapes, primarily due to the rotation of the carbon atoms in the backbone. In this diagram, light grey atoms represent alternative locations of dark grey atoms along the polymer backbone.

109.5°

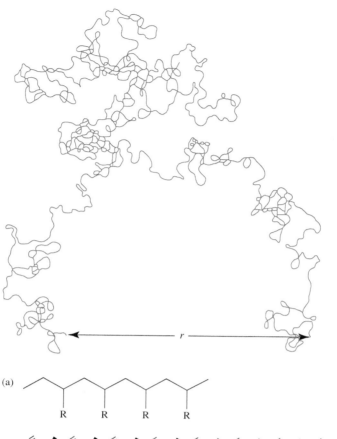

**Figure 2.25**
Depiction of a typical conformation for a polymer molecule. Note the large number of bends and kinks present. These types of molecular entanglements play a large role in the mechanical properties of polymers. The end-to-end distance of the polymer chain is denoted by $r$ [11].

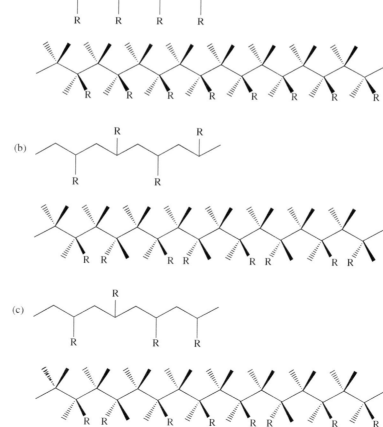

**Figure 2.26**
Common polymer configurations ("R" represents a generic side group or atom). (a) Isotactic configuration—R groups are arranged on the same side of the chain. (b) Syndiotactic configuration—R groups alternate positions on either side of the chain. (c) Atactic configuration—R groups are situated randomly. In this representation, the solid extensions are oriented out of the page and the dashed are into the page [1].

atom in poly(vinyl chloride)). If the R groups are arranged on the same side of the chain, this is an **isotactic configuration**. If they alternate positions on either side of the chain, this is a **syndiotactic configuration**. If the R groups are situated randomly, this is an **atactic configuration**. It is easy to see from these examples that conversion between two configurations requires the breaking of chemical bonds, whereas moving between different polymer conformations involves only bond rotation. In reality, any given polymer chain contains a mixture of configurations. The predominant configuration is determined primarily by the synthesis method.

In the special case where the repeat unit contains a C–C double bond, two configurations are possible (Fig. 2.27). For poly(isoprene), when both the $CH_3$ and H constituents are located on the same side of the C–C double bond, this is termed the **cis** structure (*cis*-isoprene is natural rubber). In contrast, the **trans** configuration describes the case where the $CH_3$ and H are found on opposite sides of the double bond. *Trans*-isoprene has distinctly different mechanical properties from natural rubber as a result of this difference in configuration.

### 2.4.1.4 Polymer Structure

In addition to their conformation and configuration, polymers can possess various overall structures (Fig. 2.28). As described previously, they may be **linear**, with the repeat units joined in an end-to-end fashion. In contrast, some synthesis conditions produce side reactions that result in chains that branch off of the main polymer chain; these are termed **branched** polymers.

Both linear and branched polymers may be crosslinked. In **crosslinked polymers**, adjacent chains are joined at certain points via covalent bonds, forming a three-dimensional polymer network. Crosslinking can be induced during synthesis, or afterwards using a nonreversible chemical reaction. In one sense, crosslinking increases the molecular weight of the polymer chains as they are bonded together. An alternative method of producing polymer structures in three dimensions is through the use of **network polymers**, which, as explained earlier, have tri- or multifunctional mer units that can bind monomers or other polymers in more complicated formations than bifunctional monomers, which produce primarily linear polymers.

**Figure 2.27**
Polymer configurations with a C–C double bond (above example: poly(isoprene)). (a) cis configuration—$CH_3$ and H constituents are found on the same side of the C–C double bond (*cis*-isoprene is natural rubber). (b) trans configuration—$CH_3$ and H are found on opposite sides of the double bond [1].

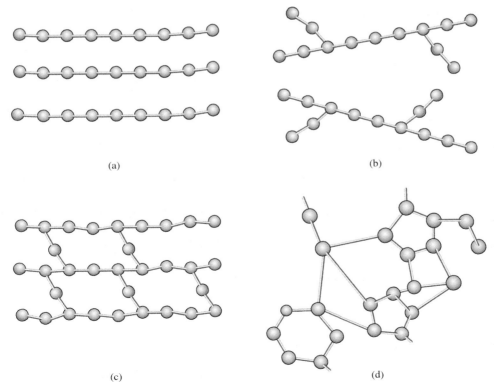

(a)

(b)

(c)

(d)

**Figure 2.28**
Overall structures of polymers. (a) Linear polymers have their repeat units joined in an end-to-end fashion. (b) Branched polymers are formed by synthesis conditions that encourage the formation of chains that branch off from the main polymer chain. (c) Crosslinked polymers possess adjacent chains that are joined at certain points via covalent bonds, forming a three-dimensional polymer network. Both linear and branched polymers may be crosslinked. (d) Network polymers have tri- or multifunctional mer units that can bind monomers or other polymers to produce three-dimensional network structures.

### EXAMPLE PROBLEM 2.7

Poly(ethylene) is a polymer used in a number of biomedical applications. One common application is the fabrication of wearing surfaces of orthopedic implants, such as the acetabular cup of a hip implant or the articulating surface of a knee implant. Consider a poly(ethylene) polymer chain with 25,000 mers.

(a) One method for estimating the length of a polymer chain is to model it as a chain stretched out end-to-end. Given that the angle between C–C covalent bonds is 109.5° and that the interatomic distance for a C–C bond is 1.54Å, calculate the length of the poly(ethylene) chain.

(b) More realistically, polymer chains can be modeled as random coils. The average end-to-end distance (L) of a randomly coiled polymer chain can be calculated from the relation $L = l\sqrt{m}$, where $l$ is the interatomic distance and $m$ is the number of bonds with that interatomic distance. Calculate the average end-to-end distance (L) for the poly(ethylene) chain, using the random coil model.

Solution:

(a) The bond angle $\phi$ is given as 109.5°. The bond length is given as 1.54Å, so $\frac{1}{2}$ the bond length can be defined as $r$ to be 0.77Å. The quantity $y$ can be defined as the distance between two covalently bonded carbons, as projected on the chain axis.

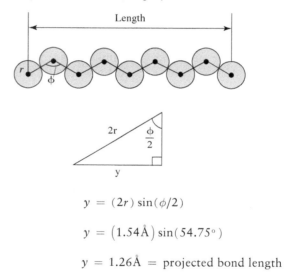

$$y = (2r)\sin(\phi/2)$$

$$y = (1.54\text{Å})\sin(54.75°)$$

$$y = 1.26\text{Å} = \text{projected bond length}$$

Since there are 25,000 mers in the polymer chain, the length of the polymer chain projected on the chain axis is as follows:

$$\text{Length} = (\text{Number of C–C bonds}) \times (\text{Projected C–C bond length})$$

$$\text{Length} = (2*25,000\text{-}1\text{ Bonds}) \times (1.26\,\text{Å})\,[\text{There are 2 carbons/mer.}]$$

$$\underline{\text{Length} = 62,999\,\text{Å} = 6.3\,\mu\text{m}}$$

(b) Using the random-coil end-to-end distance formula:

$$L = l\sqrt{m}$$

$$L = 1.54\,\text{Å}(2 \times 25,000\text{-}1)^{1/2}$$

$$\underline{L = 344\,\text{Å}}$$ ∎

## 2.4.2 Polymer Synthesis

Synthesis of polymers, also called **polymerization**, occurs through repeated chemical reactions that join individual mer units into a longer chain. There are three major types of polymerization: **addition polymerization**, **condensation polymerization**, and **polymer synthesis through genetic engineering**. The details of these reactions are described next.

**2.4.2.1 Addition Polymerization** The reaction of ethylene monomers to form poly(ethylene) via addition, or chain reaction, polymerization is shown in Figure 2.29. Bifunctional monomers are required, and, unlike condensation polymerization, the product contains the same chemical structure as the mer unit. An initiator species is needed to commence the reaction, so an initiator molecule that easily forms free radicals or ions is often used. This is depicted as **I** in Figure 2.29.

Addition polymerization reactions involve three distinct steps: initiation, propagation, and termination. **Initiation** requires the activation of a monomer through reaction with either a radical species for free radical polymerization or an anionic or cationic species for anionic and cationic polymerization, respectively. Monomers continue to successively join the polymer chain and increase its molecular weight during the **propagation** step. It is important to note that during the propagation step the active site of the growing polymer chain is simultaneously transferred to the newly added monomer upon addition. This transfer allows for the continued growth of the polymer chain.

**Termination** of addition polymerization can occur in several ways. In the case of free radical polymerization, termination occurs through destruction of the active site by the reaction of free radicals. Another method involves the reaction of the activated end on two propagating chains ($M_n\cdot$ or $M_m\cdot$) to form a longer chain, thus ending the growth of both chains (see Fig. 2.29). Another method of termination is through the reaction of the activated carbon on a propagating chain with a free radical of an initiator molecule. Chain growth can also terminate through transfer of a hydrogen atom from one growing chain to another in a process called disproportionation. In the case of anionic and cationic polymerization, however, termination generally occurs through reaction of the charged active site of the growing polymer with either trace amounts of water in the solvent in which the reaction is conducted or, depending on the nature of the solvent, with the solvent itself. Cationic polymerization can also terminate through various other side reactions, including anion-cation recombination and anion splitting.

Because termination is random with free radical polymerization, a variety of chain lengths are achieved using this method of polymerization, which leads to PI values > 1.00. Poly(ethylene), poly(propylene), poly(vinyl chloride), and poly(styrene) are examples of polymers synthesized with free radical polymerization. The polymers generated through ionic polymerization are, in general, less polydisperse than those

**Figure 2.29**
General reaction mechanism for addition, or chain reaction, polymerization. A radical species ($R\cdot$) needed to initiate the reaction is usually produced through dissociation of an initiator species (I). The radical is then added to a monomer molecule to produce a polymer chain initiating species ($M_1\cdot$) in the second part of initiation. Monomer molecules (M) are successively added to the activated chain end ($M_n\cdot$) to generate a polymer in the propagation step. Termination of chain growth may occur by a number of methods - two are depicted here: (1) reaction of the activated monomer ($M_n\cdot$ and $M_m\cdot$) on two propagating chains that react to form one longer chain (coupling) or (2) through disproportionation. Poly(ethylene), poly(propylene), poly(vinyl chloride), and poly(styrene) are examples of polymers synthesized via addition polymerization. The parameters $k_d$, $k_i$, $k_p$, $k_{tc}$, and $k_{td}$ are the kinetic constants for the initiator dissociation, initiation, propagation, termination by coupling, and termination by disproportionation steps, respectively [12].

$$\text{Initiation} \begin{cases} \text{I} \xrightarrow{k_d} 2R\cdot \\ \\ R\cdot + M \xrightarrow{k_i} M_1\cdot \end{cases}$$

$$\text{Propagation} \begin{cases} M_n\cdot + M \xrightarrow{k_p} M_{n+1}\cdot \end{cases}$$

$$\text{Termination} \begin{cases} M_n\cdot + M_m\cdot \xrightarrow{k_{tc}} M_{n+m} & \textit{Coupling} \\ \\ M_n\cdot + M_m\cdot \xrightarrow{k_{td}} M_n + M_m & \textit{Disproportionation} \end{cases}$$

generated through free radical polymerization. Examples of polymers that are synthesized through anionic polymerization include poly(styrene), poly(methyl methacrylate), and poly(ethylene glycol). Additionally, poly(styrene) can be synthesized through cationic polymerization.

#### 2.4.2.2 Condensation Polymerization

Unlike addition polymerization, condensation, or step reaction, polymerization often involves more than one monomer species, and no radical initiator is required. Because of this, there is less distinction among initiation, propagation, and termination stages, although the reaction does proceed in a stepwise manner. As shown in Figure 2.30, the polymerization occurs through elimination of one molecule (usually water). Therefore, unlike addition polymerization, the product does not have the same chemical formula as either mer.

Long reaction times and nearly complete depletion of the monomer are needed to obtain high molecular weight substances from this polymerization method. During the reaction, chains with various lengths are produced, leading to *PI* values similar to those seen for addition polymerization. Nylons and poly(carbonates) are among the polymers formed in this way. Natural polymers, such as polysaccharides and proteins, are also a product of this synthetic reaction.

#### 2.4.2.3 Polymer Production Via Genetic Engineering

Addition and condensation polymerization generally result in the synthesis of polymers with a wide range of chain lengths and sequences, due to the probabilistic nature of the reactions involved. Polymer production via genetic engineering, however, provides the potential for greater control over polymer architecture and weight distributions when synthesizing fibrous proteins and analogous natural polymers. However, it is not possible to create synthetic polymers, such as poly(ethylene) or poly(styrene), via this method.

**Figure 2.30**
Condensation, or step reaction, polymerization mechanisms can be classified into two general groups, depending upon the types of monomers involved in the reaction. (a) The first group involves bifunctional or polyfunctional monomers, with each monomer possessing only one type of functional group. (b) The second group involves a single monomer species having both types of functional groups. In this figure, the general equation for each reaction mechanism (A and B are two different types of functional groups) is followed by an example reaction [12].

Although a detailed account of this method is beyond the scope of this text, genetic engineering of protein polymers involves the expression within a host organism (usually bacteria) of a genetic vector that encodes the protein polymer of interest. This can be achieved by one of two general methods. First, DNA encoding the protein polymer can be isolated from an organism that naturally produces it, and the DNA coding units can be introduced into the DNA of the host bacteria for expression and polymer production. Alternatively, the DNA encoding the protein polymer can be chemically synthesized and subsequently introduced into the host organism. The second method is more widely used and allows for a high level of control over the sequence of the protein polymer. Additionally, the second method allows for optimization of the DNA sequence for maximal expression by the host organism used. Examples of polymers produced through genetic engineering include silks, collagens, viral proteins, and a variety of artificial structural proteins.

### 2.4.3 Copolymers

In the previous discussion, we have focused on the synthesis and structure of **homopolymers,** or polymers with one type of repeat unit. However, **copolymers** (those involving two or more repeat unit types) are often produced to create materials with improved properties. Copolymers can be formed by either traditional condensation or addition polymerization, using a blend of monomer types as the reactant species.

As shown in Figure 2.31 with the different repeat units depicted in different colors, there are several types of copolymers. In **random copolymers,** the two mer units are distributed along the chain with no pattern. As the name indicates, mer types alternate in an **alternating copolymer. Block copolymers** occur when each type of repeat unit is clustered in regions (blocks) along the chain. If homopolymer chains

**Figure 2.31**
Types of copolymers. (a) Random copolymer—the two mer units are distributed along the chain with no pattern. (b) Alternating copolymer—mer types alternate. (c) Block copolymer—each type of repeat unit is clustered in regions (blocks) along the chain. (d) Graft copolymer—homopolymer chains are attached to a main homopolymer chain containing a different repeat unit.

are attached as side chains to a main homopolymer chain containing a different repeat unit, this is called a **graft copolymer**. Graft copolymers are often branched, as depicted in Figure 2.31. One of the most common examples of copolymers for biomedical applications is the random copolymerization of lactic acid and glycolic acid to form the biodegradable, synthetic polymer poly(lactic-*co*-glycolic acid), which is used in sutures, drug delivery devices, and tissue engineering scaffolds.

## EXAMPLE PROBLEM 2.8

Given the molecular structure of the following copolymer poly(lactic-*co*-glycolic acid) (PLGA) commonly used in biodegradable sutures, determine the molecular weights for:

(a) Each repeat unit for the copolymer shown.

(b) The copolymer when $n = 5$ and $m = 7$.
(c) The copolymer when $n = 7$ and $m = 3$.

Solution:

(a) The molecular weight for the repeat unit on the left ($n$) is as follows:

$$3 \text{ carbons } (12 \text{ g/mol C}) + 2 \text{ oxygens} (16 \text{ g/mol O}) + 4 \text{ hydrogens}$$
$$(1 \text{ g/mol H}) = \underline{72 \text{ g/mol } (n)}$$

The molecular weight for the repeat unit on the right ($m$) is as follows:

$$2 \text{ carbons } (12 \text{ g/mol C}) + 2 \text{ oxygens } (16 \text{ g/mol O}) + 2 \text{ hydrogens}$$
$$(1 \text{ g/mol H}) = \underline{58 \text{ g/mol } (m)}$$

(b) The molecular weight of the given copolymer is as follows:

$$5(72 \text{ g/mol } n) + 7(58 \text{ g/mol } m) + (16 \text{ g/mol oxygen})$$
$$+ 2(1 \text{ g/mol hydrogen}) = \underline{784 \text{ g/mol}}$$

(c) The molecular weight of the given copolymer is as follows:

$$7(72 \text{ g/mol } n) + 3(58 \text{ g/mol } m) + (16 \text{ g/mol oxygen})$$
$$+ 2(1 \text{ g/mol hydrogen}) = \underline{696 \text{ g/mol}}$$

## 2.4.4 Methods of Polymerization

A variety of polymerization methods exist for polymer production. The simplest method is **bulk polymerization**, in which only monomer and a monomer-soluble initiator are present in the reaction. This technique provides a high yield of high purity polymer, but tends to present difficulties with heat dissipation, especially in large-scale reactions, since most polymerization reactions are highly exothermic.

Problems in heat dissipation can be addressed by conducting the polymerization reaction in water or an appropriate organic solvent with high thermal conductivity in another method known as **solution polymerization**. In solution polymerization, it is important that the monomer and initiator be soluble in the chosen solvent and that the solvent can be easily recovered following the reaction. Although solution polymerization addresses issues with heat dissipation, it generally has a small polymer yield per reaction volume and requires an additional step to remove the solvent.

**Suspension polymerization** is another method that presents high heat transfer capabilities. In this process, monomer and initiators that are not soluble in water are added under stirring to a reactor full of water. The insolubility of the monomer coupled with the mechanical agitation leads to the formation of monomer droplets containing initiator. These droplets can be stabilized with additives (colloids) and act as small reactors for polymerization. After the reaction, the resulting polymer beads can be recovered through filtration and washed.

A similar process, **emulsion polymerization**, involves the addition under stirring of a hydrophobic monomer, a water soluble initiator and a surfactant (emulsifier) to a reactor containing water. (See Chapter 7 for more on surfactants.) Emulsion polymerization results in the formation of polymer beads or rods, depending upon the reaction conditions and the surfactant used. The mechanism for emulsion polymerization is illustrated in Figure 2.32.

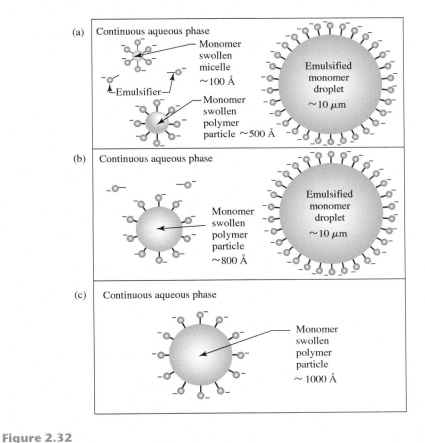

**Figure 2.32**
The mechanism for emulsion polymerization. This type of polymerization takes place in water with a water-soluble initiator, but involves a hydrophobic monomer. In order to disperse the hydrophobic monomer, a surfactant (emulsifier) is added. Because the surfactant possesses both hydrophilic and hydrophobic areas, it can be used as a coating for beads of the monomer and resulting polymer to promote their interaction with the aqueous environment. (a) At early stages of the reaction, three types of particles are present: emulsified monomer droplets, surfactant micelles containing solubilized monomer, and growing polymer particles stabilized by surfactant and swollen with monomer. (b) As the polymer particles grow, increasing amounts of surfactant are required to stabilize them until the surfactant micelles are depleted. (c) The polymer particles (swollen with monomer) continue to grow until the monomer in the emulsified monomer droplets is depleted and only surfactant stabilized polymer particles remain. (Reprinted with permission from [13].)

Additionally, polymerization can occur in the gas phase in **gaseous polymerization** and in the solid-state in **solid-state polymerization**. For solid-state polymerization, monomers in their crystalline state are polymerized through exposure to heat or irradiation. This process results in polymer chains that are oriented along the crystal structure. Lastly, polymerization can take place in a plasma environment in a process called **plasma polymerization**. This method is effective in depositing highly uniform thin films of polymer and can be used to alter surface properties, such as wettability (see Chapter 7).

### 2.4.5 Crystal Structures and Defects

**2.4.5.1 Crystal Structures**    Like metals and ceramics, polymers can form crystalline structures, although their unit cells are more complex and contain more atoms than those for other types of materials. A number of aspects of a polymer's chemical structure affect its ability to crystallize. These include the polymer's tacticity (if it is isotactic, syndiotactic, or atactic) and its degree of branching. A large amount of branching reduces the crystallinity of a polymeric material, as does the presence of bulky side groups in its repeat unit. It is rare for polymers to be 100% crystalline; many are considered to be *semi-crystalline*. A more in-depth discussion of polymer crystallinity is found in Chapter 3.

**2.4.5.2 Point Defects and Impurities**    Point defects in the form of vacancies may occur in polymer crystals. In this case, a vacancy can be seen as the space between where one chain ends and the next begins. Polymer crystals usually have a large number of defects, but their presence has less of an effect on the overall properties of the material than defects in metals or ceramics. As with other types of biomaterials, impurities also exist in polymer crystals. In some situations, such as the synthesis of copolymers, these impurities have been added intentionally. (The effects of copolymerization on crystal structure are discussed in Chapter 3.)

### 2.4.6 Hydrogels

As mentioned in Chapter 1, a specific subclass of polymeric materials called **hydrogels** are formed from hydrophilic polymers, and thus, have the ability to retain a significant fraction of water without dissolving [4]. Hydrogels are highly swellable. Swelling results from a balance between osmotic forces that encourage water diffusion into the material, and the bonds between the polymer chains, which resist water penetration and prevent the hydrogel from completely dissolving. A common biomedical use of hydrogels is in contact lenses, first commercialized in the 1970s using poly(2-hydroxyethyl methacrylate) (PHEMA) [5].

Hydrogels can be formed from either synthetic or natural polymers. Their gelation (formation of 3D network from a group of linear chains) can be due to chemical or physical means. Physical gelation is usually due to the entanglement of long polymer chains. Chemical gelation can be caused by a variety of mechanisms, including ionic interactions. A well-known example of an ionic-based hydrogel is alginate, a polysaccharide derived from seaweed, which contains mer units that are negatively charged. When a divalent cation such as $Ca^{2+}$ is introduced, it acts as a crosslink between chains, and gelation occurs. Other non-covalent chemical interactions can also be exploited to form hydrogels, including van der Waals and hydrophobic interactions. An example of gels formed using these mechanisms are protein (peptide)-based hydrogels that self-assemble into small (nm-diameter) fibers based on interactions of their hydrophobic groups. These fibers can then further assemble into 3D gel structures, based on these interactions, as well as chain entanglements.

However, to form hydrogels with more robust mechanical properties, a number of covalently crosslinked hydrogels have been developed (see Section 2.4.1.4 for a further discussion of covalent crosslinking), such as those based on derivatives of poly(ethylene glycol) (PEG) or the PHEMA mentioned earlier. Additional types of hydrogels include *interpenetrating network* hydrogels, where one polymer network is created and infiltrated with a second type of polymer, which is then gelled around the first. Such hydrogels can be fabricated to improve hydrogel toughness or to add a biological functionality to the hydrogel, depending on the chemical composition of the two networks. Recent work has also explored nanocomposite hydrogels, where nanoparticles act like additional crosslinks to further improve mechanical properties of the final material.

Regardless of the type of hydrogel, characterization of the swelling properties provides practical data about dimensional changes in environments like those found *in vivo*, as well as can reveal information about the structure of the gel formed. In particular, the volume swelling ratio,

Q = volume of gel in swollen state/volume of polymer in dry state

or the weight swelling ratio,

q = weight of gel in swollen state/weight of dry polymer

is often reported. This data (sometimes in combination with tensile testing data) can be used to calculate network parameters of the formed gels. While a detailed discussion of the basis for these calculations is outside the scope of this text (please see [6], [7] for more details), two parameters that are often reported are the molecular weight between crosslinks ($M_c$) and the physical distance between crosslinks ($\xi$), as shown in Figure 2.33. The distance between crosslinks ($\xi$) is found based on $M_c$ using assumptions such as the length of a carbon-carbon bond (see Example Problem 2.7), since most polymers have a carbon backbone, and can be particularly useful for understanding what size of molecules can easily diffuse through the hydrogel.

In addition to contact lenses, hydrogels have been explored as coating materials for medical devices, as drug delivery vehicles, and, due to their excellent water penetration, as scaffolds for cells for regenerative medicine applications. Thus, a wide range of hydrogels have been developed, many of which are designed to be sensitive to environmental factors, such as changes in pH, temperature, particular wavelengths of light, or biomolecules such as enzymes released from nearby cells.

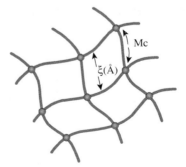

**Figure 2.33**
Diagram of a hydrogel network, with the molecular weight between crosslinks ($M_c$) and distance between crosslinks ($\xi$) depicted.

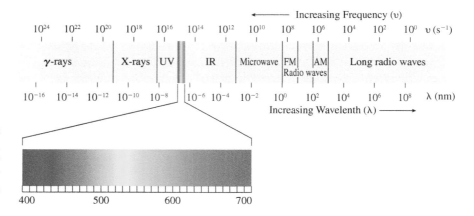

**Figure 2.34**
The spectrum of energies employed in spectroscopy. Note that higher energy results in higher frequency ($\nu$) and shorter wavelength ($\lambda$) radiation [8].

## 2.5 Techniques: Introduction to Material Characterization

Characterization of properties relating to the chemical composition of a biomaterial can be accomplished through two major techniques, *spectroscopy* and *chromatography*. In **spectroscopy**, one measures how compounds absorb different types of energy. As discussed in the previous chapter, due to the allowable energy states for electrons in the various orbitals, molecules absorb energy in discrete packets called **quanta**. The absorbed energy results in **excitation** of the sample by creating changes in electron or mechanical motion within the molecule.

Figure 2.34 and Table 2.6 depict the spectrum of energies that are employed in spectroscopy. (It is important to note in this figure that higher energy results in higher

**TABLE 2.6**

| Energies and Corresponding Atomic Transitions Found in Common Spectroscopic Techniques | | | |
|---|---|---|---|
| Type Spectroscopy | Usual Wavelength Range* | Usual Wavenumber Range, cm$^{-1}$ | Type of Quantum Transition |
| Gamma-ray emission | 0.005–1.4Å | – | Nuclear |
| X-Ray absorption, emission, fluorescence, and diffraction | 0.1–100Å | – | Inner electron |
| Vacuum ultraviolet absorption | 10–180 nm | $1 \times 10^6$ to $5 \times 10^4$ | Bonding electrons |
| Ultraviolet visible absorption, emission, and fluorescence | 180–780 nm | $5 \times 10^4$ to $1.3 \times 10^4$ | Bonding electrons |
| Infrared absorption and Raman scattering | $0.78 - 300 \,\mu\text{m}$ | $1.3 \times 10^4$ to $3.3 \times 10^1$ | Rotation/vibration of molecules |
| Microwave absorption | 0.75–3.75 mm | 13–27 | Rotation of molecules |
| Electron spin resonance | 3 cm | 0.33 | Spin of electrons in a magnetic field |
| Nuclear magnetic resonance | 0.6–10 m | $1.7 \times 10^{-2}$ to $1 \times 10^3$ | Spin of nuclei in a magnetic field |

*1Å $= 10^{-10}$ m $= 10^{-8}$ cm

1 nm $= 10^{-9}$ m $= 10^{-7}$ cm

1 μm $= 10^{-6}$ m $= 10^{-4}$ cm

(Reprinted with permission from [8].)

frequency and shorter wavelength radiation.) Each of the energy categories produces distinct changes in the atoms of a sample and thus provides different types of information about its chemical structure. In order of descending energy, X-rays promote electrons from inner subshells to outer ones, while ultraviolet/visible light excites only valence electrons (often from bonding to antibonding orbitals). Infrared energy causes vibration of bonds, and the lowest energy discussed here, radio waves (as used in nuclear magnetic resonance spectroscopy), produce transitions in nuclear spin.

In contrast to spectroscopy, ***chromatography*** uses various means to physically separate molecules on the basis of chemical characteristics such as charge or molecular weight. Both spectroscopic and chromatographic techniques are important in defining chemical compositions of biomaterials, and often provide complementary data. As explained next, each technique reveals slightly different information, and some are preferred for certain materials over others. For example, since it is possible to learn about the composition of crystalline materials by knowing the type of crystal formed, X-ray diffraction is often used for metals and ceramics, while a number of other techniques such as ultraviolet, infrared, and nuclear magnetic resonance spectroscopy, as well as mass spectrometry and high performance liquid chromatography, provide information to address questions about the composition of polymers.

## 2.5.1 X-Ray Diffraction

X-rays are a very high energy form of electromagnetic radiation used for a variety of characterization techniques. As mentioned earlier, X-rays are employed as a source for spectroscopic techniques to alter the energy state of core electrons. This is called **X-ray fluorescence**, of which there are two main types: *energy dispersive X-ray spectroscopy* (EDS) and *wavelength dispersive X-ray spectroscopy* (WDS). EDS is a more rapid spectroscopy method, but WDS has superior resolution. A more detailed description of these two methods is left to more advanced texts. X-rays are also important for biomaterial surface analysis in such techniques as electron spectroscopy for chemical analysis (ESCA), which will be discussed further in Chapter 7. A technique that uses X-rays for imaging is microcomputed tomography ($\mu$CT), and is discussed further in Chapter 14. In this section, we will focus on another characterization technique involving X-rays: **X-ray diffraction**. Rather than measuring how the absorbance of X-rays affects the sample, as in spectroscopic techniques, this method examines how X-rays, which can travel as waves like visible light, are diffracted from atoms in a material. X-ray diffraction is commonly used to determine structures of crystals, including calculation of Miller indices and unit cell size.

### 2.5.1.1 Basic Principles
Because the wavelength of X-rays (0.5–50Å) is similar to the distance between atoms in a solid, they are ideal for exploring atomic arrangement in crystal structures. **Diffraction** of X-rays occurs when incident rays are scattered by atoms in a way that reinforces the waves. As seen in Figure 2.35(a), if two waves (waves 1 and 2) of the same wavelength ($\lambda$) and amplitude ($A$) are in phase at point O/O' and are scattered so that they remain in phase (waves 1' and 2'), they will combine in a reinforcing (or **constructive**) manner and the diffracted wave will have the same wavelength, but twice the amplitude ($2A$). This occurs only if the total distance traveled by waves 1 and 2 differ by an integer number of wavelengths.

On the other hand, as shown in Figure 2.35(b), when the path lengths of two incident waves (waves 3 and 4) differ by a number of *half* wavelengths, after scattering, the waves (waves 3' and 4') are out of phase and there is **destructive interference**. The scattered waves cancel each other and no diffraction occurs. There are also a number of interactions that cause phase differences between these two extremes, leading to only partial reinforcement of incident waves.

(a)

(b)

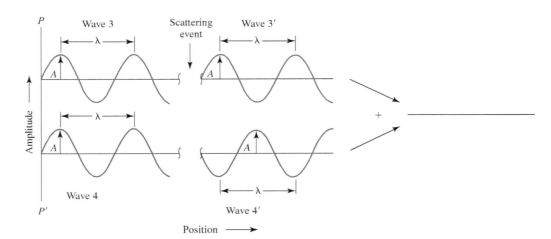

**Figure 2.35**

Constructive and destructive interference of X-rays. (a) If two waves (waves 1 and 2) of the same wavelength ($\lambda$) and amplitude ($A$) are in phase at point $O/O'$ and are scattered so that they remain in phase (waves 1' and 2'), they will combine in a constructive manner and diffraction will occur. The diffracted wave will have the same wavelength, but twice the amplitude (2$A$). This occurs only if the total distances traveled by waves 1 and 2 differ by an integer number of wavelengths. (b) When the path lengths of two incident waves (waves 3 and 4) differ by an odd number of *half* wavelengths, after scattering, the waves (waves 3' and 4') are out of phase and there is destructive interference. The scattered waves cancel each other and no diffraction occurs [1].

When X-rays enter a sample, they are scattered in all directions by the electrons associated with each atom/ion. In most cases, this leads to destructive interference and no resulting X-rays can be measured. For certain atomic arrangements, however, diffraction occurs and X-ray patterns can be recorded. In Figure 2.36, the planes of atoms marked $A/A'$ and $B/B'$ have the same Miller indices ($h\ k\ l$) and are separated by the distance $d_{hkl}$ (interplanar spacing). Consider the path of parallel X-rays (waves 1 and 2) of wavelength $\lambda$ that are in phase upon striking the sample at angle $\theta$. Wave 1 is scattered by atom $P$, and wave 2 is scattered by atom $Q$.

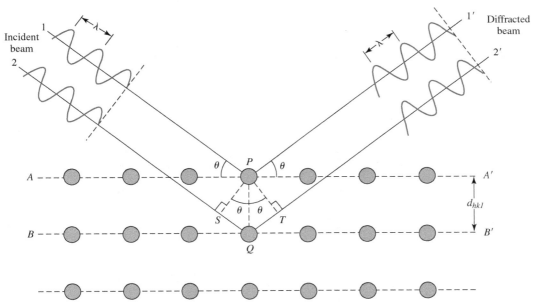

**Figure 2.36**
Scattering of X-rays by electrons in a crystalline material. The planes of atoms marked $A/A'$ and $B/B'$ have the same Miller indices ($h\,k\,l$) and are separated by the distance $d_{hkl}$ (interplanar spacing). Waves 1 and 2 are parallel X-rays of wavelength $\lambda$ that are in phase upon striking the sample at angle $\theta$. Wave 1 is scattered by atom $P$, and wave 2 is scattered by atom $Q$. For diffraction to occur, the total path length of the two waves must differ by an integral number of wavelengths. This can be expressed in terms of the crystal's interplanar spacing $(d_{hkl})$: $n\lambda = d_{hkl}\sin\theta + d_{hkl}\sin\theta = 2d_{hkl}\sin\theta$ and is called Bragg's law [1].

Since we know that for diffraction to occur, the total path length of the two waves must differ by an integral number of wavelengths, we can write

$$n\lambda = SQ + QT \qquad (2.19)$$

where $n$ is an integer. We can also rewrite this expression in terms of the crystal's interplanar spacing $(d_{hkl})$ using geometric relations:

$$n\lambda = d_{hkl}\sin\theta + d_{hkl}\sin\theta = 2d_{hkl}\sin\theta \qquad (2.20)$$

This expression is known as **Bragg's law**, and if this condition is not met, there will be no diffraction resulting from this set of planes. In the equation, $n$ refers to the type of diffraction, with $n = 1$ indicating first-order diffraction.

Interplanar spacing, as observed through X-ray diffraction experiments, is a function of a crystal's Miller indices and its lattice parameters. For cubic crystal systems, the relation is

$$d_{hkl} = \frac{a}{\sqrt{h^2 + k^2 + l^2}} \qquad (2.21)$$

where $a$ is the unit cell edge length. This relationship is more complex for other crystal systems. However, such equations can provide a means to determine the size of the unit cell and other important structural parameters based on X-ray diffraction data.

**2.5.1.2 Instrumentation** A typical X-ray diffraction pattern for aluminum powder is found in Figure 2.37. Results are plotted as intensity ($y$-axis) as a function of $2\theta$ ($x$-axis), where $\theta$ is the incident angle of the X-rays. Peaks are generated at

**Figure 2.37**
A typical X-ray diffraction pattern for aluminum powder. Peaks are generated at angles that satisfy the Bragg criteria for a certain set of atomic planes. The indices of these planes are noted in the figure. (Adapted with permission from [2].)

angles that satisfy the Bragg criteria for a certain set of atomic planes. The figure includes the indices of such planes for aluminum.

A number of X-ray diffraction techniques have been developed, but one of the most common is the powder method. Here, the sample is ground into a powder before placing it into the **diffractometer**. With so many fine particles (each crystalline) arranged randomly, there is a higher probability that, at a given angle, various particles will be oriented so that all possible atomic planes fulfill the Bragg criteria during the experiment and are recorded. For this technique, rather than changing the angular position of the X-ray source, the sample is rotated with respect to the incident beam. There are four basic components to a powder diffractometer, as shown in Figures 2.38 and 2.39:

1. Source—produces X-rays with known wavelength.
2. Sample holder—holds powdered sample and allows 360° rotation about its axis.
3. Counter—converts diffracted X-rays to an electrical signal proportional to the intensity of the rays. Rotates in conjunction with sample holder.
4. Processor (computer)—converts the signal from the counter into the appropriate plot.

As seen in the diagram (Fig. 2.39), the sample holder ($S$) containing the powdered sample is allowed to rotate about point $O$ on an axis perpendicular to the plane of the page. In this configuration, the X-ray source is located at point $T$ and the counter is found at point $C$. $S$, $T$, and $C$ all reside in the same plane. The counter is movable and can also be rotated about the axis at $O$. As the sample is rotated through an angle $\theta$, the counter is mechanically coupled so that it moves a distance $2\theta$. Its position in terms of $2\theta$ is marked on a graduated scale and is recorded by

**Figure 2.38**
Block diagram of components of a powder X-ray diffractometer. The four basic components are the source (produces X-rays with known wavelength), the sample holder (holds powdered sample and allows 360° rotation about its axis), the counter (converts diffracted X-rays to an electrical signal proportional to the intensity of the rays), and the processor/computer (converts the signal from the counter into the appropriate plot).

**Figure 2.39**
Schematic of a powder X-ray diffractometer. The sample holder (S) containing the powdered sample is allowed to rotate about point O on an axis perpendicular to the plane of the page. In this configuration, the X-ray source is located at point T and the counter is found at point C. S, T, and C all reside in the same plane. The counter is moveable and can also be rotated about the axis at O. As the sample is rotated an angle θ, the counter is mechanically coupled so that it moves an angular distance 2θ. Its position in terms of 2θ is marked on a graduated scale and is recorded by the computer. As the sample and counter move, the intensity of diffracted X-rays at various angles is monitored by the counter [1].

the computer. As the sample and counter move, the intensity of diffracted X-rays at various angles is monitored by the counter. At the end of the experiment, a summary of the diffraction pattern is plotted as a function of 2θ.

**2.5.1.3 Information Provided**  X-ray diffraction is a powerful technique for exploring atomic and molecular arrangements in solids and can be used for all crystalline materials, including metals, ceramics, and polymers. The size of a unit cell as well as its geometry can be determined from the angles at which peaks occur, and arrangement of atoms within the unit cell is indicated by the height of the peaks. In addition, compound identification may be carried out by comparing experimental results to diffraction patterns of known substances.

## 2.5.2 Ultraviolet and Visible (UV-VIS) Light Spectroscopy

**2.5.2.1 Basic Principles**  The absorption of UV-VIS radiation (wavelength ($\lambda$): approximately 185–1,100 nm) by a molecule ($M$) may promote one or more of its valence electrons to a higher energy state, resulting in molecular excitation to a new state ($M^*$)

$$M + h\nu = M^* \tag{2.22}$$

where $\nu$ is the frequency of radiation and $h$ is the Planck's constant ($6.6 \times 10^{-34}$ J-s).

Usually, this involves the transition of electrons from $\sigma$ or $\pi$ bonding to antibonding molecular orbitals (see Chapter 1 for discussion of molecular orbitals). Since different amounts of energy are required for different transitions, absorption occurs at various wavelengths, depending on the chemical structure of the molecule. Figure 2.40 provides a general idea of the energies involved in common transitions. Examples of organic molecules that demonstrate characteristic absorption at a given wavelength are given in Table 2.7.

After excitation, the molecule returns to its ground state through the conversion of the excitation energy to another form, such as thermal energy (heat). This process is known as **relaxation**:

$$M^* = M + heat \tag{2.23}$$

**Figure 2.40**
Excitation of molecules by UV-VIS radiation. Absorption of energy may promote one or more valence electrons from $\sigma$ or $\pi$ bonding to antibonding molecular orbitals. Since different amounts of energy are required for different transitions, absorption occurs at various wavelengths, depending on the chemical structure of the molecule [8].

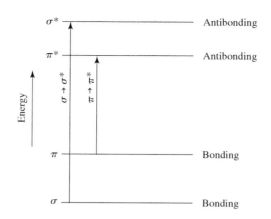

**TABLE 2.7**

| Common Chromophores and Corresponding Characteristic UV-VIS Absorption Wavelengths | | | |
|---|---|---|---|
| Chromophore | Example | Solvent | $\lambda_{max\ abs}$ (nm) |
| Alkene | | *n*-Heptane | 177 |
| Alkyne | | *n*-Heptane | 178 |
| | | | 196 |
| | | | 225 |
| Carbonyl | | *n*-Hexane | 186 |
| | | | 280 |
| | | *n*-Hexane | 180 |
| | | | 293 |
| Carboxyl | | Ethanol | 204 |
| Amido | | Water | 214 |
| Azo | | Ethanol | 339 |
| Nitro | | Isooctane | 280 |
| Nitroso | | Ethyl ether | 300 |
| | | | 665 |
| Nitrate | | Dioxane | 270 |

$\lambda_{max\ abs}$ denotes the wavelength at which maximum absorption in the spectrum occurs [8].

Return to the ground state can occur via a variety of means. An example of non-radiative relaxation is fluorescence, which will be discussed in Chapter 8 as a means to observe proteins.

**2.5.2.2 Instrumentation** A typical UV-VIS spectrum of poly(lactic-*co*-glycolic acid) (PLGA), a common suture material, is found in Figure 2.41. UV-VIS spectra are generally plotted as absorbance (*y*-axis) as a function of wavelength (or wavenumber) on the *x*-axis. In order to obtain such a plot, many types of UV-VIS

**Figure 2.41**
UV-VIS spectra of poly(lactic-*co*-glycolic acid)-polylysine (PLGA-plys) before and after deprotection. The peak with the maximum at 257 nm corresponds to the presence of the CBZ (carbobenzoxy) protecting group on the protected polymer (the large ringed structure in the diagram). In the deprotection step, this chemical group is removed, as is evidenced by the decrease in this peak in the spectrum. PLGA-plys block copolymer was synthesized by coupling PLGA with a carboxyl end group to poly($\epsilon$-carbobenzoxy-L-lysine) and is an example of a polymer that possesses both biological molecules (an amino acid) and a synthetic polymer (PLGA) [14].

**Figure 2.42**
Block diagram of components of a UV-VIS spectrophotometer. The source light beam (at a given wavelength as determined by the filter) is split and directed through both a reference chamber, usually a blank container, and a sample chamber (container + sample). The amount of transmitted energy is recorded in each path via the detector (photodiodes) and transmitted to a computer. Processing software then subtracts the transmittance of the reference path from that of the sample path to provide the amount of energy transmitted through the sample, without interference that may arise from its holder or other environmental factors. The process is then repeated at the next wavelength, if desired. At the end of the wavelength scans, the entire spectrum is plotted for that sample.

spectrophotometers have been developed. There are four basic components to a spectrophotometer, as shown in Figure 2.42:

1. Source provides energy over the wavelength range of interest.
2. Wavelength selector or filter—allows user to choose a specific wavelength if desired.
3. Detector—converts energy transmitted through the sample to an electrical signal.
4. Processor (computer)—converts the electrical signal into the appropriate spectrum.

In UV-VIS spectroscopy, the sample is placed after the wavelength selector and before the detector. We will now focus our attention on one of the most common instruments: the double beam spectrophotometer (Fig. 2.42).

As shown in the diagram, the source light beam (at a given wavelength as determined by the settings of the filter) is split and directed through both a reference chamber, usually a blank container, and a sample chamber (container + sample). The amount of transmitted energy (transmittance) is recorded in each path via the photodiodes and transmitted to a computer. Processing software then subtracts the *transmittance* of the reference path from that of the sample path to provide the amount of energy transmitted through the sample, without interference that may arise from its holder or other environmental factors. Finally, fraction transmittance ($F_t$) is converted to fraction absorbance ($F_a$)($F_a = 1 - F_t$). The process is then repeated at the next wavelength, if desired. At the end of the wavelength scans, the entire spectrum is plotted for that sample.

**2.5.2.3 Information Provided**   There are two main uses for UV-VIS spectroscopy. One is to produce spectra to help identify samples or chemical groups within samples. This is done by recording the absorbance over a wide range of wavelengths with successive scans by the spectrophotometer.

In addition, UV-VIS is often used to quantify the amount of a certain compound in a mixture or solution. Of course, this is only possible if the compound absorbs a significant amount of UV radiation at a certain wavelength, and if this wavelength is known. In this case, repeated scans are not needed—the user simply chooses the appropriate wavelength

**Figure 2.43**
Standard curve for potassium permanganate. A standard curve is generated by measuring UV-VIS absorbance at a set wavelength of known concentrations (five concentrations in this example). Using Beer-Lambert's law, an equation describing the linear relation of absorbance and concentration can then be created [15].

and the computer records the absorbance value at that setting. Concentrations of both inorganic and organic substances can be quantified using this method, but it is more commonly used in the biomaterials field for organic materials (Table 2.7).

Quantification of a sample is made possible through the use of **Beer-Lambert's law**:

$$A = \varepsilon l C \tag{2.24}$$

where $A$ is the absorbance measured by the spectrophotometer, $l$ is the thickness of the sample through which the light is passed, $C$ is the molar concentration of the compound, and $\varepsilon$ is the molar absorption coefficient for that compound at a given wavelength. The parameter $\varepsilon$ has been measured for many substances, and can be affected by temperature and the nature of the solvent, as well as the wavelength chosen.

A direct result of Beer-Lambert's law is that a standard curve of a given compound can be generated by measuring the absorbance at a fixed wavelength of the pure material at varying concentrations. An equation describing the linear relation over a certain range of absorbance and concentration can then be generated (Fig. 2.43). Using this relation, the concentration of that compound in an unknown sample can be determined by comparing the absorbance value of the unknown at the selected wavelength with values found in the standard curve.

The ease with which such quantification can take place using an UV-VIS system has made it a common technique in a variety of assays, including those for products of cellular function, as described in the second half of this book. In addition, UV-VIS detectors are often found as part of chromatographic techniques, such as HPLC (see Section 2.5.6), to measure the amount of various compounds separated from a mixture and injected into the instrument.

## 2.5.3 Infrared (IR) Spectroscopy

**2.5.3.1 Basic Principles**  IR spectroscopy includes sources that produce radiation of wavelengths 0.78−1000 μm, but the majority of analysis takes place with energy of wavelengths 2.5−25 μm. Although interaction between IR radiation and analyte molecules is complex, the basic concepts can be understood by using a simple ball and spring model representing a bond between two atoms (Fig. 2.44). It should be noted that, in order for interactions to occur, the bond must possess a permanent dipole, so that molecules such as $O_2$, $N_2$, and $Cl_2$ are relatively transparent in IR spectroscopy.

As seen in Figure 2.45, a polar bond can be thought of as oscillating or vibrating with a certain frequency. Since this is occurring in three dimensions, there are

*Mechanical oscillations*                                    *Mechanical oscillations*

**Figure 2.44**
(a&b) Basic ball and spring model of IR energy interaction with chemical bonds. (It should be noted that, in order for interactions to occur, the bond must possess a permanent dipole.) As depicted in the figure, a polar bond can be thought of as oscillating or vibrating with a certain frequency. If the frequency of the IR radiation matches the frequency of this vibration, then there is a reinforcing interaction and the amplitude of the oscillation increases, although the frequency of the oscillation remains the same. The result is that absorption at this IR frequency (wavelength) occurs for this material [15].

a number of vibrations possible for any given bond, including stretching, bending, and rocking movements. Common types of vibrations are depicted in Figure 2.45.

If the frequency of the IR radiation matches the frequency of this vibration, then there is a reinforcing interaction and the amplitude of the oscillation increases,

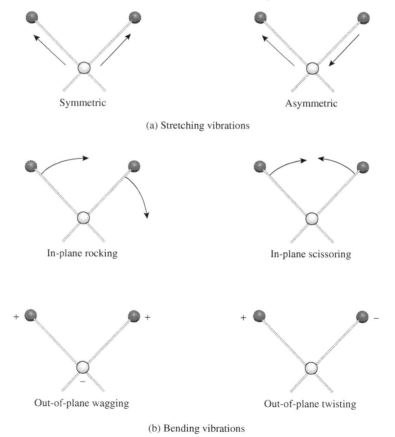

**Figure 2.45**
(a&b) Common types of three-dimensional vibrations in bonds between atoms. "+" indicates movement out of the plane of the page.

**TABLE 2.8**

| IR Frequencies Absorbed by Common Chemical Groups | | | |
|---|---|---|---|
| Bond | Type of Compound | Frequency Range, cm$^{-1}$ | Intensity |
| C—H | Alkanes | 2850–2970 | Strong |
| | | 1340–1470 | Strong |
| C—H | Alkenes $\left( \overset{}{\underset{}{}} C = C \overset{H}{\underset{}{}} \right)$ | 3010–3095 | Medium |
| | | 675–995 | Strong |
| C—H | Alkynes(–C≡C–H) | 3300 | Strong |
| C—H | Aromatic rings | 3010–3100 | Medium |
| | | 690–900 | Strong |
| O—H | Monomeric alcohols, phenols | 3590–3650 | Variable |
| | Hydrogen-bonded alcohols, phenols | 3200–3600 | Variable, sometimes broad |
| | Monomeric carboxylic acids | 3500–3650 | Medium |
| | Hydrogen-bonded carboxylic acids | 2500–2700 | Broad |
| N—H | Amines, amides | 3300–3500 | Medium |
| C=C | Alkenes | 1610–1680 | Variable |
| C=C | Aromatic rings | 1500–1600 | Variable |
| C≡C | Alkynes | 2100–2260 | Variable |
| C—N | Amines, amides | 1180–1360 | Strong |
| C≡N | Nitriles | 2210–2280 | Strong |
| C—O | Alcohols, ethers, carboxylic acids, esters | 1050–1300 | Strong |
| C=O | Aldehydes, ketones, carboxylic acids, esters | 1690–1760 | Strong |
| NO$_2$ | Nitro compounds | 1500–1570 | Strong |
| | | 1300–1370 | Strong |

(Adapted with permission from [8].)

although the frequency of the oscillation remains the same. The result is that absorption at this IR frequency (wavelength) is observed for this molecule. Since different types of bonds exist in a given sample, and there are multiple types of vibrations for each bond, absorption occurs at various wavelengths, depending on the chemical structure of the molecule. Table 2.8 provides a general idea of the frequencies absorbed for different chemical groups.

**2.5.3.2 Instrumentation**   A typical IR spectrum of poly(styrene) is found in Figure 2.46. In contrast to UV-VIS, IR spectra are generally plotted as percent transmittance (rather than absorbance) (y-axis), as a function of wavelength (or wavenumber) (x-axis). The basic instrumentation for IR spectroscopy is very similar to that for UV-VIS and includes an IR source, a wavelength selector, a detector and a processor

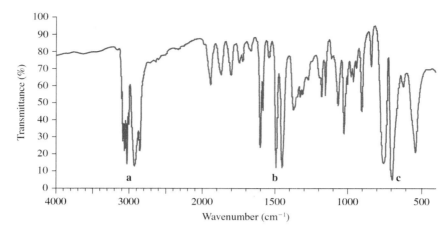

Poly(styrene) mer structure:

**Figure 2.46**
A typical IR spectrum of poly(styrene). In contrast to UV-VIS, IR spectra are generally plotted by percent transmittance (rather than absorbance) (*y*-axis), as a function of wavelength (or wavenumber) (*x*-axis) and, therefore, the peaks appear inverted. The IR spectrum, along with reference data such as shown in Table 2.8, is used to determine the structure of the material. For example, peaks are shown at 2800–3100 (a), 1400–1600 (b), and 600–900 (c) wavenumber. When used in conjunction with Table 2.8, it is evident that aromatic rings result in peaks between 3010–3100, 1500–1600, and 690–900. This would indicate that the material analyzed via IR spectroscopy contains an aromatic ring structure. This process is continued until the whole structure has been determined [9].

(Fig. 2.47(a)). Although double beam spectrophotometers are also often used for IR analysis, unlike UV-VIS, the sample is usually placed directly after the source, since the energies used in this type of analysis are not strong enough to damage the material.

Improvement in IR spectroscopy has come through the use of Fourier-transform techniques (FTIR), which involve the inclusion of mirrors in the form of an interferometer (Figs. 2.47(b) and 2.48). Although the exact mechanism of interferometer function is beyond the scope of this book, the advantage of Fourier transform is that, since information for all wavelengths reaches the detector simultaneously, the scan time is significantly shortened. Thus, it is possible to perform more scans in a given time, which significantly increases the signal strength (signal-to-noise ratio). This advantage is particularly important in analyzing samples containing a small amount of material, such as is found when examining the surface of a biomaterial. The application of FTIR to surface analysis will be discussed further in Chapter 7.

**2.5.3.3 Information Provided**   Because samples analyzed by IR spectroscopy also follow Beer-Lambert's law, like UV-VIS, IR can be used to quantify amounts of substances. However, this technique has been most often employed in biomaterial

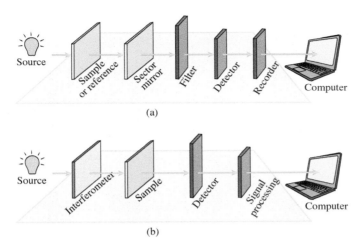

**Figure 2.47**
Block diagram of components of an IR spectrophotometer. (a) The basic instrumentation for IR spectroscopy is very similar to that for UV-VIS and includes an IR source, a wavelength selector, a detector, and a processor. Unlike UV-VIS, the sample is usually placed directly after the source, since the energies used in this type of analysis are not strong enough to damage the material. (b) Improvement in IR spectroscopy has come through the use of Fourier-transform techniques (FTIR), which involve the inclusion of mirrors in the form of an interferometer. The basic components of a FTIR instrument are shown here.

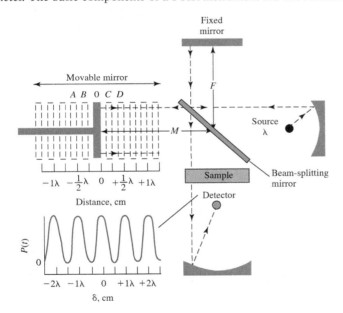

**Figure 2.48**
Detail of a Michelson interferometer. A source produces a beam of the proper wavelength that is then directed to a beam-splitting mirror, which transmits half the radiation and reflects the other half. The split beams are then reflected off mirrors (one fixed, one movable) and are joined again at the beam splitter. When the two mirrors are equidistant from the beam splitter, the recombined beam is in phase and can be observed at the detector. However, if the distance of the two mirrors is off by 1/4 of a wavelength (total difference $1/2\lambda$), destructive interference occurs and nothing is registered at the detector. Because the recombined beam is passed through the sample, Fourier-transform techniques can then be used to convert information about absorbance of this beam into a traditional IR spectrum. The advantage of Fourier transform is that, since information for all wavelengths reaches the detector simultaneously, the scan time is significantly shortened and, thus, the signal to noise ratio is increased [8].

Poly(ethylene glycol) diacrylate

**Figure 2.49**
Attenuated total internal reflectance-Fourier transform infrared spectroscopy (ATR-FTIR) spectra acquired during the photopolymerization of poly(ethylene glycol) diacrylate using a UV lamp. As the reaction proceeds, the acrylic carbon double bound (C=C) (seen at 1 on the diagram) is converted to single bonds (C–C) (seen at 2 on the diagram). The reduction in the amount of this double bond was determined by measuring the decrease in terminal C=C stretch (RHC=CH) at $1635\,\mathrm{cm}^{-1}$ and C=C–H bending at $1410\,\mathrm{cm}^{-1}$ at several time points [16].

characterization to record sample spectra, particularly of polymeric molecules. These spectra are unique for each material and form a sort of "molecular fingerprint," allowing identification of various materials via spectrum comparison. This type of analysis is very powerful, since IR provides more information about polymer structure and composition than most other characterization techniques.

Another common use for IR spectroscopy is to follow the relative change over time of certain peaks that correspond to specific types of bonds, as shown in Table 2.8. Examining the appearance of product peaks or disappearance of monomer peaks are two means to monitor a polymerization reaction, for example (Fig. 2.49).

## 2.5.4 Nuclear Magnetic Resonance Spectroscopy (NMR)

### 2.5.4.1 Basic Principles

NMR utilizes radiation in the radio-frequency region (0.5–75 m) to excite molecules. However, in contrast to the types of spectroscopy previously discussed, NMR induces changes in the nucleus, rather than the electrons, of an atom. Additionally, the presence of a strong magnetic field is needed to observe the nuclear transitions.

As introduced in Chapter 1, quantum mechanical principles can be employed to describe the configurations of electrons around the nucleus, including the concept that each electron can be characterized in part by its angular momentum, or spin. In an extension of these principles, many nuclei also behave as if they were spinning. Since nuclei are positively charged, their movement (spin) creates a small magnetic field, and each nucleus in an NMR experiment can be viewed as a small magnet. Like electrons, the nuclei of most interest to the biomaterialist ($^1$H and $^{13}$C) have two theoretical orientations to their spin. A nucleus must have unequal numbers of protons and neutrons to produce a signal in NMR analysis.

Like little magnets, when the nuclei are placed in a larger, external magnetic field, their orientation can be in the same direction as the field, which is more energetically favorable and thus represents a lower energy state, or opposite to the field, which represents a higher energy state (Fig. 2.50). The difference in these two energy states increases with increasing strength of the magnetic field.

**Figure 2.50**
Theory behind nuclear magnetic resonance. When protons (H) are placed in a larger, external magnetic field, $H_0$ their spins can be oriented in the same direction as the field, which is more energetically favorable and thus represents a lower energy state ($\alpha$), or with spin opposing the field (a higher energy state, $\beta$). The difference in energy $\Delta E$ between these two states is equal to $h\nu$. If exposed to radio energy of frequency $\nu$ (resonance frequency), then the nuclei will absorb this energy and the nuclear spin will be "flipped" from the $\alpha$ to the $\beta$ state. At this point, the nuclei are in resonance. The resonance frequency depends strongly on the local environment of each nucleus [17].

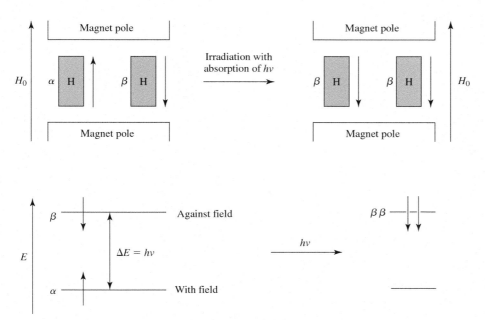

In a constant magnetic field, the addition of radio waves with just enough energy to bridge the gap in energy states will force some of the nuclei into the higher energy orientation. At this point, the nuclei are in **resonance**. This is indicated by absorbance of radio waves at a certain frequency, called the **resonance frequency**. After resonance has been achieved, as with other types of spectroscopy, molecular relaxation can occur through a variety of means.

When exposed to the same magnetic field, various molecules will require different amounts of energy to resonate (because they demonstrate different resonance frequencies). This is partially due to the local environment of the nucleus of interest (usually $^1H$). To explain, we will discuss in more detail the cases of hydrogen bonded to fluorine, as in HF, and hydrogen bonded to carbon, as in $CH_3$.

In addition to the external magnetic field, the $^1H$ nucleus is also affected by smaller magnetic fields created by the circulation of electrons around it. The movement of these electrons creates a magnetic field whose strength is proportional to the electron density. This smaller field opposes the effects of the external field (Fig. 2.51). In the case of the H–C bond, there are more electrons nearby than would normally be found in a hydrogen atom, so the nucleus is said to be **shielded** from the strength of the external field. Therefore, less energy (lower frequency of radio waves) is needed to induce resonance in this molecule.

On the other hand, if the hydrogen is bonded to a more electron-withdrawing (electronegative) atom such as fluorine (HF), the electron density around the hydrogen nucleus is less than normal, and the nucleus is **deshielded**. In this case, more energy is required and a higher resonance frequency than normal is recorded. These principles, along with more complicated aspects of a $^1H$ NMR spectrum, are used to determine molecular structure by identification of the localized environment of each proton in the sample.

**2.5.4.2 Instrumentation**  A typical NMR spectrum of poly(DL-lactic acid-b-ethylene glycol)-monomethyl ether diblock copolymer is found in Figure 2.52.[3]

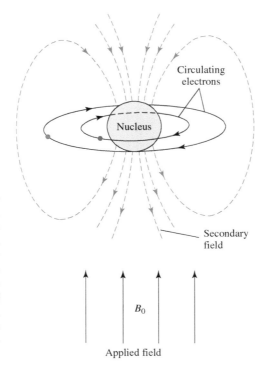

**Figure 2.51**
Effect of applied and secondary magnetic fields on the hydrogen nucleus. The nucleus is affected by small magnetic fields created by the circulation of electrons around it. This smaller field opposes the effects of the external field ($B_0$) and reduces the energy needed to induce resonance in the molecule [8].

Poly(DL-lactic acid-b-ethylene glycol)-monomethyl ether:

**Figure 2.52**

[1]H-NMR spectrum of a poly(DL-lactic acid-b-ethylene glycol)-monomethyl ether diblock copolymer. Although it is somewhat difficult to obtain absolute values for the $x$-axis of an NMR spectrum, it is easier to determine relative shifts in resonance frequency as compared to a standard included with the sample (an internal standard). In many cases, this reference material is tetramethylsilane (TMS), $(CH_3)_4 Si$, which produces the large peak seen at 0 ppm. As evidenced by the various peaks (1–4), the environment of the individual H atoms produces alterations in localized magnetic fields, resulting in different shifts that allow chemical structures to be distinguished [18].

NMR spectra are generally plotted as peak intensity ($y$-axis) versus chemical shift in parts per million ($x$-axis, ppm). Although it is somewhat difficult to obtain absolute values for the $x$-axis of an NMR spectrum, it is easier to determine relative shifts in resonance frequency as compared to a standard included with the sample (an **internal standard**). In many cases, this reference material is tetramethylsilane (TMS), $(CH_3)_4 Si$, which produces the large peak seen at 0 ppm in Figure 2.52. The remainder of the peaks in the figure represent absorption of frequencies by protons in other chemical milieus, and therefore they are shifted a certain amount (usually 1–13 ppm for [1]H NMR) from that absorbed by the TMS protons.

It is possible to obtain NMR spectra by either maintaining a constant magnetic field and varying the frequency of the radio waves produced, or holding the radio frequency constant and changing the strength of the magnetic field. Both configurations require

---

[3]DL in poly(DL-lactic acid) refers to a racemic mixture of enantiomeric repeating units of L-lactic acid and D-lactic acid. In general, polymers of enantiomeric monomers may possess different physical properties from their racemic counterparts because of their ordered configuration.

**Figure 2.53**
The components of an NMR instrument. The sample is placed into the probe, which holds it in a constant field produced by the magnet. The radio frequencies produced by the transmitter are varied in a controlled manner, and the corresponding returning frequencies are recorded by the detector. After all the frequencies have been scanned, computer software converts the sample response into the appropriate spectrum [15].

similar equipment, but for ease of explanation we will focus our attention on the former. There are five basic components to a NMR instrument, as shown in Figure 2.53:

1. Magnet—produces a strong, uniform magnetic field.
2. Sample probe—allows for insertion of the sample into the magnetic field.
3. Radio wave transmitter—produces radio waves at a variety of frequencies.
4. Radio wave receiver/detector—converts the radio frequencies not absorbed by the sample into an electrical signal.
5. Processor (computer)—translates the output from the detector into the appropriate spectrum.

As shown in the diagram (Fig. 2.53), the sample is placed into the probe, which holds it in a constant field produced by the magnet. The radio frequencies produced by the transmitter are varied in a controlled manner, and the corresponding returning frequencies are recorded by the detector. After all the frequencies have been scanned, a computer converts the sample response into the appropriate spectrum. Similar to IR spectroscopy, Fourier-transform NMR experiments are commonly performed in modern laboratories due to their increased sensitivity, but description of such techniques is beyond the scope of this text.

**2.5.4.3 Information Provided** NMR is a powerful tool for elucidating the structure of inorganic and organic molecules. Samples can be examined for the presence of certain types of bonds using characteristic chemical shifts for different groups, as listed in Table 2.9. Also, the relative amounts of atoms in various chemical states can be easily obtained. One of the most common uses of NMR in the biomaterials field is to characterize a polymer after a synthesis reaction to assure product quality and purity.

## 2.5.5 Mass Spectrometry

**2.5.5.1 Basic Principles** Despite the similarity of name and plot produced (also called a spectrum), mass spectrometry is not a type of spectroscopy, like X-ray,

Table 2.9

## Characteristic NMR Shifts for Common Chemical Groups

*¹H NMR chemical shift table*

| Type of proton | Approximate δ (ppm) | Type of proton | Approximate δ (ppm) |
|---|---|---|---|
| Alkane (—CH₃) methyl | 0.9 | C=C CH₃ allylic | 1.7 |
| Alkane (—CH₂—) methylene | 1.3 | Ph—H aromatic | 7.2 |
| Alkane (—CH—) methine | 1.4 | Ph—CH₃ benzylic | 2.3 |
| O ‖ —C—CH₃ methyl ketone | 2.1 | O ‖ R—C—H aldehyde | 9–10 |
| —C≡C—H acetylenic | 2.5 | O ‖ R—C—OH acid | 10–12 |
| R—CH₂—X (X = halogen, O) | 3–4 | R—OH alcohol | Variable, ~2–5 |
| C=C H vinyl | 5–6 | Ar—OH phenol | Variable, ~4–7 |
| | | R—NH₂ amine | Variable, ~1.5–4 |

*Note:* These values are approximate because all chemical shifts are affected by neighboring substituents. The values given here assume that alkyl groups are the only other substituents present. (Table taken from J.R. Dyer, Applications of absorption spectroscopy by organic compounds, P. 85. Engkewood Cliffs, NJ: Prentic-Hall, Unc., © 1965. with permission.)

UV-VIS, IR, or NMR, because it does not involve measuring the absorption of electro-magnetic radiation. Instead, it determines the atomic or molecular masses of various species in a material. In order to accomplish this, the sample is first ionized though bombardment with high-energy particles (usually electrons). The resulting charged species are forced through a magnetic field, which interacts with them to deflect them from a linear path. Because lighter species are deflected more than heavier ones, the

**Figure 2.54**
Spectrum from a type of mass spectrometry (matrix-assisted laser desorption/ionization time-of-flight mass spectrometry) of poly(methyl methacrylate) (PMMA). Top: Counts at each m/z (mass/charge) ratio from 2,500 to 12,500 showing relative amounts of different PMMA ion fragments. Bottom: Structure of the repeat unit of PMMA [19].

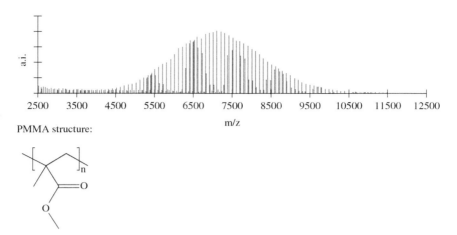

PMMA structure:

particles can be separated based on mass.[4] This technique is extremely sensitive to differences in mass, and can even distinguish between isotopes of the same element.

**2.5.5.2 Instrumentation**  A typical mass spectrum of poly(methyl methacrylate) (used as a bone cement) is found in Figure 2.54. Mass spectra are generally plotted as relative intensity (*y*-axis) as a function of mass (*x*-axis). As with traditional spectroscopy techniques, a number of mass spectrometers have been developed. There are four basic components to a mass spectrometer, as shown in Figures 2.55 and 2.56.

1. Inlet/ionization chamber allows for insertion of the sample and its ionization via bombardment by high-energy particles.
2. Mass analyzer—uses a magnetic or electric field to separate the resulting ions based on mass.

**Figure 2.55**
Block diagram of components of a mass spectrometer. The four basic components are the inlet/ionization chamber (allows for insertion of the sample and its ionization via bombardment by high-energy particles), the mass analyzer (uses a magnetic or electric field to separate the resulting ions based on mass), the detector (converts the impact of ions after separation into an electrical signal), and the processor/computer (translates the signal from the detector into the appropriate spectrum).

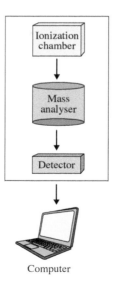

---

[4]Technically, in mass spectrometers, species are sorted on their mass to charge ratio (*m/z* ratio). However, since the ions often have a charge of +1 or −1, this is generally equivalent to separation by mass.

**Figure 2.56**
Schematic of a mass spectrometer. The sample is first ionized and the resulting particles are accelerated into the mass analyzer chamber. Because of the geometry of the mass analyzer and the strength of the magnet, only ions with a certain mass are allowed to hit the detector, while all others strike the walls of the chamber. By altering the magnetic field in a controlled manner, the detector can record the amount of ions having various masses. At the end of the sweep of magnetic field strength, the entire spectrum is plotted for that sample. (Adapted with permission from [8].)

3. Detector—converts the impact of ions after separation into an electrical signal.
4. Processor (computer)—translates the signal from the detector into the appropriate spectrum.

We will now focus our attention on one of the most common instruments: the magnetic sector spectrometer, so called because it uses only a magnetic field to separate ions (Fig. 2.56).

As shown in the diagram, the sample is first ionized and the resulting particles are accelerated into the mass analyzer chamber. Because of the geometry of the mass analyzer and the strength of the magnet, only ions with a certain mass are allowed to hit the detector, while all others strike the walls of the chamber (see path of lighter and heavier ions in Fig. 2.56). By altering the magnetic field in a controlled manner, the detector can record the amount of ions having various masses. At the end of the sweep of magnetic field strength, the entire spectrum is plotted for that sample. As indicated in Figure 2.55, mass spectrometry is performed under vacuum to prevent unwanted interactions of sample ions with reactive species in the air.

**2.5.5.3 Information Provided** Mass spectrometry can provide qualitative and quantitative assessment of both inorganic and organic molecules, although, for biomaterials, it is primarily used for analysis of natural and synthetic polymers. In particular, this is one of the few methods that allows identification of isotope ratios within a substance. By examining the type of ions produced after bombardment, it is also possible to gain insight into the strength of various bonds in the molecule. Mass spectrometry can be combined with other methods, particularly chromatographic techniques, to provide more information about the separated compounds. A variant of this method, secondary ion mass spectrometry (SIMS), is often used for surface analysis of biomaterials, as discussed further in Chapter 7.

### 2.5.6 High-Performance Liquid Chromatography (HPLC): Size-Exclusion Chromatography

Like mass spectrometry, chromatography provides information based on separation of substances by chemical properties such as size or charge. Our discussion will focus on liquid chromatography, since this is the technique most commonly used for analysis of biomaterials, particularly natural and synthetic polymers. As shown in Figure 2.57, there are many different types of liquid chromatography, but we will focus in this section on **size-exclusion chromatography** (SEC), which encompasses gel permeation and gel filtration chromatography. Affinity chromatography will be described in Chapter 8.

**2.5.6.1 Basic Principles**   SEC is based on the simple concept of filtration by size. A SEC system contains both a mobile and a stationary phase. The mobile phase is a liquid solvent into which the dissolved sample is injected. The stationary phase is composed of small (diameter ~10 μm) porous silica or polymer beads. The beads have uniformly sized open pores so that the sample and solvent can enter as the mobile phase is circulated through the system. While the analyte is in the

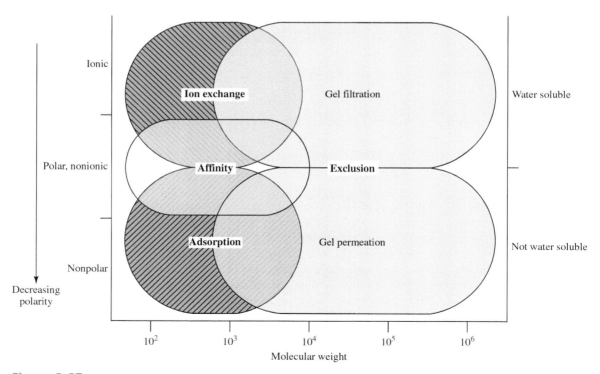

**Figure 2.57**
Classes of liquid chromatography. Chromatography provides information based on separation of substances by physicochemical properties such as size or charge.

Porous Bead

Amount polymer

Time

**Figure 2.58**
Diagram depicting how size-exclusion chromatography separates by size. The column (stationary phase) is packed with porous beads. Polymers of different sizes (lengths) are dissolved in the mobile phase (shown as the mixture of red and blue in this diagram). As the mobile phase passes through the stationary phase, the smaller polymers (shown in blue in this diagram) can enter the pores and are retained longer. In contrast, the larger polymers (shown in red) move quickly through the column and are eluted first. Results of the chromatography run are shown on the right, with the red polymer coming out of the column earlier.

porous structure, it is removed from the flow of the mobile phase and is thus considered to be **retained** in the stationary phase.

Retention time is highly affected by the size of the analyte. Molecules that are larger than the average pore size cannot enter and thus are not retained by the beads, while those that are very small can penetrate into the network and remain there for some time (see Fig. 2.58). Therefore, the first species to exit the stationary phase is the molecule with the largest size (highest molecular weight), and the smallest molecular weight compound exits (is **eluted**) last (Fig. 2.59). In between, molecules are retained for varying amounts of time depending on the extent of penetration of the porous network, which leads to separation of compounds by molecular weight.

**2.5.6.2 Instrumentation**    Figure 2.60 is an example of a typical graph obtained from SEC analysis of PEG (often used in hydrogels). Results are generally plotted as peak intensity (*y*-axis, units depend on type of detector) as a function of time (*x*-axis).

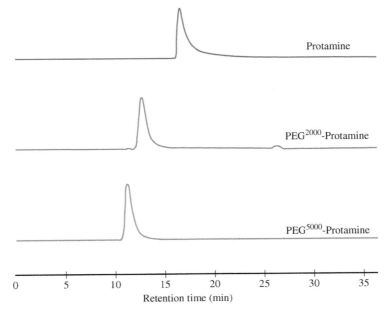

Protamine

PEG$^{2000}$-Protamine

PEG$^{5000}$-Protamine

0    5    10    15    20    25    30    35

Retention time (min)

**Figure 2.59**
Size-exclusion chromatograms of a protein (protamine), the protein bonded to a synthetic polymer (poly(ethylene glycol) (PEG)) with a molecular weight of 2 kDa, and the protein bonded to PEG of 5 kDa. In size-exclusion chromatography, higher molecular weight substances are eluted earlier than smaller molecules [20].

**Figure 2.60**

Results from SEC analysis of poly(ethylene glycol) (PEG). (a) Size-exclusion chromatographs of eight PEG standards of known molecular weight. This data can then be used to create a calibration curve (b), which is used to determine the weight ($\bar{M}_w$) and number ($\bar{M}_n$) average molecular weight of an unknown sample. To generate the calibration curve, the retention time for each peak of the known samples is plotted against their known molecular weight (as seen in (b)). An unknown sample can then be run through the SEC (c), and using the retention time and the calibration curve created in (b), the $\bar{M}_w$ and $\bar{M}_n$ of the sample can be determined. The sample's polydispersity index ($PI$) can then be calculated from $\bar{M}_w / \bar{M}_n$.

SEC can be divided into two subsets, both of which use the same instrumentation. **Gel filtration chromatography (GFC)** requires the use of aqueous solvents in the mobile phase and hydrophilic beads in the stationary phase. In contrast, **gel permeation chromatography (GPC)** employs organic solvents and a hydrophobic stationary phase.

There are five basic components to an HPLC (or SEC) instrument, as shown in Figure 2.61:

1. Pump—causes circulation of the mobile phase.

2. Injector—injects a given amount of sample into the mobile phase.

3. Column—separates different sized molecules based on retention time.

4. Detector—translates the amount of analyte in the mobile phase to an electrical signal.

5. Processor (computer)—converts the signal from the detector into plots of peak intensity over time.

**Figure 2.61**

Block diagram of components of an HPLC instrument (SEC). The basic components are the pump (causes circulation of the mobile phase), the injector (injects a given amount of sample into the mobile phase), the column (separates different sized molecules based on retention time), the detector (translates the amount of analyte in the mobile phase to an electrical signal), and the processor/computer (converts the signal from the detector into plots of peak intensity over time). It should be noted that, here, the "detector" refers to the entire spectrophotometer, not just the device that converts transmitted light to an electrical signal.

There are a wide variety of detectors for HPLC (or SEC), many of which are based on techniques previously discussed, such as UV or IR (see sections 2.5.2 and 2.5.3). Mass spectrometers as detectors are less common, but have found uses in certain systems. It should be noted that, in this list, "detector" is not used in the same manner as in lists of components for spectroscopy. Here, the detector refers to the entire spectrophotometer, not just the device that converts transmitted light to an electrical signal.

The sample is injected into the mobile phase of the system, a degassed solvent. Degassing is required to prevent any bubbles from becoming trapped in the instrument. The solvent and analyte are then pumped through a separation column at a constant flow rate. The sample is retained through interactions with the beads packing the column until it finally reaches the end, where it passes through the detector. After all of the sample has exited the column, processing software produces a plot of peak intensity versus time.

### 2.5.6.3 Information Provided

A main use of SEC is to determine the molecular weight of synthetic and natural polymers. This can be done in a quantitative manner using standards of the polymer of interest with known molecular weights. As explained earlier for UV-VIS spectroscopy, a standard curve of molecular weight versus time can be created (Fig. 2.60). By comparing the elution time for the unknown sample to that on the standard curve, the molecular weight of the unknown can be determined.

A curve generated via SEC for a polymer sample is really a version of the graphs of weight or number fraction versus molecular weight seen in Section 2.4.1.2 (Fig. 2.23). Because of this, software programs use similar methods to those described earlier to calculate values for $\bar{M}_n$, $\bar{M}_w$, and PI. This includes determination of the fraction of the total polymer that is eluted between two elution times as well as the average molecular weight for that fraction (using the values from the standard curve). Once this information is determined, equations are used to calculate the desired values. SEC is often employed as a means to monitor polymerization and/or assure the consistency of a product from a synthesis reaction.

# Summary

- The molecular structure of a material can be classified as crystalline if the constituent atoms are arranged in such a manner that long-range order is present on the molecular level. Alternatively, materials that lack such long-range order can be classified as amorphous. Various materials, including some polymers, contain both crystalline and amorphous regions and are called semi-crystalline.

- Both metals and ceramic materials are crystalline; however, due to the ionic nature of ceramics, the crystal structures are thought of as being composed of ions rather than atoms. A wider range of crystal structures are possible in ceramics than in metals, due to the vast variety of chemical compositions possible in ceramic materials. Ceramic materials can have $AX$ crystal structures, in which the anion and cation have the same charge, or $A_mX_p$ crystal structures, in which the charges are not equal. Carbon-based materials such as graphite and single walled carbon nanotubes can be considered to be ceramics.

- Various crystal structures can be characterized by their unit cells and represented by their lattice structures. Seven primary combinations of the lattice parameters ($a$, $b$, and $c$) and angles ($\alpha$, $\beta$, and $\gamma$) describe the most common crystal systems; namely, cubic, tetragonal, orthorhombic, rhombohedral, hexagonal, monoclinic, and triclinic. Miller indices can be used to notate points and planes in a lattice structure.

- Crystal structures in metals and ceramics typically contain various defects and impurities that can affect the chemical and mechanical properties of the material. Point defects in metals include vacancies (absent atoms) and self-interstitials (extra atoms) in the crystal structure. An impurity (solute) can fill spaces between the host metal (solvent) in interstitial solutions or replace solvent atoms in substitutional solutions. The atomic radii, electronegativities, and valence charges of the atoms involved strongly influence the type of impurities that may occur. Alloys are an example of materials in which impurities have been introduced in a controlled manner to impart beneficial properties.

- One type of defect in ceramic materials is the Schottky defect, in which the vacancies in both anions and cations are in the correct ratio to maintain neutrality. Frenkel defects are found in the creation of a vacancy/interstitial pair to maintain electroneutrality in a ceramic material. As with metals, impurities can be found in ceramics, but the charge of the host material and of the impurity strongly influence the stability of the impurities.

- The transport of material by atomic motion is known as diffusion. Diffusion that occurs in solid materials is known as solid state diffusion and can include vacancy and interstitial diffusion. In the case of steady-state diffusion, diffusion flux ($J$) does not change with time.

- Polymeric materials are generally long chains based upon covalently bonded hydrocarbons. The smallest building block of a polymer is a mer, a fixed number of atoms in a given structure that is repeated over and over to form the polymer. A large variety of mechanical and chemical properties are possible with polymeric materials. Hydrogels are formed from hydrophilic polymers and have the ability to swell significantly in water.

- A number of reaction mechanisms can result in polymer production from the constituent monomers, including addition polymerization and condensation polymerization mechanisms. Addition polymerization reactions, which can involve either an activated radical (free radical polymerization) or ionic moiety (ionic polymerization), involve a number of distinct steps. Condensation polymerization occurs through the elimination of a molecule (usually water). Additionally, proteins such as silk and elastin can be polymerized through genetic engineering approaches using a host organism.

- Polymers can be crystalline, amorphous, or semi-crystalline and can contain point defects in the form of vacancies between polymer chain ends. Parameters such as the chemical composition, tacticity, and degree of branching of a polymer strongly influence the ability of the polymer to form crystals. Bulky side groups along the polymer chain as well as high degrees of polymer branching impede the ability of the chains to reside close enough to one another to form crystal structures.

- Various techniques may be employed to characterize the chemical composition of a biomaterial. One broad class of techniques is spectroscopy, in which the absorption of different types of energy by the compound of interest is measured. Examples of spectroscopic techniques include X-ray diffraction, ultraviolet and visible light spectroscopy, infrared spectroscopy, and nuclear magnetic resonance spectroscopy. Another broad class of techniques of characterization is chromatography, in which molecules are physically separated based upon chemical characteristics, such as charge or molecular weight. Examples of chromatographic techniques include gel permeation chromatography and gel filtration chromatography.

## Problems

2.1  Using the diagram here, calculate the Miller indices for the following:
   (a) Plane AGDE
   (b) Plane CDGH
   (c) Plane AGCF
   (d) Point C
   (e) Point G

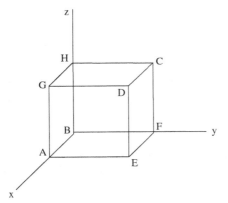

2.2    Brass is an alloy of copper and zinc. Assume the weight percent composition of brass is 80% Cu and 20% Zn. Would you expect brass to be an interstitial solution or a substitutional solution? Justify your answer based on the Hume-Rothery rules. (See Fig. 1.14 and Table 2.1.)

2.3    What is the difference in the definition of coordination number between metals and ceramics? Why are these two parameters different for the two classes of materials?

2.4    Why do point defects occur in groups in ceramics?

2.5    A polymer is made of the following fractional distribution. Calculate $\overline{M}_n, \overline{M}_w$, and PI for this polymer.

W$_i$          0.10  0.15   0.35  0.25   0.15
M$_i$ (kg/mol)  100   200   300   400   500

2.6    Using the data in Figure 2.37 and assuming first-order diffraction calculate the following:

(Note that aluminum has a FCC structure.)

(a) The interplanar spacing for peaks corresponding to planes (111), (200), and (420).

(b) The atomic radius for Al.

2.7    Based on the results in Figure 2.49, is 5 seconds of UV light exposure sufficient to polymerize the poly(ethylene glycol) completely?

2.8    In Figure 2.52, higher resonance frequencies are found to the left of the standard peak shown at 0.0 ppm (signal is shifted downfield from the standard). Given this information, provide a possible molecular explanation for the difference in location of the H signal from peak 4 versus the H signal in the solvent.

2.9    Acetone is preferred by some biomedical device manufacturers as a solvent for their polymers because it is considered by regulatory agencies to have fewer negative effects in the body than other organic solvents. Given is the mass spectrometry data and molecular structure of acetone [9]. Acetone has the molecular formula of $C_3H_6O$ and a molecular weight of 58.

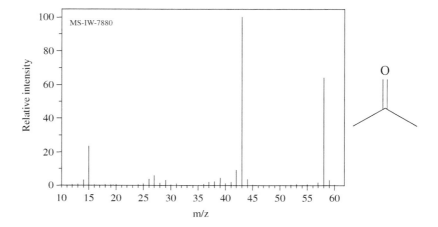

(a) How are particles separated by mass in mass spectrometry?

(b) What is the large peak at 43? Draw the molecular structure that accounts for this peak. Give a possible explanation why the peak at 43 is larger than the other peaks seen in the mass spectrum.

(c) What is the peak at 15? Draw the molecular structure that accounts for this peak. Theoretically, what is the expected relationship between the intensity of this peak and the one at 43? Why? Do the data above demonstrate this expected relationship? If not, give a possible explanation why the theory and the data do not match.

2.10 (a) You perform gel permeation chromatography (GPC) on the polymer found in Problem 2.5, which contains molecular weights of (a) 100, (b) 200, (c) 300, (d) 400, and (e) 500 kg/mol. Which of the polymer weights (a–e) would elute through the column first and which would elute last? Explain your choice based on molecular interactions between the sample and the column.

(b) You have synthesized two polymers using the same monomer, but with differing final molecular weights.

You run the two polymers on the GPC and obtain the following plots:

Using the following standards, create the standard curve and calculate the approximate molecular weight of polymer A and polymer B.

| Molecular Weight | Time of Peak (min) |
| --- | --- |
| 4,281 | 8 |
| 7,327 | 3.76 |
| 1,253 | 12.4 |
| 883 | 12.78 |
| 6,229 | 5.25 |

2.11 List all the appropriate techniques from Section 2.5 to determine the following:

(a) Chemical composition of an unknown sample (using data to determine the elements/bond types in the unknown sample)

(b) Identification of an unknown sample (comparing with known patterns to determine the unknown sample)

(c) Size of a unit cell

(d) Molecular weight of a polymeric sample

(e) Concentration of sample

# References

1. W.D. Callister Jr., *Materials science and engineering: an introduction*, 3rd ed. New York: John Wiley and Sons, 1994.

2. J. F. Shackelford, *Introduction to materials science for engineers*, 5th ed. Upper Saddle River: Prentice Hall, 2000.

3. J. P. Schaffer, A. Saxena, S. D. Antolovich, J. Sanders, and S. B. Warner, *The science and design of engineering materials*, 2nd ed. Boston: McGraw-Hill, 1998.

4. D. F. Williams, *The Williams dictionary of biomaterials*. Liverpool: Liverpool University Press, 1999.

5. P. C. Nicolson and J. Vogt, "Soft contact lens polymers: an evolution," *Biomaterials*, vol. 22, no. 24, pp. 3273–3283, Dec. 2001.

6. N. A. Peppas and A. S. Hoffman, "Hydrogels," in *Biomaterials science: an introduction to materials and medicine*, 3rd ed., B. D. Ratner, A. S. Hoffman, F. J. Schoen, and J. E. Lemons, Eds. San Diego: Academic Press, 2013, pp. 166–179.

7. N. A. Peppas and B. D. Barr-Howell, "Characterization of the cross-linked structure of hydrogels," in *Hydrogels in Medicine and Pharmacy*, vol. 1, N. A. Peppas, Ed. Boca Raton: CRC Press, 1986, pp. 27–56.

8. D. A. Skoog and J. J. Leary, *Principles of instrumental analysis*, 4th ed. Orlando: Saunders College Publishing, 1992.

9. National Institute of Advanced Industrial Science and Technology, Japan, *Spectral Database for Organic Compounds (SDBS)*. [Online]. Available: http://sdbs.db.aist.go.jp.

10. L. Jones and P. W. Atkins, P. and L. Jones, *Chemistry: molecules, matter, and change*, 3rd ed, New York: Freeman, 1997.

11. L. R. G. Treloar, *The physics of rubber elasticity*, 2nd ed. Oxford: Oxford University Press, 1958.

12. G. Odian, *Principles of Polymerization*, 3rd ed. New York: John Wiley and Sons, 1991.

13. W. H. Ray and R. L. Laurence, "Polymerization reaction engineering," in *Chemical reactor theory: a review*, L. Lapidus and N. R. Amundson, Eds. Englewood Cliffs: Prentice Hall, 1977, pp. 532–582.

14. E. B. Lavik, J. S. Hrkach, N. Lotan, R. Nazarov, and R. Langer, "A simple synthetic route to the formation of a block copolymer of poly(lactic-co-glycolic acid) and polylysine for the fabrication of functionalized, degradable structures for biomedical applications," *J Biomed Mater Res*, vol. 58, no. 3, pp. 291–4, May 2001.

15. F. Rouessac and A. Rouessac, *Chemical analysis: modern instrumental methods and techniques*. New York: John Wiley and Sons, 2000.

16. M. B. Mellott, K. Searcy, and M. V. Pishko, "Release of protein from highly cross-linked hydrogels of poly(ethylene glycol) diacrylate fabricated by UV polymerization," *Biomaterials*, vol. 22, no. 9, pp. 929–41, May 2001.

17. K. P. C. Vollhardt and N. E. Schore, *Organic chemistry*, 2nd ed. New York: W. H. Freeman, 1994.

18. A. Lucke, J. Tessmar, E. Schnell, G. Schmeer, and A. Gopferich, "Biodegradable poly(D,L-lactic acid)-poly(ethylene glycol)-monomethyl ether diblock copolymers: Structures and surface properties relevant to their use as biomaterials," *Biomaterials*, vol. 21, no. 23, pp. 2361–2370, 2000.

19. S. J. Wetzel, C. M. Guttman, and J. E. Girard, "The influence of matrix and laser energy on the molecular mass distribution of synthetic polymers obtained by MALDI-TOF-MS," *International Journal of Mass Spectrometry*, vol. 238, no. 3, pp. 215–225, 2004.

20. L. C. Chang, H. F. Lee, M. J. Chung, and V. C. Yang, "PEG-modified protamine with improved pharmacological/pharmaceutical properties as a potential protamine substitute: Synthesis and in vitro evaluation," *Bioconjug Chem*, vol. 16, no. 1, pp. 147–155, Feb. 2005.

# Additional Reading

S. V. Bhat, *Biomaterials*, 2nd ed. Alpha Science Int'l Ltd., 2005.

J. D. Bronzino and J. B. Park, *Biomaterials: principles and applications*. Boca Raton: CRC Press, 2003.

G. W. Ewing, *Analytical instrumentation handbook*, 2nd ed. New York: Marcel Dekker, 1997.

J. M. Knipe and N. A. Peppas, "Multi-responsive hydrogels for drug delivery and tissue engineering applications," *Regenerative Biomaterials*, vol. 1, no. 1, pp. 57–65, 2014.

J. L. Ong, M. R. Appleford, and G. Mani, *Introduction to biomaterials: basic theory with engineering applications*. Cambridge: Cambridge University Press, 2014.

J. B. Park and R. S. Lakes, *Biomaterials: an introduction*, 2nd ed. New York: Plenum Press, 1992.

J. F. Rabek, *Experimental methods in polymer chemistry*. New York: John Wiley and Sons, 1980.

Y. S. Zhang and A. Khademhosseini, "Advances in engineering hydrogels," *Science*, vol. 356, no. 6337, p. eaaf3627, 2017.

# 3

# Physical Properties of Biomaterials

**Main Objective**

To understand how material subunits from Chapter 2 interact to make bulk materials and to comprehend how the thermal treatment of various materials affects their three-dimensional structure.

**Specific Objectives**

1. To compare and contrast linear, planar, and volume defects in crystals.
2. To draw and use Burger's vector notation to determine types of linear dislocations.
3. To understand how dislocations lead to the possibility of material deformation for crystalline materials and to contrast this with deformation in amorphous materials (viscous flow).
4. To compare and contrast the types of planar defects in crystals and understand how their presence affects chemical reactivity of the material.
5. To give examples and uses for three-dimensional (volume) defects.
6. To understand models for crystalline structure in polymers.
7. To understand the difference between the types of thermal transitions for crystalline and noncrystalline materials.
8. To understand the basic theory behind differential scanning calorimetry (a thermal analysis technique).

## 3.1 Introduction: From Atomic Groupings to Bulk Materials

In this chapter, we move from how atoms interact to make biomaterial subunits to how the subunits interact to form bulk materials. For metals and ceramics, which are usually polycrystalline materials, the interactions of multiple crystals define the material's physical properties. Although the term "physical properties" can encompass a variety of characteristics, two of the most important for these materials are the amount and type of dislocations that occur within or between crystals. These characteristics, discussed in sections 3.2-3.4 can affect mechanical properties and material processability (see Chapters 4 and 6).

For polymers, the subunits are sections of mers, and how they interact to create crystalline and amorphous regions also defines the physical properties of this material type. In this case, one of the most important physical characteristics is the percent crystallinity of the polymer. Polymer crystallinity, discussed in more detail later in the chapter, impacts mechanical and degradative properties of the final material (see Chapters 4 and 5).

Another key aspect of all materials is how their physical properties change in response to temperature. Thermal transitions of both crystalline and amorphous materials will be explained at the molecular level in the later sections of this chapter. These properties are particularly important to the processing of biomaterials (see Chapter 6).

## 3.2 Crystallinity and Linear Defects

As discussed in the previous chapter, crystalline materials contain point defects that can affect their mechanical properties. In addition, several other defect types that involve larger areas of the crystal are possible. These include linear defects and planar defects. It is estimated that, in a metallic material, only five atoms in 100,000,000 lie on a linear defect. However, despite their low occurrence, linear defects have a large impact on the final strength of the material. It is also important to note that the presence of these defects, particularly in metals, is what allows for their fabrication into complex shapes (see Chapter 6).

### 3.2.1 Dislocations

**3.2.1.1 Edge Dislocations** Crystals can possess several types of linear, or one-dimensional, defects. One of these is an **edge dislocation**, shown in Figure 3.1. This occurs when an extra portion of a plane of atoms (half-plane) terminates in a crystal. In this case, the defect is actually the line that defines the end of the extra half-plane, called the **dislocation line**. In the figure, this line would be perpendicular to the

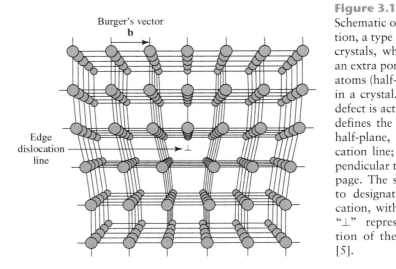

**Figure 3.1**
Schematic of an edge dislocation, a type of linear defect in crystals, which occurs when an extra portion of a plane of atoms (half-plane) terminates in a crystal. In this case, the defect is actually the line that defines the end of the extra half-plane, called the dislocation line; it would be perpendicular to the plane of the page. The symbol ⊥ is used to designate an edge dislocation, with the cross of the "⊥" representing the position of the dislocation line [5].

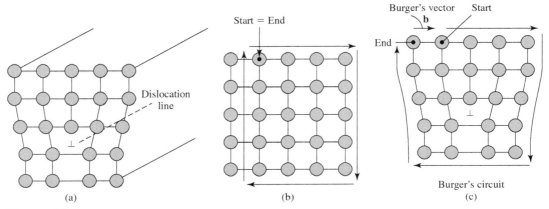

**Figure 3.2**
Depiction of Burger's vector. An edge dislocation is shown in (a), compared to the defect-free section seen in (b). The magnitude and direction of atomic displacement in a linear defect can be ascertained by drawing a circuit around the area of the crystal containing the dislocation. This circuit has the same number of atomic steps as for a similar circuit in a defect-free region. Therefore, the circuit should close on itself, except for the presence of the defect. However, due to the defect, an additional vector (Burger's vector) must be drawn to complete the atomic circuit (c) [5].

plane of the page. The symbol is used to designate an edge dislocation, with the cross of the "⊥" representing the position of the dislocation line. The addition of the half-plane of atoms in a crystal can occur for a variety of reasons, including accidents in the crystal growth process, internal stresses from other defects in the crystal, or the interaction of resident dislocations during plastic deformation (discussed in greater depth later in the chapter).

Two important characteristics of dislocations are the magnitude and direction of atomic displacement. These can be ascertained by drawing a circuit around the area of the crystal containing the dislocation. As depicted in Figure 3.2, this circuit has the same number of atomic steps as a similar circuit in a defect-free region. Therefore, the circuit should close on itself, except for the presence of the defect. However, due to the defect, an additional vector must be drawn to complete the atomic circuit. This is called the **Burger's vector (b)** for that dislocation. For an edge dislocation, the Burger's vector is perpendicular to the dislocation line (Fig. 3.1).

3.2.1.2 Screw and Mixed Dislocations  Another type of linear defect is the **screw dislocation**. This can be conceptualized as the result of shear forces on part of the material that caused the displacement of a portion of the crystal. In Figure 3.3, a part of the top section of the crystal has been moved one atomic distance to the right relative to the bottom half of the crystal. This type of dislocation is so named because of the helical pattern that the planes of atoms follow around the dislocation line. A screw dislocation is indicated with a ↻ (Fig. 3.3), and, in this case, the Burger's vector is parallel to the dislocation line.

Most linear defects exhibit both edge and screw qualities and are called **mixed dislocations**. Such a dislocation is shown in Figure 3.4. In between the two faces where the dislocation is neither pure screw nor pure edge, the defect has a mixed character. This is best demonstrated by examining the orientation of the Burger's vector, which remains constant for a given defect. For more complex defects, such as that in Figure 3.4, the dislocation line changes so that it is oriented differently

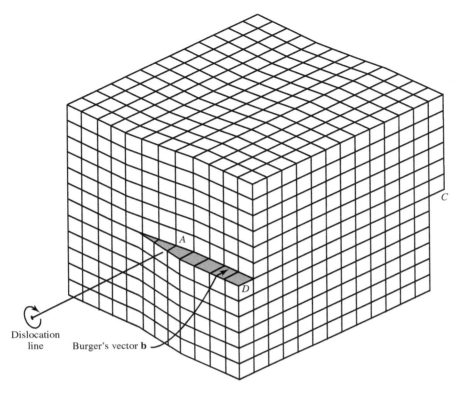

**Figure 3.3**
A screw dislocation, a type of linear defect in crystals. This can be caused by shear forces on part of the material that caused the displacement of a portion of the crystal. Here, a part of the top section of the crystal has been moved one atomic distance to the right relative to the bottom half of the crystal. This type of dislocation is so named because of the helical pattern that the planes of atoms follow around the dislocation line. A screw dislocation is indicated with a ↻ [1].

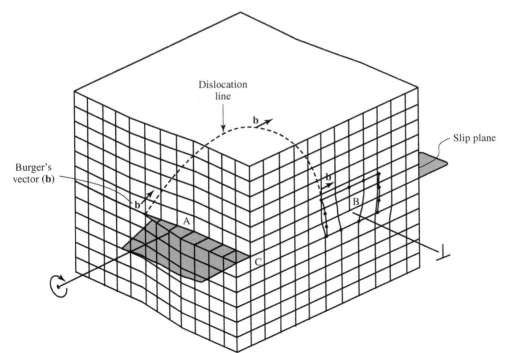

**Figure 3.4**
A mixed dislocation, a type of linear defect in crystals. The orientation of the dislocation line with respect to the Burger's vector changes in different areas of the crystal. For an edge dislocation, the dislocation line is perpendicular to the Burger's vector (section near point $B$ in the figure) and for a screw dislocation the dislocation line is parallel to the Burger's vector (section near point $A$ in the figure). When it is neither completely perpendicular nor completely parallel, this is the region of the mixed dislocation [1].

with respect to the Burger's vector in different areas of the crystal. When it is neither completely perpendicular nor completely parallel to the Burger's vector, this is the region of the mixed dislocation.

**3.2.1.3 Characteristics of Dislocations**   It should be noted that the classifications of dislocations described earlier are found in both metals and crystalline ceramics, although the electroneutrality requirement usually causes the Burger's vectors to be longer for ceramics than metals. There are a number of key characteristics associated with dislocations, no matter what their classification is. These characteristics are summarized as follows:

1. Localized lattice strains develop as a result of the dislocation. For example, in an edge dislocation, the atoms above the dislocation line are compressed together, and those below are pulled apart.
2. The classification of a dislocation is dependent on the relationship between the Burger's vector and the dislocation line.
3. The Burger's vector is invariant (does not change for a given defect).
4. A dislocation cannot end in a defect-free region of a crystal. Instead, it ends on the crystal surface, on itself, or connects with another dislocation.
5. The plane on which a dislocation may move (slip) contains both the Burger's vector and the dislocation line and is a plane of high atomic density (see Section 3.2.2 for a discussion of slip planes).

### EXAMPLE PROBLEM 3.1

Given the crystal structure illustrated here, locate the dislocation and draw the Burger's circuit around it. Draw the Burger's vector for the dislocation. Indicate the type of dislocation and rationalize your answer using the Burger's vector that you identified. Mark the dislocation with the proper dislocation symbol.

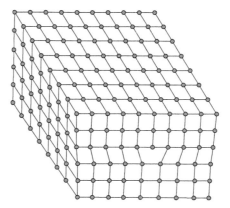

**Solution:**   The dislocation present is an edge dislocation, as the Burger's vector is perpendicular to the dislocation line.

## 3.2.2 Deformation

As mentioned earlier, the presence of even a small number of linear defects has a large effect on the mechanical properties of the overall material. This is mainly due to the fact that these dislocations allow plastic (permanent) deformation of a

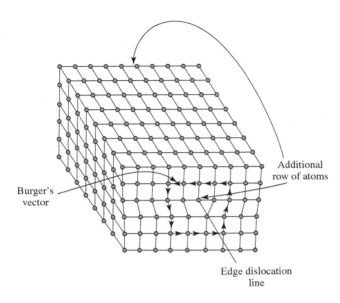

Burger's vector

Additional row of atoms

Edge dislocation line

crystalline material. Plastic deformation occurs by movement of dislocations, or **dislocation glide**.

As shown in Figure 3.5, if a shear stress ($\tau$) is applied to a crystal having an edge dislocation, there is energy added to the system that can cause the breaking of bonds between atoms in row C and row A and the formation of bonds between atoms in row B and row A. This leaves the atoms in row C without the correct coordination number and marks the new position of the edge defect (it was previously located by atoms in row B). In this manner, a dislocation can glide by one atomic spacing at a time until it exits a crystal, much as a caterpillar moves one section of its body at a time to effect total displacement (Fig. 3.5). Using this model, the amount of shear stress needed to cause deformation is relatively small, since only one row of bonds at a time must be broken, rather than all the bonds at once.

Continuing with the analogy of the caterpillar, it is apparent that if there are larger steps, it will be more difficult to move individual sections of the caterpillar's body the required distance. Similarly, dislocation glide occurs more easily on planes with higher atomic density than those with lower atomic density. When speaking about crystals, plastic deformation is referred to as **slip** and the plane in which the deformation takes place is the **slip plane**. Therefore, as mentioned earlier, slip occurs in a crystal only if the dislocation's geometric plane (defined by the Burger's vector) coincides with the crystallographic slip plane (plane with highest atomic density).

Slip planes occur in various planes for different metals, depending on the crystal structure. Table 3.1 shows major slip planes for several common crystal structures. A **slip system** is the combination of a crystallographic plane through which slip can occur and the number of directions slip can take place along this plane. It is interesting to note that those metals with a higher number of slip systems, such as aluminum, are more deformable (ductile), while those having only a few, such as magnesium, break with little deformation (are brittle).

As discussed in the previous chapter regarding point defects, similar types of linear defects are found in ceramics, but their movement is limited by the requirement of electroneutrality. This generally means that the Burger's vectors are longer for ceramics than metals (Fig. 3.6) and that the planes on which slip can occur (that for example, do not place two atoms of like charge next to each other) are not those

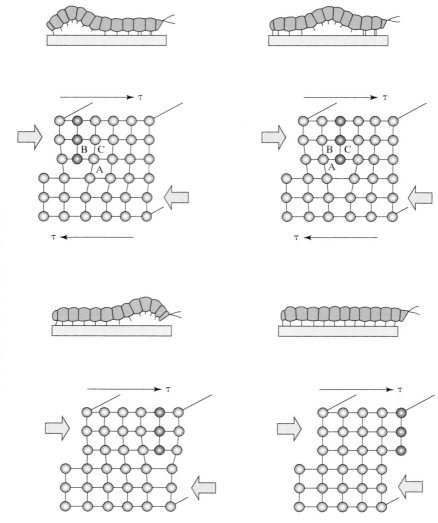

**Figure 3.5**
Diagram of dislocation glide in crystalline materials (end-on view). If enough energy is added to the system, the bonds between atoms in row C (rows extend out of the plane of the page) and row A will break and bonds between atoms in row B and row A will form. This leaves the atoms in row C without the correct coordination number and marks the new position of the edge defect (previously located by atoms in row B). In this manner, dislocations can glide by one atomic spacing at a time until they exit a crystal, much as a caterpillar moves one section of its body at a time to effect total displacement [3, 5].

**Figure 3.6**
Diagram showing the variation in slip between metals and ceramics. In a metal, the dislocation can move by one atomic position, whereas with a ceramic the dislocation must occur over two atomic positions, due to the electroneutrality requirement. This leads to a larger Burger's vector in ceramics when compared to metals. The amount of movement can be seen by the variation in the location of the squares, with each pair indicating a relating pair of atoms.

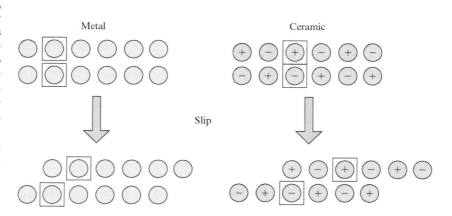

**TABLE 3.1**

| Major Slip Planes and Slip Systems for Common Crystal Structures | | | | |
|---|---|---|---|---|
| Crystal Structure | Slip Plane | Number of Slip Systems | Until Cell Geometry | Examples |
| BCC | {110} | $6 \times 2 = 12$ | | $\alpha$-Fe, Mo, W |
| FCC | {111} | $4 \times 3 = 12$ | | Al, Cu, $\gamma$-Fe, Ni |
| HCP | {001} | $1 \times 3 = 3$ | | Cd, Mg, $\alpha$-Ti, Zn |

*Note:* $\alpha$-Fe, $\gamma$-Fe and $\alpha$-Ti denote the BCC form of iron, the FCC form of iron and the HCP form of titanium, respectively. (Adapted with permission from [1].)

that contain the highest atomic density. For these reasons, there is less slip in ceramics than metals, leading to more brittle fracture for ceramic materials.

## 3.3 Crystallinity and Planar Defects

We now move our discussion from defects of one dimension to those of two dimensions (planar defects). All biomaterials possess planar defects, as they include the material surface, which is of utmost importance in biocompatibility (see Chapter 7). Other examples of planar defects include grain boundaries in metals and ceramics.

### 3.3.1 External Surface

Atoms at the surface of a material are not bonded to the maximum possible number of nearest neighbors, so they possess higher energy than those atoms located inside a crystal. This extra energy is called the surface free energy or **surface tension** and is expressed in units of energy per unit area. The existence of these sites with higher energy is thermodynamically unstable, and the need to minimize surface energy leads to chemical reactions at the surface. In particular, the effect of surface tension on the interaction of water and proteins with biomaterials is discussed in Chapter 8. The surface tension of a biomaterial can be altered via a variety of means, as described in Chapter 7.

EXAMPLE PROBLEM 3.2

Why do atoms at the surface of a crystalline material generally possess higher energy than those inside of the crystal and what is the term for this heightened energy?

**Solution:** Unlike most atoms in the interior of a crystalline material, atoms at the surface of a crystalline material are not bonded to the maximum number of nearest neighbor atoms. Consequently, the atoms at the surface generally have a higher energy than comparable atoms within the material. The term for the heightened energy of atoms at the surface of a crystalline material is "surface tension." ∎

### 3.3.2 Grain Boundaries

Most metals and ceramics are polycrystalline, composed of a large number of small, randomly oriented crystals, or grains. The interface between these grains is called the **grain boundary**. Because of the disorder of these regions, grain boundary atoms do not usually attain the optimal coordination number. Thus, as with the external surface, these atoms are in a higher energy state than comparable atoms in the center of the grain. This leads to higher chemical reactivity in these regions. For example, corrosive attack often occurs first at grain boundaries in metals (see Chapter 5). The total interfacial energy is lower in materials with larger grains, since there are fewer boundary areas than for materials with smaller grains.

There are two types of grain boundaries that can be distinguished via microscopic observation (see Fig. 3.7). If the grains on either side of the boundary have similar orientations (only a few degrees different), this is a **small-angle grain boundary**. Grains with more severe misalignment form **high-angle grain boundaries**. Since the increase in energy at the grain boundary is a result of atomic mismatch, the greater the degree of misorientation, the higher the energy of the boundary. Two common small-angle grain boundaries are the **tilt boundary**, which is composed of aligned edge dislocations, and the **twist boundary**, which is composed of aligned screw dislocations. A diagram showing how a series of edge dislocations can lead to a tilt boundary with tilt angle $\theta$ is found in Figure 3.8.

**Figure 3.7**
Classes of grain boundaries. If the grains on either side of the boundary have similar orientations (only a few degrees difference), this is termed a small-angle grain boundary. Grains with more severe misalignment form high-angle grain boundaries. Since the increase in energy at the grain boundary is a result of atomic mismatch, the greater the degree of misorientation, the higher the energy of the boundary [3].

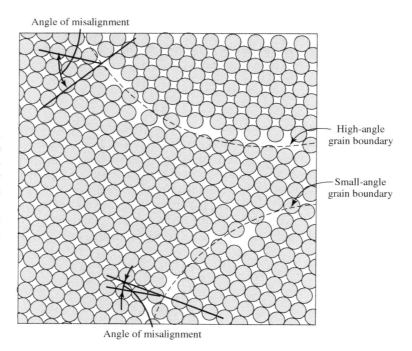

Angle of misalignment

High-angle grain boundary

Small-angle grain boundary

Angle of misalignment

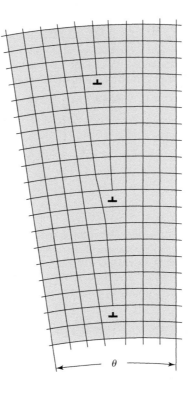

**Figure 3.8**
Formation of a tilt grain boundary. A series of edge dislocation can lead to a tilt boundary with tilt angle $\theta$ [3].

A special type of grain boundary defect is termed a **twin boundary**. This occurs when there is a mirror image of atomic placement across the boundary. The area of material between two of these boundaries is called a **twin** (Fig. 3.9). The basic crystal structure is the same both inside and outside the twin. Twinning can be caused by subjecting the material to either shear forces (deformation twin) or annealing heat treatments (annealing twin).

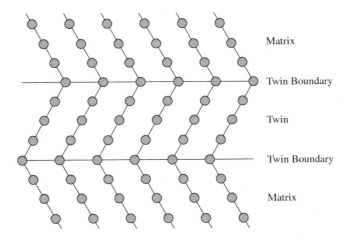

Matrix

Twin Boundary

Twin

Twin Boundary

Matrix

**Figure 3.9**
A twin boundary, a special type of grain boundary defect that contains a mirror image of atomic placement across the boundary. The area of material between two of these boundaries is called a twin. The basic crystal structure is the same both inside and outside the twin [5].

## EXAMPLE PROBLEM 3.3

Consider the two metal samples indicated below, each composed of the same metal. The only difference between the two samples is the size of the grains in the material. Which sample has the higher total interfacial energy? Why?

(A)                    (B)

**Solution:**   The sample with the smaller grains (B) would have the higher total interfacial energy due to the larger amount of boundary area present between grains. As the size of the grains decreases, the total amount of interface between grains increases. Since the energy of atoms at grain boundaries is generally higher than that of atoms at the center of a grain, the total interfacial energy would be higher.    ■

## EXAMPLE PROBLEM 3.4

Consider a polycrystalline rod of iron submerged in a beaker of brine (saltwater solution). Would one expect corrosive attack to begin first at the grain boundaries or at the center of grains? Why?

**Solution:**   As the atoms at the grain boundaries are generally at a higher energy state than those at the center of a grain, they are generally more reactive. Thus, one could reasonably expect that corrosive attack would begin first with the atoms at the grain boundaries.    ■

# 3.4   Crystallinity and Volume Defects

As the name implies, volume defects are three-dimensional regions in which the long-range order of the crystal is lost. Examples of volume defects include **precipitates** and **voids**. Precipitates are clusters of substitutional or interstitial impurities, while voids are three-dimensional aggregates of vacancies.

Voids are of particular importance in biomaterials, because in addition to their accidental formation due to the clustering of point defects, it is possible to create void space (pores) in a controlled manner to alter the biological response to the material. This is usually accomplished through the addition of porogens at some point during the fabrication of the implant, or via the creation of fibers that are then made into highly porous three-dimensional meshes.

Porogens can either be solid or gaseous. Common solid porogens include salt (NaCl), collagen-based materials (gelatin), or waxy materials such as lipids or paraffin. The concept behind the use of these porogens is that they are solid when mixed with the material, but can be easily extracted after fabrication of the implant to leave behind large void spaces (pores). Extraction can occur through dissolution in water (sodium chloride, NaCl) or via a temperature change that transforms solid porogens into liquid (gelatin or waxes). Porogens such as these have been explored mainly for use with polymeric biomaterials. Another option for ceramic materials is the addition of a second ceramic phase that decomposes during the processing procedure to leave pores in the remaining material. In either case, the amount of solid porogen included affects the amount of porosity of the final material, while the pore geometry is determined by the shape of the porogen chosen.

Gaseous porogens such as $N_2$ or $CO_2$ are most often employed to form void spaces in polymeric biomaterials. These gases can be liberated during polymerization, or can be bubbled through the polymer while it is in a molten state to form three-dimensional foams upon cooling. The amount, rate, and timing of gas introduction can be altered to form materials with different porosities and pore geometries.

Fibers have also been used successfully to make products with large void volumes, particularly for metals and polymeric materials. After drawing the appropriate material into a fiber (see Chapter 6), the fibers are bonded or woven together to form a three-dimensional mesh containing large voids. Both porosity and pore geometry for these materials depend on the size of the fibers and how densely they can be packed.

As indicated previously, the addition of pores into an implant can be accomplished in some manner for all types of biomaterials. Advantages of porous structures are that they allow for the exchange of fluids and gases deep within the material and that they encourage tissue ingrowth and implant anchoring. Allowing nearly unhampered diffusion of nutrients and waste products enables the foams to be seeded with cells for a myriad of tissue engineering applications. However, the presence of pores decreases the mechanical properties of the material and alters both the biodegradation and corrosion properties of the implant. Therefore, for a given material, the percent porosity must be optimized, keeping in mind the intended final application.

## 3.5 Crystallinity and Polymeric Materials

A key physical property of polymers is their percent crystallinity. The amount of crystallinity in polymeric materials varies much more than for metals and crystalline ceramics. As discussed briefly in Chapter 2, polymers form crystals that are significantly different in structure than those in other materials. Due to the large molecules involved, polymeric unit cells are relatively complex. A typical unit cell for poly(ethylene) (orthorhombic geometry) and its relationship to the polymer chains is shown in Figure 3.10. As with other crystalline materials, information about the structure of polymeric crystals can be obtained through X-ray diffraction experiments (see Chapter 2 for a description of this technique).

### 3.5.1 Percent Crystallinity

The fraction of crystalline areas in a polymeric material is highly dependent on the chemical structure of its mer as well as the polymer's configuration. Anything that prevents chain alignment (such as kinks) or discourages secondary bonding between chains will reduce polymer crystallinity. The following factors can influence percent crystallinity:

1. Mer side groups
2. Chain branching
3. Tacticity
4. Regularity of mer placement in copolymers

Side groups (groups of atoms that project from the backbone) are important in crystallization because if they are large and bulky, this prevents neighboring chains from coming close enough to form a crystalline structure. For example, most forms of poly(styrene), with its pendant benzene ring, are amorphous. For similar reasons, branched polymers exhibit lower percent crystallinity than linear polymers.

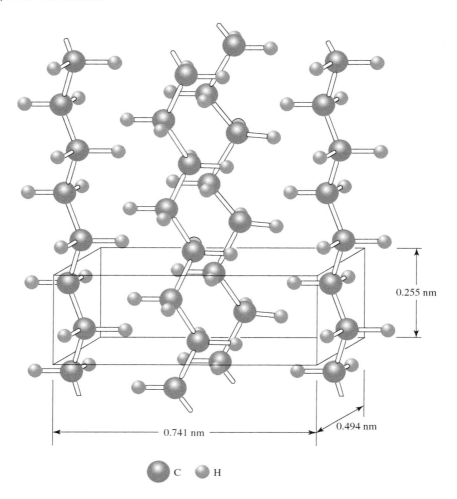

0.255 nm

0.741 nm

0.494 nm

C    H

**Figure 3.10**
A typical unit cell for poly(ethylene) (orthorhombic geometry) and its relationship to constituent polymer chains. The unit cell is composed of atoms from adjacent chains. (Adapted with permission from [6].)

The location of the side groups is also important. Atactic polymers are much more difficult to crystallize than isotactic or syndiotactic polymers, since the random placement of the side groups prevents sections of neighboring polymer chains from coming together in an ordered fashion. Extending this idea to copolymers, if the two different mers are more regularly arranged, such as for alternating and block copolymers, there is a higher probability of the formation of crystalline regions.

It is rare for a polymeric material to be 100% crystalline. This is due to the large size and flexibility of the molecules involved, which significantly increases the possibility that they will fold back on themselves or intermingle with other chains to form complex, nonordered entanglements. Calculation of percent polymer crystallinity therefore provides useful information about the physical structure of these materials. This calculation is based on the fact that crystalline regions of a polymer are denser than amorphous regions (up to 20% difference in density) because the chains are more closely packed in the crystalline regions. Therefore, with careful density measurements of the polymer sample ($\rho_s$), the same polymer in its (nearly) completely crystalline form ($\rho_c$), and the polymer in its completely amorphous form ($\rho_a$), percent *crystallinity* may be determined via the following equation:

$$\% \ crystallinity = \frac{\rho_c(\rho_s - \rho_a)}{\rho_s(\rho_c - \rho_a)} \times 100 \qquad (3.1)$$

## EXAMPLE PROBLEM 3.5

Calculate the density of a poly(ethylene) sample that is 75% crystalline, knowing that the density of completely amorphous poly(ethylene) is $0.85$ g/cm$^3$ and the density of completely crystalline poly(ethylene) is $1.00$ g/cm$^3$.

Solution:   The equation for the percent crystallinity of a polymer samples is as follows:

$$\% \; crystallinity = \frac{\rho_c \left( \rho_s - \rho_a \right)}{\rho_s \left( \rho_c - \rho_a \right)} \times 100$$

$$75\% = \frac{1.00 \; \text{g} / \text{cm}^3 \left( \rho_s - 0.85 \; \text{g} / \text{cm}^3 \right)}{\rho_s \left( 1.00 \; \text{g} / \text{cm}^3 - 0.85 \; \text{g} / \text{cm}^3 \right)} \times 100$$

In this case, the values for $\rho_a$ and $\rho_c$ are given to be $0.85$ g/cm$^3$ and $1.00$ g/cm$^3$, respectively, but the value of $\rho_s$ is unknown. However, the percent crystallinity of the sample is given to be 75%. Substituting these values into the equation above and solving for $\rho_s$, we find that the density of the sample is approximately 0.96 g/cm$^3$. ∎

## 3.5.2 Chain-Folded Model of Crystallinity

The form of polymer crystals is more complex than that for metals or ceramics. The basic unit of crystalline structure is the lamella, which is larger than the polymeric crystal's unit cell. As shown in Figure 3.10, the unit cell is composed of a few atoms from adjacent chains, while Figure 3.11 depicts a portion of a lamella, which contains a number of polymer chains folded back on themselves. This model is thus named the **chain-folded model** of polymeric crystallinity. The folds occur at the faces, with regularly aligned chain sections within the lamella.

Although Figure 3.11 shows an idealized concept of a lamella, in reality, folding may be much more complicated, given that there are several polymer chains found within each lamella. A more realistic visualization may be found in Figure 3.12. This figure includes several intermingled chains, each of which has crystalline regions located inside the lamellar structure and noncrystalline regions found outside.

~ 10 nm

**Figure 3.11**
A portion of a lamella, the basic unit of crystal structure in polymers. The lamella is larger than the polymeric crystal's unit cell and contains a number of polymer chains folded back on themselves. The folds occur at the faces, with regularly aligned chain sections found inside the lamella [3].

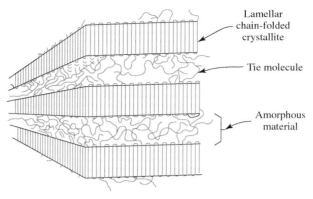

**Figure 3.12**
Folding in polymer lamella including multiple chains. Although the previous figure shows an idealized concept of a lamella, in reality, folding may be much more complicated, given that there are several polymer chains found within each lamella. This figure includes several intermingled chains where each has crystalline regions located inside the lamellar structure and noncrystalline regions found outside [3].

When a polymer is crystallized from a molten state, the formation of **spherulites** is observed. As shown in Figure 3.13, these are three-dimensional aggregates of lamellae. The lamellae form radial lines, with the folds oriented perpendicular to the radial direction. Lamellae are separated by amorphous regions that include chain folds and the tie molecules that bind lamellae into aggregates.

As shown in Figure 3.14, as the spherulites grow, they impinge on one another and deviate from their spherical shape. In this type of crystal formation, the spherulites are analogous to grains in polycrystalline metals and ceramics, although they actually contain many crystalline lamellae as well as amorphous areas.

## EXAMPLE PROBLEM 3.6

Consider the following copolymer chains:

(a)  -A-B-A-B-A-B-A-B-A-B-A-B-A-B-A-B-
(b)  -A-B-B-B-A-A-B-A-B-A-A-A-B-A-B-B-

Which chain is an alternating copolymer, and which is a random copolymer? Which chain would have a higher probability of forming crystalline regions? Why?

Solution:   The mers alternate regularly in chain (a), whereas the mers appear randomly arranged in (b). It follows that chain (a) is an alternating copolymer, while chain (b) is a random copolymer. Chain (a) would thus present a higher probability of forming crystalline regions due to the regular arrangement of its mers, relative to chain (b).   ■

## 3.5.3 Defects in Polymer Crystals

**3.5.3.1 Linear Defects**   As in metals and ceramics, dislocations can also occur in crystalline regions of polymers. However, because of the size of the unit cell, the Burger's vectors produced are longer than those for either metals or ceramics. Since the covalent bonds within the polymer chains are stronger than the secondary forces between chains, slip usually takes place along the axis of polymer chains.

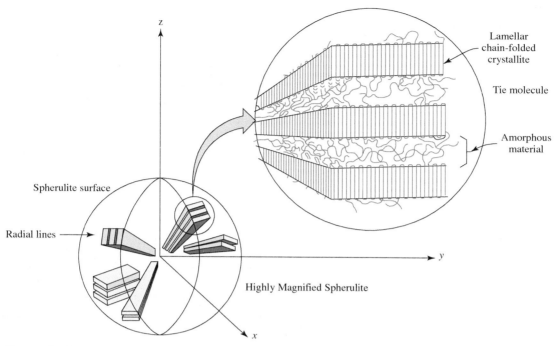

**Figure 3.13**
Composition of spherulites. When a polymer is crystallized from a molten state, the formation of spherulites is observed. As shown in the figure, these are three-dimensional aggregates of lamellae. The lamellae form radial lines, with the folds oriented perpendicular to the radial direction. Lamellae are separated by amorphous regions that include chain folds and the tie molecules that bind lamellae into aggregates [3].

**Figure 3.14**
Polymer spherulites under polarized light. Using this type of microscopy, each spherulite appears to contain a Maltese cross. As shown here, when the spherulites grow, they impinge on one another and deviate from their spherical shape. (Reprinted with permission from [5].)

Unlike metals and ceramics, dislocations do not play a large role in the deformation of polymeric materials. The unique causes of deformation in crystalline and semi-crystalline polymers will be discussed further in the next chapter.

**3.5.3.2 Planar and Volume Defects**    Like linear defects, planar crystal defects also exist in polymeric materials. Polymeric implants possess surfaces with additional energy, similar to metals and ceramics. In addition, boundaries between spherulites can be considered akin to grain boundaries in metals and ceramics. As mentioned earlier, both solid and gaseous porogens can be added to polymers to form voids, a type of volume defect.

# 3.6    Thermal Transitions of Crystalline and NonCrystalline Materials

A final physical property that is of interest for all types of biomaterials is how the material subunits described in this chapter are affected by changes in temperature. This is particularly important for processing and fabrication of biomedical implants, since, for example, there is a significant difference in how crystalline and amorphous materials behave in response to temperature changes. The definitions of several thermal transition points are based on changes in how the material deforms. Therefore, we will begin this section with a discussion of viscosity and material deformation.

## 3.6.1    Viscous Flow

As mentioned earlier in the chapter, plastic deformation takes place due to dislocation movement in crystalline materials. However, since there is no regular structure in noncrystalline materials, a different mechanism of deformation, called **viscous flow**, occurs. In viscous flow, the same type of deformation that liquids undergo, the *rate* of deformation is proportional to the applied stress (this will be discussed more fully in the following chapter). This can be written as

$$\tau = \eta \dot{\gamma} \tag{3.2}$$

where $\tau$ is the (shear) stress applied to the material; $\eta$ is the proportionality constant, also referred to as the **viscosity** of the material; and $\dot{\gamma}$ is the rate of applied (shear) strain, or rate of deformation. Viscosity, which is measured in poise (P) or pascal-seconds (Pa-s), represents a material's ability to resist deformation. The wide range of viscosities possible and the effect of viscosity on handleability (ease of handling) is easily demonstrated by comparing the properties of water ($\eta = 0.01$ P) and caramel ($\eta = 50$ P). At the upper extreme, amorphous ceramics (glasses) have a very high viscosity ($10^{25}$ P) due to the presence of strong interatomic bonds.

## 3.6.2    Thermal Transitions

**3.6.2.1 Metals and Crystalline Ceramics**    The characteristic thermal transition for crystalline materials is the **melting point** ($T_m$). This is the temperature above which atomic movement is large enough to break the material's highly ordered structure. At temperatures higher than $T_m$, the material behaves as liquid and deforms via viscous flow. Below this temperature, the substance is a highly ordered solid, with its crystal structure and grain boundaries intact.

**3.6.2.2 Amorphous Ceramics (Glasses)** In contrast to crystalline materials, glasses do not solidify below a certain temperature (there is no distinct $T_m$). Instead, the material becomes more and more viscous with decreasing temperature until it can be treated as solid. In the "solid" state, there is very little atomic movement. However, although there is no exact $T_m$ for glasses, this and other thermal transitions can be defined in terms of the viscosity of the material.

The transitions shown in Figure 3.15 are arbitrarily chosen, but are quite important to glass-shaping operations (see Chapter 6 for a more detailed discussion of glass processing). From highest temperature to lowest, $T_m$ is the temperature when the viscosity of the material is 100 P. Above this temperature, the material can be handled as a liquid. The **working point** is defined as the temperature at which the viscosity of the glass is $10^4$ P. At this temperature, the material is easily deformed, but maintains some solid-like properties. At lower temperatures, the material becomes more and more like a solid. The **glass transition temperature** $\left( T_g \right)$ is the temperature below which the material is considered to be a glass (solid).

**3.6.2.3 Polymers** Polymers may behave like a liquid, a rubbery solid, or a glass depending on their temperature and molecular structure. Figure 3.16 depicts the effect of molecular weight and temperature on polymer properties (and $T_m$ and $T_g$).

Like other crystalline materials, crystalline polymers can undergo melting at a defined $T_m$. Below this temperature, the crystals are highly ordered, while above it, there is a random ordering of chains with no repeating structure. This occurs

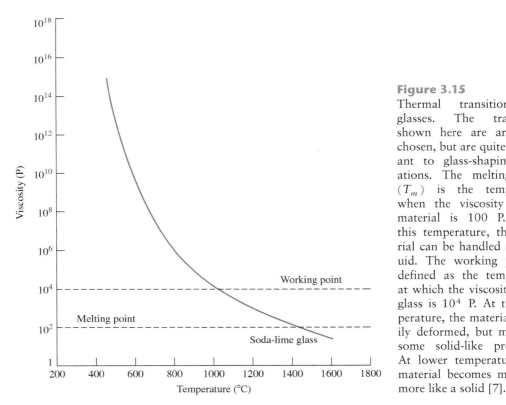

**Figure 3.15**
Thermal transitions for glasses. The transitions shown here are arbitrarily chosen, but are quite important to glass-shaping operations. The melting point $\left( T_m \right)$ is the temperature when the viscosity of the material is 100 P. Above this temperature, the material can be handled as a liquid. The working point is defined as the temperature at which the viscosity of the glass is $10^4$ P. At this temperature, the material is easily deformed, but maintains some solid-like properties. At lower temperatures, the material becomes more and more like a solid [7].

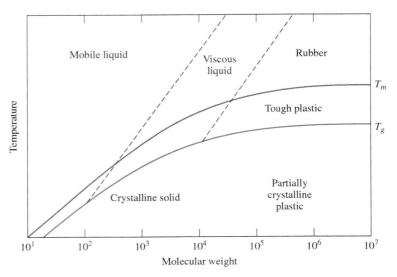

**Figure 3.16**
Effect of molecular weight and temperature on polymer properties ($T_g$ and $T_m$). Polymers may behave like a liquid, a rubbery solid, or a glass depending on their temperature and molecular structure. Crystalline polymers can undergo melting at a defined $T_m$. Below this temperature, the crystals are highly ordered, while above it, there is a random ordering of chains with no repeating structure. $T_m$ increases with increasing molecular weight. Alternatively, those polymers that are amorphous possess a glass transition point $(T_g)$. $T_g$ generally occurs at lower temperatures than $T_m$. Below the glass transition, the polymeric material is glassy and brittle, while above it, the chains are mobile enough to produce a rubbery, elastic material. Like $T_m$, a polymer's $T_g$ increases with increasing molecular weight [8].

when there are enough atoms or chain segments vibrating with sufficient energy to become coordinated and result in overall chain motion (translational motion). This motion then can overcome the secondary bonds that are formed between chains and disrupt the long-range order of the crystal.

Because of this, factors that influence a polymer's ability to form secondary bonds will impact the $T_m$. These include many of the factors affecting the percent crystallinity of a polymer (discussed previously), such as the degree of branching, and other concerns, such as the molecular weight. For example, with more chain branching, the molecules are less densely packed and therefore cannot form van der Waals interactions or hydrogen bonds as easily. This results in a decrease in $T_m$ with increasing amounts of branching.

In contrast, $T_m$ increases with increasing molecular weight (Fig. 3.16). This is due to the fact that with higher molecular weight, there are fewer polymer chain ends. Because chain ends are more free to move than other parts of the macromolecule, more energy is needed to produce the motion required to release the chains from their ordered structure if the chains have a higher molecular weight.

Alternatively, those polymers that are amorphous possess a glass transition point $(T_g)$ similar to that of ceramic glasses. $T_g$ generally occurs at lower temperatures than $T_m$ (see Table 3.2). Below the glass transition, the polymeric material is glassy and brittle, while above it, the chains are mobile enough to produce a rubbery, elastic material. This occurs when there is a high enough temperature to impart sufficient energy to cause molecular motion around the polymer backbone. The ratio of $T_m$ to $T_g$ of a polymer, in the absence of any solvent and where temperature is in degrees Kelvin, usually falls between 1.4 and 2.0, with a few exceptions [2].

**Table 3.2**

| Comparison of Typical Glass Transition Temperatures and Melting Temperatures of Common Polymers | | | |
|---|---|---|---|
| Material | Structure | Glass Transition Temperature (°C (°F)) | Melting Temperature (°C (°F)) |
| Poly(ethylene) (low density) | | −110(−166) | 115 (239) |
| Poly(ethylene) (high density) | | −90(−130) | 137 (279) |
| Poly(tetrafluoro-ethylene) | | −90(−130) | 327 (621) |
| Poly(propylene) | | −20(−4) | 175 (347) |
| Nylon 6,6 | | 57 (135) | 265 (509) |
| Poly(ethylene terephthalate) | | 73 (163) | 265 (509) |

[3]

Factors that influence chain vibration and rotation have a large effect on the $T_g$ of a polymer. Chain flexibility is one of the major determinants of the glass transition point, since more flexibility results in a greater possibility for molecular motion. Therefore, a polymer with more flexible chains will require less energy to achieve the required movement around the backbone and its $T_g$ will be lower.

Chemical constituents have the largest effect on chain flexibility. C–O bonds rotate more easily than C–C bonds, so the presence of these bonds reduces $T_g$, while the addition of bulky side groups reduces movement around the backbone and increases $T_g$. Polar side groups that promote chain interactions also increase $T_g$. For the same reasons as described for $T_m$, a polymer's $T_g$ is higher at higher molecular weight (see Table 3.3). In the same vein, crosslinking reduces overall molecular motion and thus increases $T_g$.

As may be assumed, semicrystalline polymers that contain both crystalline and amorphous regions can have both glass transition and melting points. However, $T_m$ may be undetectable for polymers with low percent crystallinity.

For those polymers possessing the ability to crystallize, at a characteristic temperature above $T_g$ known as the **crystallization temperature** ($T_c$), the polymer chains will have sufficient energy to move into a highly ordered crystalline state.

**Table 3.3**

| Comparison of Glass Transition Temperatures and Melting Temperatures of Poly(Lactic Acid) with Two Different Molecular Weights | | |
| --- | --- | --- |
| Weight Average Molecular Weight (Da) | Glass Transition Temperature (°C) | Melting Temperature (°C) |
| 50,000 | 54 | 170 |
| 300,000 | 59 | 178 |

[4]

This arrangement of the polymer chains into a crystalline state is an exothermic process. A polymer can be annealed by raising the temperature of the sample to its $T_c$, maintaining this temperature for some time $t$ and then lowering the temperature very slowly. The degree of crystallinity of the polymer developed at time $t$, $X(t)$, is described by the Avrami equation as

$$X(t) = 1 - e^{-kt^n} \tag{3.3}$$

where $k$ is the kinetic rate constant of crystal growth and $n$ is a number characteristic of the mechanism of crystal nucleation and growth. Upon further heating of the polymer at temperatures above $T_c$, the melting temperature $T_m$ of the polymer will be reached and the crystal structure will become disrupted. More details about measurement of these transitions are provided in Section 3.7.

### EXAMPLE PROBLEM 3.7

Given that the kinetic rate constant of a particular polymer sample is $2.5 \times 10^{-6}$ $1/s^3$ and that the value of $n$ is 3 for the crystallization of this particular polymer sample in the given conditions, plot the degree of crystallinity of the sample from time $t = 0$ through 125 s. What is the degree of crystallinity of the sample at time $t = 3$ hours?

**Solution:**   At three hours, the time in seconds equals $(3 \text{ hr}) * (60 \text{ min/hr}) * (60 \text{ s/min})$ $= 10,800$ s. Substituting this value along with the other given values into the Avrami equation and solving for $X_c$, we find that the degree of crystallinity is approximately 1. This value makes sense, as the degree of crystallinity of a sample cannot exceed a value of 1, which reflects 100% crystallinity. ∎

## EXAMPLE PROBLEM 3.8

Some researchers utilize the following form of the Avrami equation in their experimental studies:

$$\ln\left[\ln\left(\frac{1}{1 - X_c}\right)\right] = \ln(k) + n \cdot \ln(t)$$

Derive this form of the Avrami equation from the form of the equation given in the text.

**Solution:** $X_c = 1 - e^{-kt^n}$

Subtracting 1 from each side of the equation and then multiplying each side of the equation by $-1$ yields

$$1 - X_c = e^{-kt^n}$$

Taking the natural log of both sides of the equation gives

$$\ln(1 - X_c) = -kt^n$$

Multiplying each side of the equation by $-1$ produces

$$-\ln(1 - X_c) = kt^n$$

Recalling that $-\ln(x) = \ln(1 / x)$, we obtain

$$\ln\left(\frac{1}{1 - X_c}\right) = kt^n$$

Taking the natural log of both sides of the equation and recalling that $\ln(x \cdot y) = \ln(x) + \ln(y)$ and that $\ln(x^y) = y \cdot \ln(x)$ results in

$$\ln\left[\ln\left(\frac{1}{1 - X_c}\right)\right] = \ln(k) + n \cdot \ln(t)$$ ∎

## EXAMPLE PROBLEM 3.9

Assuming that there are amorphous regions in materials made from each of the following polymers, place the three polymers in order of lowest glass transition temperature to highest and rationalize your answer:

(a) poly(ethylene)

(b) poly(p-xylene)

(c) poly(ethylene oxide)

**Solution:** The polymers arranged in order of lowest glass transition temperature to highest are $(c) < (a) < (b)$, that is, poly(ethylene oxide) < poly(ethylene) < poly(p-xylene). Chemical constituents have the largest effect on polymer chain flexibility and glass transition temperatures. C–O bonds rotate more easily than C–C bonds, and are thus more flexible.

However, bulky groups in the chain, such as the benzene ring in the poly(*p*-xylene), prevent rotation around the polymer backbone, and result in a higher $T_g$. In this case, the C–O bond in the poly(ethylene oxide) chain makes it the most flexible polymer of the three (lowest $T_g$), and the benzene ring in the poly(*p*-xylene) chain makes it the least flexible (highest $T_g$) polymer of the three, all other factors being equal. ■

## 3.7 Techniques: Introduction to Thermal Analysis

As mentioned earlier in this chapter, how materials respond to temperature changes is important for their processing and final application. In a controlled environment, a material's response to change in temperature can also provide useful information about the chemical or physical makeup of the material. **Thermal analysis** consists of a group of characterization techniques that involve the measurement of the physical properties of a material (and/or reaction products) as a function of temperature as the sample is subjected to controlled changes in temperature.

Thermal analysis encompasses many well-known techniques, such as **thermogravimetric analysis (TGA)**, **dynamic mechanical analysis (DMA)**, and others, but the one that we shall focus on in this section is **differential scanning calorimetry (DSC)**. DSC has become one of the most popular thermal techniques since it can provide a variety of information about a material, including melting and glass transitions and percent crystallinity of polymeric materials.

### 3.7.1 Differential Scanning Calorimetry

**3.7.1.1 Basic Principles** In DSC, the difference in heat flow into a sample and reference material is recorded as a function of temperature while the two are exposed to a controlled temperature ramp. There are two types of DSC experiments: **power-compensated DSC** and **heat-flux DSC**. For power-compensated DSC, the sample and reference cells are heated by individual heaters and the temperature difference between the cells is kept near zero. The power needed to maintain this equal temperature is then compared. In heat-flux DSC, the sample and reference are heated from the same heater and the temperature difference between the two cells is measured. The temperature difference is then converted to heat flow. This difference is depicted in Figure 3.17. In the following section, we will focus on the operation of the power-compensated DSC.

**3.7.1.2 Instrumentation** A typical plot produced from a DSC experiment is found in Figure 3.18. Results are generally plotted as heat flow in units of power/mass (*y*-axis) as a function of temperature (*x*-axis). Thermal transitions are characterized as endothermic (requiring energy to proceed) or exothermic (releasing energy during the process).

There are three basic components to a differential scanning calorimeter, as shown in Figure 3.19:

1. Furnace(s)—heats sample and reference material with parameters specified by processor (computer).
2. DSC sensors—hold sample and reference and record changes in power to maintain temperatures of each cell.
3. Processor (computer)—controls ramp time and final temperature of the furnaces. Uses the electrical signal from the sensors to control the temperature of the samples in real time via the furnaces. Produces final plotted results.

a) Power-compensated DSC

b) Heat-flux DSC

**Figure 3.17**
Different types of DSC. (a) For power-compensated DSC, the sample and reference cells are heated by individual heaters and the temperature difference between the cells is kept near zero. The power needed to maintain this equal temperature is then compared. (b) In heat-flux DSC, the sample and reference are heated from the same heater and the temperature difference between the two cells is measured. The temperature difference is then converted to heat flow.

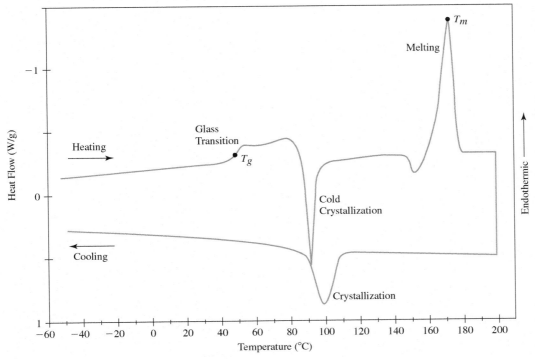

**Figure 3.18**
DSC thermogram of poly(L-lactic acid) (PLLA). During the heating ramp (10°C/min) the glass transition, cold crystallization, and melting of the material occur and during the cooling (10°C/min) the crystallization of the material is observed. The glass transition temperature $\left(T_g\right)$ and melting temperature $\left(T_m\right)$ are indicated in the figure [9].

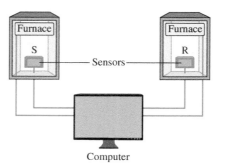

Computer

**Figure 3.19**
Block diagram of components of a differential scanning calorimeter. For a DSC measurement, the sample (S) is first placed in a holding pan made of a metal with high thermal conductivity and hermetically sealed to produce a controlled environment. The reference material (R) is often an empty pan, but can contain a material with known thermal properties. As shown in the diagram, for power-compensated DSC, the two pans are heated with separate furnaces, while processing software controls the furnaces and thus the temperature of the samples. As part of its control mechanism, the computer (via the sensors holding the samples) records how much power is required to maintain a similar temperature in the two pans and plots this as a function of temperature after the temperature ramp has been completed.

For a DSC measurement, the sample is first placed in a holding pan made of a metal with high thermal conductivity and hermetically sealed to produce a controlled environment. The reference material is often an empty pan, but can contain a material with known thermal properties. As shown in the diagram, for power-compensated DSC, the two pans are heated with separate furnaces, while processing software controls the furnaces and thus the temperature of the samples. As part of its control mechanism, the computer records how much power is required to maintain a similar temperature in the two pans and plots this as a function of temperature after the temperature ramp has been completed. Certain differential scanning calorimeters are also equipped with a cooling device, so temperature ramps can be increasing, decreasing, or even cyclical.

**3.7.1.3 Information Provided**   As seen in Figure 3.18, both $T_g$ and $T_m$ can be determined via DSC. At $T_g$, the heat capacity of the sample increases since energy is absorbed by chain rearrangement. $T_m$ refers to the peak temperature. Melting of polymers in general occurs over a range of temperatures due to the presence of crystals of different sizes. Although it may be possible to observe these changes for all types of materials, the working temperature limit on many DSC furnaces makes this technique useful primarily for the characterization of polymeric materials.

DSC is especially useful in determining percent crystallinity of polymers. Since the $T_m$ endotherm is affected by the amount of crystalline material present, comparing the area under the curve representing $T_m$ for a semicrystalline polymer with that for the same polymer in its crystalline form can provide an accurate measure of the percent crystallinity of the semicrystalline polymer (Fig. 3.20).

**Figure 3.20**
DSC thermograms of poly(ethylene glycol)-(D,L-lactic acid)-monomethyl ether diblock copolymers obtained by DSC measurements (left $y$-axis). The structure of these polymers (Me.PEG-PLAs—numbers indicate the molecular weight of the corresponding polymer blocks in kDa) is found in the bottom panel. In the graph, crystalline Me.PEG5 is used as a control (right $y$-axis). Since the $T_m$ endotherm is affected by amount of crystalline material present, by comparing the area under the curve representing $T_m$ for a semicrystalline polymer (Me.PEG-PLA) with that for a similar polymer in its crystalline form (Me.PEG5), an accurate measure of the percent crystallinity of the semicrystalline polymer may be obtained. In comparison, it can be seen that the crystallinity of the Me.PEG-PLA increases with decreasing molecular weight of the PLA block (from 25 kDa to 7.5 kDa). As the PLA molecular weight is reduced, this increases the relative amount of the crystalline Me.PEG5 within the copolymer [10].

## EXAMPLE PROBLEM 3.10

Consider the following DSC thermogram of a polycrystalline polymer. Match the transition temperatures ($A$, $B$, and $C$) with the proper landmarks: ($T_g$, $T_m$, and $T_c$). Based on

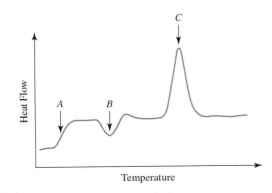

information provided in the thermogram, is the $T_c$ peak endothermic or exothermic? Support your answer. Similarly, is the $T_m$ peak endothermic or exothermic? Why?

**Solution:** A corresponds with the $T_g$ (glass transition temperature), while B denotes the $T_c$ (crystallization temperature) and C marks the $T_m$ (melting temperature). The $T_c$ transition is marked by an exothermic peak (flow of heat out of the sample) as the polymer chains arrange into a crystalline state. The $T_m$ transition is marked by an endothermic peak (flow of heat into the sample) as additional energy is required to disrupt the crystal structure of the polymer. ∎

## Summary

- Defects in crystal structures include those occurring in one dimension (linear defects), two dimensions (planar defects), and three dimensions (volume defects).

- Several types of linear defects can be present in crystal structures, including edge dislocations, screw dislocations and mixed dislocations (exhibiting both edge and screw characteristics). The Burger's vector can be used to classify a dislocation and to map the motion of linear defects in a crystal.

- The presence of linear defects causes localized strains in the crystal lattice and can lead to plastic deformation of the material through movement of the dislocations. Amorphous materials, however, do not possess highly ordered structure and deform by viscous flow, in which the rate of deformation is proportional to the applied stress.

- Planar defects include the material surface and grain boundaries. Atoms at the external surface of a material do not attain the optimal coordination number and consequently possess excess energy, which leads to chemical reactions at the material surface. Most metals and ceramics are composed of randomly oriented crystals, known as grains, of various sizes. The atoms at the disordered interface between grains (grain boundary) are not at the optimal coordination number and thus possess higher energy than comparable atoms within the grain. The higher energy at grain boundaries results in higher chemical reactivity at these sites, relative to the bulk material.

- Volume defects are three-dimensional regions in which the long-range order of the crystal is lost. Volume defects include precipitates (aggregates of impurities) and voids (aggregates of vacancies). Processing to increase void defects is particularly important for tissue engineering applications, as void volume provides a space into which new tissue may grow.

- The form of polymer crystals is generally much more complex than with metals or ceramics. The chain-folded model of polymeric crystallinity holds that the polymer chains fold back on themselves at the faces of lamellae and are regularly aligned within lamellae. Spherulites are three-dimensional aggregates of lamellae and are analogous to grains in ceramic and metallic crystals.

- The melting point $(T_m)$ of a crystalline metal or ceramic is the temperature above which sufficient atomic movement is present to break the highly ordered structure of the material and allow viscous flow and below which the material is solid. Amorphous ceramics (glasses) do not solidify below a certain temperature and do not possess a distinct melting temperature, so $T_m$ is defined in terms of the viscosity of the material. Likewise, the glass transition temperature $(T_g)$ for amorphous ceramics is defined as the temperature below which the material is sufficiently viscous to be considered a glass (solid).

- For crystalline polymers, the melting point is the temperature above which the vibrational energy of the polymer chains is sufficient to overcome secondary bonds between the chains and to allow for translational chain motion. Similarly, amorphous polymers possess a glass transition point above which the polymer chains have sufficient energy to cause molecular motion around the polymer backbone, resulting in a rubbery material. $T_g$ generally occurs at a lower temperature than $T_m$. For semicrystalline polymers, between $T_g$ and $T_m$ the chains increase in energy and mobility, which can lead to a highly ordered crystalline state.

- Techniques of thermal analysis allow for measurement of the physical properties of a material as a function of temperature and enable the characterization of the thermal transitions of a material. Differential scanning calorimetry is one such technique that allows for characterization of $T_m$, $T_g$, and other transitions as well as the percent crystallinity of a polymer under the proper conditions.

## Problems

3.1  Why does slip occur on planes of high atomic density?

3.2  Assume you are exploring using materials as a porogen for a device made of high density poly(ethylene) in order to improve anchorage in surrounding tissue. In this case, you would plan to insert the porogen during fabrication of the device and then heat the device to remove the porogen. You believe that low density poly(ethylene) may be an appropriate choice, but your boss is not convinced.

  (a) Using data in Table 3.2, describe the potential concern of use of low density poly(ethylene).

  (b) Of the characterization techniques discussed thus far in the book, which one would be most appropriate to use to address your boss's concerns? To move forward with low density poly(ethylene) as a viable option, describe the outcome of this test.

3.3  While working for Biomaterials, Inc., you realize your assistant has left an unknown substance contaminating the reference pan in the company's power-compensated differential scanning calorimeter (DSC). You are extremely upset because you realize that it will be nearly impossible to gather useful data from the run you just made, given that the reference pan was contaminated at the time. Explain why a contaminant in the reference pan will render your newly collected data useless based on how a DSC works.

3.4  Using the differential scanning calorimetry (DSC) results below for three different polymers, answer the following questions. Note that endothermic transitions are shown as positive on this graph.

  (a) Identify the approximate thermal transitions for this sample based on the graph above.

  (b) From the DSC plot, which polymer (A), (B), or (C) is most crystalline? Explain how you drew this conclusion.

  (c) Describe a possible heating/cooling regimen to improve crystallinity and explain the process from a molecular perspective. For which of the above polymers would this be a good choice, and for which ones would this process not likely work? Explain your rationale.

  (d) Which polymer (A), (B), or (C) would you expect to have the lowest molecular weight? Justify your conclusions from a molecular perspective.

(e) Studies later find that one of these polymers is actually more branched than the other two. Which polymer (A), (B), or (C) is most likely the branched polymer? Explain your reasoning from a molecular point of view.

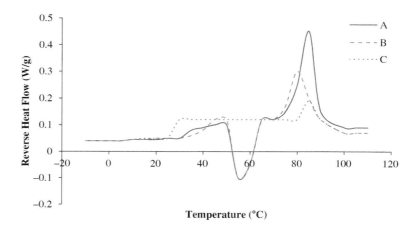

# References

1. J. F. Shackelford, *Introduction to materials science for engineers*, 5th ed. Upper Saddle River: Prentice Hall, 2000.

2. N. A. Peppas, *Structure and properties of polymeric materials: a study guide for students of CHE 544*. West Lafayette: Purdue University, 1984.

3. W. D. Callister Jr. *Materials science and engineering: an introduction*, 3rd ed. New York: John Wiley and Sons, 1994.

4. I. Engelberg and J. Kohn, "Physico-mechanical properties of degradable polymers used in medical applications: a comparative study," *Biomaterials*, vol. 12, no. 3, pp. 292–304, Apr. 1991.

5. J. P. Schaffer, A. Saxena, S. D. Antolovich, J. Sanders, and S. B. Warner, *The science and design of engineering materials*, 2nd ed. Boston: McGraw-Hill, 1998.

6. C. W. Bunn, *Chemical crystallography*. Oxford: Oxford University Press, 1945.

7. W. D. Kingery, H. K. Bowen, and D. R. Uhlmann, *Introduction to ceramics*, 2nd ed. New York: John Wiley and Sons, 1976.

8. J. B. Park and R. S. Lakes, *Biomaterials: an introduction*, 2nd ed. New York: Plenum Press, 1992.

9. Ljungberg and Wesslen, "Tributyl citrate oligomers as plasticizers for poly (lactic acid): thermo-mechanical film properties and aging," *Polymer*, vol. 44, no. 25, pp. 7679–7688, 2003.

10. A. Lucke, J. Tessmar, E. Schnell, G. Schmeer, and A. Gopferich, "Biodegradable poly(D,L-lactic acid)-poly(ethylene glycol)-monomethyl ether diblock copolymers: structures and surface properties relevant to their use as biomaterials," *Biomaterials*, vol. 21, no. 23, pp. 2361–70, Dec. 2000.

# Additional Reading

J. D. Bronzino and J. B. Park, *Biomaterials: principles and applications*. Boca Raton: CRC Press, 2003.

J. F. Rabek, *Experimental methods in polymer chemistry*. New York: John Wiley and Sons, 1980.

D. A. Skoog, F. J. Holler, and S. R. Crouch, *Principles of instrumental analysis*, 6th ed. Boston: Brooks Cole, 2006.

R. J. Young and P. A. Lovell, *Introduction to polymers*, 2nd ed. London: Chapman and Hall, 1991.

# Mechanical Properties of Biomaterials

**Main Objective**

To understand the molecular mechanisms behind the mechanical properties for each class of material as well as the principles behind events that strengthen and weaken biomaterials.

**Specific Objectives**

1. To understand and apply equations for calculation of engineering stress and strain, shear stress and strain, and true stress and strain.
2. To complete calculations based on stress-strain curves.
3. To understand the molecular mechanisms of elastic and plastic deformation in metals, ceramics and polymers.
4. To understand the need and the experimental setup for bending tests.
5. To understand the molecular mechanisms of viscoelastic behavior in metals, ceramics and polymers.
6. To create simple models of viscoelastic behavior in biomaterials.
7. To understand the molecular reasons for biomaterial weakening through degradation or due to the inclusion of pores.
8. To compare and contrast types of fracture and explain the role of stress raisers.
9. To understand how fatigue failure is different from other modes of failure and the factors that affect fatigue life.
10. To understand the molecular mechanisms behind material strengthening techniques.
11. To understand the basic theory behind and possible limitations to the mechanical testing of materials.

## 4.1 Introduction: Types of Mechanical Properties

Previous chapters have discussed the chemical makeup of various biomaterials and how this affects physical properties such as crystallinity and thermal transitions. This chapter will address how the nature of their bonds and sub-unit structures translate into distinct mechanical properties for each class of biomaterials. Mechanical properties of materials include the following:

1. Tensile/compressive properties
2. Shear/torsion properties
3. Bending properties
4. Viscoelastic properties
5. Hardness

This chapter will focus on the first four of those listed, as they are of particular interest for general biomedical applications. Specifically, testing methods and the molecular causes of each set of properties will be discussed.

## 4.2 Mechanical Testing Methods, Results, and Calculations

Mechanical assessment of materials is performed with a **mechanical testing frame** like that seen in Figure 4.1. While the specific mechanisms of its operation are discussed in more detail at the end of this chapter, in general, different fixtures can be attached to accommodate various testing modes. The design of the device allows for controlled loading in a well-defined environment for all testing modes. A number of ASTM standards (created by ASTM International) provide guidelines for most testing modes and material types. Of particular interest for biomaterials applications, the testing can be completed in the wet state, thus approximating *in vivo* conditions much more accurately.

**Figure 4.1**
A mechanical testing frame used for determining the mechanical properties of various materials [3].

## 4.2.1 Tensile and Shear Properties

### 4.2.1.1 Calculations for Tensile and Shear Tests

As shown in Figure 4.2(a–c), in mechanical testing, force can be applied as tensile, compressive, or shear. **Tensile testing** is one of the most common testing methods. A diagram of a specimen undergoing tensile testing is found in Figure 4.3. From ASTM standards, typically, the tensile sample is shaped into a "dog-bone" geometry, with either a round or rectangular cross-section (Fig. 4.4). During testing, the sample is placed in the mechanical testing frame so that one end is attached to a movable platform, which loads the specimen along the longitudinal axis. Further details about the operation of the loading frame can be found at the end of this chapter.

The two important parameters measured during tensile testing are load and specimen elongation. From these, engineering stress ($\sigma$) and engineering strain ($\varepsilon$) can be calculated. Engineering stress is

$$\sigma = \frac{F}{A_0} \tag{4.1}$$

where $F$ is the force applied perpendicular to the cross-section of the sample at any point during the test and $A_0$ is the original cross-sectional area of the sample. SI units of stress are Pascals (Pa). Engineering strain is

$$\varepsilon = \frac{l_i - l_0}{l_0} \tag{4.2}$$

where $l_0$ is the length of the sample before loading, and $l_i$ is the sample length at any point during the testing procedure. As seen in the equation, strain is a dimensionless

(a)

(b)

(c)

(d)

**Figure 4.2**
Types of forces that can be applied to a material: (a) tensile, (b) compressive, (c) shear, and (d) torsion.

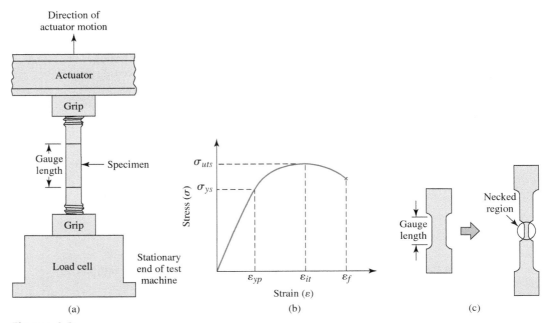

**Figure 4.3**
A sample testing setup for tensile characterization. (a) The sample material placed in a mechanical testing frame. (b) A stress-strain curve, from which the material properties of the sample can be determined. (c) A gross example of what occurs to the material when tension is applied to the sample [4].

quantity. Because they take into account the geometry of the specimen, stress and strain values can (ideally) be used to compare materials that were tested in different shapes.

**Compression testing** is also often performed on biomaterials (Fig. 4.2(b)), particularly if they are to be subjected to compressive forces while in use, such as for orthopedic implants. Typical compressive specimens are cylindrical, with a length at least twice that of their diameter. The same equations are used to calculate stress and strain as for tensile tests, but since the compressive force acts in the opposite direction to the tensile force, $F$ is taken to be negative, resulting in a negative stress. Additionally, since the sample becomes smaller along the axis of the stress, $l_0$ is larger than $l_i$, and the calculated strain is negative.

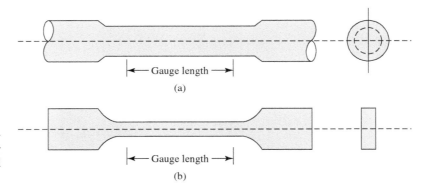

**Figure 4.4**
The dog-bone shaped geometry used for tensile testing for (a) round materials and (b) rectangular materials [1].

Unlike tensile or compressive modes, **shear testing** produces forces that are parallel to the top and bottom faces of the sample (Fig. 4.2(c)). Shear stress ($\tau$) can be calculated by

$$\tau = \frac{F}{A_0} \tag{4.3}$$

In this case, $F$ is the force imparted parallel to the upper and lower faces, while $A_0$ is the area of these faces.

As seen in Figure 4.2(c), the shear force causes sample deformation of angle $\theta$. Therefore, shear strain ($\gamma$) is defined as

$$\gamma = \tan \theta \tag{4.4}$$

In many cases, instead of pure shear, **torsion forces** may be applied to the sample. As depicted in Figure 4.2(d), a torque force ($T$) twists a cylindrical specimen to cause deformation of angle $\phi$ on one end relative to the other end. Calculation of shear stress and strain is completed via modification of equations 4.3 and 4.4.

### 4.2.1.2 Stress-Strain Curves and Elastic Deformation

A composite diagram showing a range of stress-strain responses for various materials is found in Figure 4.5. Looking at Material I of Figure 4.5 and at Figure 4.6, it can be seen that the stress and strain are proportional to each other at all values. This relationship is known as **Hooke's law** and can be written as

$$\sigma = E\varepsilon \tag{4.5}$$

where $E$ is the **modulus of elasticity** or **Young's modulus** (MPa). In the area of the curve where the stress and strain follow this linear relationship, the sample undergoes **elastic deformation**. The slope of the curve in this region is the modulus of elasticity, or stiffness of the material. For materials with high $E$, a large stress is required before deformation will occur. Elastic deformation is not permanent; upon release of the load, the sample returns to its original shape.

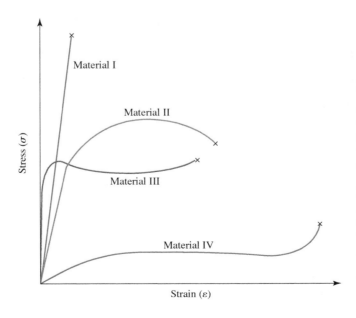

**Figure 4.5**
The wide variations possible on the stress-strain curve depending on the tested material. Ceramics are often brittle and demonstrate behavior similar to Material I, while metals produce curves similar to Material II. Polymers fall into a wide range of categories, from very brittle materials (Material I), to materials exhibiting plastic deformation (Material III), to highly elastic materials (Material IV) [1] and [4].

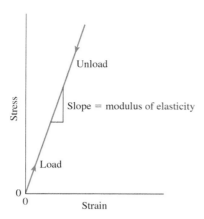

**Figure 4.6**
A sample stress-strain curve showing a linear relationship, from which the modulus of elasticity can be calculated (slope of the curve) [1].

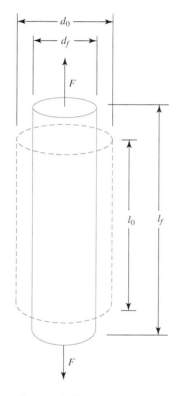

**Figure 4.7**
Schematic showing the radial contraction that occurs when a material undergoes tensile deformation. The ratio of the strain in the transverse direction to the strain in the longitudinal direction (direction of the applied force $F$) is the Poisson's ratio [4].

The relationship described in equation 4.5 is valid for both tensile and compressive testing. Similarly, shear stress and strain can be related by

$$\tau = G\gamma \tag{4.6}$$

where $G$ is the **shear modulus**, which, as for tensile/compressive testing, also represents the slope of the stress-strain curve in the elastic region.

As shown in Figure 4.7, when elastic elongation occurs along the axis of loading, there is contraction in the directions perpendicular to this loading. For cylindrical specimens, this perpendicular (transverse) strain is represented as $\varepsilon_t = \Delta d / d_0$, where $\Delta d$ is the change in diameter and $d_0$ is the original diameter of the specimen. The ratio of the strain that occurs in the transverse direction to the strain that occurs along the loading axis ($\varepsilon_a$) is called the **Poisson's ratio** ($\nu$):

$$\nu = -\frac{\varepsilon_t}{\varepsilon_a} \tag{4.7}$$

The negative sign is included to ensure that the Poisson's ratio is a positive number. This value is dimensionless and for completely isotropic materials (those which have identical properties in all directions) should be 0.25. The theoretical maximum, assuming no volume change, is 0.5. Typical values range from 0.25 to 0.35.

Using the Poisson's ratio, the shear and elastic moduli for an isotropic material can be related via the formula

$$E = 2G(1 + \nu) \tag{4.8}$$

## EXAMPLE PROBLEM 4.1

A cylindrical chicken bone specimen is tested in compression. The original outer diameter of the bone is 7.40 mm, and the original length of the bone specimen is 45.00 mm. At one point during the compressive testing, the bone specimen is compressed to a length of 42.75 mm. One researcher hypothesizes that the Poisson's ratio of the sample at this point is 0.3. What would the outer diameter of the bone specimen need to be at this point for the Poisson's ratio of 0.3 to be correct?

**Solution:**  The Poisson's ratio is defined as the ratio of the strain of a sample in the transverse direction to the strain in the axial direction: $\nu = -\varepsilon_t/\varepsilon_a$. In this case, the strain in the axial direction can be calculated from the information given and is

$$\varepsilon_a = (42.75 \text{ mm} - 45.00 \text{ mm})/(45.00 \text{ mm}) = -0.05$$

Since the hypothesized Poisson's ratio is given to be 0.3, and the axial strain has been calculated to be $-0.05$, the transverse strain can be calculated as follows:

$$\varepsilon_t = -(\nu\varepsilon_a) = -(0.3(-0.05)) = 0.015$$

Recalling that $\varepsilon_t = (\Delta d/d_0$, where $d_0$ equals 7.40 mm in this case, the equation can be solved to find the outer diameter of the sample required to give the hypothesized Poisson's ratio as follows:

$$\varepsilon_t = (d_t - 7.40 \text{ mm})/(7.40 \text{ mm}) = 0.015$$

$$0.111 \text{ mm} + 7.40 \text{ mm} = d_t$$

$$d_t = \underline{7.511 \text{ mm}}$$

■

### 4.2.1.3  Molecular Causes of Elastic Deformation

On a molecular level, elastic deformation is a result of small changes in atomic spacing and stretching of bonds. The resistance to this deformation is provided by the interatomic bonding forces. Those materials with stronger bonds will be less easily deformed (have a higher modulus of elasticity). Revisiting the force-separation curves described in Chapter 1 (Fig. 1.15), it is found that $E$ is proportional to the slope of these curves at the equilibrium bond length $r_0$:

$$E \propto \left(\frac{dF}{dr}\right)_{r_0} \tag{4.9}$$

As can be seen in Figure 4.8, those materials that possess a high $E$ (very stiff materials) demonstrate a force-separation curve with very steep sides, so more energy is required to move the atoms away from their equilibrium positions. As a result of the nature of their chemical bonds, values for $E$ are generally greater for ceramics than metals, and both ceramics and metals are stiffer than most polymers. It should be noted, however, that due to the structure of their chains, mechanical properties in polymeric materials are highly direction dependent. Therefore, along the axis of the chain, where primary (covalent) bonds exist between atoms, polymers can possess similar strength and stiffness to metals or ceramics. However, in other directions, where the material is held together mainly by secondary forces, mechanical properties are usually significantly lower.

### 4.2.1.4  Stress-Strain Curves and Plastic Deformation

As mentioned in Chapter 3, **plastic deformation** can also occur and plays a large role in forming operations, particularly for metals and polymers. In contrast to elastic deformation, plastic deformation is permanent, so that the sample never returns completely to its original shape. Evidence of plastic deformation is apparent for Materials II, III, and IV in Figure 4.5 in the nonlinear portion after the elastic region.

In the following discussion, plastic deformation of materials in tension is considered. The beginning of plastic deformation is the point where the stress-strain relationship no longer follows Hooke's law; hence, the curve changes from a linear region to a nonlinear region. The stress corresponding to the end of the elastic

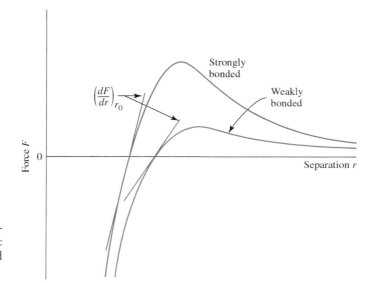

**Figure 4.8**
Diagram showing the relationship between elastic modulus (E) and bond strength [1].

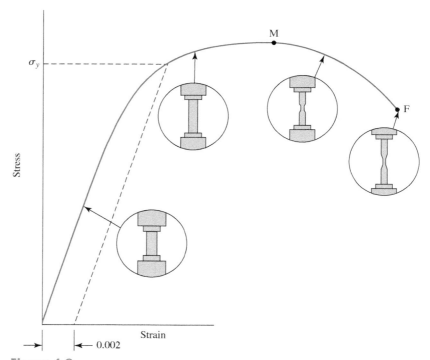

**Figure 4.9**
Stress versus strain curve showing elastic and plastic deformation of a material. During the elastic region no necking of the sample occurs, and if the stress is removed, the sample will return to its original state. In this scenario, it is difficult to find the point between the linear and nonlinear regions, so a 0.2% strain offset is used. To do this, a line parallel to the elastic portion is created, with the origin of the line having an offset of 0.002 (0.2%) strain. Where this line connects with the curve is considered the yield point, and is used to determine the yield strength ($\sigma_y$). From this point until the ultimate tensile strength (point M), plastic deformation occurs, meaning that if the stress is removed, the sample will not return to its native state. After this point, necking will occur in the sample until fracture (point F) [1].

region of the curve is known as the **yield strength** $(\sigma_y)$ and the strain at this value is the **yield point strain** $(\varepsilon_{yp})$. However, this transition is not always readily apparent for certain materials and the change can be difficult to pinpoint (Fig. 4.9). In this case, it is common to use a 0.2% strain offset to determine the yield point.

After yielding, there is an increase in stress required to continue plastic deformation until a maximum is reached (the **ultimate tensile strength** or just **tensile strength**, $\sigma_{uts}$). After this value, necking of the specimen occurs (Fig. 4.9), and there is no longer uniform strain across the entire specimen (deformation occurs at the necked area only). With the onset of necking, the stress required to cause further plastic deformation decreases until the point of material fracture (**fracture strength**, $\sigma_f$). It should be noted that of these values, the yield strength is often used as a key design parameter, since by the time the material reaches its ultimate tensile strength, it has undergone significant plastic deformation and may no longer meet the shape requirements for the application.

An important property associated with plastic deformation is the ductility of a material. **Ductility** reflects the ability of a material to deform plastically before breaking. Those materials that have low ductility will fracture with very little plastic deformation (Fig. 4.10) and are considered **brittle**. Many ceramics behave in this manner.

Ductility values can be calculated as % elongation (%$EL$) or % area reduction (%$AR$). The former gives

$$\%EL = \frac{l_f - l_0}{l_0} \cdot 100 \qquad (4.10)$$

where $l_f$ is the length at fracture and $l_0$ is the gauge length (the original length of the thin portion of the dog-bone specimen; see Fig. 4.4). The latter yields

$$\%AR = \frac{A_0 - A_f}{A_0} \cdot 100 \qquad (4.11)$$

where $A_0$ is the original sample's cross-sectional area and $A_f$ is the cross-sectional area at fracture. %$EL$ depends on the gauge length of the specimen, and this information should be included when reporting these results. In contrast, %$AR$ is independent of sample parameters. %$EL$ and %$AR$ are not expected to be equal for a given sample.

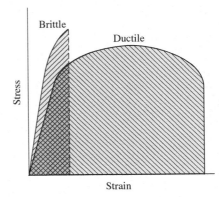

**Figure 4.10**
Stress-strain diagram of a brittle and ductile material. Note that the area under the curve is small in the brittle material compared to the ductile material [1].

It should be noted that plastic deformation for polymers, particularly semi-crystalline polymers, is slightly different from what was described before for crystalline materials such as metals (Fig. 4.9). Figure 4.11 depicts macroscopic deformation of a semi-crystalline polymer in tension. After the yield point, a neck develops, like that seen for metals. However, within this neck, the polymer chains become oriented with the direction of the load. As mentioned earlier, the chains have more of an ability to resist deformation along their axes due to strong primary bond interactions. Therefore, specimen elongation occurs by the growth of the necked region along the gauge length, with an accompanying increase in chain order in this region. This contrasts with sample deformation in metals, in which the extension is confined only to the original necked area (Fig. 4.9). Just before fracture, there is a dramatic increase in stress needed to deform the polymer sample, which corresponds to the energy needed to overcome the strength of the primary bonds within the aligned chains.

Although this discussion of plastic deformation has focused on changes associated with tensile loading, similar stress-strain curves are found for materials undergoing compressive, shear, or torsional loading. In each of these cases, the stages of deformation and fracture may differ from those seen in tension. For example, there is no maximum strength after yield for compressive testing, since there is no necking of the specimen.

To this point, calculations of stress and strain have been based on the original sample dimensions, assuming that there is negligible change in size during testing. These values are referred to as **engineering stress and strain**. However, these are not entirely accurate, especially once specimen necking begins. Therefore, it is sometimes more useful to speak of **true stress and strain**. True stress ($\sigma_t$) is the force ($F$) divided by the area at any point (instantaneous area, $A_{in}$):

$$\sigma_t = \frac{F}{A_{in}} \tag{4.12}$$

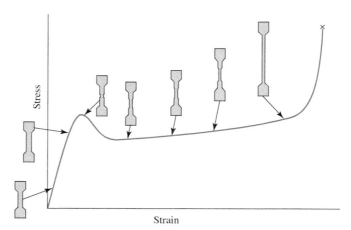

**Figure 4.11**
Stress-strain diagram depicting the macroscopic deformation of a semi-crystalline polymer in tension. After the yield point, a neck develops, like that seen for metals. Within this neck, the polymer chains become oriented with the direction of the load, due to their ability to resist deformation along their axes (strong primary bond interactions). Therefore, specimen elongation occurs by the growth of the necked region along the gauge length, with an accompanying increase in chain order in this region [4, 5].

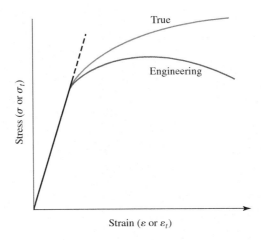

**Figure 4.12**
Diagram demonstrating the difference between an engineering stress-strain curve and a true stress-strain curve. Note that there is no decrease in stress throughout the test on the actual sample; this decrease is simply an artifact of the engineering stress-strain calculations [4].

Similarly, the expression for the true strain ($\varepsilon_t$) can be derived from that for engineering strain (eq. 4.2, restated here as 4.13):

$$\varepsilon = \frac{l_i - l_0}{l_0} \tag{4.13}$$

Modifying this equation from the reference of a single point in the testing procedure, the numerator becomes the differential change in length ($dl_i$) and the denominator, rather than the original length, is the instantaneous length at that point in time ($l_i$). To find the total strain up to that moment in the test, an integral is needed:

$$\varepsilon_t = \int_{l_0}^{l_i} \frac{dl}{l} \tag{4.14}$$

This can be reduced to

$$\varepsilon_t = \ln\left(\frac{l_i}{l_0}\right) \tag{4.15}$$

where $l_0$ is the original length of the sample. Figure 4.12 demonstrates the difference between a typical engineering stress-strain curve and its corresponding true stress-strain values.

## EXAMPLE PROBLEM 4.2

Consider the following test specimens that were subjected to tensile testing. Label each series with the type of deformation that occurs and justify your answer. Match each series to the corresponding stress-strain curve. For which series is the mechanical deformation subject to Hooke's law throughout the testing illustrated?

Series A

Series B

Curve 1

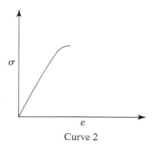

Curve 2

**Solution:**   In both of the illustrated cases, the sample changes from its original dimensions during the course of the tensile testing. However, in Series A, the sample does not return to its original dimensions at the end of the testing. Thus, Series A demonstrates plastic deformation. Series B, however, does return to its original dimensions at the end of the tensile testing. Thus, Series B demonstrates elastic deformation. Consequently, Series B was subject to Hooke's law throughout the testing, as this applies to samples that remain within the region of linear elasticity. Curve 1 illustrates elastic deformation, as the curve remains linear throughout. Curve 2, on the other hand, demonstrates plastic deformation, as the curve deviates from the region of linearity at higher strains as the sample begins to yield. Thus, Curve 1 corresponds with Series B, and Curve 2 corresponds with Series A.   ▪

## EXAMPLE PROBLEM 4.3

A strip of chicken skin was excised for mechanical testing in tension. The initial dimensions of the rectangular specimen were 30 mm long and 15 mm wide, with an average thickness of 3 mm. The mechanical testing was conducted at a rate of 5 mm/sec. The following data were obtained:

| Gauge Length (mm) | Force (N) |
|---|---|
| 20.0 | 0.0 |
| 20.5 | 0.1 |
| 21.0 | 0.3 |
| 21.5 | 0.5 |
| 22.0 | 0.8 |
| 22.5 | 1.1 |
| 23.1 | 1.6 |
| 23.6 | 2.0 |
| 24.2 | 2.7 |
| 24.6 | 3.6 |
| 25.2 | 4.7 |
| 25.7 | 6.2 |
| 26.3 | 7.9 |
| 26.8 | 9.7 |
| 27.4 | 11.4 |
| 27.9 | 12.9 |
| 28.5 | 14.5 |
| 29.0 | 16.4 |
| 29.6 | 18.3 |
| 30.1 | 19.6 |

(a) Calculate the engineering stresses and strains from the information given and plot the engineering stress-strain curve. Assume that 5 mm of the specimen length is clamped by the testing grips at each end, such that the initial gauge length of the specimen is 20 mm.
(b) It was found that immediately before the last data point, the average width of the sample was 8 mm and the average thickness of the sample was 0.75 mm. Considering this information, determine the true stress and true stain of the sample at the last data point.

(c)  Compare the true stress and strain values for the final data point with the engineering stress and strain values for the final data point.

Solution:

(a)  Since the initial gauge length of the specimen is given to be 20 mm and the gauge length for each data point is given, the engineering strain can be calculated at each point as follows:

$$\varepsilon = (l_i - l_0)/l_0$$

$$\varepsilon = (l_i - 20 \text{ mm})/20 \text{ mm}$$

The engineering stress can be calculated by dividing the force at each point by the cross-sectional area of the sample. In this case, the cross-sectional area of the sample is the width of the sample (15 mm) times the average thickness of the sample (3 mm). Thus,

$$A = 15 \text{ mm} \cdot 3 \text{ mm} = 45 \text{ mm}^2$$

$$\sigma = F/A_0 = F/45 \text{mm}^2$$

The calculated stresses and strains are as follows:

| Strain | Stress (N/mm$^2$) |
|---|---|
| 0.00 | 0.00 |
| 0.02 | 0.00 |
| 0.05 | 0.01 |
| 0.07 | 0.01 |
| 0.10 | 0.02 |
| 0.12 | 0.02 |
| 0.15 | 0.03 |
| 0.18 | 0.05 |
| 0.21 | 0.06 |
| 0.23 | 0.08 |
| 0.26 | 0.10 |
| 0.29 | 0.14 |
| 0.31 | 0.18 |
| 0.34 | 0.22 |
| 0.37 | 0.25 |
| 0.39 | 0.29 |
| 0.42 | 0.32 |
| 0.45 | 0.36 |
| 0.48 | 0.41 |
| 0.51 | 0.44 |

The engineering stress-strain plot is as follows:

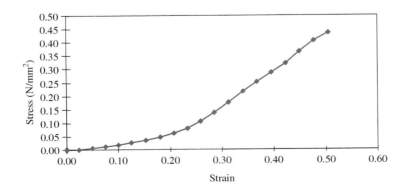

(b) The true stress of a sample takes into account the changes in the sample dimensions that may occur with time. As a result, the true stress is determined by the formula

$$\sigma_t = F/A_t,$$

where $A_t$ is the cross-sectional area at the time of interest. In this case, the dimensions of the sample at time $t$ are given to be 8 mm in width and 0.75 mm in thickness. Thus, the cross-sectional area of the sample at the time point of interest is $(8 \text{ mm})(0.75 \text{ mm}) = 6 \text{ mm}^2$.
So, the true stress at this point can be calculated as follows:

$$\sigma_t = (19.6 \text{ N})/(6 \text{ mm}^2) = \underline{3.27 \text{ N/mm}^2}$$

The true strain of the sample at the final point can be calculated from the equation $\varepsilon_t = ln(l_i/l_0)$ as follows:

$$\varepsilon_t = \ln(30.1 \text{ mm}/20 \text{ mm}) = \underline{0.41}$$

(c) The calculated true stress of 3.27 N/mm$^2$ is much greater than the engineering stress of 0.51 N/mm$^2$ for the last data point. The difference is due mainly to the large changes in the cross-sectional area of the sample from the initial value (changed from the initial value of 45 mm$^2$ to 6 mm$^2$). If a given force is distributed across a smaller cross-sectional area, as was the case in this exercise, then the stress increases. There was little difference observed between the engineering strain and the true strain for the sample at the final point. ∎

### 4.2.1.5 Molecular Causes of Plastic Deformation

Figure 4.5 depicts the stress-strain response for a number of material types. As mentioned previously, ceramics are often brittle and demonstrate behavior similar to Material I, while metals produce curves similar to Material II. Polymers fall into a wide range of categories, from very brittle materials (like Material I) to materials exhibiting plastic deformation (like Material III) to highly elastic materials (like Material IV).

Although the first two types of polymer mechanical behavior are similar to those discussed for ceramics and metals, the third type, **elasticity**, is characteristic only of a subset of polymers called **elastomers**. The most common elastomer is rubber. Elastic materials are defined as those that allow large recoverable strains at low stress levels. The molecular causes for this particular mechanical behavior are discussed next.

### 4.2.1.6 Causes of Plastic Deformation—Metals and Crystalline Ceramics

At this point, a detailed look at what happens on an atomic scale to produce plastic deformation of the various classes of materials is warranted. As discussed in Chapter 3, metals and crystalline ceramics undergo deformation due to dislocation glide along a plane called the **slip plane**. The slip plane is usually the plane with the highest atomic density. However, the number of possible slip planes in ceramics is limited by requirements of electroneutrality. Therefore, it is difficult for ceramic materials to deform plastically, resulting in their brittleness.

Slip occurs when there is a great enough force in an orientation that coincides with a slip plane. For simplicity, we will take a material composed of a single crystal as an example. As seen in Figure 4.13, for such a material in tension, shear forces exist along all planes except those completely perpendicular to the direction of the tensile force. It is these shear forces that provide the energy to induce the dislocation

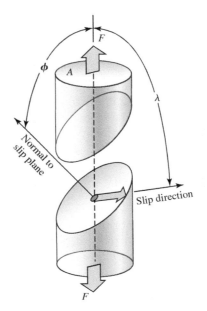

**Figure 4.13**
Schematic showing slip in a tensile specimen. Slip is caused by shear stress in a tensile specimen, which can occur in any direction with the exception of perpendicular to the tensile force. This stress in the slip plane can be calculated using the tensile stress on the sample, and the two angles shown in the figure ($\phi$ and $\lambda$) [1].

glide described in the previous chapter. Therefore, the magnitude of the shear stress felt by the slip plane (**resolved shear stress**, $\tau_r$) is of particular interest and can be determined by the equation

$$\tau_r = \sigma \cos \phi \cos \lambda \qquad (4.16)$$

where $\sigma$ is the tensile stress, $\phi$ is the angle between the normal to the slip plane and the direction of applied force, and $\lambda$ is the angle between the slip direction and the direction of applied force. When the resolved shear stress along a slip plane exceeds a certain value, called the critical resolved shear stress ($\tau_{crss}$), slip is initiated. $\tau_{crss}$ varies according to the material and is a factor in determining the yield strength of the material.

Deformation of polycrystalline materials is more complex, since each grain is oriented randomly. Therefore, some grains may be arranged favorably with the applied force to allow slip, while others may not. For each grain, slip occurs along the plane with the most appropriate orientation. As shown in Figure 4.14, macroscopic deformation of polycrystalline materials occurs due to deformation of individual grains, rather than alterations or opening of grain boundaries.

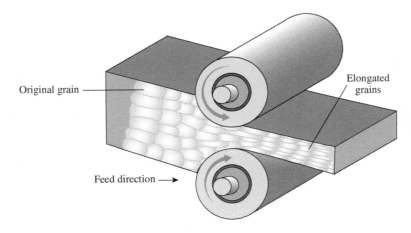

Original grain

Feed direction →

Elongated grains

**Figure 4.14**
During hot rolling of metals, which is used to produce a final product with smaller cross-sectional area (see Chapter 6), macroscopic elongation occurs. As shown in this diagram, this is due to deformation of individual grains, rather than opening of the grain boundaries.

Polycrystalline materials are usually stronger (have higher yield strengths) than their equivalent single-crystal materials due to constraints imposed by neighboring grains. Even if a certain grain is orientated to allow slip at a low level of stress, a contiguous grain may have a much less favorable orientation, and the first grain cannot deform until the neighboring grain also deforms. Therefore, a stress with high enough magnitude to cause deformation of the less-favorably arranged grains must be applied. (Another way of thinking of this is that the presence of grain boundaries hinders overall slip in the material—see Section 4.5 for further discussion of this topic.)

### 4.2.1.7 Causes of Plastic Deformation—Amorphous Polymers and Ceramics (Glasses)

Also as discussed in Chapter 3, noncrystalline polymers and ceramics (glasses) deform by viscous flow. Here, atoms or ions slide past each other by breaking and reforming bonds, but, in contrast to dislocations, there is no prescribed direction of movement. As with slip, shear stress also plays an important role in viscous deformation. From Chapter 3, we have seen that

$$\tau = \eta \dot{\gamma} \tag{4.17}$$

or, in viscous flow, the *rate* of deformation is proportional to the applied stress. The proportionality constant $\eta$ is the viscosity of the sample, and $\dot{\gamma}$ is the rate of shear deformation $\left(\dfrac{d\gamma}{dt}\right)$. This is called **Newton's law**.

Now that we understand more about the different types of mechanical properties of materials, we can derive this relationship. Newton's law can be seen as an extension of the shear stress/shear-strain relationship for solids discussed earlier (Fig. 4.15):

$$\tau = G\gamma \tag{4.18}$$

As depicted in Figure 4.15, here, another form of $\gamma$ is used:

$$\gamma = \tan \theta = \frac{dy}{dx} \tag{4.19}$$

However, as discussed in the previous chapter, amorphous materials can be thought of as cooled liquids, so when we replace the solid sample in the figure with an equal volume of liquid, we obtain a relationship like that shown in Figure 4.16. In this case, the shear force does not cause a single strain value, but the deformation

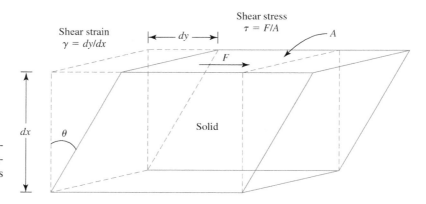

**Figure 4.15**
Schematic of the deformation that occurs when a crystalline material undergoes shear stress [4].

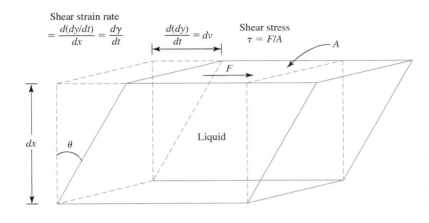

**Figure 4.16**
Schematic of the deformation that occurs when an amorphous material undergoes shear stress [4].

continues with time. The rate of deformation $(d(dy/dt))$ is proportional to the shear force $F$:

$$F \propto d(dy/dt) \qquad (4.20)$$

If the force is normalized by the area to obtain shear stress $(\tau)$ and the displacement rate is normalized by the height $(dx)$ the expression becomes

$$\tau \propto \frac{d(dy/dt)}{dx} \qquad (4.21)$$

Because $dx$ is a constant, the equation can be rearranged:

$$\tau \propto \frac{d(dy/dx)}{dt} \qquad (4.22)$$

Replacing $dy/dx$ with $\gamma$, and including $\eta$ as a constant of proportionality yields

$$\tau = \eta\left(\frac{d\gamma}{dt}\right) = \eta\dot{\gamma} \qquad (4.23)$$

**4.2.1.8  Causes of Plastic Deformation—Polymers (General)**  The results of mechanical testing of polymers are more dependent on testing conditions than are the results for metals and ceramics. Temperature has striking effects on the behavior of the material. Similarly, the properties observed can be influenced by the rate of testing. Either increasing the testing temperature or decreasing the strain rate causes a reduction in $E$, a decrease in tensile strength and an increase in ductility. The molecular reasons for these phenomena are described next.

For all polymers containing amorphous regions, whether the material is tested at temperatures above or below its $T_g$, has a very large impact on its mechanical properties. Below $T_g$, the polymer chains are "frozen" and the resulting material is brittle. Above $T_g$, the polymer chains begin to rotate around their backbones and move relative to one another, so the material becomes more ductile.

The effect of strain rate on mechanical properties can be related, in part, to the necking phenomenon described earlier. If a polymeric sample is pulled too quickly, the chains do not have enough time to rearrange and orient themselves along the axis of loading in the neck region. Therefore, at higher strain rates, less deformation occurs; therefore the specimen behaves in a more brittle manner and has a higher overall strength.

## EXAMPLE PROBLEM 4.4

Consider a sample of poly(methyl methacrylate) (PMMA) in tension. For increasing strain rates, would the stress-strain curve below be expected to shift from 1 to 3 or from 3 to 1 and why? Assuming an initial temperature significantly higher than the $T_g$ for PMMA, would the stress-strain curve be expected to shift from 1 to 3 or from 3 to 1 as the temperature decreases and why?

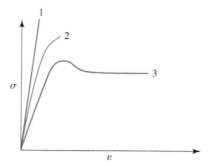

Solution:    For increasing strain rates, the stress-strain curve would be expected to shift from 3 to 1. As the strain rate increases, the polymer chains are given less time to orient themselves along the axis of loading. Thus, at higher strain rates, the sample behaves in an increasingly brittle manner and with a higher strength. Starting at a temperature much higher than $T_g$ for PMMA, the sample would behave in a manner similar to curve 3, as the polymer chains have a large amount of energy to rearrange with the applied force. As the temperature decreases toward $T_g$, one would expect the stress-strain curve to shift toward curve 1, as the energy available for polymer chain movement decreases and the material acts in a more brittle manner.    ∎

### 4.2.1.9   Causes of Plastic Deformation—Semi-Crystalline Polymers and Elastomers    Because two particular subclasses of polymers, semi-crystalline polymers and elastomers, possess unique stress-strain properties, their deformation is discussed here in more detail. This description follows that of Callister [1] for both polymer types. Semi-crystalline polymers are composed of spherulites, as depicted in Figure 3.13. These spherulites contain crystalline lamellar regions that radiate from the center. In between the lamellae are amorphous regions that contain tie molecules to connect neighboring lamellae.

Plastic deformation for these polymers can be conceptualized as interactions between the lamellar and amorphous regions in response to a tensile force. As shown in Figure 4.17, there are several stages of elongation. In the first stage, the tie chains extend and the lamellae slide past each other. In the second stage, the lamellae themselves become reoriented so that the chain folds are aligned along the axis of loading. After this, blocks of the crystalline phases separate from each other. However, adjacent lamellae within the blocks are still attached via the tie molecules. Finally, the blocks and tie molecules become oriented along the axis of the applied tensile force. In this way, tensile forces can induce significant chain orientation in semi-crystalline polymers (as seen in the necking phenomena described before). As in grains in polycrystalline metals and ceramics, this also induces a change in shape of the spherulites.

An interesting aspect to semi-crystalline polymers is that synthesis and processing parameters can easily affect their deformation behavior, as seen in Figure 4.18. Any changes that inhibit chain motion within these polymers increase the observed strength and decrease the ductility. Such changes include increasing the polymer

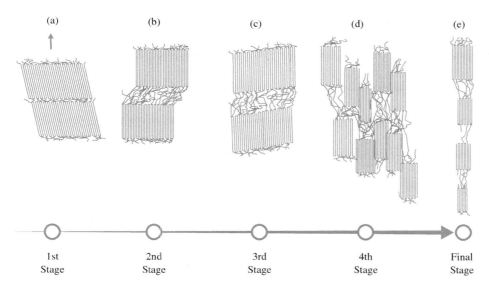

**Figure 4.17**
Plastic deformation for semi-crystalline polymers (a) can be conceptualized as interactions between the lamellar and amorphous regions in response to a tensile force. There are several stages of elongation. (b) In the first stage, the tie chains extend and the lamellae slide past each other. (c) In the second stage, the lamellae themselves become re-oriented so that the chain folds are aligned along the axis of loading. (d) After this, blocks of the crystalline phases separate from each other. However, adjacent lamellae within the blocks are still attached via the tie molecules. (e) Finally, the blocks and tie molecules become oriented along the axis of the applied tensile force. In this way, tensile forces can induce significant chain orientation in semi-crystalline polymers [3].

crystallinity, increasing the molecular weight, or crosslinking the polymer. Secondary bonds that exist in crystalline areas where the chains are more tightly packed are effective in restricting chain motion. Thus, percent crystallinity can have a significant effect on the mechanical properties of a polymer. An increase in molecular weight will also strengthen a polymer, since physical entanglements between larger chains will inhibit chain movement (Fig. 4.18). Finally, covalent linkages, such as those formed during crosslinking, will also prevent chain movement and increase the strength and brittleness of the polymer.

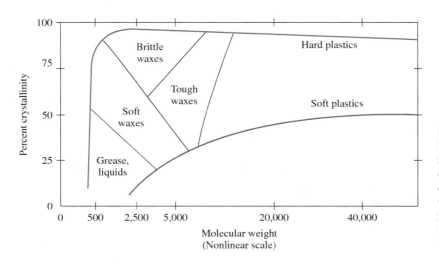

**Figure 4.18**
Effect of crystallinity and molecular weight on properties of polymers. As the crystallinity and molecular weight increase, the same material can be found in liquid, wax, or stiff solid form [6].

## EXAMPLE PROBLEM 4.5

An extrusion technique was employed to fabricate a square polymer sample 4 cm × 4 cm × 0.5 cm. The extrusion process has resulted in the vast majority of the polymer chains being aligned preferentially in one direction as shown. In which direction, then, should a tensile force be applied to the sample to result in the greatest resistance to the applied force? Why?

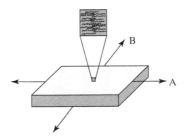

**Solution:** The tensile force should be applied along the direction indicated by arrow "A" as this direction is parallel to the axis of orientation of the majority of the polymer chains in the material, as illustrated. Although secondary forces may exist between the polymer chains, the strongest forces in the material are found in the covalent bonds along the backbones of the polymer chains. In this case, the majority of the polymer chains are oriented along one axis; thus, the greatest resistance to force would occur along this axis. The resistance to force in the direction of arrow "B" would stem primarily from chain entanglements and any secondary forces that might be present between the polymer chains. These forces are much weaker than the covalent bonds found in the polymer chains themselves. ∎

As depicted in Material IV in Figure 4.5, elastomers are unique in that they allow large elastic deformation at low stresses, due to their distinctive chain structure. Elastomers are amorphous materials in their unstressed state, composed of coiled chains with nearly-free bond rotations around the backbone, as shown in Figure 4.19. The chains are crosslinked at given points to prevent chains from slipping past each other, which would result in plastic deformation of the material.

An example of an elastomer found in the human body is **elastin**, which confers resiliency and extensibility to many tissues (see Chapter 9 for more

**Figure 4.19**
Diagram of elastin, a type of elastomer, showing its relaxed and stressed states. Elastomers are amorphous materials in their unstressed state, composed of coiled chains with nearly free bond rotations around the backbone. Tensile forces cause the individual elastin molecules to unfold and align in the direction of loading. The network is held together by the crosslinks between the elastin molecules. If the applied stress is removed, the elastin will return to its unstretched state due to thermodynamic considerations.

information on elastin). Elastin is a particularly important constituent of tissues that must undergo many stretch-relaxation cycles, such as the air sacs in the lungs. Like other elastomers, elastin fibers exist as crosslinked coiled protein chains.

When elastomers are above their $T_g$, a tensile force applied to the sample will cause the uncoiling of the chains and their alignment along the axis of tension, as seen in Figure 4.19. The driving force for the elastomer to return to its prestressed state after the removal of the tensile force is thermodynamic. The entropy of the system is greater in the amorphous than in the ordered state that occurs after tension. Since greater disorder is favored, entropic concerns cause the material to return to its original state. Elastomers can be modeled as little springs that obey Hooke's law. This model and its uses will be explained further in the next section.

## 4.2.2 Bending Properties

The stress-strain behavior of materials can also be determined through bending tests. While these tests can be performed on a variety of materials, they are usually used on ceramics, due to the inherent brittleness of the material (simply clamping a ceramic specimen can lead to fracture; hence, it is a difficult material to test under tension).

Bending tests can be performed on specimens having rectangular or circular cross-sections, as shown in Figure 4.20. The sample can be subjected to three-point (seen in figure) or four-point bending. A disadvantage of bending tests is that the magnitude and type of stress is not constant across the sample. For the experiment shown in the figure, the top of the specimen experiences compressive forces, while the bottom experiences tensile forces. This makes calculation of the stress on the sample complicated—sample thickness, bending moment (M), and moment of inertia (I) of the cross-section must all be taken into account. Important parameters are illustrated in the figure.

One of the main parameters determined from this type of testing is the **modulus of rupture** ($\sigma_{mr}$) (also known as flexural strength), or the stress required to fracture a sample (note that this is not the same as the modulus of elasticity). For specimens having a rectangular cross-section, this is calculated via the relationship

$$\sigma_{mr} = \frac{3F_f L}{2bd^2} \tag{4.24}$$

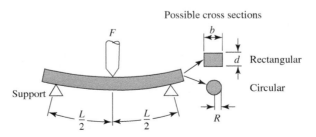

Possible cross sections

**Figure 4.20**
Schematic of a three-point bending test. If the applied load $F$ causes fracture of the specimen, then the modulus of rupture can be calculated. This test can be carried out with either rectangular or cylindrical specimens (see inset of cross-sections) [3].

where $F_f$ is the load at fracture, $L$ is the distance between the supports and $b$ and $d$ are the specimen dimensions as depicted in Figure 4.20. For samples having a circular cross-section, the equation becomes

$$\sigma_{mr} = \frac{3F_f L}{\pi R^3} \qquad (4.25)$$

where $R$ is the radius of the sample.

Stress-strain curves similar to those resulting from tensile tests can be produced from bending data. Since there is little plastic deformation of these materials, there exists a linear relationship between stress and strain until sample fracture. As with tensile testing, the slope of this curve is the modulus of elasticity.

## EXAMPLE PROBLEM 4.6

The following is a stress-strain curve resulting from a three-point bending test on an alumina (ceramic) test sample:

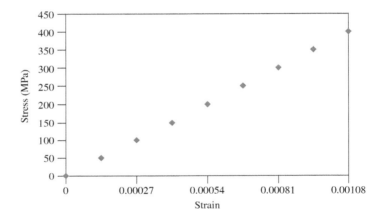

(a) Calculate the modulus of elasticity of the alumina sample.
(b) Using this information, what is the modulus of rupture?
(c) The sample is a cylindrical specimen with a radius of 1 cm and a distance of 10 cm between the lower supports. What force was necessary to cause this fracture?
(d) Given the following diagram of the three-point bending test of a rectangular sample, which portion of the sample is in compression and which portion is in tension?

Solution:

(a)  The modulus of elasticity can be determined from the slope of the linear portion of the stress-strain curve:

$$E = \frac{\Delta \sigma}{\Delta \varepsilon} = \frac{400 - 0 \text{ MPa}}{0.00108 - 0} = \underline{370 \text{ GPa}}$$

(b)  The modulus of rupture is the stress at the point of fracture, around 400 MPa.

(c)  Solve equation 4.25 for $F_f$ and determine the force at fracture:

$$F_f = \frac{\sigma_{mr} \pi R^3}{3L} = \frac{400000 \pi 0.01^3}{3 \times 0.1} \approx \underline{4.2\text{N}}$$

(d)  The portion of the sample at the top facing the indenting attachment is in compression, while the portion of the sample at the bottom facing the two supporting points is in tension under the load.   ■

## 4.2.3 Time-Dependent Properties

Traditional mechanical tests like those described before do not provide a full picture of the stress-strain behavior of materials, since they measure response to loading over a relatively short time. However, some materials experience changes at the molecular level that result in alterations in mechanical properties when loaded for longer times. Two of these time-dependent properties, creep and stress relaxation, are described in the following sections.

### 4.2.3.1 Creep
**Creep** can be defined as plastic deformation of a sample under constant load over time. Creep can be observed in all materials, but it is usually only a concern at temperatures greater than $0.4T_m$ ($T_m$ = absolute melting temperature) for metals and even higher temperatures for ceramics. In contrast, creep can occur at or around room temperature for some polymer systems.

Creep tests are performed by exerting a constant (usually tensile) load on the specimen while maintaining the system at a fixed temperature. The resulting strain is recorded as a function of time. A typical creep curve for metal and ceramic materials is found in Figure 4.21.

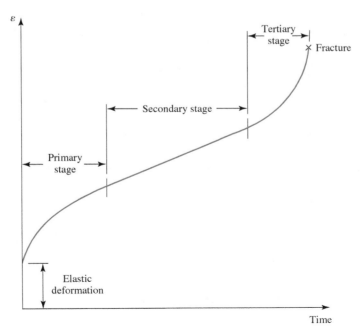

**Figure 4.21**

A typical creep curve for a metal or ceramic material. The strain observed by the sample varies as a function of time. This curve can be divided into three distinct regions. After the initial deformation, the first stage, primary creep, is characterized by an increase in strain with time, while the creep rate (slope of curve) decreases. As the load continues, an equilibrium is established within the material substructure and secondary creep is achieved. In this area, there is a linear relationship between creep strain and time. Finally, tertiary creep rapidly leads to failure [4].

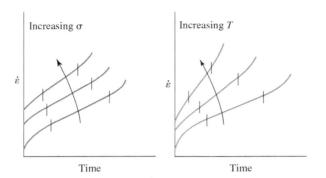

**Figure 4.22**
Effect of stress and temperature on creep response. Steady state creep rate ($\dot{\varepsilon}$) increases with increasing stress and increasing temperature [7].

This curve can be divided into three distinct regions. After the initial deformation, the first stage, **primary creep**, is characterized by an increase in strain with time, while the creep rate (the slope of the curve) decreases. This is due to repositioning of aspects of the material, such as dislocations, in response to loading. As the load continues, an equilibrium is established within the material substructure and a minimum creep rate is attained. This is **secondary creep**, and in this area, there is a linear relationship between creep strain and time. Secondary creep usually lasts for the longest period. Finally, **tertiary creep** leads to failure. In this stage, gross defects appear inside the material, such as grain boundary separation, cracks, or voids. Here, elongation proceeds rapidly until material failure.

Important parameters obtained from creep testing are the **steady state creep rate**, $\dot{\varepsilon}$, and the time to rupture ($t_r$). $\dot{\varepsilon}$ is calculated by taking the slope of the creep curve in the secondary stage. However, because both the applied stress and the testing temperature have a large effect on a material's creep response, these parameters must be specified for each value of $\dot{\varepsilon}$ and $t_r$. As seen in Figure 4.22, $\dot{\varepsilon}$ increases with increasing stress and increasing temperature. In contrast, $t_r$ decreases at higher temperatures or stresses.

Creep curves for polymers, like those shown in Figure 4.23, are similar to those for metals and ceramics, but with less distinct stages of creep deformation. This figure

**Figure 4.23**
A typical creep curve for a porous polymeric material (poly(lactic-*co*-glycolic acid), PLGA 50:50) under applied stress of 9.5 kPa. (In this case, strain is negative because the load applied was compressive, rather than tensile, but the continual change in length with time still occurs.) Creep curves for polymers are similar to those for metals and ceramics, but with less distinct stages of creep deformation. Creep in polymeric materials can be a concern even at relatively low temperatures and stresses [8].

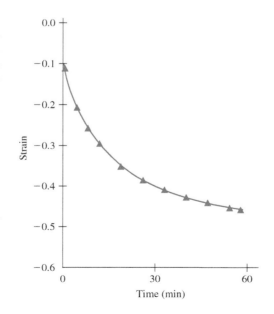

also demonstrates that creep in polymeric materials can be a concern even at relatively low temperatures and stresses. The possibility of creep at body temperature is extremely important to recall when designing polymeric implants that must maintain specific dimensions in order to function. For example, one of the reasons for failure of previous polymer-based ligament replacements over years in the body is creep of the material, which leads to the inability of the device to maintain the joint in its proper position.

### 4.2.3.2  Molecular Causes of Creep—Metals

On an atomic scale, creep is caused by a variety of mechanisms, depending on the material type. In metals, creep can be a result of grain boundaries sliding relative to one another, or migration of vacancies. Vacancy migration is promoted at high temperatures due to greater atomic diffusion with increasing temperature (see Chapter 2). In particular, there are two main creep mechanisms involving vacancy migration: stress-induced vacancy diffusion and dislocation climb.

**Stress-induced vacancy diffusion** is depicted in Figure 4.24. As a result of loading, extra vacancies are produced on the faces of the grains perpendicular to the applied stress (AB and CD), and these have a tendency to migrate to the faces parallel to the stress axis (AC and BD). As with all vacancy diffusion, atomic diffusion is in the opposite direction, resulting in an elongation of the grain along the line of applied stress. This type of stress-induced vacancy diffusion is called **Nabarro-Herring creep**. If the vacancies migrate along the grain boundaries rather than through the bulk of the grain, this is termed **Coble creep**.

As the name implies, in **dislocation climb** a dislocation moves (climbs) one atomic spacing by diffusion of an entire row of vacancies to the extra partial plane of atoms found in an edge dislocation. Atomic movement is opposite to this, as shown in Figure 4.25.

### 4.2.3.3  Molecular Causes of Creep—Ceramics

Creep mechanisms for ceramics are similar to those in metals, but ceramics are more resistant to creep deformation for a variety of reasons. Ion and vacancy diffusion are more difficult in

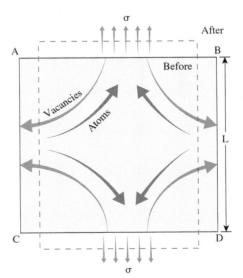

**Figure 4.24**

A schematic of stress-induced vacancy diffusion. As a result of loading, extra vacancies are produced on the faces of the grains perpendicular to the applied stress (AB and CD), and these have a tendency to migrate to the faces parallel to the stress axis (AC and BD). As with all vacancy diffusion, atomic diffusion is in the opposite direction, resulting in an elongation of the grain along the line of applied stress. The parameter $L$ is the original length of the grain and $\sigma$ is the applied stress.

**Figure 4.25**
A diagram of dislocation climb (end-on view). In this scenario, a dislocation moves (climbs) one atomic spacing by diffusion of an entire row of vacancies to the extra partial plane of atoms found in an edge dislocation.

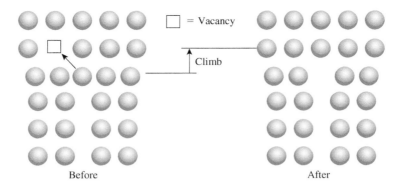

ceramics because of the need to maintain electroneutrality of the material, and the difference in diffusivities between cations and anions. In addition, there are generally fewer point defects in ceramics as compared to metals. With these constraints, grain boundary sliding is a main means for microstructural rearrangement and creep deformation in this class of biomaterials.

**4.2.3.4   Molecular Causes of Creep—Polymers**   Creep deformation in semi-crystalline and amorphous polymers depends on movement of chains in the amorphous regions via viscous flow. Therefore, the percent crystallinity and whether testing occurs above or below the polymer's $T_g$ have a large influence on the creep properties observed. Susceptibility to creep decreases as the crystallinity of the polymer increases since there is a smaller fraction of amorphous areas in more highly crystalline samples. Below $T_g$, the chains in the amorphous regions are not able to rotate or slide and no time-dependent deformation is observed. At these temperatures, generally only elastic deformation is recorded up to the point of fracture. On the other hand, above $T_g$, the polymer chains can move past each other, so time-dependent properties indicative of viscous flow (creep and stress relaxation) can be seen.

**4.2.3.5   Stress Relaxation and its Causes**   A related time-dependent mechanical property is termed **stress relaxation**. While creep involves plastic deformation of a sample under constant load over time, stress relaxation is the decrease in stress seen over time under constant strain, and is most often found in polymeric materials. Creep and stress relaxation behavior are depicted graphically in Figure 4.26.

**Figure 4.26**
(a) The creep response of a polymeric material, which involves plastic deformation (increased strain) of a sample under constant load over time. (b) Stress relaxation response in a polymeric material, where a decrease in stress is seen over time under constant strain. $I$ represents the input on the sample and $R$ indicates the response of the material [9].

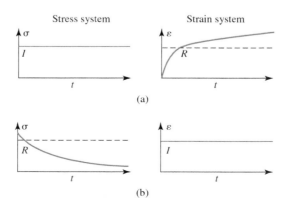

A common example of stress relaxation is provided by a rubber band binding a stack of items for a period of time. As time progresses, the rubber band relaxes and no longer tightly binds the stack.

Stress relaxation experiments are conducted in a similar manner to creep experiments. However, in this case, the specimen is loaded with sufficient stress to produce a small strain. The changes in stress needed to maintain a constant strain are then monitored as a function of time as the system is maintained at a constant temperature.

The molecular causes for stress relaxation involve movement of chains in the amorphous regions of the polymer, as for creep. Therefore, the percent crystallinity and testing temperature relative to the $T_g$ of the polymer also affect stress relaxation behavior. Like creep, stress relaxation behavior is observed only at temperatures above $T_g$, where viscous flow of the polymer chains is possible.

**4.2.3.6 Mathematical Models of Viscoelastic Behavior** At temperatures below $T_g$, polymers behave mainly as elastic solids, and at temperatures above $T_m$, they are viscous liquids. However, at temperatures between $T_g$ and $T_m$, polymeric materials exhibit both viscous and elastic properties, and thus are considered to be **viscoelastic**. Figure 4.27 depicts the difference in responses between the three types of materials. For the applied step load shown in Figure 4.27(a), the strain in the entirely elastic material occurs instantaneously and remains constant (Fig. 4.27(b)), while the strain in the entirely viscous material increases linearly with time (Fig. 4.27(d)). The viscoelastic material demonstrates intermediate properties—an instantaneous strain occurs, but it is followed by further deformation, the magnitude of which is time-dependent (Fig. 4.27(c)). Thus, the nature of viscoelastic materials leads to the demonstration of time-dependent mechanical properties such as creep and stress relaxation, described in the preceding section.

A common example of a viscoelastic substance is a silicone-based polymer known by the brand name as Silly Putty.® If one forms this material into a ball and throws it, it will bounce (behave elastically). However, one can also pull it slowly and it will elongate/flow like a viscous liquid. As with other viscoelastic materials, the rate of strain in Silly Putty determines how it behaves. At high rates of deformation (strain), such as during bouncing, the elastic component of the response dominates. At slower deformation rates, the viscous portion dominates.

**Figure 4.27**
A schematic of the response of different materials to a step load. The parameter $t_a$ indicates when the step load is applied and $t_r$ indicates when the load is released. (a) The applied step load. (b) The strain seen in an entirely elastic material, which is instantaneous and remains constant. (c) The strain seen in a viscoelastic material, which demonstrates intermediate properties—an instantaneous strain occurs, but it is followed by further deformation, the magnitude of which is time-dependent. (d) The strain seen in an entirely viscous material, which increases linearly with time [1].

**Figure 4.28**
Schematic of the Maxwell model, which consists of a spring and dashpot in series. (A dashpot can be likened to a shock absorber in a car, which contains a damping fluid and thus has a similar time-dependent response). $E$ represents the elastic modulus of the elastic portion of the response, while $\eta$ represents the viscosity of the viscous portion of the response [9].

To more fully explore viscoelastic responses such as creep and stress relaxation, a number of models have been developed. The following discussion is based on that of [1]. For an idealized model, it is assumed that the elastic component of the response obeys Hooke's law. It is modeled with a mechanical analog, a **spring**, whose deformation follows the equation

$$\sigma = E\varepsilon \tag{4.26}$$

or, in differential form,

$$\frac{d\sigma}{dt} = E\frac{d\varepsilon}{dt} \tag{4.27}$$

Similarly, the viscous portion of the response is assumed to follow Newton's law and its mechanical model is a **dashpot** (Fig. 4.28). (A dashpot can be likened to a shock absorber in a car, which contains a damping fluid and thus has a similar time-dependent response.) For these simplified models, no distinction is made between shear stress and strain and tensile/compressive stress and strain. Instead, it is the nature of the relationship between the stress and strain that is of most importance. Therefore, for ease of notation, Newton's law can be rewritten as

$$\tau = \eta\frac{d\gamma}{dt} = \sigma = \eta\frac{d\varepsilon}{dt} \tag{4.28}$$

There are many different ways to combine these elements to model viscoelastic behavior. Complicated models involving multiple springs and dashpots have been derived, but we will focus in this section on two simple models: the Maxwell model and the Voigt model.

### 4.2.3.7 Viscoelastic Behavior—Maxwell Model

The **Maxwell model** proposes a spring and dashpot in series, as shown in Figure 4.28. When a stress $\sigma$ is applied, there will be a resulting strain $\varepsilon$ in the system that is the addition of the strain in each of the components; that is,

$$\varepsilon = \varepsilon_1 + \varepsilon_2 \tag{4.29}$$

where $\varepsilon_1$ is the strain in the spring and $\varepsilon_2$ is the strain in the dashpot. Because the components are in series, the stress will be equal in each:

$$\sigma_1 = \sigma_2 = \sigma \tag{4.30}$$

Equations 4.27 and 4.28 can then be rewritten as

$$\frac{d\sigma}{dt} = E\frac{d\varepsilon_1}{dt} \tag{4.31}$$

$$\sigma = \eta\frac{d\varepsilon_2}{dt} \tag{4.32}$$

for the spring and dashpot. Equation 4.29 can be differentiated to give

$$\frac{d\varepsilon}{dt} = \frac{d\varepsilon_1}{dt} + \frac{d\varepsilon_2}{dt} \tag{4.33}$$

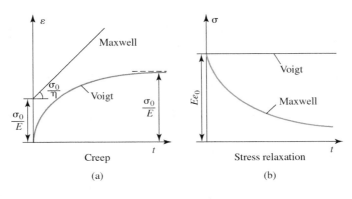

**Figure 4.29**
The responses predicted by the Maxwell model and the Voigt model for both (a) creep and (b) stress relaxation [9].

Substitution of the expressions for $d\varepsilon_1/dt$ and $d\varepsilon_2/dt$ results in

$$\frac{d\varepsilon}{dt} = \frac{1}{E}\frac{d\sigma}{dt} + \frac{\sigma}{\eta} \qquad (4.34)$$

The validity of this model in predicting behavior of polymers can be examined by applying it to creep and stress relaxation situations. During creep, the stress is held constant at $\sigma_0$ and, thus, $d\sigma/dt = 0$. The previous equation can then be written as

$$\frac{d\varepsilon}{dt} = \frac{\sigma_0}{\eta} \qquad (4.35)$$

This equation shows that the Maxwell model predicts Newtonian flow during creep, and the strain would then be expected to increase linearly with time. This is obviously not what occurs (Fig. 4.26(a)), so this model has minimal predictive value for creep conditions.

However, during stress relaxation, a constant strain is maintained $\varepsilon = \varepsilon_0$ and, therefore, $d\varepsilon/dt = 0$. In this case, the equation becomes

$$0 = \frac{1}{E}\frac{d\sigma}{dt} + \frac{\sigma}{\eta} \qquad (4.36)$$

or

$$\frac{d\sigma}{\sigma} = -\frac{E}{\eta}dt \qquad (4.37)$$

Assuming that at $t = 0$, $\sigma = \sigma_0$, this expression can be integrated to give

$$\sigma = \sigma_0 e^{\frac{-Et}{\eta}} \qquad (4.38)$$

so, an exponential decrease in stress is expected over time, as is observed in polymers during stress relaxation (Fig. 4.26(b)). The responses predicted by the Maxwell model for both creep and stress relaxation are depicted in Figure 4.29.

### 4.2.3.8 Viscoelastic Behavior—Voigt Model

The **Voigt** (or Kelvin) **model** uses the same components as the Maxwell model, but in a different order. As seen in Figure 4.30, in this system, the elements are in parallel. In contrast to the previous

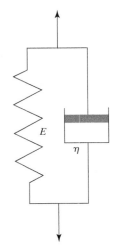

**Figure 4.30**
Schematic of the Voigt model, which consists of a spring and dashpot in parallel. $E$ represents the elastic modulus of the elastic portion of the response, while $\eta$ represents the viscosity of the viscous portion of the response [9].

model, this means that the strains are equal between the elements, but the stresses are additive:

$$\varepsilon = \varepsilon_1 = \varepsilon_2 \tag{4.39}$$

$$\sigma = \sigma_1 + \sigma_2 \tag{4.40}$$

Here, again, the subscript 1 designates the spring and the subscript 2 refers to the dashpot. From equations 4.26 and 4.27, expressions for the stresses $\sigma_1$ and $\sigma_2$ can be obtained:

$$\sigma_1 = E\varepsilon \tag{4.41}$$

and

$$\sigma_2 = \eta \frac{d\varepsilon}{dt} \tag{4.42}$$

These can be placed into equation 4.40 to yield

$$\sigma = E\varepsilon + \eta \frac{d\varepsilon}{dt} \tag{4.43}$$

or

$$\frac{d\varepsilon}{dt} = \frac{\sigma}{\eta} - \frac{E\varepsilon}{\eta} \tag{4.44}$$

As with the Maxwell model, the validity of the Voigt model can be examined for both creep and stress relaxation phenomena. During creep, $\sigma = \sigma_0$ and equation 4.44 becomes

$$\frac{d\varepsilon}{dt} = \frac{\sigma_0}{\eta} - \frac{E\varepsilon}{\eta} \tag{4.45}$$

The solution to this equation is

$$\varepsilon = \frac{\sigma_0}{E}\left(1 - e^{\frac{-Et}{\eta}}\right) \tag{4.46}$$

which shows an exponential increase in strain over time, as is observed during creep experiments. The predicted response is shown in Figure 4.29.

However, this model does not hold for stress relaxation conditions. When the strain is held constant at $\varepsilon_0$ and $d\varepsilon/dt = 0$, equation 4.45 becomes

$$\frac{\sigma}{\eta} = \frac{E\varepsilon_0}{\eta} \tag{4.47}$$

or

$$\sigma = E\varepsilon_0 \tag{4.48}$$

This is Hooke's law, so in this case, the Voigt model does not take into account the viscous portion of the response (Fig. 4.29) and thus is not useful for predicting polymer behavior under these conditions.

From this discussion, it is clear that the Maxwell system can provide a simple model of polymeric stress relaxation behavior, while the Voigt model can be employed for creep conditions. In this vein, several combinations of these models have been developed to simultaneously predict creep and stress relaxation behavior. A simple combination called the **standard linear solid model** is shown in Figure 4.31. It should be noted that, regardless of the complexity of the model, spring-dashpot systems can be used to describe the general behavior of a polymer, but do not provide information about the molecular causes for the time-dependent phenomena observed.

## EXAMPLE PROBLEM 4.7

Consider the standard linear solid model illustrated in Figure 4.31. Derive the differential equation for this model and use this equation to explore (a) the case of stress relaxation and (b) the case of creep for this system.

Solution:

$$E_1 = \sigma_1/\varepsilon_1$$

$$E_2 = \sigma_2/\varepsilon_2$$

$$\eta = \sigma_\eta/(d\varepsilon_\eta/dt)$$

$$\varepsilon_1 = \varepsilon_2 + \varepsilon_\eta = \varepsilon \rightarrow \varepsilon = \varepsilon_1 \text{ and } d\varepsilon/dt = d\varepsilon_1/dt$$

$$d\varepsilon_1/dt = d\varepsilon_2/dt + d\varepsilon_\eta/dt = d\varepsilon/dt$$

$$\sigma_2 = \sigma_\eta$$

$$\sigma = \sigma_2 + \sigma_1 = \sigma_\eta + \sigma_1$$

$$d\sigma/dt = d\sigma_2/dt + d\sigma_1/dt = d\sigma_\eta/dt + d\sigma_1/dt$$

$$d\varepsilon/dt = \sigma_\eta/\eta + [d\sigma_2/dt]/E_2$$

$$\sigma_\eta = [d\varepsilon/dt - [d\sigma_2/dt]/E_2]\eta$$

$$d\sigma_2/dt = d\sigma/dt - d\sigma_1/dt$$

$$\sigma_1 = E_1\varepsilon_1 = E_1\varepsilon$$

$$d\sigma_1/dt = E_1 d\varepsilon_1/dt = E_1 d\varepsilon/dt$$

$$\rightarrow \sigma_\eta = [d\varepsilon/dt - (d\sigma/dt - E_1 d\varepsilon/dt)/E_2]\eta$$

$$\sigma_{E1} = E_1\varepsilon_1$$

$$\rightarrow \sigma = [d\varepsilon/dt - (d\sigma/dt - E_1 d\varepsilon/dt)/E_2]\eta + E_1\varepsilon$$

$$\sigma/\eta = d\varepsilon/dt - (d\sigma/dt - E_1 d\varepsilon/dt)/E_2 + E_1\varepsilon/\eta$$

$$\sigma(E_2/\eta) = E_2 d\varepsilon/dt - d\sigma/dt + E_1 d\varepsilon/dt + (E_1 E_2/\eta)\varepsilon$$

$$\rightarrow \underline{d\sigma/dt + \sigma(E_2/\eta) = d\varepsilon/dt(E_1 + E_2) + \varepsilon(E_1 E_2/\eta)}$$

For the case of stress relaxation, $\varepsilon = \varepsilon_0$ and $d\varepsilon/dt = 0$.
Plugging these conditions into the previous differential equation yields

$$d\sigma/dt + \sigma(E_2/\eta) = \varepsilon_0(E_1 E_2/\eta)$$

$$d\sigma/dt = \varepsilon_0(E_1 E_2/\eta) - (E_2/\eta)\sigma$$

**Figure 4.31**
Schematic of the standard linear solid model, which is a combination of the Maxwell and Voigt models. $E$ represents the elastic modulus of the elastic portion of the response, while $\eta$ represents the viscosity of the viscous portion of the response [9].

$$d\sigma/dt = (1/\eta)[E_1 E_2 \varepsilon_0 - E_2 \sigma]$$

$$[d\sigma/dt]/[E_2\sigma - E_1 E_2 \varepsilon_0] = -(1/\eta)$$

$$d/dt(\ln|\sigma E_2 - E_1 E_2 \varepsilon_0|) = -E_2/\eta$$

$$\ln|\sigma E_2 - E_1 E_2 \varepsilon_0| = (-E_2/\eta)t + C, \text{ where } C \text{ is a constant}$$

$$|\sigma E_2 - E_1 E_2 \varepsilon_0| = e^C \exp[(-E_2/\eta)t]$$

$$\sigma E_2 = E_1 E_2 \varepsilon_0 + k \exp[(-E_2/\eta)t], \text{ where } k \text{ is a constant}$$

$$\underline{\sigma(t) = E_1 \varepsilon_0 + K \exp[(-E_2/\eta)t], \text{ where } K \text{ is a real constant greater than zero.}}$$

For the case of creep, $\sigma = \sigma_0$ and $d\sigma/dt = 0$.
Plugging these conditions into the differential previous equation gives

$$d\sigma/dt = -\sigma_0(E_2/\eta) + d\varepsilon/dt(E_1 + E_2) + \varepsilon(E_1 E_2/\eta) = 0$$

$$d\varepsilon/dt(E_1 + E_2) + \varepsilon(E_1 E_2/\eta) = \sigma_0(E_2/\eta)$$

$$d\varepsilon/dt + [E_1 E_2 \varepsilon]/[\eta(E_1 + E_2)] = \sigma_0 E_2/[\eta(E_1 + E_2)]$$

$$d\varepsilon/dt = -[E_1 E_2 \varepsilon]/[\eta(E_1 + E_2)] + \sigma_0 E_2/[\eta(E_1 + E_2)$$

$$(d\varepsilon/dt)/[E_1 E_2 \varepsilon - \sigma_0 E_2] = -1/[\eta(E_1 + E_2)]$$

$$d/dt(\ln|E_1 E_2 \varepsilon - \sigma_0 E_2|) = -(E_1 E_2)/[\eta(E_1 + E_2)]$$

$$\ln|E_1 E_2 \varepsilon - \sigma_0 E_2| = -(E_1 E_2)/[\eta(E_1 + E_2)]t + C, \text{ where } C \text{ is a constant}$$

$$|E_1 E_2 \varepsilon - \sigma_0 E_2| = e^C \exp[-(E_1 E_2)t/[\eta(E_1 + E_2)]]$$

$$\varepsilon E_1 E_2 = \sigma_0 E_2 + k \exp[-(E_1 E_2)t/[\eta(E_1 + E_2)]], \text{ where } k \text{ is a constant}$$

$$\varepsilon = \sigma_0/E_1 + k \exp[-(E_1 E_2)t/[\eta(E_1 + E_2)]]$$

$$\underline{\varepsilon(t) = \sigma_0/E_1 + K \exp[-(E_1 E_2)t/[\eta(E_1 + E_2)]], \text{ where } K \text{ is a real constant}}$$
$$\underline{\text{greater than zero.}} \qquad \blacksquare$$

### 4.2.4 Influence of Porosity and Degradation on Mechanical Properties

As discussed in Chapter 3, pores can be created in a biomaterial in a controlled manner through the addition of porogens. Alternatively, they may be an unwanted by-product of material processing in which gas was trapped in the sample, or in which incomplete sintering occurred (metals and ceramics only, see Chapter 6). No matter what their origin, the presence of pores will decrease the elastic modulus and the strength of a biomaterial. Fracture strength is reduced with the addition of pores for two main reasons. Pores decrease the cross-sectional area across which the sample is loaded. In addition, they act as stress concentrators (see Section 4.3.3) and can increase significantly the stress applied to localized areas of the sample.

The use of biodegradable materials for implants is particularly challenging, since their mechanical properties vary with time. For example, poly(glycolic acid) of 50% crystallinity, used as a biodegradable suture, loses most of its mechanical strength after two to four weeks of degradation (Fig. 4.32) [2]. Many parameters, including

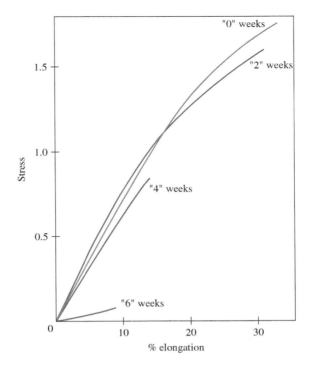

**Figure 4.32**
Change in mechanical properties of poly(glycolic acid) of 50% crystallinity with time. Degradation of the polymer over two to four weeks results in a loss of the majority of its mechanical strength [2].

chemical structure and the presence of pores, can affect the degradation rate (this is discussed further in Chapter 5). These must be taken into account when designing a tissue engineering scaffold so that it maintains sufficient mechanical properties until enough tissue has been generated to take over the function of the scaffold. Thus, the timing of degradation and the concomitant decrease in mechanical properties is a crucial design parameter for biodegradable implants.

## 4.3 Fracture and Failure

### 4.3.1 Ductile and Brittle Fracture

If either time-dependent or time-independent deformation is continued, eventually the material will fracture. If the material undergoes plastic deformation before breaking, it experiences **ductile fracture**. If there is little plastic deformation, the material demonstrates **brittle fracture**. For simplicity, in the following section we will focus on fracture that occurs during tensile testing only.

Ductile failure is characterized by plastic deformation in the area of the crack, as demonstrated by the cone-shaped appearance of the fractured specimen in Figure 4.33. Crack propagation occurs fairly slowly, and the crack is considered to be **stable**, since there is no further elongation unless additional stress is applied. Ductile fracture is the preferred mode of failure, since there is warning available in the form of change in shape of the specimen during plastic deformation. This is particularly important in biomedical applications, where sudden failure of certain devices, such as replacement heart valves, could lead to immediate death. In addition, generally more strain energy is needed to cause ductile than brittle fracture. Metals and some types of polymers exhibit ductile fracture.

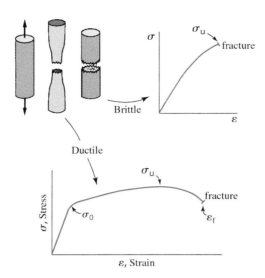

**Figure 4.33**
Ductile failure in a metallic material, is characterized by plastic deformation in the area of the crack, as demonstrated by the cone-shaped appearance at the fracture of the specimen. In contrast, brittle failure is characterized by a flat fracture surface and shows little plastic deformation before fracture. (Reprinted with permission from [10]).

On the other hand, in brittle fracture, there is little evidence of plastic deformation around the crack (Fig. 4.33). This type of fracture proceeds quickly with little warning and can lead to catastrophic failure. Brittle fracture is more common in ceramics than metals because there is usually less slip in ceramics. Certain types of polymers also demonstrate failure via this means.

Two standard testing mechanisms, the **Charpy and Izod impact tests,** have been developed to assess the fracture properties for various materials. Although the specifics of these tests are beyond the scope of this text, the general experimental apparatus is depicted in Figure 4.34 and is designed to measure impact energy as the hammer hits the sample. In particular, these experiments are used to determine the **ductile-to-brittle transition temperature.** This characteristic temperature, which is similar to the glass transition temperature in polymers, is the temperature below which the material fractures in a predominately brittle manner. This transition occurs in metals at a range of temperatures and ceramics only at temperatures greater than $1000°C$.

### 4.3.2 Polymer Crazing

As mentioned earlier, polymers can undergo ductile or brittle fracture, depending on their chemical composition and the temperature of the specimen. **Crazing** is another phenomenon that can be involved in the fracture of some amorphous thermoplastic polymers (polymers that can be cooled and heated repeatedly—see Section 6.6.1). Like cracks, crazes are initiated in regions near scratches or other flaws that are exposed to high levels of stress. Crazes are generally found perpendicular to the axis of tensile stress.

As a part of crazing, there are areas of localized yielding, which cause the formation of fibrils containing oriented polymer chains. Interconnected small void areas are also created. Unlike cracks, crazes can support a load, but the maximum before fracture is less than that for the noncrazed material. If the stress applied is great enough, the fibrillar structure will degrade and the voids will expand, leading to crack formation in the crazed area.

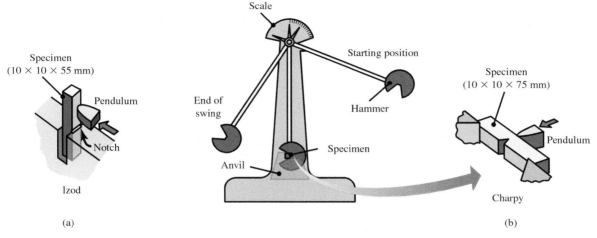

**Figure 4.34**
Charpy and Izod impact tests. Testing machine/setup is shown in the center of the figure. Although the specimen configuration varies between the Charpy and Izod tests (see a and b), in both cases, the testing hammer is raised to various heights until the height necessary for specimen fracture is determined, and the corresponding impact energy can be then read from the scale. (Reprinted by permission of Pearson Education, Inc., Fig 2.19 in Kalpakjian, S *et al*, in "*Manufacturing, Engineering and Technology*," 8th Ed, 2020.)

### 4.3.3 Stress Concentrators

As mentioned in the previous section, small flaws or cracks in a material can cause the formation of larger cracks or crazes in neighboring regions. This is because the applied stress can be amplified at the tip of the flaw. Figure 4.35 depicts an elliptical crack in the center of a material and Figure 4.36 shows the corresponding increase in stress at the edges of the crack. Farther away, the stress is reduced to a value equal to the overall applied stress ($\sigma_0$). Because these flaws cause a localized increase in stress, they are termed **stress concentrators** or **stress raisers**.

For an elliptical crack such as this, the following equation has been developed to estimate the maximum stress at the crack tip ($\sigma_m$):

$$\sigma_m = 2\sigma_0 \left( \frac{a}{\rho_t} \right)^{1/2} \tag{4.49}$$

In this equation, $\rho_t$ is the radius of curvature of the crack tip, and $a$ is the length of a crack on the surface or half the length of an internal crack (Fig. 4.35).

Other stress raisers include notches, sharp corners, and pores (discussed previously). Similar equations can be derived to determine the maximum stress experienced for each type of flaw. The presence of stress concentrators is more significant in brittle than ductile materials, since plastic deformation reduces the localized stress in the area around the flaw. The idea of stress raisers also helps explain why ceramics usually have higher fracture strengths in compression than in tension. Although stress-raising flaws occur in both cases, there is lower localized stress amplification in compression than tension, resulting in a higher applied stress ($\sigma_0$) required before failure for compression.

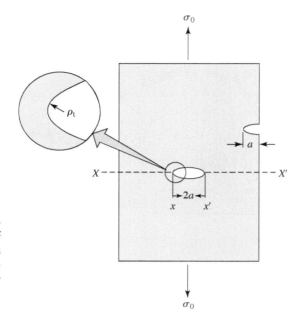

**Figure 4.35**
Schematic showing an elliptical crack in the center of a material. This crack is responsible for an effective local stress that is greater than $\sigma_0$ [1].

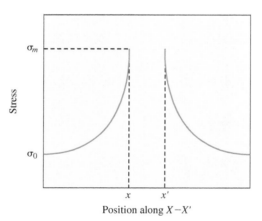

**Figure 4.36**
Diagram showing the increase in stress at the edge of the crack in Fig. 4.35. The parameter $\sigma_0$ is the overall applied stress on the material and $\sigma_m$ is the maximum stress, seen at the crack tip.

# 4.4   Fatigue and Fatigue Testing

## 4.4.1   Fatigue

Another mechanical property of extreme importance is how biomaterials behave under repeated loading as would occur in the use of many medical devices. Repeated loading can lead to failure at stresses significantly less than the tensile or yield strengths as determined by the static testing methods described previously. This type of failure, known as **fatigue fracture**, occurs suddenly after the material has been subjected to many cycles of altering stress or strain. Fatigue is the cause of up to 90% of metallic fractures, and both ceramics and polymers can also undergo this type of failure.

Fatigue fracture is brittle, with little plastic deformation around the fracture, even in ductile materials. Although loading can actually strengthen a crystalline (or semi-crystalline) material (see Chapter 6 for further discussion of this phenomenon, called strain hardening), repeated stress increases the number of dislocations and creates more and more imperfections in the crystal structure. These flaws then can act to nucleate cracks, which eventually lead to failure of the material. Fatigue failure occurs in three main stages:

1. Crack initiation—a small crack is created at an area of high stress.
2. Crack propagation—the crack increases in size with each successive loading cycle.
3. Final failure—occurs rapidly after the crack has reached a certain size.

Therefore, the fatigue life ($N_f$, see Section 4.4.2) of a material can be estimated as the number of cycles required for crack initiation ($N_i$) plus the number of cycles needed for propagation to the critical size for failure ($N_p$):

$$N_f = N_i + N_p \tag{4.50}$$

## 4.4.2  Fatigue Testing

Material fatigue testing is completed using a rotating-bending apparatus like that shown in Figure 4.37 or a uniaxial tension-compression machine, which employs a mechanical testing frame like that described at the end of this chapter. In this testing procedure, specimens are exposed to cycles of stress at relatively high stress values (usually two-thirds of the static tensile strength) and the number of cycles to failure is observed. Other specimens are subjected to lower levels of stress and the corresponding number of cycles is recorded for each set of samples. This allows the generation of stress ($S$) versus number of cycles to failure ($N$) plots. For such graphs, $S$ usually represents the **stress amplitude,** or the difference in the maximum ($\sigma_{max}$) and minimum ($\sigma_{min}$) applied stress divided by two:

$$S = \frac{\sigma_{max} - \sigma_{min}}{2} \tag{4.51}$$

Two typical S–N curves are shown in Figure 4.38. For some metals, including certain titanium alloys, below a certain stress level fatigue failure will not occur, regardless of the number of cycles the sample experiences. This stress value is called the **fatigue limit** or endurance limit, and the S–N graph becomes horizontal at this level (Fig. 4.38(a)).

In contrast, many alloys containing metals such as aluminum do not demonstrate a clear fatigue limit, but the curve continues downward with decreasing values of applied stress. These materials are instead characterized by their **fatigue strength,**

**Figure 4.37**
A rotating-bending apparatus used for material fatigue testing. In this example, both tensile and torsion forces are applied to the sample.

(a)

(b)

**Figure 4.38**
Two typical S–N curves seen in fatigue testing. (a) A material that demonstrates a fatigue limit (it will not fracture under a certain load, regardless of the number of cycles experienced). (b) A material that does not have a fatigue limit. From this information, the number of cycles necessary for fatigue fracture at a certain stress can be determined [1].

which is defined as the stress level that will cause failure after a given number of cycles. Figure 4.38(b) depicts the fatigue strength for $N_1$ cycles.

As mentioned earlier, **fatigue life** ($N_f$) is an important parameter for all types of materials. This is the number of cycles required to cause fatigue fracture at a specified stress (Fig. 4.38(b)), and it depends on the kinetics of crack propagation, as explained earlier.

### 4.4.3 Factors that Affect Fatigue Life

As with other types of failure, increased stress resulting from flaws in a biomaterial can act to nucleate cracks, which eventually result in fatigue fracture. Therefore, anything that acts to increase regional stresses can impact the fatigue life of the device. As seen from the S–N curves in Figure 4.38, one of these factors is the amplitude of the applied stress. With increasing stress, the number of cycles to failure decreases significantly.

Since in many cases the maximum stress occurs at the surface of a component, impurities in the surface region can also reduce fatigue life. Therefore, particular care should be taken to understand how surface treatments of biomaterials may affect the localized stress experienced in this region. In the same vein, the avoidance of other stress raisers, such as notches or sharp corners, in the design of the implant is encouraged in order to improve fatigue life. Biodegradable materials may be particularly susceptible to fatigue fracture at later time points due to a combined decrease in mechanical properties and potential production of flaws within the implant due to the degradation process.

In addition to internal parameters, the environment of the implant may affect its fatigue properties. As discussed in more detail in the next chapter, the body's tissues contain a number of active substances, including water, salts and proteins, that can react chemically with biomaterials. Failure that occurs because of the presence of cyclic stresses in combination with chemical attack is called **corrosion fatigue**, and this type of fracture is a serious concern for implants designed to remain in the body for long periods of time.

## 4.5   Methods to Improve Mechanical Properties

As discussed earlier in the chapter, metals, crystalline ceramics, and polymers undergo plastic deformation due to dislocation glide or slip. Therefore, to strengthen these materials, it is necessary to reduce the movement of dislocations. A detailed discussion of various methods to do this is reserved for Chapter 6. However, a brief overview is presented in this section, with particular emphasis on concepts described in this chapter.

Slip can be reduced in materials either by the inclusion of additives or through various processing techniques. Additives include metal alloys, since the impurity atoms can help to cancel the lattice strains that result from dislocations and thus "stabilize" the dislocation and prevent its movement. In polymers, **fillers** can be added. Fillers (usually particulates of ceramics or other polymers) increase strength by acting as additional entanglements or crosslinks and thus restricting chain motion. A popular class of fillers for mechanical reinforcement are the single-walled carbon nanotubes discussed in Chapter 2.

Processing can also affect the ease of dislocation motion in a sample. As mentioned previously, polycrystalline materials are generally stronger than those composed of only one crystal, in part because grain boundaries discourage dislocation movement. Materials with smaller grains have more grain boundaries per volume, and thus are usually stronger than materials with larger grains. In metals and ceramics, the cooling rate of the material (after it has been formed into a specific shape, for example) affects the grain size, with grain growth preferred at higher temperatures.

As in metals and ceramics, the cooling rate also influences the strength of polymeric materials. For polymers, crystalline regions have more interactions between adjacent chains and, thus, the higher percent crystallinity of a semi-crystalline polymer, the stronger it is expected to be. A plot of strength as a function of percent crystallinity of poly(ethylene) is found in Figure 4.39. In this case, the polymer chains must be allowed time to align to form crystalline structures, so very rapid cooling may result in a low percent crystallinity and reduce the overall strength of the material.

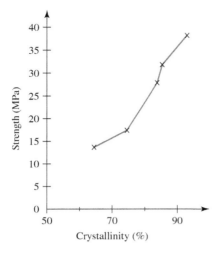

**Figure 4.39**
A plot of strength as related to percent crystallinity of poly(ethylene). Crystalline regions have more inter-actions between adjacent chains and, thus, the higher percent crystallinity of a semi-crystalline polymer, the stronger it is expected to be [11].

From these examples, it can be seen that the thermal history of a material can have a large impact on its mechanical properties. This is explored further in the discussion of processing of biomaterials found in Chapter 6.

## EXAMPLE PROBLEM 4.8

Assume that a pure and perfectly crystalline (no crystal defects or impurities) aluminum bar can be formed.

(a) Would more or less energy be required to break the perfect aluminum bar when compared with a real aluminum bar (containing defects and impurities), all other things being equal (dimensions, temperature, strain rate, etc.)?

(b) If one were to start with an aluminum bar with a sufficient number of defects such that an average person could bend it easily with their hands, would one expect the bar to become more or less difficult to bend as the number of bending cycles increases? Why?

(c) Would the slope of the elastic portion of the stress-strain curve be higher for the perfect aluminum bar or the real aluminum? Why?

Solution:

(a) A perfect aluminum bar would have no impurities or defects; thus, it would have a perfect crystal structure. Normally, impurities and defects are present in the metal, and the movement of these defects and impurities allows for material deformation without necessarily having to break bonds between the metal atoms. In this way, the macroscopic mechanical properties of metals are conferred by the defects present in the metal. However, in the case of a crystal with absolutely no defects, deformation of the material with applied force would break the atomic bonds in a plane of the crystal. Thus, a much higher energy would be required to break the perfect aluminum bar.

(b) Starting with an aluminum bar with a number of dislocations and defects just sufficient to allow for bending of the bar, the bar could initially bend quite easily as the defects and dislocations do not have many interactions. However, as the bar is bent, the dislocations move and additional edge and line defects are created. As the bending cycles continue, the movement of the bar becomes increasingly difficult, as the increasing defect interactions raise the energy barrier needed to continue to bend the bar. One can think of the work-hardening a blacksmith imparts upon a piece of metal while hot through repeated hammerings as an analogous example. With each stroke of the hammer, more defects and dislocations are created and the number of interaction between these defects increases, thereby increasing the hardness of the material.

(c) The slope of the elastic portion of the stress-strain curve would be the same for the perfect aluminum bar and the real aluminum bar because the slope reflects the strengths of interatomic bonds within the material. In this case, the atomic composition of both materials is the same; it is the absence or presence of defects that is different.  ■

# 4.6 Techniques: Introduction to Mechanical Analysis

The major piece of equipment for mechanical testing as described in this chapter is the mechanical testing frame shown in Figure 4.1. Although it was already described briefly, this method is treated in more depth here for comparison with characterization techniques discussed in other chapters. It should be noted that a common means of obtaining mechanical properties during oscillatory loading is **dynamic mechanical analysis (DMA)**, but a description of this method is beyond the scope of this text.

## 4.6.1 Mechanical Testing

**4.6.1.1 Basic Principles**  The testing frame is designed to subject a sample to uniaxial loading at a controlled amplitude and rate. This can occur once per sample, or can be repeated, as in fatigue testing. The shape of the sample is dictated by ASTM standards, taking into account the amount of material available and the form it will take in the final application. For tensile testing, a rod or film is often shaped into a "dog-bone" geometry, as shown in Figure 4.4. This effectively raises the stress in the portion with the smaller cross-section and causes a reproducible region of breakage in all samples. This geometry mitigates artifacts, such as specimen fracture near the gripping mechanisms due to stress raisers caused by the clamps. Mechanical tests are normally **destructive**—that is, the test continues until the specimen breaks.

**4.6.1.2 Instrumentation**  A typical plot produced from a mechanical testing experiment is found in Figure 4.5. Results are generally plotted as stress (y-axis) as a function of strain (x-axis). Equations to calculate stress and strain were presented earlier in this chapter (equations 4.1 and 4.2).

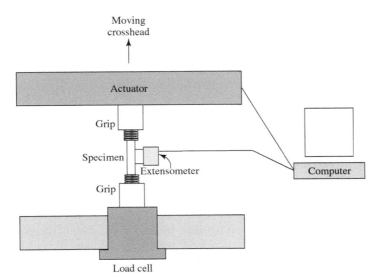

**Figure 4.40**
A block diagram of a mechanical testing apparatus [12].

The basic components to the mechanical testing apparatus, as shown in Figure 4.40 are as follows:

1. Grips/actuator—holds sample; through the movement of the grip attached to the actuator, load is applied along the axis of the sample.
2. Load cell—records instantaneous load on the sample and sends this information to the processor/computer.
3. Extensometer—records instantaneous length of the sample and sends this information to the processor/computer.
4. Processor (computer)—converts the electrical signals from the load cell and extensometer into a stress-strain plot.

During testing, the sample is placed in the mechanical testing frame and clamped tightly with the grips. As depicted in Figure 4.40, one of the grips is attached to a moveable platform (actuator), which moves at a constant speed, thus loading the specimen along the longitudinal axis. As the actuator moves, the load cell records the load on the sample, while another transducer, the extensometer, measures the change in length of the specimen. The computer then converts load-elongation information into a stress-strain curve.

**4.6.1.3 Information Provided**   Mechanical testing produces stress versus strain or stress/strain versus time curves for a variety of testing modes. The most common of these are tensile, compressive, bending, creep, and stress relaxation tests. From these curves, a number of characteristic values, such as modulus and yield and tensile strengths, can be calculated. As mentioned earlier, fatigue life and other parameters can be determined from uniaxial fatigue experiments performed on a mechanical testing frame. Mechanical testing is crucial to determine if a biomaterial will be suitable for a certain application, given the loading parameters of the tissue of interest.

## Summary

- The mechanical properties of a material can be characterized through mechanical testing in tension, compression, bending, shear, or torsion. During tensile testing, the load and specimen elongation are measured and can be normalized with respect to specimen geometry to give stress (force/area) and strain (length/length), respectively. Stress-strain curves can vary widely, depending upon the nature of the material tested.

- Elastic deformation of a sample occurs when, upon release of the load, the sample returns to its original shape. The linear portion of a stress-strain curve in which the curve obeys Hooke's law ($\sigma = E\varepsilon$) represents elastic deformation of the sample. The slope of this linear region is known as the modulus of elasticity (force/area) or Young's modulus of the material.

- Elastic deformation results from slight changes in atomic spacing and stretching of bonds. The stiffness of a material directly reflects the amount of energy required to move atoms in a material from their equilibrium positions. Thus, ceramics are generally stiffer than metals. The stiffness of polymers is typically directionally dependent.

- Plastic deformation is permanent deformation from which the sample cannot return to its original shape following loading. The stress corresponding to the end of the elastic region is called the yield stress, and the strain at this value is the yield point strain. Beyond the yield point, an increase in stress is required to continue plastic deformation until the ultimate tensile strength is met. After this point, further stress results in necking of the specimen and finally fracture.

- Metals and crystalline ceramics deform plastically through dislocation glide along a slip plane. Requirements of electroneutrality in ceramics limit the number of possible slip planes; thus, ceramics are typically brittle. Plastic deformation of polycrystalline materials occurs through deformation of individual grains rather than alternations or openings of grain boundaries.

- Plastic deformation of semi-crystalline polymers occurs through interactions between amorphous regions and lamellae in response to the load. First, tie chains extend and lamellae slide past one another. Then, the lamellae reorient so that the chain folds are aligned along the axis of loading and blocks of the crystalline phases separate from each other. Finally, the blocks and tie chains orient along the axis of applied force.

- Amorphous polymers and ceramics deform plastically by viscous flow, in which atoms slide past one another through the breaking and reforming of bonds. However, unlike deformation in crystalline materials, there is no prescribed direction of movement.

- Three- or four-point bending tests are often used with ceramic materials as an alternative to tensile testing to determine the modulus of rupture (stress at fracture).

- Some materials present time-dependent mechanical properties. Creep is one such property, in which the sample deforms plastically with time under constant load. Stress relaxation is another such property, in which the stress of a sample decreases with time under constant strain.

- Creep in metals can result from grain boundaries sliding relative to one another or from migration of vacancies. Although mechanisms of creep in ceramics are similar to those in metals, ceramics are generally more resistant to creep, due in part to the requirement of electroneutrality. Creep deformation in semi-crystalline and amorphous polymers depends upon the movement of chains in the amorphous regions of the material via viscous flow.

- A number of models have been developed to more fully explore viscoelastic responses of materials. The Maxwell model consists of a spring and dashpot in series and is typically appropriate for predicting stress-relaxation behavior. The Voigt model consists of a spring and dashpot in parallel and is typically appropriate for predicting creep behavior.

- Various modes of material fracture exist. If a material undergoes plastic deformation before it fractures, then it experiences ductile fracture. Fractures that involve little plastic deformation are called brittle fractures. Small flaws or cracks in a material that cause a localized increase in stress are called stress raisers. The presence of stress concentrators is more significant in brittle than ductile materials, since plastic deformation reduces the localized stress in the area around the flaw.

- Voids or pores in biomaterials, necessary for many tissue engineering applications, act as stress raisers and considerably weaken the overall material. In addition, degradation *in vivo* can decrease mechanical properties significantly and must be taken into account in the original implant design.

- Fatigue failure of a material occurs following repeated cycles of stress or strain. The repeated stresses of fatigue testing result in an increased number of imperfections and dislocations in the crystal structure of a material. These flaws can act to nucleate cracks, which can propagate and lead ultimately to the failure of the material. Any factor that acts to increase regional stresses can impact the fatigue life of the material.

- Various methods can be employed to improve the mechanical properties of materials, such as the inclusion of fillers in polymers to increase chain entanglements.
- Although a variety of mechanical testing modes are possible, a typical mechanical testing apparatus includes grips, an actuator, load cell, extensometer and a data processor.

## Problems

4.1 Prove when a cylindrical isotropic material has constant volume and undergoes a very small deformation, its Poisson's ratio ($\nu$) is equal to 0.5.

4.2 Assume the Young's modulus of poly(styrene) at 25°C is $4.9 \times 10^5$ Pa, and its Poisson's ratio is 0.35. Calculate its shear modulus.

4.3 Explain why polycrystalline materials are stronger than the same material made of a single crystal.

4.4 The mechanical properties of orthodontic wires are temperature dependent. Force-distance measurements were taken for a wire with a diameter of 1.3 mm at 25°C and 37°C.

(a) Graph the engineering stress-engineering strain diagrams for both temperatures. Label the elastic and plastic regions of each plot. Show all work.

| Length (mm) | Force (N) at 25°C | Force (N) at 37°C |
|---|---|---|
| 100 | 0 | 0 |
| 100.5 | 1.5 | 1.5 |
| 101 | 3 | 3 |
| 101.5 | 3.7 | 4.5 |
| 102 | 3.9 | 6 |
| 102.5 | 4 | 7.5 |
| 103 | 4.2 | 9 |
| 103.5 | 4.4 | 10.5 |
| 104 | 4.5 | 12 |
| 104.5 | 4.4 | 13.5 |
| 105 | 4.3 | 15 |
| 105.5 | 4.2 | 16.5 |
| 106 | 4.1 | 17 |
| 106.5 | 4 | 17.3 |
| 107 | 3.9 | 16.8 |
| 107.5 | 3.8 | 16.3 |
| 108 | 3.7 | fracture |
| 108.5 | 3.6 | |
| 109 | 3.5 | |
| 109.5 | fracture | |

(b) How does this temperature dependence benefit the orthodontic use of the wire?

(c) Calculate the modulus of elasticity, yield strength, ultimate tensile strength, and fracture strength of this material at the two different temperatures.

(d) For each of the four parameters that you calculated in (c), state whether the parameter changed with the change in temperature or not and briefly (in one sentence each) describe what that indicates about the material properties.

(e) When this material fractures, what will the shape of the fracture surface look like?

4.5 It is known that articular cartilage has viscoelastic properties. In particular, it is known to undergo stress relaxation. Using the definition of stress relaxation and your knowledge of articular cartilage's role in the knee joint, explain why stress relaxation is actually desirable in articular cartilage.

4.6 You are investigating metal alloys for applications in bone replacement. You generate two materials: Alloy A and Alloy B. The following diagram shows the structures of each alloy.

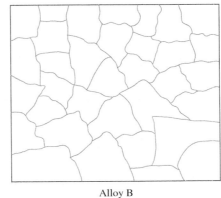

Alloy A                    Alloy B

(a) Because this material is of interest to the orthopedic field, it is necessary for it to be able to have a high fatigue life. Using the graph here, determine the following parameters:

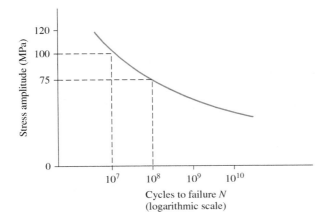

$\sigma_{max}$

$\sigma_{min}$

Fatigue life at a stress amplitude of 100 MPa

Fatigue strength at $10^{10}$ cycles

(b) Would you expect Alloy A or Alloy B to have a shorter fatigue life in the wet state? Why?

# References

1. W.D. Callister Jr., *Materials science and engineering: an introduction*, 3rd ed. New York: John Wiley and Sons, 1994.

2. J. E. Mark, *Physical properties of polymers handbook*. Woodbury, New York: American Institute of Physics, 1996.

3. Instron Corporation, "Instron: Materials testing machines for tensile, fatigue, impact, rheology and structural testing" [Online]. Available at http://www.instron.us/en-us.

4. J. P. Schaffer, A. Saxena, S. D. Antolovich, J. Sanders, and S. B. Warner, *The science and design of engineering materials*, 2nd ed. Boston: McGraw-Hill, 1998.

5. J. M. Schultz, *Polymer materials science*, 1st ed. Englewood Cliffs: Prentice Hall, 1974.

6. R. B. Richards, "Polyethylene-structure, crystallinity and properties," *Journal of Applied Chemistry*, vol. 1, no. 8, pp. 370–376, 1951.

7. J. F. Shackelford, *Introduction to materials science for engineers*, 5th ed. Upper Saddle River: Prentice Hall, 2000.

8. A. G. Mikos, G. Sarakinos, S. M. Leite, J. P. Vacanti, and R. Langer, "Laminated three-dimensional biodegradable foams for use in tissue engineering," *Biomaterials*, vol. 14, no. 5, pp. 323–30, Apr. 1993.

9. R. J. Young and P. A. Lovell, *Introduction to polymers*, 2nd ed. London: Chapman and Hall, 1991.

10. N. E. Dowling, S. L. Kampe and M. V. Kral, Mechanicals behaviour of materials, 5th ed.: Pearson Education, Inc, 2019.

11. H. V. Boeing, *Polyolefins: structure and properties*. Lausanne: Elsevier Press, 1966.

12. J. F. Shackelford, *Introduction to materials science for engineers*, 4th ed. Upper Saddle River: Prentice Hall, 1996.

# Additional Reading

F. W. Cooke, "Bulk properties of materials," in *Biomaterials science: an introduction to materials and medicine*, 2nd ed., B. D. Ratner, A. S. Hoffman, F. J. Schoen, and J. E. Lemons, Eds. San Diego: Elsevier Academic Press, 2004, pp. 23–32.

J. A. Koski, C. Ibarra, and S. A. Rodeo, "Tissue-engineered ligament: cells, matrix, and growth factors," *Orthopedic Clinics*, vol. 31, no. 3, pp. 437–452, 2000.

C. T. Laurencin and J. W. Freeman, "Ligament tissue engineering: an evolutionary materials science approach," *Biomaterials*, vol. 26, no. 36, pp. 7530–7536, 2005.

J. B. Park and R. S. Lakes, *Biomaterials: An Introduction*, 2nd ed. New York: Plenum Press, 1992.

# Biomaterial Degradation

**Main Objective**

To understand the molecular mechanisms behind environmental degradation of metals, ceramics, and polymers in the human body.

**Specific Objectives**

1. To distinguish between controlled and uncontrolled material degradation.
2. To understand how redox reactions cause corrosion.
3. To compare and contrast types of corrosion.
4. To understand the contribution of the location of the implant to its corrosion rate.
5. To compare and contrast the degradation of metals, ceramics, and polymers.
6. To distinguish between polymer chain scission by hydrolysis and by oxidation.
7. To understand the factors that influence controlled polymer and ceramic degradation.
8. To distinguish between bulk and surface erosion of biodegradable polymer systems.

## 5.1 Introduction: Degradation in the Biological Environment

In the previous chapters, we have explained how the physical and mechanical properties of different classes of biomaterials are dependent on the atomic/molecular structure of the materials. In this chapter, we will describe how the degradation of materials in the body is also affected by this structure, and how the degradation process affects the physical and mechanical properties of the overall material.

Biomaterial degradation can occur in an **uncontrolled** manner, which is usually undesirable because it often leads to structural breakdown of the material and premature failure of the device. In contrast, some materials have been designed to degrade in a **controlled** manner, and these are often employed in tissue engineering or drug delivery applications, where the overall goal is temporary tissue replacement and/or release of bioactive factors. This chapter begins with a discussion of

TABLE 5.1

| Concentration of Various Ionic Components of Blood Plasma and Extracellular Fluid | | |
|---|---|---|
| Anion, Cation | Blood Plasma (mM) | Extracellular Fluid (mM) |
| $Cl^-$ | 96–111 | 112–120 |
| $HCO_3^-$ | 16–31 | 25.3–29.7 |
| $HPO_4^{2-}$ | 1–1.5 | 1.93–2 |
| $SO_4^{2-}$ | 0.35–1 | 0.4 |
| $H_2PO_4^-$ | 2 | – |
| $Na^+$ | 131–155 | 141–145 |
| $Mg^{2+}$ | 0.7–1.9 | 1.3 |
| $Ca^{2+}$ | 1.9–3 | 1.4–1.55 |
| $K^+$ | 3.5–5.6 | 3.5–4 |

[1]

undesired biomaterial degradation and closes with a section on materials in which biodegradation is expected as a part of device function.

Although the body provides a relatively mild environment with a neutral pH and constant temperature, the presence of aqueous media containing ions (see Table 5.1 for the composition of blood and extracellular fluid) facilitates the corrosion of metallic implants. Also, specific reactions, such as the actions of inflammatory cells, can change the local chemistry around a device after implantation. As discussed further in Chapter 10, specific inflammatory cells may attach to the biomaterial surface and excrete strong oxidizing agents, such as peroxides, as well as lower the pH drastically in the area, which can further encourage corrosion or degradation of the material.

These unique properties of the biological environment make it difficult to predict the extent of decomposition *in vivo* for materials undergoing either controlled or uncontrolled degradation. Therefore, *in vivo* testing of new biomaterials is necessary to assess degradation at the site of proposed implantation before they can be used clinically (see the last section in this chapter for more information on this topic).

## 5.2    Corrosion/Degradation of Metals and Ceramics

Given the chemical composition of physiologic fluids, metals are, in general, more susceptible to degradation *in vivo* than ceramic-based materials. Degradation of metals is referred to as **corrosion**, and, due to its common occurrence in biomedical implants, will be the subject of a large portion of this section. Characterization and prediction of corrosion is very important in order to forecast how long the metal may stay in the body before it undergoes structural changes or failure. Moreover, knowledge of corrosion is also crucial in predicting the biocompatibility of an implant. During corrosion, leaching of ions from the metallic surface into the surroundings may have deleterious short- or long-term biological consequences that must be taken into account when determining the suitability of a certain metal for use in the body.

## 5.2.1 Fundamentals of Corrosion

### 5.2.1.1 Oxidation-Reduction Reactions

Corrosion is an **electrochemical** process that involves transfer of electrons from one substance to another. Corrosion occurs through coupling of two reactions: **oxidation**, which generates electrons, and **reduction**, which consumes electrons. Combined, these are termed **redox** reactions. For a metal $M$ with $n$ valence electrons, oxidation can be represented as

$$M \rightarrow M^{n+} + ne^-$$

where $e^-$ indicates a free electron. The place where oxidation occurs is called the **anode.**

The corresponding reduction reaction depends on the environment in which the corrosion is taking place. If the milieu is acidic (such as may occur under or around inflammatory cells attached to biomaterials), $H^+$ ions are reduced to form hydrogen gas:

$$2H^+ + 2e^- \rightarrow H_2$$

Since dissolved oxygen is also present in body fluids, alternate reactions include the reduction of oxygen in acidic solutions, namely,

$$O_2 + 4H^+ + 4e^- \rightarrow 2H_2O$$

or, in neutral or basic solutions,

$$O_2 + 2H_2O + 4e^- \rightarrow 4(OH^-)$$

These reduction reactions take place at the **cathode.**

A simple example of coupled redox reactions is the formation of an electrochemical (or galvanic) cell, also called a battery, using a strip of solid zinc immersed in a solution containing zinc ions and a strip of copper in a separate container with a solution of copper ions (Fig. 5.1). The two solutions are connected with a **salt bridge** composed of a substance that readily dissociates into ions, such as KCl. The circuit is completed by connecting the two metal strips (**electrodes**) with a wire so that electrons can flow from one piece of metal to the other. A voltmeter is also placed in the circuit to record the potential difference between the electrodes.

In each compartment (called a **half-cell**), a reaction occurs. In this example, zinc is oxidized:

$$Zn \rightarrow Zn^{2+} + 2e^-$$

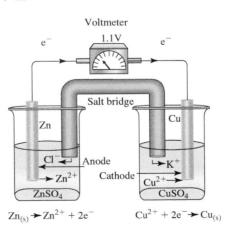

**Figure 5.1**
An electrochemical (or galvanic) cell. A strip of solid zinc and solid copper are immersed in corresponding solutions containing zinc ions and copper ions, respectively. The two solutions are connected with a salt bridge composed of a substance that readily dissociates into ions, such as KCl. A completed circuit is formed by connecting the two metal strips (electrodes) with a wire so that electrons can flow from one piece of metal to the other. A voltmeter is used to record the potential difference between the electrodes—in this case, 1.1V [10].

while, in the other half-cell, copper ions are reduced:

$$Cu^{2+} + 2e^- \rightarrow Cu$$

This results in slow dissolution of the solid zinc anode, with concomitant deposition of copper at the cathode. The role of the salt bridge is to provide ions that maintain a neutral charge in each half-cell. If the concentrations of the solutions in each compartment are 1M and the cell is tested at room temperature (**standard conditions**), the voltmeter in the circuit should read 1.1V.

**5.2.1.2 Half-Cell Potentials**   Why is it that for the system depicted in Figure 5.1, zinc is always the anode and the copper the cathode? This depends on how easily each metal will release electrons (be oxidized). In order to rank the oxidation behavior of different metals, the concept of **standard reduction potentials** for half-cells was developed. In this case, the potential difference for each metal is measured with respect to a **standard hydrogen electrode**. As illustrated in Figure 5.2, a hydrogen electrode is formed by bubbling hydrogen through a 1M solution of HCl containing a strip of platinum. The solid platinum does not participate in the reaction, but provides a surface on which the hydrogen ions can be oxidized or reduced.

The use of the standard electrode in an electrochemical cell (Fig. 5.2) is the same as that described for the zinc-copper system described previously. This set-up has been employed to determine the reduction potentials for a number of metals, some of which are listed in Table 5.2. As one moves down the table [called the **standard electromotive force (emf) series**], the metals' propensity for oxidation becomes higher and they are more active (anodic), as indicated in the table.

**Figure 5.2**
In order to rank the oxidation behavior of different metals, the potential difference for each metal is measured with respect to a standard hydrogen electrode. A hydrogen electrode is formed by bubbling hydrogen through a 1M solution of HCl containing a strip of platinum (an inert surface on which the hydrogen ions can be oxidized or reduced). From this particular setup, the standard reduction potential can be measured for zinc (a) and copper (b) [10].

TABLE 5.2

| Standard Electromotive Force (emf) Series | | |
|---|---|---|
| | Electrode Reaction | Standard Electrode Potential, $E^0$ (V) |
| | $Au^{3+} + 3e^- \rightarrow Au$ | +1.420 |
| | $O_2 + 4H^+ + 4e^- \rightarrow 2H_2O$ | +1.229 |
| | $Pt^{2+} + 2e^- \rightarrow Pt$ | ~+1.2 |
| | $Ag^+ + e^- \rightarrow Ag$ | +0.800 |
| Increasingly inert (cathodic) | $Fe^{3+} + e^- \rightarrow Fe^{2+}$ | +0.771 |
| | $O_2 + 2H_2O + 4e^- \rightarrow 4(OH^-)$ | +0.401 |
| | $Cu^{2+} + 2e^- \rightarrow Cu$ | +0.340 |
| | $2H^+ + 2e^- \rightarrow H_2$ | 0.000 |
| | $Pb^{2+} + 2e^- \rightarrow Pb$ | −0.126 |
| | $Sn^{2+} + 2e^- \rightarrow Sn$ | −0.136 |
| | $Ni^{2+} + 2e^- \rightarrow Ni$ | −0.250 |
| | $Co^{2+} + 2e^- \rightarrow Co$ | −0.277 |
| | $Cd^{2+} + 2e^- \rightarrow Cd$ | −0.403 |
| | $Fe^{2+} + 2e^- \rightarrow Fe$ | −0.440 |
| Increasingly active (anodic) | $Cr^{3+} + 3e^- \rightarrow Cr$ | −0.744 |
| | $Zn^{2+} + 2e^- \rightarrow Zn$ | −0.763 |
| | $Al^{3+} + 3e^- \rightarrow Al$ | −1.662 |
| | $Mg^{2+} + 2e^- \rightarrow Mg$ | −2.363 |
| | $Na^+ + e^- \rightarrow Na$ | −2.714 |
| | $K^+ + e^- \rightarrow K$ | −2.924 |

[2]

As demonstrated by the zinc-copper example, the metal with the more negative standard reduction potential will always act as the anode.

Although standard reduction potentials are useful for comparing activities of various metals, in reality, it is rare to encounter pure metals in a 1M solution of their ions. While effects from changes in ion concentration can be taken into account using the Nernst equation (see equation 5.2), alterations in the nature of the solvent are more difficult to model. Therefore, the **galvanic series** has been developed from data collected on metal corrosion in seawater, which provides a good indication of the relative activity of various metals in a salt solution, similar to that found in the human body. A summary of the galvanic series is given in Table 5.3. Although no exact potentials have been assigned, like the emf series, the metals towards the bottom of the list are more easily oxidized than those at the top.

**5.2.1.3 Nernst Equation**   As mentioned earlier, the potential measured between the electrodes of an electrochemical cell depends in part on temperature and the concentration of the metal ions in each half-cell. Alterations in either of these parameters will affect the overall potential, as described by the Nernst equation.

TABLE 5.3

| Galvanic Series in Seawater | |
|---|---|
| Platinum | ↑ |
| Gold | Cathodic |
| Graphite | |
| Titanium | |
| Silver | |
| Stainless steel (passive) | |
| Nickel-base alloys (passive) | |
| Cu-30% Ni alloy | |
| Copper | |
| Aluminum bronze | |
| Cu-35% Zn brass | |
| Nickel-base alloys (active) | |
| Manganese bronze | |
| Cu-40% Zn brass | |
| Tin | |
| Lead | |
| 316 stainless steel (active) | |
| 50% Pb-50% Sn solder | |
| 410 stainless steel (active) | |
| Cast iron | |
| Low carbon steel | |
| 2024 aluminum | |
| 2017 aluminum | |
| Cadmium | |
| Alclad | |
| 1100 aluminum | |
| 5052 aluminum | |
| Galvanized steel | |
| Zinc | |
| Magnesium alloys | Anodic |
| Magnesium | ↓ |

[3]

For a generic two-metal cell, like the zinc-copper example discussed earlier, the reactions and corresponding measured potentials are as follows:

$$M_1 \rightarrow M_1^{n+} + ne^- \qquad -E_1^0 \,(\text{metal } M_1 \text{ is oxidized})$$

$$M_2^{n+} + ne^- \rightarrow M_2 \quad E_2^0 \,(\text{metal } M_2 \text{ is reduced})$$

Here, the values for $E_1^0$ and $E_2^0$ are those from the standard reduction potential table (see Table 5.2). Because $M_1$ is oxidized, the sign of its reduction potential must be reversed $(-E_1^0)$.

The overall reaction for metals $M_1$ and $M_2$ with the same number of valence electrons is

$$M_1 + M_2^{n+} \rightarrow M_1^{n+} + M_2$$

and, adding the standard half-cell potentials, the corresponding electrochemical potential for the entire cell is

$$\Delta E^0 = (E_2^0 - E_1^0) \tag{5.1}$$

In order to take into account deviations from the conditions in which the standard reduction potentials were measured (changes in temperature or ion concentration), the equation becomes

$$\Delta E^0 = (E_2^0 - E_1^0) - \frac{RT}{nF} \ln \frac{[M_1^{n+}]}{[M_2^{n+}]} \tag{5.2}$$

where $R$ is the gas constant ($8.314 \text{ JK}^{-1}\text{mol}^{-1}$), $T$ is the absolute temperature (K), $F$ is Faraday's constant (96,500 C/mol), and $n$, $E_1^0$ and $E_2^0$ are as previously described. This is the **Nernst equation.**

## EXAMPLE PROBLEM 5.1

Consider an electrochemical cell of zinc and copper as described in the text and illustrated in Figure 5.1.

(a) Assuming that the concentrations of the solutions in each compartment are 1M and that the cell is tested at room temperature (standard conditions), show that the potential difference between the electrodes is 1.1V.
(b) Consider now that the conditions of the cell have changed as follows. The cell is tested at body temperature (37°C) and the concentrations of the zinc and copper solutions in each compartment are typical serum concentrations of these ions ($107 \, \mu\text{g/dL}$ and $115 \, \mu\text{g/dL}$, respectively). Calculate the potential difference between the electrodes under these conditions.
(c) Assuming the same ion concentrations as given in part (b), at what temperature would the system need to be tested for the potential difference between the electrodes to equal 1.15V?

Solution:

(a) In this electrochemical cell, the zinc is being oxidized and the copper is being reduced, as described in the text. Thus, the following chemical reactions are occurring:

$$\text{Zn} \rightarrow \text{Zn}^{2+} + 2e^-$$
$$+ \ \underline{\text{Cu}^{2+} + 2e^- \rightarrow \text{Cu}}$$
$$\text{Net:} \quad \text{Zn} + \text{Cu}^{2+} \rightarrow \text{Zn}^{2+} + \text{Cu}$$

Looking up the standard electrode potentials from Table 5.2, we find that $E_1^o = -0.763\text{V} (\text{Zn})$ and $E_2^o = +0.340\text{V} (\text{Cu})$. Under standard conditions, the potential difference between the two electrodes is calculated by simply subtracting the standard emf of the anode from the cathode, as follows:

$$E^\circ = E_2{}^\circ - E_1{}^\circ = 0.340\text{V} - (-0.763\text{V}) = \underline{1.103\text{V}}$$

(b) In nonstandard conditions, the potential difference between the electrodes should be calculated using the Nernst equation:

$$\Delta E^\circ = (E_2{}^\circ - E_1{}^\circ) - \frac{RT}{nF} \cdot \ln \frac{[M_1{}^{n+}]}{[M_2{}^{n+}]}$$

Here, the emf values are as before, $R$ is the gas constant ($8.314 \ JK^{-1}mol^{-1}$), $F$ is Faraday's constant ($96,500 \ C/mol$), $n$ is 2, and the absolute temperature $T$ is given ($37°C = 310K$). The concentration of zinc can be calculated from the given information as follows:

$$(0.00107 \ g/dL)(mol/65.39 \ g \ Zn)(10 \ dL/L) = 0.0164 \ \mu M \ Zn$$

Similarly, the concentration of copper can be calculated as

$$(0.00115 \ g/dL)(mol/63.55 \ g \ Cu)(10 \ dL/L) = 0.0181 \ \mu M \ Cu$$

Plugging these values into the equation gives

$$\Delta E° = (0.340V - (-0.763V)) - \frac{8.314\left(\frac{J}{K \cdot mol}\right)310K}{2 \cdot 96,500(C/mol)} \cdot \ln\frac{[.0164 \ \mu M]}{[.0181 \ \mu M]}$$

$$\Delta E° = 1.104V$$

(c) Using the same equation as in (b), and solving for $\Delta E° = 1.15V$ yields

$$1.15V = (0.340V + 0.763V) - \frac{8.314\left(\frac{J}{K \cdot mol}\right)T}{2 \cdot 96500(C/mol)} \cdot \ln\frac{[.0164 \ \mu M]}{[.0181 \ \mu M]},$$

and solving for T, we find that the temperature must be approximately 11,061K for the potential difference between the electrodes to equal 1.15V!    ∎

**5.2.1.4 Galvanic Corrosion**    One of the most common forms of corrosion corresponds well to the description of typical electrochemical cells, and thus is termed **galvanic corrosion**. In this case, two different types of metals are electrically coupled when placed in the body, like the wire connecting the two electrodes in Figure 5.1. Physiological fluid becomes the salt bridge completing the circuit. In this situation, the more active metal will dissolve at an accelerated pace. For example, if stainless steel is used in conjunction with another alloy, it often undergoes anodic dissolution.

However, it is difficult to predict metal degradation in such a system solely based on the activities listed in the galvanic series (see Table 5.3) because corrosion is a very complex process. One important consideration is that the oxidation and reduction rates must be equal so that if localized changes reduce one reaction, then the overall corrosion may be significantly slowed. An example of this is metal *passivation*, which is discussed in the next section.

### 5.2.2 Pourbaix Diagrams and Passivation

In addition to the parameters discussed earlier, corrosion activity for a certain metal also depends on the pH of the solution in which it is immersed. In order to further refine predictions of corrosion in various environments, a Pourbaix diagram may be created. As shown in Figure 5.3 for iron, a **Pourbaix diagram** for a given metal depicts regions of corrosion and noncorrosion as a function of cell potential and pH. Pourbaix diagrams are formed using results from the Nernst equation and the solubilities of possible degradation products, as well as other factors. The diagonal dashed lines in the figure represent the stability of water. Aqueous corrosion, if it occurs, will take place in environments falling between these two lines.

The Pourbaix diagram is divided into three main regions: corrosion, immunity, and passivation. Corrosion is arbitrarily defined as a region in which greater than $10^{-6}$ M of the metal's ions are found in solution at equilibrium. If less than this

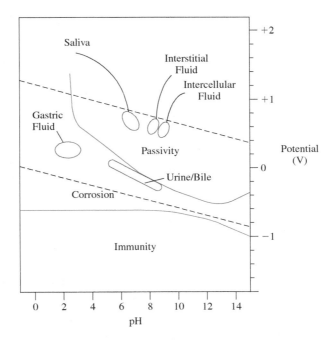

**Figure 5.3**
An example of a Pourbaix diagram for iron, depicting regions of corrosion and noncorrosion as a function of cell potential and pH. The regions depicted in this particular example assume that a surface film of lepidocrocite (an iron oxide-hydroxide mineral, $\gamma$ FeOOH) forms under proper conditions and that this film is protective against corrosion. The stability of water is represented via the diagonal dashed lines. Aqueous corrosion, if it occurs, will take place in environments falling between these two lines. Sample physiological environments, such as saliva and gastric fluid, are also shown [11].

concentration is measured, the metal may fall into either of the other categories (immune or passive). In the **immune** region, it is not energetically favorable for the metal to corrode (dissolve). This phenomenon is also called **cathodic protection** because the metal cannot act as an anode under these conditions.

**Passivation** occurs when surface oxidation leads to the formation of a stable solid film (usually an oxide or hydroxide) that coats the surface of the metal. In this region, although it may be energetically favorable, corrosion can be slowed or stopped due to this thin, insulative barrier that prevents transfer of electrons in and out of the metal. In particular, metals such as chromium, iron, nickel, titanium, and aluminum have a tendency to form these coatings.

The diagram in Figure 5.3 also includes areas representing the composition of different body fluids, so that it is possible to predict the response of a metal in various locations in the body. The regions found in Pourbaix diagrams give an idea of which reactions are possible *in vivo*, but cannot predict the rate of these reactions. This rate, which is often defined in terms of current flow per surface area, is dependent on other factors, such as possible depletion of ions around the cathode. A detailed discussion of corrosion rate calculation is beyond the scope of this text.

## EXAMPLE PROBLEM 5.2

The pH of a wound site created through the implantation of a material can drop considerably to acidic values of 5 or lower. Imagine the hypothetical case of a surgeon implanting a bone plate composed of stainless steel with an iron coating. Assume that the pH of the tissue surrounding the implant drops to 5 during the wound healing response and that the surgical team did not notice an aluminum screw that was accidentally dropped into the patient near the implant. Assume also that an electrochemical cell is created through the interaction among the iron, aluminum, and extracellular fluid. Using the Pourbaix diagram for iron given in Figure 5.3, would you expect the iron coating to corrode with a cell potential of $+0.10$V? Would you expect the iron coating to corrode with a cell potential of $-0.40$V?

**Solution:** The dashed lines on the Pourbaix diagram indicate the range of conditions for which water is stable, with the conditions falling between these lines being conducive to the presence of water. Using the Pourbaix diagram for iron, at a pH of approximately 5, aqueous corrosion can occur when the cell potential lies between approximately $+0.30V$ and $-0.30V$. Thus, at a cell potential of $+0.10V$, one would expect the iron to begin to corrode in the aqueous environment at a pH of 5. However, at a cell potential of $-0.40V$ and a pH of 5, one would not expect aqueous corrosion of the iron to occur, as the conditions exceed the stability of water (as indicated by the dashed lines on the diagram).  ■

### 5.2.3 Contribution of Processing Parameters

A number of additional factors besides metal composition can enhance corrosion *in vivo*. These include metal processing and handling techniques, discussed here, as well as mechanical loading and the presence of proteins, cells, and bacteria, which are addressed in subsequent sections. Anything that causes the presence of different microstructures within an implant can change localized ion concentrations and thus affect the corrosion rate. These can be the result of tiny flaws or cracks introduced during fabrication, or overall device design.

**5.2.3.1 Crevice Corrosion**   As the name implies, **crevice corrosion** occurs in areas with a narrow, deep crack—for example, in between the screw and plate of a bone fixation device (Fig. 5.4). Certain metals commonly used in orthopedic applications, such as stainless steels, can exhibit this type of corrosion, while others, like titanium and cobalt-chromium alloys, are less susceptible. Although the exact mechanism of crevice corrosion is not fully understood, it is thought to begin with the depletion of oxygen within the crevice. At this point, only the anodic reaction is possible in the crevice, which results in oxidation of the metal in this area, while the remainder of the piece becomes the cathode. Outside the crevice, oxygen reduction results in an increase in pH. A diagram of this process is found in Figure 5.5.

In the presence of sodium chloride solution, as found in the body, crevice corrosion is further accelerated by the diffusion of $Cl^-$ ions into the crevice to balance the charge of the $M^{n+}$ ions created. The compound formed can react further to produce an insoluble hydroxide and liberate $H^+$:

$$MCl_n + nH_2O \rightarrow M(OH)_n + nH^+Cl^-$$

**Figure 5.4**
An example of crevice corrosion on the plate of a bone fixation device. Corrosion occurred in the narrow, deep crack between the screw (not shown) and plate. Arrows indicate where corrosion has occurred [1].

**Figure 5.5**
A theoretical mechanism of crevice corrosion. Depletion of oxygen occurs within the crevice, causing oxidation of the metal in that location, while the remainder of the piece becomes the cathode [12].

This decreases the local pH and provides a more corrosive environment, thereby significantly increasing the rate of metal dissolution within the crevice.

**5.2.3.2 Pitting Corrosion** **Pitting corrosion** is caused by the same mechanism as crevice corrosion. As shown in Figure 5.6, stainless steels can also undergo this type of corrosion. In this case, processing or handling may lead to a small flaw or area in which the passivation film on the surface is disrupted, leading to the formation of a relatively small anode and large cathode. Because of this inequality in surface area and the fact that the rates of both reactions must be equal, the anodic regions undergo significant dissolution. This is a particularly dangerous type of corrosion because it can go undetected until device failure, due to the small overall material loss.

**5.2.3.3 Intergranular Corrosion** Devices fabricated by casting (see Chapter 6) often have multiple grains and thus are particularly susceptible to **intergranular corrosion**. As discussed in Chapter 3, the grain boundaries are at a heightened energy state and therefore may represent more active (anodic) regions of the material. Particularly in alloys, this can lead to intergranular attack by a similar mechanism as that described for crevice corrosion (Fig. 5.7). A common example of this is corrosion of stainless steel at the grain boundaries due to depletion of chromium in the area. Chromium is required to form a passivating layer on the metal; if this is removed, the area quickly undergoes corrosion and, in the extreme case, may crumble into many tiny pieces.

**Figure 5.6**
Pitting corrosion seen on a sample of stainless steel. Small defects on the surface of the material act as an anode, resulting in corrosion at that location [13].

**Figure 5.7**
An example of intergranular corrosion. The same process seen in crevice corrosion occurs in this situation, with the grain boundaries acting as the anode [14].

## 5.2.4 Contribution of the Mechanical Environment

In addition to fabrication and handling parameters, the location of an implant has a large effect on the length of time elapsed before substantial corrosion occurs. If a device is used in a tissue that undergoes continued movement and is constantly under load, the corrosion rate can be significantly higher than for a similar device located in a less stressed environment. The presence of mechanical stress can potentiate corrosion by increasing the number of microcracks in a metal. Also, a material under stress is in a higher energy state, so it is more susceptible to the chemical reactions that produce corrosion.

**5.2.4.1 Stress and Galvanic Corrosion**    Bending a metal rod or plate will cause the tensile side to be anodic compared to the side in compression. This encourages galvanic corrosion in a material that otherwise would have no difference in electrochemical potential between the two sides. This same effect can be observed near stress raisers (see Chapter 4) such as holes or sharp corners.

**5.2.4.2 Stress Corrosion Cracking**    **Stress corrosion cracking** occurs to a metal that is both under tension and subjected to a corrosive environment. This combination results in small cracks that form perpendicular to the direction of applied stress, and is particularly dangerous because it can occur at relatively low loads (below the ultimate tensile strength) and in solutions that would normally be well tolerated by the material. Once formed, the cracks propagate and lead to brittle fracture, even though metals traditionally exhibit substantial ductility. Alloys, especially stainless steel, are susceptible to this type of degradation in the presence of saline solutions like those found *in vivo*.

**5.2.4.3 Fatigue Corrosion**   In **fatigue corrosion**, continued bending, loading, or motion around the implant may disrupt the passivating film formed on the metal and expose the underlying surface, leading to corrosion of this area. As discussed in Chapter 4, fatigue properties are measured by recording how many cycles of loading a device can undergo at a certain stress without failure (fatigue life). In corrosion fatigue, the maximum stress at failure decreases continually as the number of loading cycles increases. Therefore, this type of corrosion may significantly shorten the fatigue life of the implant and result in premature device failure.

**5.2.4.4 Fretting Corrosion**   Unlike the other types of corrosion listed in this section, **fretting corrosion** is not related to loading, but is dependent on motion near the implant. This type of corrosion involves removal of the metal's passivating layer by mechanical means. This can be the creation of a nick in the surface that does not repassivate, or a cyclic process in which the passive layer is formed and then destroyed repeatedly. It is thought that fretting corrosion plays a role in the degradation seen around connections between fixation plates and bone screws (Fig. 5.4).

### 5.2.5 Contribution of the Biological Environment

Besides the effects of mechanical factors, the implant's location in the body can influence corrosion in other ways. Chemical and cellular constituents of the biological milieu may affect the corrosion rate substantially. It is important to remember that the localized environment is rarely constant, with diffusion of ions, migration of cells, and chemical reactions taking place continuously, which adds yet another level of complexity to predicting corrosion rates *in vivo*.

The physiological fluids and tissues surrounding an implant are rich in proteins and cells. The recruitment of inflammatory cells to the area after biomaterial implantation can result in drastic changes in the chemistry surrounding the implant, including a drop in pH and release of strong oxidizing agents. Although it may seem that both of these responses would promote corrosion, it has been found for some metals that the oxidizing agents released during inflammation actually contribute to the growth of the passive layer on the surface, so the effects of surrounding cells on corrosion must be evaluated for the specific system of interest before use in the body.

The attachment of proteins to the metallic surface (see Chapters 7 and 8 for why this occurs) may also have a number of effects. Proteins can alter the nature of the passive layer on the metal by creating a barrier that reduces oxygen diffusion to the surface. This, in turn, reduces the stability of the oxide layer formed on the implant. Electrochemical potential can also be affected by proteins that act as electron carriers, thereby shifting cell parameters so that they fall outside the passive region on the Pourbaix diagram. Finally, certain proteins require metal ions to function, so they have a natural affinity to scavenge metals. If they consume a product of the corrosion reaction, their presence may alter the equilibrium and favor further dissolution.

As discussed further in Chapter 14, bacteria may attach to the implant during insertion or at some later point, leading to infection of the device. The by-products of bacterial metabolism can change the regional pH near the material, which affects the stability of the passive layer. Additionally, bacteria can consume hydrogen, an ion often found at the cathode. Like metal scavenging by proteins, this change in reaction equilibrium may encourage anodic dissolution.

### 5.2.6 Means of Corrosion Control

Although corrosive attack due to the nature of the biological environment cannot always be controlled, reduction of corrosion is possible via key decisions in the design and fabrication of the implant. For example, stress-induced corrosion can be mitigated by designing devices with few stress raisers. Similarly, galvanic corrosion may be prevented through selection of combinations of metals that are close together in the galvanic series. Ideally, the device would be fabricated from only nonreactive (cathodic) metals like gold, silver, or platinum, but in many cases, the mechanical properties of these materials limit their usefulness. Therefore, as a compromise, metals known to form passive oxide coatings are often employed, either in their pure or alloyed form, to create implants with corrosion resistance as well as sufficient mechanical strength.

In addition, extra processing steps may be included to prevent specific types of corrosion. For instance, heat-treating stainless steels may reduce intergranular corrosion. Additionally, pre-treating a metal with nitric acid forms a passive surface layer before implantation (see Chapter 7 and ASTM standard F86 for more about these methods). This is one example of a protective layer that may be applied to metallic implants. Others, including metallic, ceramic, or polymeric coatings, are added on the surface via a variety of means (see Chapter 7) to provide a barrier between the active metal and its surroundings, thereby decreasing dissolution of the implant.

### 5.2.7 Ceramic Degradation

While the dissolution of metals is called corrosion, breakdown of ceramic materials is termed **degradation**. Passivating layers on metals are usually a form of ceramic material, so this indicates that ceramics are, in general, more stable than metals in the physiologic environment. This is because ceramics are composed of bonds with a largely ionic character, so much energy is required to break them.

However, some ceramic formulations are highly soluble in an aqueous environment. This has led to the classification of ceramics as either **inert, resorbable,** or having **controlled surface reactivity** in the body. Resorbable and surface reactive ceramics are treated in more detail in Section 5.4.

Regardless of type, degradation of ceramics, like metals, depends on their mechanical environment, as well as the implant design. Stress-induced degradation can occur in ceramics under tension. If a crack is formed in these materials, the tensile stress may lead to further dissolution at the crack tip and, eventually, material fracture. Ceramic porosity also plays a large role in an implant's degradation characteristics. Pores are stress raisers, and thus may increase the formation of cracks or the rate of their propagation. Additionally, the presence of pores promotes degradation by creating more surface area for reaction with the environment (see Section 5.4 for further discussion of the effect of porosity on degradation).[1]

## 5.3 Degradation of Polymers

Like metals and ceramics, polymeric biomaterials may undergo unwanted degradation in the body due to interactions with surrounding fluids and tissues. Indications that this has occurred include discoloration of the implant, appearance of crazes, or a significant change in mechanical properties. These characteristics result from specific degradation mechanisms discussed in the following sections. As with other

---

[1]Although porosity in metals has the same effect on corrosion rate, the formation of pores in ceramic implants is more common and, therefore, plays a larger role in ceramic than metallic degradation.

types of biomaterials, the implant location within the body, including access to water, proteins, inflammatory cells, and mechanical stress, plays a large role in the rate of polymer degradation.

### 5.3.1 Primary Means of Polymer Degradation

Polymers usually degrade by two main mechanisms: swelling/dissolution or chain scission. Many polymers with hydrophilic domains will **swell** in the physiologic environment. Here, the solvent (water) molecules are absorbed into the polymer and are small enough to occupy spaces between the macromolecular chains. In this way, they act as plasticizers and make the material more ductile by reducing secondary bonding between chains. They may also affect the crystallinity of the polymer. Both mechanical and thermal properties (e.g., glass transition temperature) can be influenced by the presence of the absorbed solvent. In extreme cases, if the chains are soluble enough and there are few covalent bonds between chains, the polymer may **dissolve** completely in an aqueous environment.

In contrast, **chain scission** involves breaking primary, rather than secondary, bonds. There is a separation in chain segments at the point of bond rupture, which leads to an overall decrease in molecular weight. As discussed in previous chapters, this can have a significant impact on both the mechanical and thermal properties of the polymer. Chain scission may occur via hydrolysis or oxidation reactions, as described in the following sections.

### 5.3.2 Chain Scission by Hydrolysis

Depending on the susceptibility of chemical groups in the polymer, water molecules may facilitate the cleavage of certain bonds within a macromolecule. This process is called **hydrolysis**, and is a common degradation mechanism of polymers formed by condensation. Many of the chemical moieties that can be cleaved in this manner are found in Figure 5.8. There are a number of factors that affect the extent of polymer hydrolysis, including the following:

1. Reactivity of groups in the polymer backbone (chemical susceptibility of the material)
2. Extent of interchain bonding
3. Amount of media (water) available to the polymer
4. Material surface area to volume ratio

As an example of how chemical and physical material properties affect hydrolysis rates, a polymeric implant that is highly susceptible to hydrolytic cleavage will contain a large number of highly cleavable groups like those shown to the left in Figure 5.9, as well as hydrophilic domains to allow the influx of water deep into the material. It will have a relatively low initial molecular weight and low crosslink density so there are fewer chain entanglements or covalent interactions between chains to be broken. It will possess low or no crystallinity and its $T_g$ will be below body temperature, so the material is in an amorphous, rubbery state to encourage water penetration. To further promote hydrolytic degradation, the polymer will be formed into an implant that has a high surface area to volume ratio so that the aqueous media reaches many areas of the implant simultaneously.

### 5.3.3 Chain Scission by Oxidation

In addition to hydrolysis, chain scission of polymers may occur via oxidation reactions. Here, **oxidation** means that highly reactive species (usually free radicals) attack and break covalent bonds in susceptible chemical groups within the macromolecule.

**Figure 5.8**
Examples of chemical moieties susceptible to cleavage via hydrolysis [17].

**Figure 5.9**
Chart demonstrating relative susceptibilities of various groups to bond cleavage by hydrolysis [16].

High rate of hydrolysis

Polyanhydrides > Polycarbonates > Polyesters >

Polyurethanes > Polyorthoesters > Polyamides

Low rate of hydrolysis

Unlike hydrolysis, this reaction involves initiation, propagation, and termination steps, similar to those described in Chapter 2 for addition polymerization. The initiation step can involve either homolysis or heterolysis of the polymer chain (Fig. 5.10). An example of initiation and stabilization of radicals by polymers can be seen in Figure 5.11. This stabilization in essence increases the lifetime of the radicals, so that they may catalyze the scission of multiple bonds on nearby chains before eventually terminating.

The extent of oxidative degradation depends on many of the same parameters as discussed earlier for hydrolysis:

1. Reactivity of groups in the polymer backbone (chemical susceptibility of the material)

2. Extent of interchain bonding

Examples of some of chemical domains susceptible to oxidation reactions are found in Figure 5.12. Additionally, lower molecular weight polymers and those that are less tightly crosslinked will degrade more quickly because there are fewer primary and secondary interactions holding the material together.

Oxidation occurs most often in the body due to active agents released during the inflammatory process, such as highly reactive oxygen radicals (see Chapter 10 for more on inflammation). In addition, it has been observed that irradiating certain polymers, such as the ultra-high molecular weight poly(ethylene) (UHMWPE) used in orthopedic implants, in air as a part of a sterilization process (see Chapter 6 for more information on sterilization) prior to implantation caused the formation of oxygen radicals that led to oxidative degradation of the polymer. **Metal-catalyzed oxidation** has also been found, particularly in the case of pacemaker leads. Unlike cracks induced by environmental stress (see the next section), which most often appear on the exterior of the implant, fissures resulting from metal-catalyzed oxidation are found on the interior of a polymer coating that is in contact with a metal wire. It is believed that this is caused by corrosion of the metal, which results in the formation of strong oxidizing agents that then, in turn, attack the polymer coating. This type of degradation is characterized by brittle fracture of the polymer, as seen in Figure 5.13.

Homolysis

$$R{-}R \longrightarrow 2R\cdot$$

Heterolysis

$$R{-}R \longrightarrow R^+ + R^-$$

**Figure 5.10**
The two different initiation steps (homolysis and heterolysis) that can lead to oxidation of a polymer chain [15].

(a)

(b)                                   "Hyperconjugation"

**Figure 5.11**
Examples of resonance stabilization of radicals during polymer oxidation for (a) ethers and (b) hydrocarbons [17].

Branched Aliphatic Hydrocarbon

Ar = Aromatic Ring-Containing Polymer

Allylic Hydrocarbon

Ether

Phenol

Alcohol

Aldehyde

Amine

**Figure 5.12**
Examples of chemical domains that are susceptible to oxidative degradation. * denotes sites of homolysis or heterolysis [15].

### 5.3.4 Other Means of Degradation

In addition to the main mechanisms for polymer degradation described earlier, the presence of the physiological environment may encourage material dissolution in other ways. As with metals and ceramics, the addition of mechanical stress, due either to the implant location or the design of the device, can encourage degradation. Also, the presence of certain proteins with an affinity for chemical groups present in the polymer may facilitate bond cleavage.

**5.3.4.1 Environmental Stress Cracking**   **Environmental stress cracking** seen in polymers is similar to stress corrosion cracking in metals. When a polymer is subjected to sufficient tensile stresses in the biological environment, the exterior of the implant develops deep cracks perpendicular to the primary loading axis (Fig. 5.14). However, unlike in metal-catalyzed oxidation, it is believed that in this case the material fractures in a ductile manner. Although the exact mechanism of this type of

**Figure 5.13**
A brittle fracture is seen in the polymer, which is a sign of metal-catalyzed oxidation. In this case, corrosion first occurs on the metal that the polymer is contacting, and the resultant strong oxidizing agents then attack the polymeric material [15].

**Figure 5.14**
Environmental stress cracking seen in a polymer sample. This sample has undergone tensile loading in a biological environment, resulting in the development of deep cracks perpendicular to the primary loading axis [15].

degradation is not well understood, it is known that the presence of inflammatory cells (or reactive species released from these cells) is required before environmental stress cracking will occur.

**5.3.4.2 Enzyme-Catalyzed Degradation**    Of the many proteins present in the tissue and fluid surrounding a biomedical implant, **enzymes** have a particular affinity for certain chemical groups present in polymers. They then act as *catalysts*, lowering the required activation energy for specific reactions, usually involving those chemical groups. A variety of enzymes are used in the body to achieve efficient synthesis, as well as cleavage, of natural polymers (see Chapter 9 for more information on the structure and function of enzymes). However, in some cases, these same molecules can cause either hydrolytic or oxidative degradation of synthetic polymers, if the polymers possess chemical functional groups similar to the target moieties for the enzymes. Because each person produces different amounts of enzymes, it is difficult to predict to what extent enzyme-catalyzed degradation will affect polymeric materials in a given individual.

### 5.3.5  Effects of Porosity

The effects of porosity on polymer degradation are similar to those for ceramic (and metallic) degradation. Because pores represent additional stress raisers, mechanically induced degradation may be increased in porous polymers. Also, porosity increases the surface area of the implant, thereby providing more space for cleavage by environmental factors such as water or oxidative species. Thus, in general, degradation occurs more quickly in porous than nonporous polymeric materials.

## 5.4   Biodegradable Materials

In contrast to the uncontrolled degradation discussed in the previous sections, which is generally undesirable, controlled biomaterial degradation can be used as an important part of tissue engineering and drug delivery therapies. For these applications, the temporary nature of the material is ideal to promote localized tissue healing or release of a bioactive agent without the need for a second surgery to remove the implant.

However, before materials with designed degradation properties can be described in detail, a few definitions should be clarified. Although international organizations have attempted to standardize the terminology associated with biodegradable implants, many expressions remain redundant and poorly defined. The following discussion is based, in part, on that presented by Kohn et al. [4]. In general, degradation refers to breaking chemical bonds within the material, while erosion involves a change in the size or shape of the material that may or may not be caused by degradation. Although the prefix "bio" was defined to mean that specific actions by a biological agent, such as an enzyme, cell, or bacterium, cause the material breakdown, often in the literature "biodegradation" or "bioerosion" is used simply to indicate that these processes are occurring in the body.

Therefore, in this book, we will refer to **biodegradation** as the chemical breakdown of a material mediated by any component of the physiological environment (such as water, ions, cells, proteins, and bacteria). **Bioerosion** is an even broader term indicating breakdown, including chemical degradation or other processes in which bond cleavage is not required (e.g., physical dissolution), of a material mediated by any component of the physiological environment.[2]

Although the use of biodegradable materials provides several advantages for the patient, particularly in the applications discussed earlier, degradable materials also exhibit more complex biocompatibility issues since not only the original materials, but also any degradation products, must be nontoxic. More information on *in vitro* and *in vivo* tests for biocompatibility of biodegradable materials can be found in Chapters 10 and 11. Biodegradable implants have, to date, been fabricated primarily from specially formulated ceramics and polymers, and therefore these materials are the subject of the remainder of this section.

### 5.4.1 Biodegradable Ceramics

Biodegradable ceramics are often a type of calcium phosphate, such as calcium hydroxyapatite $(HA, Ca_{10}(PO_4)_6(OH)_2)$, or tricalcium phosphate $(TCP, Ca_3(PO_4)_2)$, but they can be composed of hydrated calcium sulfate $(CaSO_4 \cdot 2H_2O)$, or types of phosphorous oxides (containing $P_2O_5$), including bioactive glasses. While fully biodegradable ceramics will be resorbed (see section 5.4.1.1 for mechanisms), bioactive glasses undergo a reaction at their surface through a slow exchange of ions with the physiological fluid surrounding the material, which results in a silica-rich layer that affects eventual protein and cell interactions with the material over weeks to months. For more detailed description of bioactive glasses, see [5]. The remainder of this section will focus on degradable ceramics. However, both bioglasses and biodegradable ceramics are often used in orthopedic applications due to their similarity to forms of calcium-based mineral found naturally in bone tissue.

#### 5.4.1.1 Erosion Mechanisms
Biodegradable ceramics actually erode under physiological conditions due to a combination of dissolution and physical disintegration. The extent of dissolution depends both on the solubility of the particular formulation

---

[2]"Bioresorption" and "bioabsorption" are other terms commonly found in texts referring to biodegradable materials. These words are not well defined and, in general, can be considered to be synonyms of "biodegradation."

in aqueous media and the local pH around the implant. For example, for phosphate-containing materials, the following reactions may occur at different pH [6]:

$$H_3PO_4 \leftrightharpoons H_2PO_4^- + H^+ \qquad pKa_1 = 2.1192$$
$$H_2PO_4^- \leftrightharpoons HPO_4^{2-} + H^+ \qquad pKa_2 = 7.2076$$
$$HPO_4^{2-} \leftrightharpoons PO_4^{3-} + H^+ \qquad pKa_3 = 12.0000$$

Physical disintegration then occurs after preferential dissolution of the material at the grain boundaries.

### 5.4.1.2 Factors that Influence Degradation Rate

Because ceramic bioerosion occurs mainly due to interactions with water, the factors that control the erosion rate are similar to those discussed earlier for polymer hydrolysis and include the following:

1. Chemical susceptibility of the material
2. Amount of crystallinity
3. Amount of media (water) available
4. Material surface area to volume ratio

It has been found that the chemical composition of the ceramic can have a significant impact on the degradation rate, with hydrated forms such as hydrated calcium sulfate eroding faster than their nonhydrated counterparts. In addition, ionic substitutions of $CO_3^{2-}$, $Mg^{2+}$, or $Sr^{2+}$ in hydroxyapatite decrease the overall degradation time, while $F^-$ substitutions make this material less susceptible to dissolution.

Because ceramic degradation depends on water penetration, a more tightly packed crystalline material is less susceptible to dissolution than a ceramic that is mainly amorphous. Polycrystalline materials degrade more quickly than ceramics created from a single crystal due to the presence of grain boundaries. For the same reason, a material containing many smaller crystals is more susceptible to dissolution than one with fewer, larger crystals.

Degradation rates are also affected by the total amount of aqueous media available as well as the surface area of the implant. Therefore, highly porous materials will dissolve more quickly than the same ceramic with fewer pores due to the increase in area for interaction with the environment.

In addition to the factors listed previously, ceramic bioerosion is encouraged in areas of high mechanical stress, either due to the implant site location or the presence of stress raisers in the device. As discussed in previous sections, dissolution can also be mediated by biological factors such as a pH drop caused by the presence of inflammatory cells.

## 5.4.2  Biodegradable Polymers

### 5.4.2.1 Introduction to Biodegradable Polymers and Definitions

Biodegradable polymers can be either natural or synthetic-based. Synthetic polymers can be designed to degrade in aqueous environments due to hydrolysis, as explained earlier, or in response to the actions of specific enzymes. In contrast, naturally derived materials, which are often based on molecules found in mammalian tissues, usually undergo enzymatically induced cleavage. Hydrolytic degradation depends solely on the availability of water and is more consistent between patients. Enzyme levels may vary from patient to patient, creating potential problems in predicting material degradation rates for enzyme-responsive substances. However, because active enzymes are usually only found in particular tissues, enzymatically cleavable polymers allow for localized degradation, which may be an important advantage for applications like targeted drug delivery.

A wide variety of synthetic, hydrolytically degradable polymers have been synthesized. These include the common suture materials poly(lactic acid) and poly(glycolic acid), as well as poly(dioxanone), poly(propylene fumarate), and poly(trimethylene carbonate) for orthopedic applications. In addition, poly($\varepsilon$-caprolactone), poly(anhydride)s, poly(orthoester)s, poly(phosphazene)s, and poly(hydroxybutyrate)/poly(hydroxyvalerate) have been used for controlled drug delivery, while poly(cyanoacrylate)s have been utilized as tissue adhesives. The chemical structure of the repeat unit for each of these polymers is found in Figure 5.15.

**Figure 5.15**
Biodegradable polymers that have been explored for use in medical devices [16].

For polymers undergoing biodegradation via hydrolysis, two mechanisms can be distinguished: bulk and surface degradation. In **bulk degradation,** the rate of water ingress into the polymer is greater than the rate at which the polymer is converted into its (water-soluble) degradation products. Often, the implant will develop cracks and fissures before complete degradation occurs. Although most polymers degrade in this manner, the tendency of these materials to undergo a rapid decrease in mechanical properties leading to collapse of the implant in many small pieces may limit the potential applications of these polymers, particularly in load-bearing applications.

On the other hand, **surface degradation** occurs when the rate of water penetration into the material is less than the rate of polymer hydrolysis. In this case, the implant will decrease in thickness, but maintain much of its mechanical integrity during the degradation process. Surface-degrading materials represent a smaller subset of synthetic polymers. Of the biodegradable polymers mentioned earlier, only the poly(anhydrides) degrade via surface erosion. Such materials must possess highly hydrolytically labile bonds as well as hydrophobic moieties to prevent significant water penetration into the interior of the device. A potential disadvantage of surface-eroding polymers is that the continual turnover of the implant surface may make it difficult to establish good integration with the surrounding tissue *in vivo*.

## EXAMPLE PROBLEM 5.3

Identify which of the following is representative of bulk polymer degradation and which is representative of polymer surface degradation. Which series of stress–strain curves best represents each of the degradation series shown?

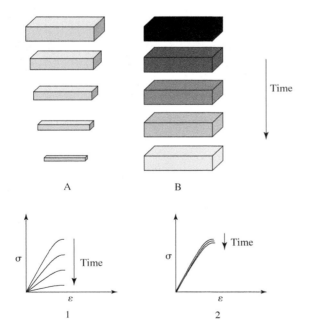

**Solution:** The series A is representative of surface degradation, as the dimensions of the polymer construct are decreasing with time as the surface of the material degrades. However, the structure of the material remains approximately the same with time; thus, the mechanical properties of the construct should change little with time, as illustrated in the stress–strain curve series 2. The degradation series B, however, represents bulk degradation, as the material maintains approximately the same gross dimensions, while polymer chains in the bulk of the material undergo increasing degradation with time. In this case, the mechanical properties of the bulk material would decrease substantially with time, as illustrated in the stress–strain curve series 1. ∎

**5.4.2.2 Degradation Mechanisms** Three general mechanisms exist for polymer biodegradation, regardless of whether the polymer is degraded via hydrolysis or enzymatic means. This is because the goal of both types of degradation is usually to produce relatively low-molecular weight products that are water soluble so that they may be cleared by the body's natural processes.

As depicted in Figure 5.16, degradation can be achieved by breaking bonds in crosslinks between the polymer chains, which are water soluble (Mechanism I). Alternatively, hydrophobic side chains may be cleaved to reveal hydrophilic groups, thus rendering the overall polymer water soluble (Mechanism II). In Mechanism III, there is attack of the polymer backbone itself, which is degraded into water-soluble monomers. In reality, two or more of these mechanisms often occur simultaneously during polymer biodegradation.

**5.4.2.3 Factors That Influence Degradation Rate** For enzymatically degradable materials, the rate of bioerosion depends most strongly on the amount of enzyme present at the implant site, as well as the number of cleavable moieties included in the polymer. Other types of polymers degrade via hydrolytic cleavage, so the factors governing degradation rate are the same as those discussed in the previous section on hydrolysis. These include the reactivity of the chemical groups in the polymer, the extent of primary and secondary bonding between chains, the amount of media available, and the surface area of the implant. A common example of the influence of secondary bonding on hydrolytic degradation is that it has been found that 50:50 copolymers of poly(L-lactic-co-glycolic acid) (PLGA, a suture

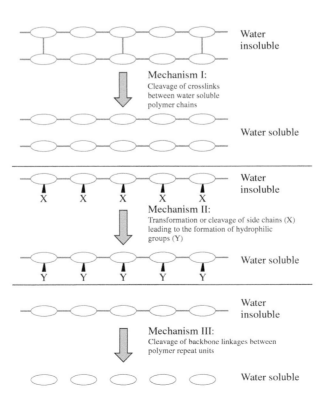

**Figure 5.16**
Three general mechanisms for polymer biodegradation [4].

material) degrade more quickly than either poly(L-lactic acid) or poly(glycolic acid), which has been attributed to the fact that the copolymer is amorphous, while the homopolymers are highly crystalline [7].

# 5.5 Techniques: Assays for Extent of Degradation

Quantification of biomaterial degradation (desired or undesired) can be carried out via either *in vitro* or *in vivo* testing. Often, *in vitro* experiments are first performed on new materials, and, if the degradation rate is acceptable, further *in vivo* assays are then undertaken. For *in vitro* testing, the material is cut to standard dimensions and then placed in vials containing a simulated body fluid with pH and ion content similar to what would be found *in vivo*.

*In vivo* experiments are more complicated and care must be taken to choose an animal model and an implantation site with characteristics similar to the intended location of final application in humans. This is extremely important, since, as discussed previously, implant-site parameters like pH and mechanical loading can have a large effect on the extent of material degradation during device function. More information on selection of appropriate animal models is found in Chapter 11.

For both *in vitro* and *in vivo* experiments, samples are taken at set time points during the course of the study and are then analyzed for signs of degradation (see Figure 5.17 for an example). This includes weighing the sample to determine mass loss and measuring different physical and chemical properties, as well as visual inspection to appreciate changes in properties such as color and the appearance of cracks. Often, the material surface is further characterized using light or electron microscopy, as well as other surface analysis techniques like those described in Chapter 7.

To estimate corrosion of metallic implants *in vitro*, however, measuring changes in weight is often insufficient since the total amount of material lost in this process can be very small. A number of alternative methods for corrosion analysis have been developed (see [8], [9]). One of the most common techniques involves *electrochemical testing*, which measures the current in a test metal resting in simulated body fluid as the potential is changed. This method is based on the concept that oxidation and reduction reactions that cause corrosion are, in essence, producing electron movement, or current. The data are then plotted as potential (*y*-axis) vs. current density (*x*-axis) and the resulting curves are used to estimate corrosion rates in various *in vivo* environments.

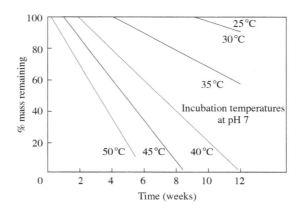

**Figure 5.17**
Example of data from in vitro degradation experiments conducted in saline at various temperatures [7].

# Summary

- Uncontrolled degradation of a biomaterial is usually undesirable, as it often leads to the structural decomposition of a material and failure of the device. Controlled degradation, however, occurs in accordance with designed and expected parameters to serve a desired purpose, such as the controlled release of bioactive factors.

- Degradation of metals (corrosion) occurs through the coupling of oxidative and reductive processes in redox reactions. These reactions result in the slow dissolution of the metal at the site at which oxidation occurs (anode).

- Corrosion of metals depends upon a number of factors. The Nernst equation and Pourbaix diagrams facilitate the prediction of the corrosion activity of a metal under certain conditions.

- Various aspects of the processing and handling of a metal can contribute to its corrosion. Narrow cracks or crevices within a metal or between two metal surfaces can lead to crevice corrosion, in which the metal in the crevice acts as an anode. Pitting corrosion occurs by the same process in small flaws or breaks in the passivation layer on the surface of a metal. Intergranular corrosion can occur as a result of the high energy at grain boundaries, which may serve as anodic regions.

- The mechanical environment can also contribute to the corrosion of a metal. The bending of a metal rod or plate will cause the side under tension to be anodic with respect to the side under compression, leading to galvanic corrosion. Small cracks can form and propagate in a metal under tension in a corrosive environment leading to brittle fracture (stress corrosion cracking). The passivating film on a metal implant may become disturbed through cyclic bending, loading, or motion and lead to corrosion in the area (fatigue corrosion). Fretting corrosion, however, does not involve loading, but is dependent on the removal of the metal's passivating layer by mechanical means.

- The biological environment of a metal (e.g., presence of proteins, cells, or bacteria) can influence its corrosion rate.

- Ceramics degrade primarily via dissolution and are susceptible to failure via stress-induced degradation. Polymers typically degrade by either swelling/dissolution or chain scission. The chain scission mechanism of degradation can occur through hydrolysis (caused by presence of water) or oxidation (caused by presence of reactive free radical species).

- Biodegradable ceramics generally degrade by dissolution (influenced by the solubility of the ceramic formulation in the media and the pH of the media) coupled with physical disintegration. The rate of degradation of ceramics is controlled by the chemical susceptibility of the material, the degree of crystallinity, the amount of water available and the surface area to volume ratio of the material. Degradation can be additionally influenced by the mechanical environment.

- The degradation of enzymatically degradable polymers depends on the number of enzyme-cleavable groups and the concentration of available enzyme. Degradation of polymers by hydrolysis can be controlled through the reactivity of the chemical groups in the polymer, the extent of primary and secondary bonding between the polymer chains, the amount of available water, and the surface area of the material.

- Bulk hydrolytic degradation occurs when the rate of water ingress into the polymer is greater than the rate at which the polymer is converted into its water-soluble degradation products. Surface degradation, however, takes place when the rate of water ingress into the material is less than the rate of polymer hydrolysis.

# Problems

5.1 How would the following affect the rate of corrosion of a stainless steel bone fixation plate? Increase, decrease, or not affect? Justify your answer.

    (a) Presence of proteins on the surface of the plate
    (b) Presence of small scratches on the surface of the implant
    (c) Presence of a screw that attaches the plate to the underlying bone

5.2 One method to quantify amount of metal corrosion is to assay the amount of metal ions released into the surrounding environment over a certain period of time. Why is this a good method? Justify your answer based on how corrosion works at a molecular level.

5.3 Dumbbells of the polymer poly(L-lactic acid) (PLLA) were stretched a small amount using a mechanical testing device (not to the point of failure) as a way to alter the material properties. A 1 cm cube of each of these samples (stretched vs. non-stretched) is placed in water. One degrades much more quickly than the other. Which degrades faster and why?

5.4 Why does one need a hydrophobic component in a surface-degrading polymer? Explain from a molecular perspective.

5.5 You want to achieve controlled, linear drug release from a biomaterial to be used in a wide variety of applications. Provide a rationale for your choices below.

    (a) Would you choose a synthetic or natural material?
    (b) Do you think enzymatic or hydrolytic degradation would be preferred? If hydrolytic, would you choose surface or bulk degradation?
    (c) What is one major chemical or physical property that you would alter to tune the rate of degradation? Explain why at a molecular level this would affect overall degradation.

# References

1. D. F. Williams and R. L. Williams, "Degradative effects of the biological environment on metals and ceramics," in *Biomaterials science: an introduction to materials and medicine*, 2nd ed., B. D. Ratner, A. S. Hoffman, F. J. Schoen, and J. E. Lemons, Eds. San Diego: Elsevier Academic Press, 2004, pp. 430–439.

2. W.D. Callister Jr., *Materials science and engineering: an introduction*, 3rd ed. New York: John Wiley and Sons, 1994.

3. American Society for Metals, *Metals handbook. Vol. 1. Properties and selection of metal*, 8th ed., vol. 1. Materials Park, OH: ASM International, 1961.

4. J. Kohn, S. Abramson, and R. Langer, "Bioresorbable and bioerodible materials," in *Biomaterials science: an introduction to materials and medicine*, 2nd ed., B. D. Ratner, A. S. Hoffman, F. J. Schoen, and J. E. Lemons, Eds. San Diego: Elsevier Academic Press, 2004, pp. 115–127.

5. L. L. Hench and S. M. Best, "Ceramics, glasses, and glass-ceramics: basic principles," in *Biomaterials science: an introduction to materials and medicine*, 3rd ed., B. D. Ratner, A. S. Hoffman, F. J. Schoen, and J. E. Lemons, Eds. San Diego: Elsevier Academic Press, 2013, pp. 128–151.

6. A. Krajewski and A. Ravaglioli, "Bioceramics and biological glasses," in *Integrated biomaterials science*, 1st ed., R. Barbucci, Ed. New York: Springer Science & Business Media, 2002, pp. 189–254.

7. A. M. Reed and D. K. Gilding, "Biodegradable polymers for use in surgery—poly (glycolic)/poly (lactic acid) homo and copolymers: 2. In vitro degradation," *Polymer*, vol. 22, no. 4, pp. 494–498, 1981.

8. K. J. Bundy, "Corrosion and other electrochemical aspects of biomaterials," *Critical Reviews in Biomedical Engineering*, vol. 22, no. 3–4, pp. 139–251, 1994.

9. J. E. Lemons, R. Venugopalan, and L. C. Lucs, "Corrosion and biodegradation," in *Handbook of biomaterials evaluation*, 2nd ed., A. von Recum, Ed. Taylor Francis Inc., 1999, pp. 155–170.

10. R. Myers, *The basics of chemistry*. Westport: Greenwood Press, 2003.

11. M. Pourbaix, "Electrochemical corrosion of metallic biomaterials," *Biomaterials*, vol. 5, no. 3, pp. 122–134, 1984.

12. E. Angelini, A. Caputo, and F. Zucchi, "Degradation process on metallic surfaces," in *Integrated biomaterials science*, R. Barbucci, Ed. New York: Kluwer, 2002, pp. 297–324.

13. M. G. Fontana, *Corrosion engineering*, 3rd ed. New York: McGraw-Hill, 1986.

14. D. F. Williams and R. L. Williams, "Degradative effects of the biological environment on metals and ceramics," in *Biomaterials science: an introduction to materials and medicine*, 1st ed., B. D. Ratner, A. S. Hoffman, F. J. Schoen, and J. E. Lemons, Eds. San Diego: Elsevier Academic Press, 1996, pp. 260–267.

15. A. J. Coury, "Chemical and biochemical degradation of polymers," in *Biomaterials science: an introduction to materials and medicine*, 2nd ed., B. D. Ratner, A. S. Hoffman, F. J. Schoen, and J. E. Lemons, Eds. San Diego: Elsevier Academic Press, 2004, pp. 411–430.

16. M. Treiser, S. Abramson, R. Langer, and J. Kohn, "Degradable and resorbable materials," in *Biomaterials science: an introduction to materials and medicine*, 3rd ed., B. D. Ratner, A. S. Hoffman, F. J. Schoen, and J. E. Lemons, Eds. San Diego: Elsevier Academic Press, 2013, pp. 179–195.

17. A. J. Coury, "Chemical and biochemical degradation of polymers intended to be biostable," in *Biomaterials science: an introduction to materials and medicine*, 3rd ed., B. D. Ratner, A. S. Hoffman, F. J. Schoen, and J. E. Lemons, Eds. San Diego: Elsevier Academic Press, 2013, pp. 698–715.

# Additional Reading

W. C. Billotte, "Ceramic biomaterials," in *Biomaterials*, J. Y. Wong and J. D. Bronzino, Eds. Boca Raton: CRC Press, 2007, pp. 2–1 through 2-34.

J. Black, *Biological performance of materials: fundamentals of biocompatibility*, 4th ed. New York: CRC Press, 2005.

J. Black and G. Hastings, *Handbook of biomaterial properties*. London: Chapman and Hall, 1998.

F. Burny, Y. Andrianne, M. Donkerwolke, and J. Quintin, "Clinical manifestations of biomaterials degradation in orthopaedics and traumatology," in *Biomaterials degradation*, M. A. Barbosa, Ed. Amsterdam: Elsevier Science, 1991, pp. 291–326.

N. M. K. Lamba, K. A. Woodhouse, and S. L. Cooper, *Polyurethanes in biomedical applications*. New York: CRC Press, 1998.

H.-Y. Lin and J. D. Bumgardner, "Changes in surface composition of the Ti–6Al–4V implant alloy by cultured macrophage cells," *Applied Surface Science*, vol. 225, no. 1–4, pp. 21–28, 2004.

H.-Y. Lin and J. D. Bumgardner, "In vitro biocorrosion of Co- Cr-Mo implant alloy by macrophage cells," *Journal of Orthopaedic Research*, vol. 22, no. 6, pp. 1231–1236, 2004.

S. Lyu and D. Untereker, "Degradability of polymers for implantable biomedical devices," *International Journal of Molecular Sciences*, vol. 10, no. 9, pp. 4033–4065, 2009.

J. B. Park and R. S. Lakes, *Biomaterials: an introduction*, 2nd ed. New York: Plenum Press, 1992.

D. W. Oxtoby, N. H. Nachtrieb, and W. A. Freeman, *Chemistry: science of change*. Philadelphia: Saunders College Publishing, 1990.

J. F. Shackelford, *Introduction to materials science for engineers*, 6th ed. Upper Saddle River: Prentice Hall, 2004.

# Biomaterial Processing

C H A P T E R

6

**Main Objective**

To understand the need and techniques for processing to improve strength, form desired shapes, and sterilize all classes of biomaterials.

**Specific Objectives**

1. To understand the molecular mechanisms behind strengthening techniques for metals and polymers.
2. To understand how thermal processing affects microstructure and bulk properties of metals and polymers.
3. To compare and contrast types of forming techniques for metals, ceramics, and polymers.
4. To understand the need for, killing mechanisms of, and limitations of various sterilization techniques.

## 6.1 Introduction: Importance of Biomaterials Processing

In previous chapters, chemical principles underlying both the creation and degradation of metallic, ceramic, and polymeric biomaterials were explained. This chapter concentrates on the practical processes relating to the formation of these materials into shapes, and how these processes affect their chemical compositions.

Processing of biomaterials is usually undertaken to change the bulk or surface properties of the material, obtain a desired shape, or sterilize or otherwise improve the biocompatibility of the material. This chapter will describe mechanisms for altering bulk properties and then discuss shaping techniques and processing for biocompatibility. Methods for altering surface properties of biomaterials are the subject of the following chapter.

## 6.2 Processing to Improve Bulk Properties

Most often, the bulk property targeted in material processing is mechanical strength. A number of methods for improving the strength of various classes of biomaterials have been developed. As mentioned in Chapter 4, in order to create stronger or

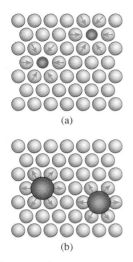

**Figure 6.1**
Localized lattice strain caused by alloying. (a) If the impurity atom is smaller than those in the base metal, a tensile strain will be created on the surrounding environment. (b) Conversely, a substitute atom that is larger than the host atoms will cause localized compressive strains.

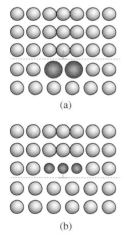

**Figure 6.2**
Crystal distortion around a dislocation. Any impurity atoms will cluster around the area of a dislocation to help cancel the lattice strains. (a) Larger atoms will cluster on the tensile side of a dislocation, whereas (b) smaller atoms will cluster on the compressive side.

harder materials, dislocation motion should be reduced so that more energy is needed before plastic deformation can occur. Methods to prevent dislocation movement, as well as the reasons they are effective, are outlined in the following paragraphs.

### 6.2.1 Metals

Processing is a very efficient means to affect mechanical properties in metals. In these materials, defects can be added to the crystal structure to prevent dislocation motion. These can be in the form of point, line, planar, or volume defects and are introduced via the mechanisms described later in the chapter. A summary of how different processes detailed here and in section 6.3 affect the strength of metals is found in Table 6.1.

**6.2.1.1 Alloying** In addition to having greater corrosion resistance, alloys are almost always stronger than pure metals. This is because alloys are a type of solid solution, and thus, alloying is like adding many substitutional point defects to the base metal. These point defects cause localized lattice strain, as seen in Figure 6.1. If the impurity atom is smaller than those in the base metal, a tensile strain will be created locally as the atoms cannot optimally bond with their neighbors (see Fig. 6.1(a)). Similarly, a substitute atom that is larger than the host atoms will cause localized compressive strain (Fig. 6.1(b)).

At the same time, there is crystal distortion around a dislocation, of either a tensile or compressive nature, depending on which side of the dislocation the atoms are located. Therefore, as depicted in Figure 6.2, impurity atoms can cluster around the area of a dislocation to help cancel the lattice strains imposed by both of these phenomena. For example, it would be more stable for large atoms to lie on the "tensile side" of an edge dislocation where the atoms are already slightly farther apart due to the presence of the dislocation. If the dislocation is moved away from the impurity, the overall lattice strain in the system would increase. This must be overcome by increasing the shear stress required to cause dislocation movement, thus strengthening the material.

### EXAMPLE PROBLEM 6.1

316L stainless steel is an alloy containing about 70% iron with 30% other metals, usually chromium and nickel. Consider an alloy of about 70% iron, 18% chromium, and 12% nickel.

(a) Would the alloy be mechanically weaker or stronger than pure iron? Why?
(b) Given that the atomic radius of an iron atom is 1.24Å, the radius of a chromium atom is 1.25Å, and the radius of a nickel atom is 1.25Å, will the chromium and nickel atoms in the lattice cause localized tensile or compressive strain? Why?
(c) Name the type of defect created by the addition of copper atoms.

**TABLE 6.1**

| Processing Methods and Their Effect on the Properties of Metals | |
|---|---|
| Strengthens | Weakens |
| Alloying | Annealing |
| Cold working | Hot working |
| Precipitation hardening | Porosity (due to casting and powder processing) |

[1]

**Solution:**

(a) The alloy would be mechanically stronger than the pure iron, as the other atoms serve as point defects in the lattice, introducing lattice strains and increasing the energy needed for dislocation motion.

(b) As the chromium and nickel (impurity) radii are slightly larger than that of the iron, the presence of the impurity atoms in the material will cause localized compressive strain.

(c) The impurity atoms serve as substitutional point defects.  ∎

**6.2.1.2  Strain Hardening**   Just as adding point defects improves the strength of a metal, additional line defects also create a stronger material. The phenomenon in which a metal becomes stronger as it is plastically deformed is known as **strain hardening**, and is due to an increase in the number of dislocations (line defects) during this process. As mentioned above, there is lattice strain associated with each dislocation, and it requires more energy to move the stress field of a dislocation through the combined localized strains resulting from other dislocations. Because during plastic deformation there is a continual increase in the number of dislocations, it is logical that higher and higher forces will be required to continue deformation.

Strain hardening is also called **cold working** since it is carried out at low temperatures relative to the melting point of metals. Although this process improves the strength of the material, there is a concomitant reduction in ductility. If the ductility of the cold-worked metal is not sufficient for the intended application, the effects of strain hardening can be reduced by annealing procedures (discussed later in this chapter).

**6.2.1.3  Grain Size Refinement**   Most commonly used metals are polycrystalline, consisting of grains with different orientations sharing a common boundary. In order for plastic deformation to occur, dislocations must cross between grains. However, if the orientations of the neighboring grains are not the same, the direction of dislocation motion must be altered at the grain boundary. This becomes more difficult with increasing misalignment between grains. Additionally, this mismatch will result in a discontinuity of slip planes between grains, further discouraging dislocation motion.

For these reasons, a material with many smaller grains is usually stronger than the same material with larger grains. In essence, planar defects have been added to the smaller-grained material in the form of grain boundaries. Grain size can be affected by thermal processing, as described in the following section. However, as discussed above, not only the size, but also the relative orientations of the grains are important to the overall mechanical properties of the material, since smaller-angle grain boundaries are not as effective in preventing dislocation motion as larger-angle boundaries.

**6.2.1.4  Annealing**   Cold working improves the strength of metals, but decreases material ductility and can negatively affect corrosion resistance. Therefore, heat treatment may be employed to recover some of these properties. **Annealing** is a form of heat treatment in which the material is exposed to high temperatures for relatively long periods of time in order to increase the ductility or toughness of the material, reduce internal stresses (these often promote corrosive attack, see Chapter 5), or produce a specific grain structure.

Although there are a number of means by which heat treatment affects grain size, one of the most important is that, due to the excess energy associated with the grain boundary, reduction in the total amount of these boundaries is favored thermodynamically. Thus, at high temperatures where atomic diffusion is encouraged, larger grains will spontaneously grow while the smaller ones shrink, leading to an overall increase in the size of the grains and concomitant decrease in area of the grain boundaries.

Annealing occurs in three distinct stages: heating to the required temperature, maintaining or "soaking" the material at that temperature, and controlled cooling (**quenching**). Parameters that affect the product resulting from the annealing process include the material composition and the quenching rate. The quenching rate actually refers to the rate of heat extraction from the material, which is important because the outside of the specimen will always cool more quickly than the inside. This leads to the formation of a temperature gradient that can affect the final grain structure and thus the overall properties of the metal.

Heat extraction depends on the media in which the material is quenched—water causes a faster cooling rate than oil, which is faster than air. Movement of the quenching media over the surface also increases heat extraction and causes a more rapid quench. Similarly, because cooling occurs primarily at the surface, pieces with a higher surface area to volume ratio will experience faster quenching.

## EXAMPLE PROBLEM 6.2

Imagine a material scientist (in this case a blacksmith) in late Medieval Europe trying to fashion a metallic hip implant. The blacksmith was able to cast a femoral stem-shaped implant from steel, but has hypothesized that the mechanical properties are not sufficient for use in a hip application. After some thought, the blacksmith grips the implant with tongs, submerges it among blazing hot coals for several minutes, then removes it and strikes it repeatedly with a hammer against an anvil. When the red glow of the implant begins to dim, the smithy replaces it in the coals and repeats the hammering process for several cycles.

(a) Will the cycles of hammering the hot implant increase the mechanical strength of the implant? Why or why not?
(b) If the strength of the implant increases with the hammering cycles, would the ductility of the material potentially be affected? Why or why not?
(c) Name the processing technique that the blacksmith has employed.
(d) The blacksmith thinks that the material has become too strong and brittle after his hammering cycles. He has decided to place the implant in hot coals overnight then remove it to cool in the air in the morning. Could this process increase the ductility of the implant? How?
(e) After heating the implant in coals overnight, the blacksmith realizes that he has several options for cooling the glowing hot implant. He can (1) submerge it in a bucket of water from the stream behind his shack, (2) submerge it in the flowing stream behind his shack, (3) submerge it in a bucket of oil, or (4) stick with the original plan of letting it cool in the air. Rank the methods of cooling the implant in order from the slowest to the quickest.

Solution:

(a) The cycles of hammering the hot implant will increase the strength of the implant through introduction of line defects into the crystal structure of the metal. As the number of dislocations increases with increasing hammering, they begin to interact on an increased basis. The increased number of dislocations and the lattice strains that they create result in an increase in the energy or force required to deform the material plastically. Thus, the material becomes stronger through the introduction and interaction of dislocations.
(b) The increase in strength introduced through the hammering cycles comes at the potential cost of a loss in ductility. As more energy is required to plastically deform the metal, the metal does not yield as easily with applied forces, making it less ductile.
(c) The blacksmith employed the process of strain hardening or cold working. Interestingly, the term "blacksmith" (one who works in metal) is derived from the word "smite" (to hit or strike).
(d) The proposed process of heating the implant to a high temperature below the melting point of the metal for an extended time, then cooling it could increase the ductility of

the implant through reducing some of the internal stresses in the metal. The energy associated with the high temperature facilitates the diffusion of atoms in the lattice to form larger grains (decrease in the area of the grain boundaries). The decrease in grain boundaries increases the ductility of the material by lowering the energy required to plastically deform the implant.

(e) Cooling in air < cooling in bucket of oil < cooling in bucket of water < cooling in running stream of water. ∎

**6.2.1.5 Precipitation Hardening** In the previous sections, means to insert point, linear, and planar defects into metals to reduce dislocation motion have been reviewed. In the same vein, volume defects may be added to a material via **precipitation hardening**. Here, precipitates are included within the host crystal, which causes local lattice strains. These strains then provide a barrier to dislocation motion in the area, thereby strengthening the material.

## 6.2.2 Ceramics

Due to the nature of the ionic bonds involved, dislocation motion in ceramics is difficult, and therefore there is little use for techniques to further reduce dislocation movement. On the contrary, a large problem in ceramics processing is how to increase the number of slip systems to improve ductility of this class of materials. Descriptions of these techniques are beyond the scope of this text.

## 6.2.3 Polymers

As with ionic materials, dislocation motion is difficult in covalent crystals, but many polymers are semi-crystalline, so it is possible to improve the strength of polymeric materials by increasing their percent crystallinity. One way to achieve this is through thermal processing methods. If the polymer is cooled slowly after being heated, this will allow time for the chains to become more fully aligned, thus increasing the crystallinity of the material. This increase in crystallinity is described by the Avrami equation discussed in Chapter 3 (equation 3.3).

Another means to improve the strength of polymers is to use pre-drawing procedures, which are analogous to strain hardening in metals. As mentioned in Chapter 4, polymer chains become aligned in response to deformation, such as in the necked region of a sample undergoing tensile testing. If such a method is applied to a material during or after fabrication (such as may occur with polymer fibers, see below), this can increase the overall strength along the axis of loading.

The strength and hardness of polymeric materials can also be augmented with additional crosslinking, which reduces the ability of chains to slide past each other. This can be accomplished by exposing the polymer to either chemical initiators or high-energy radiation after it has been formed into the desired geometry.

### EXAMPLE PROBLEM 6.3

A graduate student finished a six-pack of soda and decided to pull on the polymer rings that formerly held the cans together. The student placed the index and middle finger of each hand through opposite sides of one of the rings and moved her hands outward in opposite directions, stretching the polymer ring. The student found that pulling the ring required a lot of force initially, then less force, and finally a great deal more force just before the ring broke. Draw a generalized stress–strain curve that could be used to describe the mechanical behavior of the polymer ring (no numerical values needed). Explain the observed behavior on a molecular level. How did the tensile force likely affect the crystallinity of the polymer in the area of greatest stress?

**Solution:** The polymer sample underwent necking during the tensile testing by hand. A general stress–strain curve for what was described is as follows:

It can be assumed that the polymer is a semi-crystalline material. As the polymer is initially pulled with tensile force, the polymer chains (lamellae and tie molecules) begin to align along the axis of the applied force. This process of chain alignment along the axis of force is represented in the initial slope of the curve. The next region of the curve illustrating great increases in strain with little stress represents blocks of crystalline phases separating from each other and aligning along the axis of force. Once the polymer chains are aligned and extended, more force is needed for further strains to disrupt primary interactions in the polymer backbone, leading to breakage of the soda can ring. The alignment of the polymer chains along the axis of force in the area of greatest stress resulted in an increased percent crystallinity of the polymer in that region.  ∎

## 6.3 Processing to Form Desired Shapes

Although strengthening mechanisms that involve the reduction of plastic deformation can be very useful to improve the final properties of biomaterials, it should be noted that plastic deformation is crucial to the utility of many materials because it allows for fabrication of complex shapes. Processing methods to produce implants with desired geometries include forming, casting, powder processing, machining, and joining operations. In addition, the past decade has brought significant development of rapid manufacturing (also called rapid prototyping) technologies. Examples of these techniques as applied to processing of each class of biomaterials are discussed in the following sections.

## 6.4 Processing of Metals

### 6.4.1 Forming Metals

**Forming** operations are those in which the shape of a metal is altered via plastic deformation. Forging, rolling, extrusion, and drawing are all common forming techniques. If these processes are conducted at temperatures at or above about $0.3T_m$ (the recrystallization temperature), this is termed **hot working**. If the deformation occurs at a lower temperature, this is cold working, which was discussed previously. The advantages of hot working are that large deformations are possible and the energy required for these deformations is less than would be needed in cold working. However, during this process, materials often undergo surface oxidation, which results in a poor finish.

**Figure 6.3**
Diagram of closed-die forging process. In this manufacturing technique, a force is exerted on two die halves, which causes the deformation of the stock material (blank) into the desired shape.

**Figure 6.4**
Schematic of rolling process. Here, the metal is placed between two rollers that exert compressive forces on the material and cause a reduction in thickness as the material is fed through the rollers. This process can be performed at room temperature or higher.

In contrast, cold-worked metals are stronger and have a more appealing surface finish. Additionally, there is better control of the dimensions of the final product if the forming procedure is carried out at lower temperatures. Disadvantages of cold working include that smaller amounts of deformation may be possible than in hot working and that materials often experience a decrease in ductility and corrosion resistance after undergoing this process.

**6.4.1.1 Forging Metals** **Forging** has been used for centuries by blacksmiths in order to create items such as tools, horseshoes, and jewelry. A common type of modern forging, closed-die forging, is depicted in Figure 6.3. In this procedure, a force is exerted on the two die halves so that the stock metal is deformed and takes the shape of the cavity between them. This method is one of those commonly used for forming orthopedic implants from a variety of metals, including titanium and stainless steel.

**6.4.1.2 Rolling Metals** As the name implies, **rolling** involves moving a metal between two rollers, which exert compressive forces on the material and cause a reduction in thickness. An illustration of this process can be found in Figure 6.4. Rolling is employed to form stock shapes (bars, rods, etc.) for further processing to create orthopedic and dental implants.

**6.4.1.3 Extrusion of Metals** As shown in Figure 6.5, in **extrusion,** the stock metal is pushed through a die containing an orifice via forces generated by the ram. The final piece that emerges has the required shape and a smaller cross-sectional area than the stock. This technique can be used to form wires, such as those utilized in orthodontics.

**6.4.1.4 Drawing Metals** **Drawing** is similar to extrusion, but rather than pushing on the entrance side, the metal is pulled from the exit side through a die having a

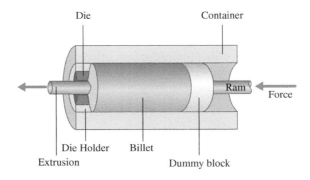

Die    Container

Ram    Force

Die Holder    Billet
Extrusion    Dummy block

**Figure 6.5**
Schematic of extrusion process. The stock metal is pushed (via the forces generated by a ram) through a die containing an orifice of the desired shape. Altering the die can allow the piece that emerges to have a variety of cross-sectional shapes.

**Figure 6.6**
Schematic of drawing process. This is similar to extrusion, except that the stock material is pulled through the die, not pushed through.

Tensile force

tapered orifice (see Fig. 6.6). The result is a product with a smaller cross-sectional area and greater length than the original. Drawing devices can be used in series to obtain final pieces with a variety of dimensions. Metal wire and tubing are often manufactured in this manner. Drawing is also used to form stock shapes for orthopedic and dental applications.

As mentioned in Chapter 3, after extrusion or drawing, fine metal fibers may be fabricated into three-dimensional meshes, which have been explored recently as substrate materials for tissue engineering applications. Although a variety of techniques exist for mesh formation, often nonwoven meshes are created from metals. In this case, the fibers are aligned and then bonded together in a specific structure using thermal or mechanical means (e.g., sintering/pressing techniques described below). However, it must be kept in mind that metal meshes have limited use in the tissue engineering field because they are not intrinsically biodegradable.

### 6.4.2 Casting Metals

**Casting** is another means of forming complex shapes from metallic materials. In this procedure, molten metal is poured into a mold and cooled. When it solidifies, it retains the shape of the mold, although some shrinkage occurs. The advantage of this fabrication technique is that complicated shapes can be easily created, even with less ductile metals than those that are commonly used in forming. In addition, it is relatively inexpensive. However, internal defects (such as pores) and less desirable grain structures are found more often in cast products than in pieces produced by other methods. Two of the many types of casting, sand and investment casting, are described in the following sections.

**6.4.2.1 Sand Casting of Metals**   One of the most simple and commonly used casting methods is **sand casting**. In this procedure, sand is packed around an object that has the shape of the intended piece (the pattern) to make a two-piece mold. The pattern is then removed and the molten metal is poured into the mold. After cooling, the mold is removed, as shown in Figure 6.7.

**6.4.2.2 Investment Casting of Metals**   **Investment casting** (or lost-wax casting) is similar to sand casting, but here the pattern is created from a wax or polymer with a low melting point. The pattern is encased in a slurry (usually plaster of Paris) to produce the mold, and the entire object is heated to melt and/or burn out the pattern. The mold (now containing a void space) is then filled with molten metal and allowed to cool. This process is illustrated in Figure 6.8. Cobalt-chromium alloys, often used in hip and knee implants, are commonly investment cast.

### 6.4.3 Powder Processing of Metals

Powder processing, or **powder metallurgy** (**P/M**), techniques are often used to create shapes from metals with low ductility or very high melting points. First the metal is ground into a fine powder. The powder is then placed in a mold and compressed to

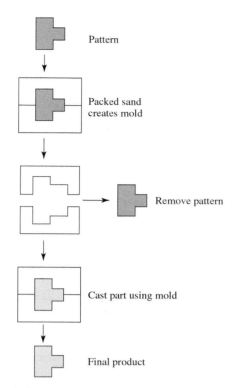

**Figure 6.7**
Diagram of sand casting process. First, sand is packed around an object that has the shape of the intended piece (the pattern) to make a two-piece mold. The pattern is removed and the molten metal is poured into the mold. After cooling, the mold is separated, resulting in the final product.

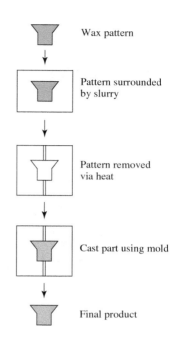

**Figure 6.8**
Diagram of investment casting process. A pattern is first created from a wax or polymer with a low melting point. The pattern is encased in a slurry to produce the mold, and the entire object is heated to melt and/or burn out the pattern. The empty mold is then filled with molten metal and allowed to cool, resulting in the final piece when the mold is separated.

create a denser material with good particle-to-particle contact. After this stage, the piece is termed a green compact.

The green compact then usually undergoes further compaction at elevated temperatures, known as **hot isostatic pressing (HIP)**. Pressures of up to 100 MPa and temperatures up to 1100°C are typically used for this process. During HIP, the metal powder is **sintered**, or densified by removal of small voids between particles, as shown in Figure 6.9. The driving force for sintering is the high energy associated with the many surfaces present due to the small size of the metal particles. Therefore,

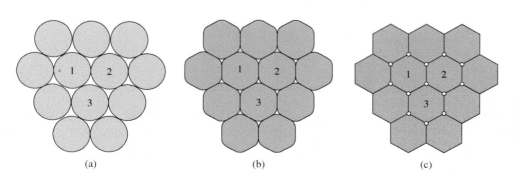

**Figure 6.9**
Diagram of sintering process used in powder metallurgy. The green compact (a) is compressed and heated (b) until the small pores between the particles have been removed (c) [4].

at high temperatures, amalgamation of these particles is favored to reduce the overall energy of the system. In this way, it is possible to create virtually non-porous materials. P/M techniques are also useful in fabricating products requiring very close tolerances. Cobalt-chromium alloys can undergo HIP as well as investment casing.

### 6.4.4 Rapid Manufacturing of Metals

In the past decade, technologies allowing for rapid fabrication of objects with very precise dimensions have become increasingly common. Although originally named rapid prototyping, these methods have been developed to the extent that they can now quickly produce final pieces, rather than just prototypes. Therefore, a more accurate term for these processes is **rapid manufacturing**, also known as **solid freeform fabrication (SFF)**. Rapid manufacturing begins with the creation of a three-dimensional image of the final product using computer-aided design (CAD) software. This rendering is then processed and signals are sent to the manufacturing apparatus to accurately reproduce the desired geometry.

Although many types of rapid manufacturing methods exist, one of the most common for metallic materials, **selective laser sintering (SLS)**, involves many of the same principles as for P/M. In this case, a powdered metal is spread evenly on a moveable platform and a laser is scanned over the surface, providing enough localized energy to selectively sinter the top layer of powder according to CAD instructions, creating a solid cross section that will become a part of the final product. As shown in Figure 6.10, the platform is then moved down and the next layer of powder is added, after which the process is repeated to build subsequent layers. Because the laser can be directed at very small areas, complicated internal geometries including fibers, channels, or interconnected pores can be produced during the fabrication process. Additionally, because the powder bed provides support for subsequent layers, complex, branching macro-architectures can be developed without needing to sinter artificial supports.

### 6.4.5 Welding Metals

Welding is a process used to join two materials together. During welding, the contact location of the metals is heated to their melting point, a metallic filler is added,

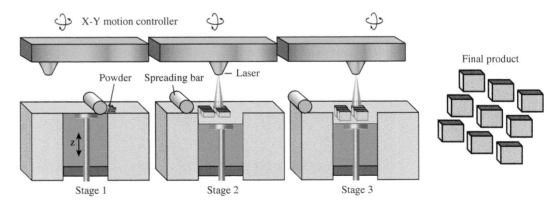

**Figure 6.10**
Diagram of selective laser sintering (SLS) process. In stage 1, a powdered metal is spread evenly on a moveable platform and, in stage 2, a laser is scanned over the surface, providing enough localized energy to sinter the top of the powder where required and create a small solid layer that will become part of the final product. The platform is then moved down and the process is repeated to build the next layer (Stage 3). In this way, products with complex shapes can be created.

and the connection is allowed to cool, resulting in a solid bridge of metal between the two materials. Welding is a technique that is used after the previously-mentioned manufacturing techniques to allow for the formation of more complex shapes.

### 6.4.6 Machining of Metals

During machining, a cutting implement (such as a blade rotated at high speeds or a laser) is used to remove material from a stock piece, resulting in shapes that are too complex or costly to construct using one of the previously-mentioned techniques. Machining is commonly performed on metals and polymers (ceramics are generally too brittle) as a second step after one of the other manufacturing techniques.

## 6.5 Processing of Ceramics

There are several types of ceramic biomaterials, including glasses, crystalline ceramics, and glass-ceramics (defined later in the chapter). Each has different processing methods as well as distinct final properties. Although many variants exist, the most common procedures for creating specific shapes from each type of ceramic are discussed in this section. Layering of ceramics on top of preshaped materials is also possible through plasma spray coating techniques, which are discussed in Chapter 7.

### 6.5.1 Glass Forming Techniques

Because glasses are completely amorphous (no grains present), heat treatment is required to form them into shapes, but it does not significantly affect their mechanical properties. The **softening point** for a glass is arbitrarily defined as the temperature when its viscosity is $4 \times 10^7$ P This is the maximum temperature at which the piece can be handled without significant changes in shape. At higher temperatures, such as the **working point** (the temperature when its viscosity is $10^4$ P ), the glass is easily deformed. Therefore, the glass is usually shaped between these two temperatures.

In this temperature range, the glass may be formed via several methods, including pressing, blowing, and drawing. **Pressing** is similar to forging of metals and involves applying an even pressure to a softened glass placed in a heated mold. Upon cooling, the glass will retain the shape of the mold. In modern commercial glass **blowing** operations, pressing techniques are first used to form the stock glass into a shape generally similar to the final product, called a **parison** (see Fig. 6.11). The parison is then placed into a more detailed mold (a finishing mold) and a jet of air forces the soft glass to conform to the shape of the mold.

**Figure 6.11**
In modern commercial glass blowing operations, pressing techniques are first used to form the stock glass into a shape called a parison, which is of similar shape to the final product. The parison is then placed into a more detailed mold (finishing mold) and a jet of air forces the soft glass to conform to the shape of the mold.

**Figure 6.12**
The drawing processes in glasses are analogous to those for metals. Here, molten glass is pulled over a series of rollers to form long pieces such as sheets or tubing [3].

Drawing processes in glasses are analogous to those for metals. Here, molten glass can be pulled over rollers to form long pieces such as sheets or tubing (see Fig. 6.12). Alternatively, the glass may be drawn through small orifices at the bottom of a heating tank to form fibers. As discussed above for metals, it is possible to use glass fibers to form three-dimensional scaffolds for tissue engineering applications, but glass-based scaffolds have not been widely explored due to their lack of biodegradability. (However, certain bioactive glasses have been used to improve bone bonding in orthopedics; see Chapter 7.)

### 6.5.2 Casting and Firing of Ceramics

**6.5.2.1 Casting Ceramics**   As with metals, *casting* can also be used for ceramics to produce specific geometries. This method is preferred for work with crystalline ceramic materials and glass-ceramics rather than with amorphous glasses. After the formation of a relatively non-porous mold via a variety of means, small ceramic particles are mixed with water and an organic binder material and then are poured/pressed into the mold.

After molding, the piece is left to dry and, as the water evaporates, the ceramic shrinks away from the walls of the mold, which aids in mold removal. At this point, the cast object is considered green ware because it still contains water and binding agents, and is more porous (and thus weaker) than the final piece. Further drying will remove additional water; however, this process must be monitored because if the surface of the object dries more quickly than the internal portions, shrinkage and cracking can result.

**6.5.2.2 Firing Ceramics**   Once dried, the cast piece is then fired, or exposed to temperatures between 900°C and 1400°C. This is done to burn out the binding agent, as well as increase the density and mechanical properties of the final object. As mentioned in Chapter 3, porous ceramic materials may be created during this process by including a second ceramic type that is burnt out at a lower temperature than that at which densification occurs, leaving voids within the sample. Casting and firing is the most common way to make ceramic implants for both orthopedic and dental applications.

Different classes of ceramics may be formed depending on the temperature and length of firing. In this way, firing can be considered similar to annealing processes in metals. Polycrystalline ceramics are created by heating and holding the object above the melting temperature of the ceramic, followed by rather rapid cooling.

This allows time for crystal growth, but produces large-grained materials that are not often used commercially due to their inferior mechanical properties.

Vitrified materials are created when powdered ceramics are fired and held at a temperature below the melting point. **Vitrification** is the gradual formation of soft glass that flows around the particulates to fill some of the void areas. After cooling, this results in a solid comprised of glassy areas surrounding unreacted particles and any residual pores. The amount of vitrification depends both on the firing time and temperature.

**Glass-ceramics** are so named because the materials begin as glasses, but become polycrystalline ceramics during processing. To accomplish this, the original, glassy material is first heat treated at 500–700°C to form a large concentration of crystal nuclei. Then, like with grain growth in metals, the temperature of the ceramic is increased to promote enlargement of these crystals. The final material is fine-grained and contains randomly oriented crystals.

### 6.5.3 Powder Processing of Ceramics

Although casting also begins with a ceramic powder/water mixture, powder processing in ceramics usually refers to a technique similar to that described above for metals (P/M) that is most often used for crystalline materials. In this procedure, a powdered ceramic and small amount of water and/or a binding agent are pressed into the desired shape and the object is then subjected to sintering. High temperatures are required to allow sufficient atomic diffusion to reduce to the overall surface area present in the material. However, this process occurs well below the melting point of the ceramic. Like with metals, this technique results in a significant reduction in material porosity (see Fig. 6.9), with individual crystals ionically bonded to each other. Also analogous to P/M, pressing and sintering can take place simultaneously with hot pressing procedures.

### 6.5.4 Rapid Manufacturing of Ceramics

As with metals, rapid manufacturing techniques using powdered ceramics have been developed to efficiently create products with complicated geometries. Sintering techniques like those described in section 6.4.4 can be employed for ceramics. However, a wide variety of other processes are also common, collectively referred to as **three-dimensional printing (3DP)** techniques.

**Powder fusion printing (PFP)** is similar to selective laser sintering, but in this case, instead of a laser, a liquid binder solution is selectively dropped onto the powder bed as directed by the computer (see Fig. 6.10). For ceramics, this is often a type of silica binder, which encourages the aggregation of the particles into a solid. As for other SFF techniques, the platform is then lowered, more powder is spread, and the process is repeated until the entire object has been fabricated.

Ceramic constructs are also developed using **extrusion printing,** in which a stock of ceramic powder is melted at high temperature and mechanically fed through a computer-controlled nozzle, after which it cools and hardens into the designed construct. Like other methods presented here, extrusion printing occurs layer by layer, where extruded fibers are deposited and then the print head moves up and deposits the next layer on top of the previous one. A variation of this process, known as **cold plotting,** mixes the ceramic into a sacrificial paste and prints constructs at low temperatures (see Fig. 6.13). The constructs harden once the paste has been removed, leaving the ceramic intact. Finally, ceramics can be used as an additive to other printed materials, such as hydrogels, by mixing the powder within another bulk solution in order to tailor the physicochemical properties of the new construct.

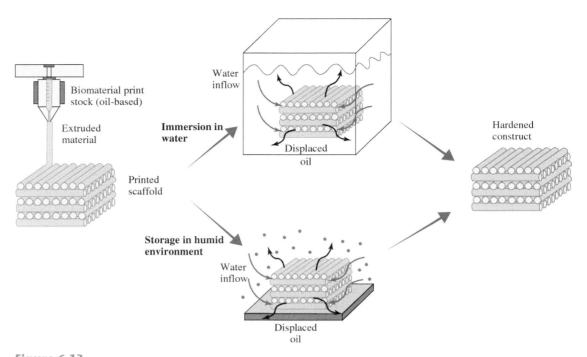

**Figure 6.13**
Schematic of the cold-plotting process. As with other extrusion printing methods, the biomaterial print stock is loaded into a cartridge, where it is extruded via pressure or a mechanical plunger. (Since many biomaterials are not water-soluble, the stock is often dissolved in oil or another solvent.) Scaffolds are constructed by layer-by-layer deposition of fibers. After the oil-based biomaterial scaffold is printed, it can be immersed in an aqueous environment (water bath) or stored in a humid environment, at which time water selectively removes the oil phase, allowing the construct to harden into its final structure.

Although rapid manufacturing of ceramic pieces is often achieved by building them using the methods above, it is also possible to use SFF to produce a mold, rather than the final object itself. Additional material is then cast into this mold in a traditional fashion. As shown in Figure 6.14, this method has been used to create ceramic molds for metallic orthopedic implants having a textured surface (this is used to improve implant integration with the surrounding bone). It must be remembered that, for such applications, the mold created in the rapid manufacturing procedure should have void space in the shape of the final object.

**Figure 6.14**
Rapid prototyping can be used to create a mold for a metallic object. The figure shows a ceramic mold on the right that was created via rapid prototyping, which was then used to create a textured bone screw on the left (pencil is used to indicate relative scale). The formation of complex shapes is possible with this manufacturing method. (Adapted with permission from [5].)

# 6.6 Processing of Polymers

## 6.6.1 Thermoplasts versus Thermosets

Similar to ceramics, transition temperatures such as $T_g$ and $T_m$ are important in selecting appropriate processing methods for polymers. Another key parameter is whether a particular polymer is a thermoplast or a thermoset. **Thermoplastic polymers** soften (liquify) when heated and harden when cooled. This is due to a reduction in secondary bonding between chains at higher temperatures, allowing the macromolecules to slide past each other. Most linear polymers are thermoplastic. During processing, it should be remembered that these polymers can be heated and cooled repeatedly, but that degradation occurs at temperatures where there is enough molecular motion to break the covalent bonds in the backbone.

In contrast, **thermosetting polymers** become permanently hardened when heated to a high temperature and do not subsequently soften. This is because, as the temperature is increased, covalent crosslinks are created between polymer chains. These highly crosslinked macromolecules are then unable to slide past each other and deform plastically. Thermosetting polymers include vulcanized rubbers, epoxies, and resins. As in thermoplastic materials, heating these polymers excessively will cause degradation due to cleavage of the crosslinks.

Complex shapes can be produced from either of these types of polymers. The most common technique to form shapes from thermosets is casting, especially compression molding, whereas all of the following forming and casting methods are employed for creation of objects from thermoplastic polymers. In addition, as discussed in Chapter 3, gases may be bubbled through the molten thermoplast during these procedures to produce porous foams. During processing, it should be kept in mind that thermosets can be removed from the mold at high temperatures, while pressure must be maintained as thermoplastic polymers are cooled below their $T_g$ to assure that the proper shape is maintained before removal from the mold.

## EXAMPLE PROBLEM 6.4

A production manager at a biomaterials plant made 40,000 artificial heart valve leaflets out of a proprietary thermosetting polymer resin. The fabrication process involved heat treatment of the leaflets at a high temperature to cure them. Unfortunately, it was discovered after the production run that a calculation error was made, resulting in all of the artificial heart valve leaflets being too large to be used. Interested in lessening the economic impact of the mistake, the production manager asks you (the resident biomaterials expert) if the leaflets can be melted to recycle the polymer resin in order to produce a new batch of leaflets of the proper dimensions. How would you respond (justify your answer)?

**Solution:** Since a thermosetting polymer resin was used to fabricate the leaflets, and a high temperature treatment was applied to cure the resin, the material cannot be recycled. The setting of the polymer resin resulted in the formation of covalent crosslinks between the polymer chains. Thus, the material cannot be melted and reused, as any heat applied to the polymer sufficient to break the crosslinks would be sufficient to break the bonds in the backbones of the polymer chains as well, thereby decomposing the polymer. ∎

## 6.6.2 Forming Polymers

**6.6.2.1 Extrusion of Polymers**  Polymer extrusion is similar to extrusion of metals and is based on plastic deformation of the material. A screw moves within a heated chamber filled with polymer pellets, causing them to melt and form a continuous feed stock. This viscous fluid is then forced through an orifice, while jets of air or water on the exterior cool and solidify the polymer into its final shape.

**Figure 6.15**
Schematic of fiber spinning process. A molten polymer is pumped through a plate (spinneret) containing many small holes. The polymer exiting from each hole forms a single fiber, which cools upon contact with air. These filaments are then packaged on spools for storage and shipping.

Polymer extruder

Metering pump

Spinneret

Filaments

Quench air

Convergence guide

Take-up spool

As with metals, this method is often used to produce lengths of polymeric rods or tubing. In the biomedical field, extrusion is commonly employed in the fabrication of expanded PTFE (GORE-TEX™) vascular grafts.

**6.6.2.2 Fiber Spinning of Polymers** A variant of extrusion for polymers is **fiber spinning**. In this procedure, a molten polymer is pumped through a plate (spinneret) that has many small holes (see Fig. 6.15). The polymer exiting from each hole forms a single fiber, which cools upon contact with air. As mentioned in Section 6.2.3, the strength of the polymer along the main fiber axis can be improved after formation by applying tension along this axis (called drawing[1] or pre-drawing).

As with metal and ceramic fibers, meshes may be produced from polymeric fibers. Because many polymers can be degraded *in vivo*, polymer meshes are popular as carriers for cells or bioactive agents in tissue engineering applications. Several methods for organizing these fibers in three dimensions have been developed, and some of these are illustrated in Figure 6.16. They include weaving, knitting and braiding the fibers into specific structures. In these meshes, the porosity is dependent on the diameter as well as the packing density of the fibers. Braided, woven, and knitted materials have been used in artificial blood vessels as well as replacement tendon/ligaments.

If fiber diameters less than about 10 $\mu$m are required, it is necessary to employ alternative spinning procedures to those described above. One such method that is currently under investigation is **electrospinning**, depicted in Figure 6.17. In this case, the molten polymer is extruded from a nozzle into a strong electrostatic field (voltages of 5–30 kV). This field acts to overcome the surface tension of the liquid and accelerates parts of this liquid in the general direction of a (grounded) target. Each part of the liquid cools upon contact with air, forming fine, looping fibers that can be collected. However, because of the looping nature of the fibers, the collected material is usually formed into a three-dimensional nonwoven mesh, rather than one of the woven or knitted structures illustrated in Figure 6.16.

---

[1]This is similar, but not identical, to drawing of metals and glasses, a type of forming procedure described in sections 6.4.1.4 and 6.5.1.

**Figure 6.16**
Several methods for organizing fibers into three dimensions have been developed. Some examples include (a) weaving, (b) weft knit, and (c) regular braid. These different structures can affect the porosity and mechanical properties of the material.

**Figure 6.17**
In electrospinning, molten polymer is extruded from a nozzle into a strong electrostatic field, which acts to overcome the surface tension of the liquid and accelerates parts of this liquid in the general direction of a (grounded) target, in this case a rotating spool. Each part of the liquid cools upon contact with air, forming fine, looping fibers.

### 6.6.3 Casting Polymers

Like metals and ceramics, polymers can be cast into a mold and allowed to solidify. However, for polymeric materials, this process is usually called *molding*. Three of the most common types of molding are described in this section.

#### 6.6.3.1 Compression Molding of Polymers

In **compression molding**, the stock polymer is placed in a heated mold (die). One half of the mold is then moved down to come in contact with the stock material. This applies pressure and forces the polymer into the desired shape (see Fig. 6.18). As mentioned previously, this is a common shaping method for thermosets, but is also used with thermoplastic polymers.

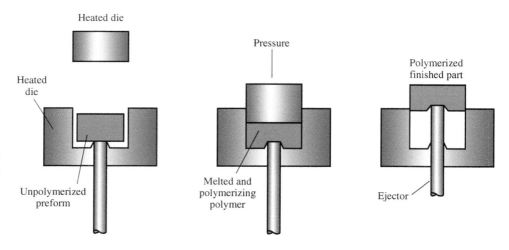

**Figure 6.18**

In compression molding, the stock polymer (preform) is placed in a heated die (mold). Part of the mold is then moved down to come in contact with the stock material, applying pressure and forcing the polymer into the desired shape. An ejector pin is manufactured into the mold to facilitate rapid removal of the final, polymerized product.

For example, high-molecular weight poly(ethylene) can be processed in this manner to form orthopedic implants.

**6.6.3.2 Injection Molding of Polymers**   Injection molding requires first melting the stock polymer in a heated chamber. As depicted in Figure 6.19, the viscous liquid polymer is then forced through the nozzle due to pressure applied by the ram. After the correct amount of polymer has exited the nozzle to fill the die, the pressure is maintained until the polymer has cooled and solidified, when it is removed from the mold. A main advantage of injection molding is its speed—a new piece may be fabricated every few seconds using this method.

**6.6.3.3 Blow Molding of Polymers**   Blow molding is very similar to glass blowing operations and is used to make hollow objects. The molten polymeric parison is placed in a heated mold, and then blowing air or steam forces the polymer to conform to the shape of the mold.

## 6.6.4 Rapid Manufacturing of Polymers

Research into rapid manufacturing technologies for polymers has grown steadily. Lower cost, open source variants of these techniques have allowed for 3D printing

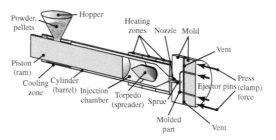

**Figure 6.19**

Schematic of injection molding process. First, polymer (in pellet form) is added to the feed hopper, where it is carried to the heating chamber. After it is melted, the viscous liquid polymer is forced through a nozzle due to pressure applied by a ram. After a measured amount of polymer has exited the nozzle and filled the die, the pressure is maintained until the polymer has cooled and solidified. At this point the final product is removed via ejector pins, similar to the compression molding process [3].

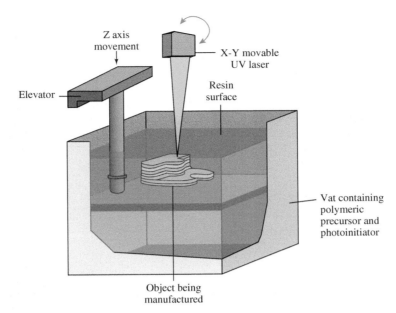

Z axis movement

X-Y movable UV laser

Elevator

Resin surface

Vat containing polymeric precursor and photoinitiator

Object being manufactured

**Figure 6.20**
Schematic of stereolithography process. This is a rapid manufacturing method that uses a liquid stock. In this process, the moveable platform is located in a pool containing a polymeric precursor (usually monomers or low-molecular weight polymers) and a light-responsive initiator molecule (photoinitiator). A small amount of the liquid is wiped onto the platform (attached to the elevator) and then a laser emitting light at a controlled wavelength is scanned across the material to create a particular profile. This causes the initiator to commence a polymerization reaction in certain areas on the resin surface, converting the stock from a liquid into a solid. The platform is then lowered and the next layer is formed in the same manner. This process is repeated until the final desired three-dimensional shape is produced.

and other manufacturing methods to be used more extensively in both industrial and academic environments. In addition to extrusion and powder fusion, which have been addressed above for other material types, other common techniques for polymers include stereolithography, laser-assisted bioprinting, and inkjet bioprinting.

In **stereolithography**, a projected light source polymerizes or cross-links a solution of a photo-polymerizable polymeric precursor (usually monomers or low molecular weight polymers) into a model pattern, as shown in Figure 6.20. Traditional stereolithography uses deflected lasers to solidify the liquid stock, while projection lithography projects patterns of light and dark pixels, polymerizing or crosslinking areas of the liquid that are exposed to the light. Stereolithography methods operate via a layer-by-layer process, where each 2D layer is cured before the next layer is added. In one of the more common types of stereolithography printers shown in Figure 6.20, after each layer, the platform is lowered and new liquid precursor flows over the top to be polymerized.

**Laser-assisted bioprinting** uses a laser to heat and evaporate an absorbing solution and/or a biological "ink," generating vapor bubbles that push ink droplets onto the platform upon which the construct will be built (see Fig. 6.21). The laser intensity and absorbing solution can be designed to evaporate without transferring heat to the

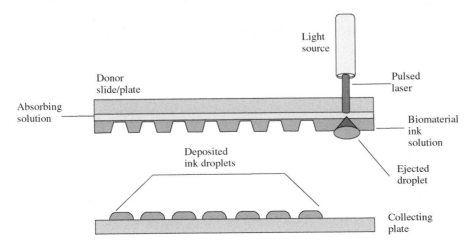

Light source

Donor slide/plate

Pulsed laser

Absorbing solution

Biomaterial ink solution

Deposited ink droplets

Ejected droplet

Collecting plate

**Figure 6.21**
Diagram of the laser-assisted bioprinting technique. A pulsed laser is used to vaporize the absorbing solution and/or ink, creating small vapor bubbles that push and eject ink droplets at precise locations. The ejected ink droplets are deposited onto a collecting plate.

**Figure 6.22**
Schematic of inkjet bioprinting. Here, small volumes of a biological ink solution are loaded into printheads and deposited as tiny droplets following transmitted coordinate instructions. In thermal inkjet printers (left), heating units near the nozzle create vapor bubbles of the solution which ultimately collapse and fall onto the platform. Piezoelectric printers (right) operate similarly, ejecting droplets via a pressure change due to crystal vibration.

ink itself, which allows the user to precisely print these materials without damage from the laser. This protection is particularly important for tissue engineering, as heat from the laser could have an adverse effect on printed cells or damage the added biochemical factors inside the ink. Laser-assisted techniques do not use a nozzle, which allows for solutions with a wide range of mechanical properties to be printed.

In **inkjet bioprinting**, tiny volumes of biological "ink" solutions are deposited following specific xyz coordinate instructions. Inkjet printers have been used for several biological applications, including cell and DNA printing. The most common inkjet bioprinters use either thermal or piezoelectric print heads (see Fig. 6.22). In thermal inkjet printers, heating the nozzle creates a pressure change within the head, causing vapor bubbles of the solution to form, collapse, and drop onto the platform. In piezoelectric printing, electric charge buildup causes internal crystals to vibrate within the print nozzle, increasing the chamber pressure and ejecting the ink. Similar to other printing methods, inkjet printing can be used to create objects with localized, specific property gradients, and this technique is particularly useful for printing heterogeneous constructs with multiple cell lines and bioactive molecules.

## 6.7   Processing to Improve Biocompatibility

As introduced in Chapter 1, biocompatibility is a broad term suggesting that a material produces an acceptable host response in a given application. Although there are many aspects to biocompatibility, many of which are governed by biomaterial surface properties, as described in the next chapter, two important considerations are that the material does not induce infection or a deleterious immune response (rejection). Postfabrication processing can play a significant role in reducing both of these responses. Techniques for sterilization of both synthetic and naturally derived materials are outlined in this section, followed by a discussion of methods for reducing the immune response to natural materials.

### 6.7.1  Sterilization

Sterilization of biomedical implants prior to implantation is extremely important because the presence of a biomaterial may promote serious infection from even normally innocuous pathogens (see Chapter 14 for further discussion of biomaterials-related infections). In addition, pre-sterilization decreases the possibility of the transfer of viruses associated with naturally derived materials. This section, based on a discussion by Kowalski and Morrissey [2], will focus on the most common sterilization/decontamination methods. More information on other sterilization methods, such as dry heat sterilization and UV sterilization, can be found in the references mentioned at the end of this chapter. Depending on key properties of the material (such as the melting point), these methods can be used for both natural and synthetic biomaterials.

Because it is virtually impossible to remove all pathogens from an implant, the concept of a **sterility assurance level (SAL)** was developed. The SAL for a given device is measured by culturing implants in nutrient media after various sterilization times and determining how many bacterial colonies remain. From these data, manufacturers can choose the time and dose of sterilization to maintain a certain SAL (probability that the implant will remain sterile). For biomedical implants, the acceptable SAL is usually $10^{-6}$, or 1 in 1 million devices will show evidence of contamination after a sterilization process. Therefore, in selecting from the sterilization methods described next, biomaterialists must consider both the ability of the technique to achieve a desired SAL and the compatibility of the process with the material and packaging material, so that the biomaterial is not degraded or deformed during the sterilization procedure.

**6.7.1.1 Steam Sterilization** As the name indicates, biomaterials can be sterilized by exposure to high pressure at a temperature of at least 121°C. Also known as autoclaving, this technique damages protein and lipid constituents important to microorganism survival. Advantages of this method include that it is effective, relatively quick and simple, and leaves no toxic residues within the sample. However, the high temperatures employed limit its use with materials having low melting points. Additionally, hydrolytically cleavable materials are particularly susceptible to degradation in such an environment, so this technique is not suitable for sterilization of this class of polymers.

**6.7.1.2 Ethylene Oxide Sterilization** A specialized sterilization apparatus is required to expose implants to ethylene oxide (EtO) gas. Because EtO is toxic, may cause cancer, and is potentially flammable, it is often mixed with an inert gas within the machine. Sterilization occurs when a chamber holding the implants at 30–50°C is first evacuated, then flooded with EtO, held for 2–16 hours, and finally purged several times with air. Following this, further aeration outside the sterilizer aids in removal of any remaining EtO.

EtO causes pathogen death primarily through permanent, chemical alteration of nucleic acids (DNA, RNA). This sterilization method is effective, even deep within crevices or pores, and, because it is carried out at a low temperature, it can be used for a wide variety of materials. However, toxic residues of EtO that may be left in the device are of great concern. In addition, due to the reactivity and possible carcinogenic nature of the gas, personnel must be properly protected while performing the sterilization procedure.

**6.7.1.3 Radiation Sterilization** The radiation used in radiation sterilization can be provided in the form of gamma rays or an electron beam. In both cases, the samples are placed in an irradiator and monitored to assure they have received the proper dosage of radiation. The gamma ray source is a $^{60}$Co isotope, while an accelerator creates the electron beam. The advantage to the electron beam method is that when the accelerator is turned off, no radiation is produced, while the $^{60}$Co source is constantly decaying and releasing radiation, which can be detrimental to the operator's health.

Radiation acts by ionizing important cellular elements, including nucleic acids, thus killing adherent microorganisms. Advantages of radiation sterilization are that it is rapid, effective, and compatible with many materials. Disadvantages are that it requires a large capital investment to install an irradiator and that certain polymers, such as poly(tetrafluoroethylene) or poly(propylene), or hydrolytically cleavable polymers like poly(lactic acid), are susceptible to radiation degradation. While this has been a common means of sterilizing orthopedic implants, when irradiated in air, ultrahigh molecular weight poly(ethylene) (UHMWPE) components have demonstrated evidence of oxidative degradation (see Chapter 5 for discussion of oxidation-based degradation of polymers). Additionally, the electron beam method has a very small penetration depth, so only thin devices may be sterilized in this manner.

## EXAMPLE PROBLEM 6.5

Consider a novel vascular stent made from a surgical grade steel. The stent has been coated with a novel polymer to help integration with native tissue and prevent further narrowing of the vessel. Would steam sterilization, ethylene oxide sterilization, or radiation sterilization be preferred for this device? Why?

**Solution:** Ethylene oxide would generally be preferred for sterilization of the coated stent. Recalling that polymers have lower melting temperatures than metals, steam sterilization would not be appropriate because it may melt the polymer coating. Although both radiation and EtO treatment may damage polymeric materials, this is often more of a concern with radiation. Therefore, the recommended method would be to sterilize the device with EtO and characterize both the metal and polymer components post-treatment to assure that no degradation has occurred.

■

## 6.7.2 Fixation of Natural Materials

In addition to harboring potential pathogens, naturally derived materials can evoke an immune response (be immunogenic) because certain areas of the material may be recognized as "foreign" by the body. If this occurs, a cascade of events (see Chapters 11 and 12) is initiated that may lead to degradation or walling off of the implant, thus reducing the efficacy of the device.

In order to decrease immunogenicity, particularly in collagen-derived materials, the implants are often crosslinked with fixatives such as gluteraldehyde after fabrication into the appropriate shape. Although the exact reason for the efficacy of this treatment has not been elucidated, it is thought that the crosslinking process alters the chemical structure of the regions in the material that are recognized as foreign to the body, thus reducing any unwanted immune response.

# Summary

- Metals can be strengthened by a number of techniques whereby defects are added to the crystal structure to prevent dislocation motion. Alloying strengthens a metal by introducing point defects that increase the shear stress required for dislocation motion. Strain hardening introduces line defects into a metal, which increase the energy needed to move the stress field through the combined localized strains from other dislocations. Precipitation hardening occurs through the introduction of precipitates in a metal, which create local strains that inhibit dislocation motion in the area.

- Strengthening techniques for polymers include heat treatment; predrawing procedures, in which the polymer chains become aligned along the axis of loading; and additional crosslinking, in which the ability of chains to slide past one another is reduced.

- Annealing generally results in an increase in grain size, decrease in grain boundaries, reduction of internal stresses and an increase in the ductility of a metal. The rate of heat extraction strongly influences the resulting grain structure of an annealed metal. The percent crystallinity of semi-crystalline polymers can be increased through heat treatment during which polymer chains are free to align with the increased energy. As with the annealing of metals, the rate of cooling strongly influences the final structure of the annealed polymer.

- Metals can be formed into desired shapes through a number of processes. The application of force to the metal to achieve the desired form is required with forming methods, which include forging, rolling, extrusion, and drawing. Casting methods involve filling a mold with molten metal and can typically result in more ductile, intricately shaped materials than forming techniques. Powder processing involves filling a mold with a fine powder of the metal of choice, condensing it with high pressure, and then sintering it at high temperature.

- Glasses can be formed into desired shapes through pressing, blowing, and drawing, all of which require the application of mechanical force. Casting techniques can be used with crystalline ceramics and glass-ceramics. Ceramic casting involves filling a mold with small ceramic particles mixed with water and an organic binder, drying the ceramic, and firing it to burn out remaining water and binding agent. Powder processing techniques can be used with ceramic materials and, although conducted at high temperatures, occur well below the melting point of the ceramic.

- Certain parameters of a polymer material, including $T_g$, $T_m$, and whether a polymer is a thermoplast or a thermoset, must be considered before identifying an appropriate processing technique. As with metals and ceramics, forming techniques, including extrusion, fiber spinning, and electrospinning, and casting techniques, including compression, injection, and blow molding, can be used to produce products of desired form.

- It is important that biomaterials be sterile prior to contact with the recipient to ensure prevention of pathogen and/or other biological contaminant transmission. Biomaterial sterilization via autoclaving involves treatment with high pressure steam to denature proteins and lipid constituents necessary to the survival of microorganisms. Ethylene oxide exposure under controlled conditions sterilizes the material by chemically altering nucleic acids of microorganisms. Biomaterials can also be sterilized through radiation exposure techniques, including gamma ray sterilization and electron beam sterilization.

# Problems

6.1 You have produced a new metallic biomaterial Material A. Use the plot below from tensile testing of your material to answer the following questions.

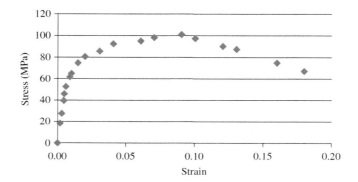

(a) You are now developing a second generation biomaterial, Material B. This material will be an alloy of Material A with other elements. In particular, you are thinking of alloying with chromium (it is known that there is a very strong atomic bonding between Cr and Material A). Based on the graph above, draw the expected stress–strain curve for Material B after alloying. Indicate how it is different than Material A and why this would occur from a molecular perspective. What is another advantage of adding Cr to this metal?

(b) Another option for your second generation biomaterial is to use a new thermal treatment on Material A whereby you quench it so that the temperature is reduced more quickly. On the same graph you drew for (a), draw the expected stress–strain curve for Material A' after the new thermal treatment. Indicate how it is different than Material A and why this would occur from a molecular perspective.

6.2 Compare and contrast forming methods in metals, polymers, and ceramic glasses. Why is forming not possible for crystalline ceramics?

6.3 Based on concepts in Chapter 5, explain at a molecular level why radiation sterilization in air resulted in ultra high molecular weight poly(ethylene) degradation. One way that companies have overcome this is to complete radiation sterilization in an inert gas. Why would this be effective? Based on literature, describe one other possible mechanism of overcoming this problem.

6.4 You are trying to decide between compression and injection molding the acetabular cup of a hip implant from a new polymer.

(a) What characteristics of the polymer would you need to know to determine which method is best? Explain your rationale.

(b) What sterilization technique would be best for this implant. Justify your answer

# References

1. J. F. Shackelford, *Introduction to materials science for engineers*, 5th ed. Upper Saddle River: Prentice Hall, 2000.

2. J. B. Kowalski and R. F. Morrissey, "Sterilization of implants and devices," in *Biomaterials science: an introduction to materials and medicine*, 2nd ed., B. D. Ratner, A. S. Hoffman, F. J. Schoen, and J. E. Lemons, Eds. San Diego: Elsevier Academic Press, 2004, pp. 754–760.

3. Kalpakjian S. and Schmid S., in *Manufacturing engineering and technology*, 8th ed., Pearson Education, 2020. (Images 18.8a, 19.7a).

4. M. F. Ashby and D. R. H. Jones, *Engineering materials 2: an introduction to microstructures, processing, and design*. Oxford: Elsevier Science, 1986.

5. M. C. Melican, M. C. Zimmerman, M. S. Dhillon, A. R. Ponnambalam, A. Curodeau, and J. R. Parsons, "Three-dimensional printing and porous metallic surfaces: a new orthopedic application," *Journal of Biomedical Materials Research*, vol. 55, no. 2, pp. 194–202, May 2001.

# Additional Reading

C.M. Agarwal, J. L. Ong, M. L. Appelford, and G. Mani, *Introduction to biomaterials: basic theory with engineering applications*. Cambridge: Cambridge University Press, 2014.

T.Ahlfeld *et al.*, "Design and fabrication of complex scaffolds for bone defect healing: combined 3D plotting of a calcium phosphate cement and a growth factor-loaded hydrogel," *Annals of Biomedical Engineering*, vol. 45, no. 1, pp. 224–236, 2017.

J.Black and G. Hastings, *Handbook of biomaterial properties*. London: Chapman and Hall, 1998.

J.B. Brunski, "Metals," in *Biomaterials science: an introduction to materials and medicine*, 2nd ed., B. D. Ratner, A. S. Hoffman, F. J. Schoen, and J. E. Lemons, Eds. San Diego: Elsevier Academic Press, 2004, pp. 137–153.

K.P. Cooper, "Layered manufacturing: challenges and opportunities," *MRS Proceedings*, vol. 758, p. LL1.4, 2002.

J.P. Fisher and D. M. Yoon, "Polymeric scaffolds for tissue engineering applications," in *Tissue engineering and artificial organs*, 3rd ed., J. D. Bronzino, Ed. New York: Taylor and Francis, 2006, pp. 1–18.

L.L. Hench and S. M. Best, "Ceramics, glasses, and glass-ceramics: basic principles," in *Biomaterials science: an introduction to materials and medicine*, 3rd ed., B. D. Ratner, A. S. Hoffman, F. J. Schoen, and J. E. Lemons, Eds. San Diego: Elsevier Academic Press, 2013, pp. 128–151.

B.Lambert and J. Martin, "Sterilization of implants and devices," in *Biomaterials science: an introduction to materials and medicine*, 3rd ed., B. D. Ratner, A. S. Hoffman, F. J. Schoen, and J. E. Lemons, Eds. San Diego: Elsevier Academic Press, 2013, pp. 1339–1353.

M.B. Murphy and A. G. Mikos, "Porous scaffold fabrication for tissue engineering," in *Principles of tissue engineering*, 3rd ed., R. P. Lanza, R. Langer, and J. P. Vacanti, Eds. San Diego: Elsevier Academic Press, 2007, pp. 309–321.

A.Park, B. Wu, and L. G. Griffith, "Integration of surface modification and 3D fabrication techniques to prepare patterned poly(L-lactide) substrates allowing regionally selective cell adhesion," *Journal of Biomaterials Science Polymer Edition*, vol. 9, no. 2, pp. 89–110, 1998.

J.B. Park and R. S. Lakes, *Biomaterials: an introduction*, 2nd ed. New York: Plenum Press, 1992.

J.P. Schaffer, A. Saxena, S. D. Antolovich, J. Sanders, and S. B. Warner, *The science and design of engineering materials*, 2nd ed. Boston: McGraw-Hill, 1998.

L.V. Yannas, "Natural Materials," in *Biomaterials science: an introduction to materials and medicine*, 2nd ed., B. D. Ratner, A. S. Hoffman, F. J. Schoen, and J. E. Lemons, Eds. San Diego: Elsevier Academic Press, 2004, pp. 127–137.

# 7

# Surface Properties of Biomaterials

**Main Objective**

To understand how biomaterial surface properties affect thermodynamics of protein adsorption and how different surface treatments can affect these properties.

**Specific Objectives**

1. To understand basic thermodynamic principles and how thermodynamics relates to protein adsorption to biomaterial surfaces.
2. To understand how physical and chemical properties of the biomaterial surface affect protein adsorption and why protein adsorption is important to the biological response.
3. To distinguish between physicochemical and biological surface modification techniques.
4. To compare and contrast various physicochemical surface modification methods and to understand which are appropriate for each class of biomaterial.
5. To distinguish among covalent coatings, non-covalent coatings, and physicochemical surface modification with no overcoat.
6. To compare and contrast various biological surface modification methods and to understand which are appropriate for each class of biomaterial.
7. To understand how surface characteristics differ on degradable vs. nondegradable materials over time.
8. To distinguish between two types of processing for substrate surface patterning.
9. To understand the theory behind and possible limitations to the surface characterization techniques presented.

## 7.1 Introduction: Concepts in Surface Chemistry and Biology

Chapters 1 to 6 have discussed bulk properties of biomaterials, such as their thermal, mechanical, and degradative characteristics, and the corresponding atomic causes. However, since the biomaterial surface is extremely important in determining the biological response and thus implant success, this chapter will focus solely on surface properties of biomaterials. This includes a description of both physico-chemical and biological means to modify solid surfaces, as well as processing techniques to form patterned biomaterial surfaces.

## 7.1.1  Protein Adsorption and Biocompatibility

As described in Chapter 3, the surface of a material can be considered a type of planar defect. Because the atoms at the surface are not bonded on all sides to other atoms, there is extra energy associated with this region due to unfilled valence shells. This excess energy is often called (due to historical reasons) the **surface tension** ($\gamma$). Since this state is thermodynamically unstable, there is a driving force to minimize the surface tension by the adsorption of atoms or molecules, which satisfy the unfilled bonds at the material surface. **Adsorption** is the adhesion of molecules to a solid surface. This can be distinguished from **absorption**, which is the penetration of molecules into the bulk of another material, such as how water is absorbed by a sponge. We focus in the next few chapters on protein adsorption to biomaterials.

At physiological conditions, the **adsorbate** on the biomaterial surface is composed primarily of ions, water, and proteins. It is to this coated surface, rather than to the "pure" biomaterial, that the body reacts. Therefore, controlling protein adsorption to biomaterial surfaces is a key aspect to assuring biocompatibility. We begin this chapter with a discussion of the impact of the biomaterial surface on the thermodynamics of protein adsorption.

## 7.1.2  Surface Properties Governing Protein Adsorption

Although a driving force exists at the biomaterial surface in the form of surface tension, in order to predict the adsorption of proteins or other molecules, one must examine the entire system, which includes the material surface (discussed in this chapter), the proteins, and the solvent (discussed in more detail in Chapter 8). In particular, the system before and after prospective adsorption must be analyzed from a thermodynamic standpoint to see if it is energetically favorable for the adsorption to occur. The following section discusses the contribution of the biomaterial surface to protein adsorption, while the contributions of the other components will be addressed in Chapter 8.

Using thermodynamic principles[1] to examine the system before adsorption occurs, we see that two surface properties have the largest effect on the favorability of adsorption:

1. Surface hydrophobicity
2. Surface charge

As discussed previously, the **hydrophobicity** of a material describes how it responds to the presence of water. To quantify hydrophobicity, a biomaterial surface is subjected to contact angle analysis, which is described later in the chapter. An example of a **hydrophobic** (water-fearing or water-repelling) surface is a freshly waxed car—water forms small balls ("beads up") on this surface. In contrast, after the wax coating has worn away, water drops spread on the more **hydrophilic** (water-loving) metallic painted surface. Examples of hydrophobic biomaterials include most of the synthetic polymers listed in Table 2.5, particularly

---

[1]It should be noted that these thermodynamic models can be most directly used to explain only nonspecific adsorption to surfaces, not protein-receptor interactions, which are discussed later in this chapter and again in Chapter 9.

**Figure 7.1**

Schematic of steric hindrance due to PEG chains. (a) On a material without steric hindrance, proteins have free access to adhere to the material surface. (b) PEG chains inhibit the attachment of proteins by physically blocking access to the surface.

those containing pendant methyl (e.g., poly(methyl methacrylate)) or aromatic (e.g., poly(styrene)) groups. Ceramic and metallic biomaterials are often more hydrophilic than these polymers in their unmodified state. Although it is difficult to predict exactly how surface hydrophobicity affects protein adsorption for a specific system, it has been found that protein adsorption generally increases with increasing hydrophobicity of the surface and the protein.

The effects of surface charge cannot be completely separated from the effects of hydrophobicity, especially when using contact angle methods to determine hydrophobicity, since contact angle is also sensitive to surface charge. However, a significant surface charge can have the additional effect of attracting or repelling charged areas of proteins. Surface charge occurs via dissociation of ionizable surface groups or through specific adsorption of ions from the solution. Again, how this property affects protein adsorption depends on both the charge of the surface and that of the protein.

In addition to the properties that affect the thermodynamics of protein adsorption to biomaterials mentioned earlier, the physical characteristics of the biomaterial surface are also important. These include **steric concerns** and **surface roughness**. For example, adding large, flexible hydrophilic polymer chains such as poly(ethylene glycol) (PEG) to a biomaterial surface will result in a decrease in protein adsorption (Fig. 7.1). This is due to the fact that a large volume at the surface is taken up by these bulky chains that are in constant motion. Since they move too quickly to allow the proteins to adsorb to them and are too large for the proteins to move through, they form a type of wall, using **steric repulsion** to prevent adsorption to the surface. In contrast, a surface with a high degree of roughness may promote protein adsorption in certain areas by physically "trapping" the proteins in the valleys on the surface.

Thus, the hydrophobicity, charge, steric hindrance, and/or roughness of a biomaterial surface can be altered during formation or processing to change the protein adsorption profile of the final material. Because this is the most accessible control point to influence the final biocompatibility of the material, many methods have been developed to modify biomaterial surfaces. In some cases, these were designed to impart surface properties other than those directly relating to protein adsorption (such as increased hardness or reduced friction), but it is important to remember that any changes in surface chemistry will affect the type and/or amount of protein on the surface. An overview of the means to effect surface modifications for various classes of biomedical materials is the subject of the remainder of this chapter.

## EXAMPLE PROBLEM 7.1

Consider the following hypothetical protein and two materials (A) and (B). Assume that in this case the water contact angle correlates directly with the hydrophobicity of the material surface. To which material would greater adsorption of the given protein be expected? Why?

Highly hydrophobic
protein X

**Solution:**   Although the contact angles for the materials are not given directly, it can be deduced through visual examination of the figure that Material B has a greater contact angle than A. Given that in this case we are to assume that the contact angle corresponds directly with the hydrophobicity of the material, it can be concluded that Material B is more hydrophobic than Material A. Consequently, one would expect greater adsorption of the highly hydrophobic protein X to the surface of Material B, through hydrophobic interaction, assuming that the surface charges of Materials A and B are comparable.                                ■

## 7.2   Physicochemical Surface Modification Techniques

### 7.2.1   Introduction to Surface Modification Techniques

There are a wide variety of surface modification techniques designed to treat all types of biomaterials, including naturally based and synthetic polymers, metals, and ceramics (see Table 7.1). Many of these can be considered as postfabrication processing techniques, similar to those discussed in Chapter 6, while in other cases, final surface modification is designed into the chemical nature of the biomaterial (e.g., surface-modifying additives, discussed in section 7.2.3.4). Surface modification possesses the advantage that bulk characteristics such as mechanical properties are not altered. However, the possibility of delamination *in vivo* is a serious concern.

Therefore, an ideal technique would produce a surface treatment with the following characteristics:

1. Thin (to minimize effects on bulk properties)
2. Resistant to delamination
3. Simple and robust (to promote commercialization)

In addition, a means to discourage surface rearrangement, which happens continually due to the free energy at the surface (see Section 7.1) and can destroy the modification, should be included. A number of methods have been developed to produce surface treatments that meet these criteria. They are generally grouped into **chemical** and **biological** modifications, and each type is discussed in more detail in the following sections.

### 7.2.2   Chemical Surface Modification: Covalent Interactions

As summarized in Table 7.1, chemical surface treatments use physical principles or chemical reactions to alter the surface chemical composition of the sample. However, in contrast to biological methods, none of these modifications involves the attachment of active biological molecules. Surface modification can be based on covalent (described in this section) or other types of bonds with the surface (described in the following section).

We begin our discussion with coatings that are covalently bonded to the surface. The following methods do not represent an exhaustive list, but are included as examples to demonstrate the variety of techniques that result in covalent coatings.

**TABLE 7.1**

| Various Surface Modification Techniques and the Materials on Which They Can Be Used | | | | | | |
|---|---|---|---|---|---|---|
| | Polymer | Metal | Ceramic | Glass | Advantages | Disadvantages |
| **Non-covalent** | | | | | | |
| Solvent coating | √ | √ | √ | √ | Simple procedure | Possible delamination |
| Plasma etching (e.g., nitrogen, argon, oxygen, water vapor) | √ | √ | √ | √ | Changes surface topography | Equipment generally expensive |
| Vapor deposition of carbons and metals[a] | √ | √ | √ | √ | Strong bonds with surface | Equipment generally expensive |
| Ion beam etching (e.g., argon, xenon) | √ | √ | √ | √ | Changes surface topography | Equipment generally expensive |
| Ion beam implantation (e.g., nitrogen) | √ | √ | √ | √ | Strong bonds with surface | Equipment generally expensive |
| Langmuir–Blodgett film deposition | √ | √ | √ | √ | Large range of surface chemistries possible | Possible delamination |
| Layer-by-layer deposition | √ | | √ | √ | Simple procedure | Possible delamination |
| Surface-active additives | √ | √ | √ | √ | Modification occurs before fabrication | Limited choices in reagents that will achieve this modification |
| Chemical reaction | | | | | Strong bonds with surface | Equipment generally expensive |
| • Nonspecific oxidation (e.g., ozone) | √ | √ | √ | √ | | |
| • Functional group modifications (oxidation, reduction) | √ | — | — | — | | |
| • Addition reactions (e.g., acetylation, chlorination) | √ | — | — | — | | |
| Conversion coatings (phosphating, anodization) | — | √ | — | — | Simple procedure | Only can be used on metals |
| Mechanical roughening and polishing | √ | √ | √ | √ | Simple procedure | Does not change chemistry of surface |
| **Covalent** | | | | | | |
| Radiation grafting (electron accelerator and gamma) | √ | — | — | — | Strong bonds with surface | Equipment usually expensive |
| Photografting (UV and visible sources) | √ | — | — | √ | Strong bonds with surface | Can be low through-put, depending on size of sample and light source |
| Plasma (gas discharge) (RF, microwave, acoustic) | √ | √ | √ | √ | Strong bonds with surface | Equipment usually expensive |

*Continued*

**TABLE 7.1** *Continued*

| | Polymer | Metal | Ceramic | Glass | Advantages | Disadvantages |
|---|---|---|---|---|---|---|
| Gas-phase deposition | | | | | Strong bonds with surface | Equipment usually expensive |
| • Ion beam sputtering | √ | √ | √ | √ | | |
| • Chemical vapor deposition (CVD) | √ | √ | √ | √ | | |
| • Flame spray deposition | — | √ | √ | √ | | |
| Chemical grafting (e.g., ozonation + grafting) | √ | √ | √ | √ | Strong bonds with surface | Equipment usually expensive |
| Self-assembled monolayers | √ | √ | √ | √ | Strong bonds with surface | Limited choices in reagents that will achieve this modification |
| Biological modification (biomolecule immobilization) | √ | √ | √ | √ | Confer biological function | Possible denaturation |

*a*Some covalent reaction may occur.
(Adapted with permission from [32].)

Some of these methods, which include plasma discharge, chemical or physical vapor deposition, radiation or photografting, and self-assembled monolayers, have been used to create biological coatings as well (see Section 7.3).

**7.2.2.1 Plasma Treatment    Plasma discharge** is a broad term that encompasses several methods of physicochemical surface modification, some of which result in surface coatings, while others do not. Additionally, exposure to a plasma environment can also be used as a pretreatment to other surface modification techniques. **Plasma** refers to an assembly of species in an atomically/molecularly dissociated gaseous environment. The gaseous species present can include positive and negative ions, free radicals, electrons, atoms, molecules, and photons. Plasma discharge can occur at a range of temperatures (usually 25°C and higher) and is most often created under vacuum. A plasma environment is obtained by applying an electric potential across a gas. A simplified depiction of one of the means to achieve plasma discharge treatment is found in Figure 7.2. As shown in the figure, the cathode is the surface to be treated and has a negative potential relative to the anode. To travel from the cathode to the anode, electrons must traverse the gas in the chamber and collide with the molecules to form gaseous ions and radicals. These species can then interact with the sample and cause a variety of surface reactions. The plasma is sustained because electrons flow from the sample while positive ions flow toward the sample.

At the sample surface, there is competition between deposition and ablation/etching. Since the formed species are very energetic, they can result in significant changes to surface chemistry simply through etching. If this process is very rapid, no deposition will be observed. However, in many instances, a mixed process takes place. For these cases, deposition can occur via at least two possible methods. For example, free radicals may polymerize other molecules from the gas phase onto the surface, or small molecules may combine into larger particulates that settle on the surface.

Plasma discharge is often used for cleaning or addition of hydroxyl (OH) or amine ($NH_2$) groups to biomaterials as a precursor to further modification (see the self-assembled monolayer and the biological modification sections later in

**Figure 7.2**

Schematic of plasma discharge treatment. The cathode is the surface to be treated and has a negative potential relative to the anode. Electrons must traverse the gas in the chamber to travel from the cathode to the anode. During this stage, they collide with molecules in the gaseous environment to form gaseous ions and radicals. These species can then interact with the sample and cause a variety of surface reactions. The plasma is sustained because electrons flow from the sample while positive ions flow toward the sample.

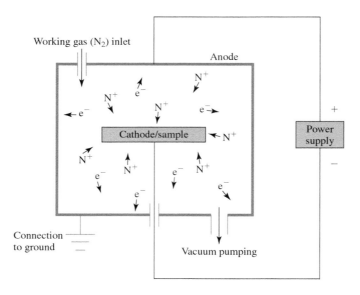

this chapter). As mentioned earlier, the energetic plasma may also be employed to directly polymerize molecules on the sample. For example, a copolymer can be placed on the surface of another polymer and exposed to plasma to crosslink the copolymer to the surface.

Plasma discharge treatments possess several advantages. According to Ratner and Hoffman [1], they

1. are conformal.
2. are free of voids/pinhole defects.
3. are easily prepared.
4. are sterile when removed from the reactor.
5. produce a low amount of leachable substances.
6. demonstrate good adhesion to underlying substrate.
7. allow unique film chemistries to be produced.
8. can be characterized relatively easily.

Due to these advantages, plasma treatment has been explored for polymeric, metallic, and pyrolytic carbon-based biomaterials for use in a wide range of applications, including replacement heart valves, vascular grafts, contact lenses, and even tissue culture dishes. However, as with any modification technique, disadvantages of plasma-based treatments also exist:

1. The chemistry within the reactor can be ill defined.
2. The equipment is often expensive.
3. Uniform reaction within long, narrow pores may be difficult.
4. Particular care must be taken in sample preparation to prevent contamination during or after processing.

Another important application of plasma technology uses an alternative configuration, called a plasma torch, to melt substances with high melting points, such as ceramics, and accelerate the molten particulates to a high velocity. Using this method, the torch can produce **plasma spray coatings**. This technique is commonly used in biomaterials to add ceramic coatings to metallic orthopedic or dental implants to improve their integration with the surrounding bone.

**Figure 7.3**
Schematic of a chemical vapor deposition apparatus. The sample chamber is surrounded by a heater and is filled with gas appropriate to the reaction that will occur inside the chamber. As shown, this setup was used to create pyrolytic carbon nanotubes.

**7.2.2.2 Chemical Vapor Deposition**  Chemical vapor deposition (CVD) is a surface treatment in which a mixture of gases is exposed to a sample at a high temperature. This environment causes a variety of reactions resulting in the decomposition of one or more components of the gas mixture and subsequent deposition on the substrate (see Fig. 7.3). Both covalent and non-covalent coatings can be formed via this method. To form these coatings, equipment providing control of the gas sources, heating of the coating chamber, and means to dispose of waste gases is required. In order to reduce the reaction temperature, plasma environments are often used to increase the reactivity of the gaseous species. This is termed **plasma-assisted chemical vapor deposition**.

CVD techniques are commonly used in biomaterials applications to deposit **pyrolytic carbon** coatings on substrates such as tantalum, molybdenum/rhenium, or graphite. In this case, the gases are hydrocarbons and they undergo thermal decomposition, or **pyrolysis**, within the reaction chamber, allowing carbon deposition on the surface of the material. CVD is also employed to deposit parylene (para-xylylene) on biomaterials using pyrolysis. Parylene coatings are often found on implanted sensors and electronics as they are insulators and provide moisture protection.

**7.2.2.3 Physical Vapor Deposition**  Physical vapor deposition (PVD) results in surface coating via deposition of atoms generated through physical processes onto the sample. PVD techniques have been employed successfully for applications such as orthopedic implants, surgical tools, and orthodontic appliances. For example, metal alloy coatings have been deposited using this method to increase wear resistance of metallic hip implants.

This class of techniques includes sputtering and thermal evaporation, among others. We will focus in this section on sputtering techniques since they can be used for biomaterials surface modification, and are often employed to coat nonconductive samples with a thin layer of metal before imaging with an electron microscope (see Section 7.6.6. for a further description of electron microscopy).

**Sputter deposition** is a two-step process. First, energetic ions or atoms bombard a target material and transfer their momentum to atoms within the target. This causes the ejection of a certain number of target surface atoms. In the second step, the released target atoms strike the sample surface and condense to form a thin film. Both covalent and non-covalent coatings are possible via this method.

Like for CVD, there are also **plasma-assisted PVD** techniques in which the formation of plasma is used to create high-energy species to collide with the target. An example of such a process is shown in Figure 7.4. Here, the target is held at a large negative potential compared to the sample to be coated. Under sufficient vacuum, this environment will initiate formation of plasma near the target, much like that which was described in Section 7.2.2.1. Species from the plasma then strike the target to release atoms that can be deposited on the substrate surface.

**Figure 7.4**
Schematic of a type of physical vapor deposition. The formation of plasma is used to create high-energy species which collide with the target in plasma-assisted physical vapor deposition. The target is held at a large negative potential compared to the sample to be coated. An environment of sufficient vacuum will initiate formation of plasma near the target. Species from the plasma then strike the target to release atoms that can be deposited on the substrate surface [7].

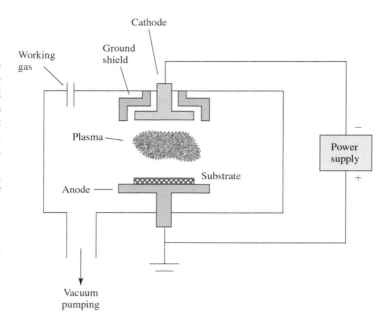

### 7.2.2.4 Radiation Grafting/Photografting

Both **radiation grafting** and **photografting** form well-bonded surface coatings via similar mechanisms. The substrate is exposed to a radiation source of high energy, such as ionizing radiation, electron beams, or UV light, which forms reactive species at the surface to create covalent bonding of the coating to the underlying material (see Fig. 7.5). These methods are often employed to bind hydrogels to hydrophobic substrates. This technique also provides a means to easily tailor the properties of the coating since a mixture of monomers or other precursors can be used.

In one type of radiation grafting (**mutual irradiation**), the biomaterial substrate is placed in a monomer solution and then irradiated by electrons or gamma rays to produce the polymerized coating. Alternatively, the substrate may be irradiated at low temperature or in an inert atmosphere to stabilize the surface free radicals and then the sample is exposed to the coating precursors in a separate step. Another type of radiation grafting occurs in air rather than in an inert environment. In this case, reactive oxygen species such as peroxides are formed on the substrate surface

**Figure 7.5**
Schematic of a type of irradiation grafting. In this example, gamma irradiation was used to covalently bond an amine-containing molecule to the surface of poly($\varepsilon$-caprolactone) nanofibers as the basis for further subsequent biological surface modification. (Adapted with permission from [8].)

as a result of the interaction between the radiating species and oxygen. Heating the substrate will further decompose the peroxides, leaving free radicals to initiate polymerization of the coating on the biomaterial.

Photografting is similar to radiation grafting, but here the radiation is UV or visible light. A number of photoresponsive chemical moieties have been developed to facilitate this type of surface modification. Two common methods involve either phenyl azide or benzophenone chemistry. If these functional groups are present in the coating precursor, they will be excited by exposure to the light and form free radicals or other reactive species. The activated molecules can then participate in reactions at the substrate surface resulting in covalent linkage of the coating to the underlying biomaterial.

**7.2.2.5 Self-Assembled Monolayers**   Surface treatment using **self-assembled monolayers (SAMs)** is based on different principles than those coating methods described previously. In this technique, the molecules composing the coating are designed so that it is thermodynamically favorable for them to align on and form covalent bonds with the surface of the biomaterial. Therefore, in contrast to the previous treatment methods, no specialized equipment is required, and the modification can be carried out at room temperature and under normal atmospheric pressure.

Self-assembling molecules are **amphiphilic**, meaning they have both hydrophilic (polar) and hydrophobic (nonpolar) areas. These molecules possess three key regions, as depicted in Figure 7.6:

1. Attachment group
2. Long hydrocarbon (alkyl) chain
3. Functional (polar) head group

Of these, both the attachment group and the nonpolar hydrocarbon chains play a large role in self-assembly. The functional group can be used to alter the

**Figure 7.6**
The three key regions of amphiphilic self-assembling molecules: the attachment group, a long hydrocarbon (alkyl) chain, and a functional (polar) head group [1].

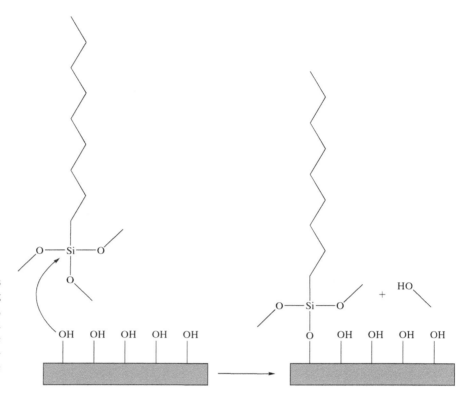

**Figure 7.7**
Self-assembly of alkyl silanes on substrates containing hydroxyl groups. A strong, exothermic reaction between the hydroxyl groups on the substrate and the silane attachment group is the driving force for self-assembly [1].

hydrophobicity of the substrate material, or it can be a point of further chemical reaction to attach biologically active molecules, for example.

A strong, exothermic reaction between the substrate and the attachment group is the driving force for assembly. For example, silanes are commonly-used attachment groups (Fig. 7.7) because they react readily with amine ($NH_2$) or hydroxyl (OH) groups. Therefore, materials containing large amounts of hydroxyl groups, such as glass and metal oxides, are preferred substrates for these types of SAMs. Alternatively, other biomaterials may be pretreated (via plasma discharge or other methods) to increase the number of appropriate reactive groups present on the surface.

Once the SAM molecules begin to gather on the surface, the properties of the alkyl chains become important, as van der Waals forces between the nonpolar regions in each molecule will cause crystallization once they are sufficiently close. High molecular mobility of the coating species is required to assure that tight packing of attachment groups and alkyl chains is achieved.

The advantages of SAMs as a surface modification technique include the ease of their formation, the chemical stability of the coating (usually significantly greater than Langmuir-Blodgett films, which are discussed in the following text), and the variety of chemical moieties that can be included either in the attachment or the functional groups. In addition to changing the chemical properties of the underlying biomaterial, SAMs can also be used to form molecularly smooth surfaces, thus altering the physical properties of the substrate.

### 7.2.3 Chemical Surface Modification: Non-Covalent Interactions

In this section, we continue our discussion of chemical coating methods by considering those that are not covalently bonded to the surface. Examples of these techniques include solution coating, Langmuir-Blodgett films, layer-by-layer coatings, surface-modifying additives, ion beam implantation, and conversion coatings. Some of these procedures have also been employed to coat biologically active molecules on biomaterials (see Section 7.3 of this chapter).

**7.2.3.1 Solution Coatings**   The least complex of the surface modification procedures producing coatings that are not covalently bound to the biomaterial surface are **solution coating** methods. In this technique, the substrate is dipped in a solution containing the dissolved coating material (usually a polymer dissolved in an organic solvent). The substrate is then left to dry and, as the solvent evaporates, the coating is deposited on the surface. This method can also be employed as a simple means to coat substrates with bioactive molecules. In this case, however, the solvent is often aqueous rather than organic.

**7.2.3.2 Langmuir-Blodgett Films**   **Langmuir-Blodgett film (LB film)** deposition involves molecules with similar properties as those used for SAMs. Like SAMs, the coating molecules are amphiphilic with two regions—a hydrophilic head and a hydrophobic tail. Using a piece of equipment called a **Langmuir trough**, shown in Figure 7.8, these molecules can be transferred to a biomaterial surface. As illustrated in the figure, the substrate to be coated is placed into aqueous media and the amphiphilic molecules are added so that the polar head groups interact with the water and the remainder of the molecule rests in the air. By changing the position of the moveable barrier depicted in the right of the figure, the coating is slowly compressed until all of the molecules are orientated so they are standing on end.

**Figure 7.8**
A Langmuir trough, which is used for Langmuir-Blodgett film deposition. In this process, coating molecules that are amphiphilic (have a hydrophilic head and a hydrophobic tail) are transferred to a biomaterial surface using a Langmuir trough. (a) As illustrated in the figure, the substrate to be coated is placed into aqueous media and the amphiphilic molecules are added so that the polar head groups interact with the water and the remainder of the molecule rests in the air. (b) By changing the position of the moveable barrier, the coating is slowly compressed until all of the molecules are orientated so they are standing on end. (c) At this point, the area per molecule reaches a minimum and is nearly constant, even as the barrier is further compressed (the surface pressure increases). This value is called the critical area and is a function of the size and type of hydrophobic tail on the molecule. By maintaining a surface pressure corresponding to the critical area as the material to be coated is slowly removed from the trough, a homogenous, well-orientated coating can be deposited [1].

As depicted in the figures, at this point the area per molecule reaches a minimum and is nearly constant, even as the barrier is further compressed (the surface pressure increases). This value is called the **critical area** and is a function of the size and type of hydrophobic tail on the molecule. By maintaining a surface pressure corresponding to the critical area as the material to be coated is slowly removed from the trough, a homogenous, well-orientated coating can be deposited.

In addition to the uniformity of the overlying layer, LB films have the advantage, like SAMs, of providing many possibilities for altering the chemistry of the coating molecules. A major disadvantage is the relative instability of the coating, due in large part to the fact that it is not chemically bonded to the surface. The addition of moieties on the head groups of the LB coatings to allow for crosslinking to other coating molecules or to the biomaterial surface is one way to overcome this limitation.

### 7.2.3.3 Layer-by-Layer Coatings

Using **layer-by-layer deposition** (LbL) to form coatings on biomedical materials has been explored extensively in the last decade. Originally, this technique was developed using the attraction between anionic and cationic materials to stabilize the layers. A general schematic of the process is found in Figure 7.9, which shows a positively charged substrate first placed in a solution of anionic material, which adsorbs to the surface, making the surface negatively charged. After a rinsing step, the substrate is then placed in a solution of a cationic material, which can then absorb to the now negatively charged surface. These steps are repeated until the desired coating thickness is reached (usually on the order of nm). Parameters such as the concentration of the coating solutions, time in each solution, and pH can be altered to affect the thickness and degree of intermingling of the layers.

More recently, the chemistries of the coating materials for this technique have been expanded and now exploit hydrophobic, hydrogen bonding, and even covalent interactions between layers. The LbL method has been utilized to immobilize both synthetic and natural polymers, as well as biological molecules and small molecule drugs to the surface of materials. Advantages of this technique include that it can attain highly conformal coatings, is relatively straightforward to execute, and like LB films and SAMs, provides a wide variety of possible surface chemistries. However, like other non-covalent coatings, long-term stability may be a concern, depending on the exact chemistries employed in the layers.

**Figure 7.9**
A schematic of the process for layer-by-layer (LbL) deposition based on electrostatic attraction. Step 1: A positively charged substrate is placed in an anionic solution, which deposits on the surface due to electrostatic attraction and causes the surface to become negatively charged. Step 2: The coated substrate is then rinsed to remove loosely attached material. Step 3: The now negatively charged surface is placed in a cationic solution, and adsorption of the positively charged material occurs, making the surface positively charged. Step 4: Substrate is rinsed again. Steps 1–4 are then repeated as many times as required to produce a coating of a desired thickness.

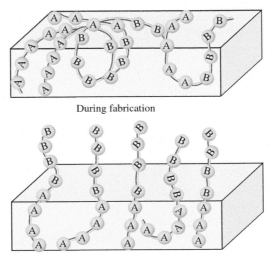

**Figure 7.10**
A depiction of the use of surface-modifying additives in a polymeric material. In this example, the additive is a block copolymer in which block A is compatible with the bulk polymer, while block B is incompatible and possesses an affinity for the surface (has a lower surface energy than the bulk polymer/A block). Block A then serves as an "anchor" to hold the molecule in the bulk, while the surface characteristics will be provided by block B, as seen in the post-fabrication diagram.

**7.2.3.4 Surface-Modifying Additives**   **Surface-modifying additives (SMAs)** are atoms or molecules that, when added in the material bulk, will spontaneously rise to the surface, thus producing a coating with characteristics dictated by the properties of the SMA. The driving force for this rearrangement is the reduction of surface free energy. Therefore, whether or not a given SMA is effective at forming a surface coating depends on the difference in surface tension with and without the SMA, the mobility of the SMA in the bulk material, and the environment surrounding the biomaterial (e.g., air or water). It should be noted here that, unlike the surface modification techniques previously discussed in this chapter, SMA treatment is not a post-fabrication procedure, but rather a part of the formation/synthesis of the biomaterial.

Examples of SMAs for metals include copper in gold alloys. Additionally, chromium will move preferentially to the surface of steels to impart corrosion resistance. SMA systems for ceramics are less likely because there is less atomic mobility within the bulk due to the nature of the ionic bonds that are found within these materials.

Design of SMAs for polymeric biomaterials is considerably easier. As shown in Figure 7.10, one possibility would be the use of a block copolymer in which block A is compatible with the bulk polymer, while block B is incompatible and possesses an affinity for the surface (has a lower surface energy than the bulk polymer/A block). In this case, block A will serve as an "anchor" to hold the molecule in the bulk, while the surface characteristics will be provided by block B.

With all of these systems, care must be taken to design the SMAs with consideration of the final (usually aqueous) environment of biomaterials. An additive with a large hydrophobic group may spontaneously move to the surface when the material is in contact with air, but after implantation in a hydrophilic milieu, it may favor the more hydrophobic material bulk.

**7.2.3.5 Ion Beam Implantation**   **Ion beam implantation** is a process whereby accelerated ions with high energies are directed at the surface of a biomaterial. This method is usually employed for metals and ceramics, although some work with polymers has been undertaken. Because the ions are very energetic, there is a high probability that they will penetrate into the surface (Fig. 7.11).

As the ion interacts with the material surface, there are many possible results. Formation of a cascade of vacancies and interstitials is triggered, with each atom usually displaced several times before slowing to rest in a new location. At the same

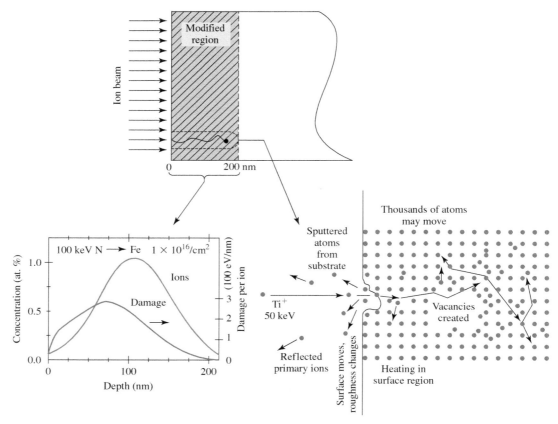

**Figure 7.11**
Schematic representation of ion beam implantation. Ions with high energy states are projected at the surface of the material at high speed, where they break the surface. Once within the material, some atoms from the material are ejected, while others collide with each other and create vacancies and changes within the crystal structure. Using different ions at various concentrations can alter the degree of modification [1, 9].

time, atoms may be sputtered from the substrate due to the high energy of the bombarding ions. Such changes can affect the overall surface roughness of the sample. Localized heating at the surface also occurs, which can alter crystal structure or kinetics of defect formation in this area.

Although specifics regarding equipment for ion beam implantation are beyond the scope of this text, the procedure usually occurs through the formation of plasma from which the ion beam is extracted and focused on the sample. Examples of ion beam implantation for biomaterial applications include the addition of nitrogen to titanium to increase wear resistance and the implantation of boron and carbon into stainless steel to improve fatigue life. Since all of these materials are used in orthopedic implants, good wear and fatigue properties are crucial to success in their final applications.

One of the main advantages to ion beam implantation is that, because almost all elements can be subjected to ionization, there exists a variety of possibilities to affect properties such as hardness, wear, corrosion, and biocompatibility. However, much of what occurs in the sample during this procedure must be more fully understood before surfaces with very well controlled characteristics can be created. Additionally, vacancy and interstitial defects often remain after treatment, so subsequent heating

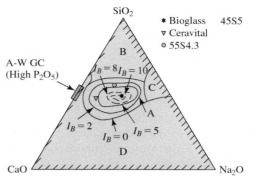

**Figure 7.12**
A phase diagram depicting the range of compositions for bioactive glasses, often used as orthopedic biomaterials. The $I_B$ index is a measurement of the bioactivity of these materials, with a higher number indicating that the material integrates with the surrounding bone more quickly [10].

to remove them may be necessary (this is similar to heat treatment for mechanical strengthening, described in Chapter 6).

**7.2.3.6 Plasma Treatment** As mentioned previously (see Section 7.2.2.1), plasma discharge processes can result in deposition of a coating, or can alter the surface properties through etching and cleaning processes. For these applications, the plasma is created as described previously using an inert gas and the energy of the plasma species causes ablation as the atoms/ions strike the biomaterial surface.

**7.2.3.7 Conversion Coatings** Despite its name, a **conversion coating** is not an overlay coating, but a modification of atoms at the surface of a metallic implant to form an oxide layer. As discussed in Chapter 5, this very thin (5–500 nm) region is chemically inert and acts as a barrier to electron transfer to prevent corrosion. These layers can be created by treating the material directly with acid (steel) or by employing an electrochemical process called *anodization* (aluminum and titanium).

**7.2.3.8 Bioactive Glasses** The phase diagram in Figure 7.12 depicts the range of compositions for a type of ceramic used in orthopedics called **bioactive glasses**. There are many classes of biological response to these glasses, from fibrous encapsulation (see Chapter 11) to complete material dissolution, depending on the ratio of CaO, $Na_2O$, and $SiO_2$ used in the fabrication. The $I_B$ index included on the diagram is a measurement of the bioactivity of these materials, with a higher number indicating that the material is integrated with the surrounding bone more quickly.

Certain compositions of bioactive glasses cause coating of the surfaces with layers of $CaO/P_2O_5$ and $SiO_2$ under physiological conditions. This protective layer allows calcium-phosphate films to precipitate on the material and promote bonding with the native bone, thus increasing the $I_B$ of that formulation. Therefore, this is an example of another surface treatment strategy: *in vivo* modification of a bulk material to produce a surface-active layer.

## 7.2.4 Laser Methods for Surface Modification

In many cases, *lasers* can be used to carry out the previously mentioned surface modifications. By focusing a high-powered light beam at the sample, a large amount of energy can be quickly deposited in a small area, which facilitates reactions such as annealing/alloying, etching, film deposition, and polymerization at the surface.

When deciding on the laser source or treatment regime to perform a particular modification, one must consider whether a pulsed or continuous wave beam would be more appropriate, as well as the effects of possible surface heating by the laser. Much of this depends on the degree of laser energy absorption by the substrate and the amount of interfacial reflection and scattering.

The use of lasers in surface modification technology presents the advantages that treatment can often be performed at atmospheric conditions and with a wide range of very precise wavelengths. In addition, with this equipment there is specific control of reaction time as well as the spatial location of the excitation beam. Lasers also allow the use of a combination of heat and light-induced excitation to initiate the desired reaction.

### EXAMPLE PROBLEM 7.2

As a biomaterials expert, you are asked to consult on surface modification for a new client. This company manufactures polymeric catheters and wishes to add a poly(ethylene glycol) (PEG)-based hydrogel coating to the outside to reduce irritation to surrounding tissues. This company wants to maintain the use of its proprietary polymer and change as few of the current processing steps as possible. What type of surface modification technique would you recommend and why?

**Solution:** The best option is radiation grafting (or plasma treatment). Polymerization of the hydrogel onto the surface of the polymer would produce the most robust coating due to the covalent bonds between the hydrogel and the surface. This can be done through radiation grafting as free radicals can polymerize PEG derivatives (or plasma treatment if the monomer can withstand the plasma environment). In theory, this technique can be applied after the device is formed, so no current processing steps would be altered. ∎

## 7.3 Biological Surface Modification Techniques

**Biological surface modification techniques** involve attachment of biologically active molecules to a substrate through a variety of means, including many of the physicochemical methods described in the previous sections. The attached molecules are then free to interact with specific target areas on cells or other tissue components (these interactions are explained in detail in Chapter 9). Therefore, a primary concern with these techniques is that the molecule of interest remains attached while maintaining its biological activity. Since many biologically based molecules are sensitive to changes in conformation, particular attention must be paid to the orientation and rotational ability of individual molecules after coating.

A list of the types of biomolecules used in surface modifications and their potential applications is found in Table 7.2. Although the specifics of many of these will be discussed in future chapters, biomolecules for surface treatment are often either proteins or carbohydrates derived from various tissues and are attached to facilitate interactions with certain cell types. Other major categories include nucleic acid derivatives (DNA or RNA) or drugs, which are added to the surface in order to alter specific cellular functions in a controlled manner.

Although biological modification of all types of biomaterials is possible, most of the work in this area has centered on polymeric substrates. Biomolecule attachment has been successfully achieved on soluble polymers, solid polymers, solid polymers containing pores to form three-dimensional scaffolds, and hydrogels.

**TABLE 7.2**

| Types of Biomolecules Used in Surface Modifications and Applications | |
|---|---|
| Enzymes | Bioreactors (Industrial, Biomedical) |
| | Bioseparations |
| | Biosensors |
| | Diagnostic assays |
| | Biocompatible surfaces |
| Antibodies, peptides, and other affinity molecules | Biosensors |
| | Diagnostic assays |
| | Affinity separations |
| | Targeted drug delivery |
| | Cell culture |
| Drugs | Thrombo-resistant surfaces |
| | Drug delivery systems |
| Lipids | Thrombo-resistant surfaces |
| | Albuminated surfaces |
| Nucleic acid derivatives and nucleotides | DNA probes |
| | Gene therapy |

(Adapted with permission from [2].)

## 7.3.1 Covalent Biological Coatings

A range of immobilization technologies exist, including both covalent and non-covalent means to link the biomolecule and the substrate. A few of these techniques will be discussed here to provide an overview of the types of reactions commonly employed for immobilization. Like physicochemical techniques, covalently linked coatings may impart additional stability and thus are preferred in many applications. However, they require the presence of a reactive substrate surface, often containing hydroxyl (OH), carboxyl (COOH), or amine ($NH_2$) groups. If these are not found on the chosen biomaterial surface, it may be modified (via plasma discharge, for example) to add appropriate functionality before proceeding with the reaction.

Figure 7.13 depicts several schemes for covalent attachment of biomolecules. In any of these, the molecule can be bound to the substrate directly or by a **spacer arm**, which is an inert molecule that provides physical space between the biomolecule and the substrate. The spacer arm may allow for greater rotational freedom and thus improve the activity of the biological molecule. In addition, it is possible to design biodegradable spacer arms to release the biomolecule in a localized region after biomaterial implantation.

Biomolecules may be attached to a substrate surface using post-fabrication reactions, as shown in Figure 7.13(a–c), or may be included as part of the material synthesis (Fig. 7.13(d–e)). In the former case, a type of binding agent is often used to facilitate interaction of the molecule with the surface. The binding agent can then remain as "glue" or catalyze the reaction and be released. For combined conjugation/synthesis reactions, there are two main methods: (1) The biomolecule may be bound to a precursor (monomer) that is then polymerized in three dimensions or as

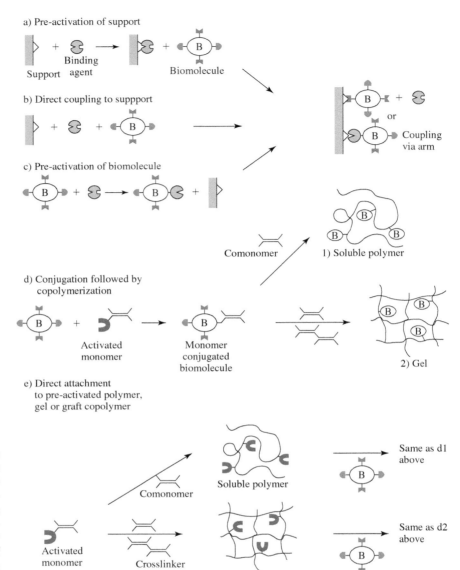

**Figure 7.13**
Methods for the covalent attachment of biomolecules to a biomaterial surface. (a–c) Attachment via postfabrication methods, (d–e) attachment during synthesis. The biomolecule may be attached with or without a spacer arm in any of these methods. (Adapted with permission from [2].)

a surface coating (Fig. 7.13(d)). (2) An activated precursor containing groups with affinity for the biomolecule is polymerized and the formed biomaterial is subsequently exposed to the molecule of interest (Fig. 7.13(e)).

## EXAMPLE PROBLEM 7.3

A researcher has created a biodegradable polymeric implant material that degrades through a surface erosion mechanism. The material is intended to serve as a tissue engineering scaffold, in which long-term cell adhesion to the material is important. Initial studies have found that cells will not adhere to the surface of the material. The researcher is considering covalent attachment (with a poly(ethylene glycol) spacer of 3400 Da) of a peptide sequence known to improve cell attachment to other materials to the surface of this material. The researcher asks if you support the idea. Will you support the idea? Why or why not? Would bulk modification with the peptide sequence be a more or less appropriate method of modification for the intended result?

**Solution:** The idea is not feasible to yield the intended effect for the given application and should not be supported. Recalling that degradation by surface erosion involves the continual loss of the material at the surface of the construct (much like a bar of soap disappears with time of exposure to water as the surface continually erodes away), it follows that any modification to the surface of this material would only be viable for a short period of time until the modified surface degrades away. Following the initial surface degradation, the cells will be exposed to the bulk unmodified material, to which cell attachment has been shown to be nil. Thus, although the cells may attach initially, long-term cell attachment could not feasibly be attained with this modification technique. Bulk modification, however, would be a more appropriate technique because the cell adhesion peptide would be present throughout the bulk of the material, unlike surface modification. As a result, cells could potentially attach to the material throughout the stages of degradation. ■

## 7.3.2 Non-Covalent Biological Coatings

For applications where covalent biological coatings are undesired or the required chemistry is unduly difficult, modification based on non-covalent interactions between the biomolecule and the substrate is possible. This usually involves adsorption of the biomolecule to the biomaterial, and then possible crosslinking to improve the coating stability. Although the principles governing adsorption are explained further in Chapter 8, it has been found that whether or not a certain molecule will gather at a given surface is often dictated by *hydrophobic* and *electrostatic* interactions. These forces can therefore be exploited to couple biomolecules to particular substrates.

For example, one method to coat heparin, a very hydrophilic carbohydrate-based biomolecule important in anticoagulation, on a hydrophobic surface is the addition of a hydrophobic region to the heparin. Thus, interaction of the hydrophobic regions of the biomolecule and the substrate in an aqueous environment will result in extension of the heparin portion away from the surface, effectively coating the biomaterial (Fig. 7.14).

In contrast, adsorption of heparin to positively charged surfaces requires no modification of the biomolecule (Fig. 7.14). Because heparin possesses significant negative charge, electrostatic attraction drives the formation of a heparin layer at the surface of positively charged biomaterials.

## 7.3.3 Immobilized Enzymes

As discussed further in Chapter 9, enzymes are a subclass of proteins that act to promote specific chemical reactions involving other biomolecules. Many of the methods discussed earlier can be used to attach enzymes to solid substrates (carriers). This process, called **enzyme immobilization**, has been highly developed over the past 50 years and now has a variety of applications in such areas as biosensors, controlled release devices, and protein analysis. Regardless of the application, because the function of the device depends on the action of the enzyme, the bioactivity of this molecule is of utmost importance. Thus, much research has been devoted to immobilization techniques, which range from simple adsorption to more complex mechanisms involving covalent linkages with spacer arms. Both hydrophilic hydrogel carriers, such as poly(acrylamide) or poly(ethylene glycol), and hydrophobic carriers, such as nylon or poly(styrene), have been explored, with optimal results dependent on the properties of the enzyme of interest.

An additional concern for these devices is that the biomolecule that the enzyme targets (its **substrate**) must be able to diffuse into the area to physically interact with the immobilized enzyme. Thus, the geometry of the carrier is crucial to allow a sufficiently large surface area for enzyme contact with the substrate. Both parameters

**Figure 7.14**
Two methods for coating a surface with heparin, a hydrophilic biomolecule. (a) A hydrophobic region is added to the heparin. Thus, interaction of the hydrophobic regions of the biomolecule and the substrate in an aqueous environment will result in extension of the heparin portion away from the surface, effectively coating the biomaterial. (b) The adsorption of heparin to positively charged surfaces requires no modification of the biomolecule. Because heparin possesses significant negative charge, electrostatic attraction drives the formation of a heparin layer at the surface of positively charged biomaterials. (Adapted with permission from [2] and [11].)

relating to the chemical activity of the enzyme and to the availability of substrate continue to be optimized to produce more efficient biomedical devices, such as glucose sensors, that depend on the actions of these immobilized enzymes to produce reliable readings.

## 7.4 Surface Properties and Degradation

Surface treatments are particularly susceptible to alteration caused by degradation, either of the surface coating itself, or of the underlying substrate. In some cases, such as conversion coatings, the surface treatment is designed as a method to decrease unwanted degradation (corrosion) of the underlying material. However, even in cases where controlled degradation of the bulk material is desired, such as for biodegradable polymers, the removal of the supporting material or actions of degradation reaction by-products may have significant deleterious effects on the surface coating. In extreme cases, such as surface-eroding materials, it may be impossible to find an effective, lasting surface treatment method.

## 7.5 Patterning Techniques for Surfaces

**Surface** or **substrate patterning** is a term that encompasses several methods developed to alter the surface properties of biomaterials in a controlled manner, resulting in a geometric design of well-defined regions with very different characteristics. Surface patterning can be used to alter either the topography or the chemistry the surface, including the attachment of biomolecules. As can be seen in Figure 7.15, it is important consider the size of the patterns desired when choosing a patterning technique. Specifically, patterns can be developed at the nanoscale (size similar to proteins and other biomolecules) or with μm-sized domains (size similar to cells). This section provides examples of common patterning techniques at each of these size scales, with a focus on methods to modify 2D surfaces. For a more complete list of techniques, including those that are appropriate for patterning in 3D, please see [3], [4].

Patterning methods generally fall into two categories: a form of direct writing on the surface, or a type of pattern transfer technique, such as using molds or masks. For fabrication of nanoscale features, the most common are direct writing methods. In one class of these techniques, a beam of high energy is directed at the surface in particular locations to form the pattern (see Fig. 7.16). This beam can be made of photons, often

**Figure 7.15**
Schematic demonstrating the relationship between the size of biological molecules/cells and the feature size obtained by various surface patterning techniques. (Adapted with permission from [3].)

(a)

(b)

**Figure 7.16**
Diagram of lithography by high energy beams (a) [3] and fabrication of a diamond nanowire by using e-beam lithography and reactive ion etching (b) [Argonne National Laboratory/Science Source Christman].

produced by lasers (**direct-write photolithography**); electrons, often produced as part of a scanning electron microscope, see Section 7.6.6 (**e-beam lithography**); or ions (**ion beam lithography**). In all of these cases, the beam is focused on small areas of the sample and can either remove material from the surface in these areas (etching) or, if the surface contains reactive molecules, can initiate polymerization or activation of molecules. The main advantage of these techniques is the small spatial resolution for patterns (on the order of nanometers). However, disadvantages include low throughput (each sample must be patterned sequentially), and large cost of the equipment needed.

Another type of direct writing is dip-pen nanolithography, which employs atomic force microscropy (AFM) equipment (see Section 7.6.7 for detailed description of AFM). In this technique, the small tip used in AFM is "inked" with a certain molecule (see Fig. 7.17). As the tip is scanned across the surface, the molecule will be transferred to the sample in a pattern determined by the location of the tip on the surface. This technique is very versatile as many different types of biomolecules have been explored as "inks," and, because of the extremely small size of the tip, nanoscale patterns can be achieved. However, like the beam writing methods explained earlier, low throughput can be a concern as each sample must be treated sequentially unless multiple tips are mounted in the AFM.

For the formation of μm-scale patterns, both direct writing and pattern transfer techniques are utilized. The most common direct writing method is **ink-jet printing**, which, in some cases, employs commercially available printers used to print on paper. In this method (Fig. 7.18), a solution containing the molecules to be patterned is dispersed

(a)

(b)

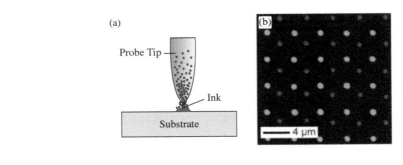

**Figure 7.17**
Diagram of dip-pen nanolithography (a) and a fluorescent microscopy image showing an array of DNA molecules patterned using this method (b) [3, 13].

(a)

(b)

**Figure 7.18**
Diagram of ink-jet printing for surface modification (a) and an optical microscopy image showing a pattern generated by ink-jet printing mussel-derived adhesive proteins on a silicon substrate (b). (Adapted with permission from [3] and [14].)

**Figure 7.19**
Photolithography for surface modification showing the use of a mask to polymerize a coating in the areas exposed to light (bottom left) or photo-cleaving to remove an area after light exposure (bottom right). (Adapted with permission from [15].)

into droplets and deposited by a printhead. Once the solvent evaporates, the molecules form a pattern on the surface that is controlled by the location of the printhead above the substrate. A wide range of molecules have been employed as "inks," making this technique very versatile, and many samples can be patterned simultaneously with the use of multiple printhead nozzles. Similarly, using different nozzles simultaneously on the same sample allows for complex patterning of multiple molecules next to each other. This technique also provides good control of the volume deposited in each spot. The main disadvantage is that patterns smaller than ~10 microns are difficult to achieve with ink-jet printing, mainly due to droplet volume and spreading on the surface.

**Photolithography** was first developed for the microelectronics industry, but for biomaterials, the most common use of this technique is to form masters or masks that can be used in pattern transfer. As shown in Figure 7.19, photolithography involves the use of opaque masks to block light penetration to form a pattern on a substrate that contains chemical moieties that are reactive to light. Depending on the chemistry of the surface, either removal of material, or adding of material due to polymerization or crosslinking, in the area bombarded by light can occur. The advantages of this technique are that large areas can be patterned easily and multiple masks can be used to produce complex patterns. However, patterns smaller than tens of microns are difficult to achieve with this method.

In **microcontact printing**, a mold of the desired pattern is first created, often via photolithographic techniques on a silicon wafer (Fig. 7.20). A silicone rubber material (poly(dimethylsiloxane), PDMS) is then polymerized in the mold to make a positive "stamp." The stamp is "inked" with the surface-modifying substance by dipping it into a solution containing the molecule of interest, and the inked stamp is then pressed onto the substrate. After carefully removing the stamp, the biomaterialist can repeat the process to modify the portion of the substrate that was not stamped the first time, thus creating multifunctional surfaces. The stamps can be re-used, making it relatively quick to produce multiple samples. This technique has been employed successfully with physicochemical approaches such as SAMs to modify the hydrophilicity of portions of a surface, and it is equally useful for biological modification methods. The main disadvantage of this technique is that the size of the pattern must be on the order of microns or larger.

**Figure 7.20**
In microcontact printing, a mold of the desired pattern is first created, often via photolithographic techniques on a silicon wafer. A silicone rubber material (PDMS) is then polymerized in the mold to make a positive "stamp" (1–3). The stamp is "inked" with the surface-modifying substance by dipping it into a solution containing the molecule of interest (4) and the inked stamp is then pressed onto the substrate (5). After carefully removing the stamp, the process can be repeated to modify the portion of the substrate that was not stamped the first time, thus creating multifunctional surfaces. (Adapted with permission from [15].)

As depicted in Figure 7.21, **microfluidics** employs many of the same materials as microcontact printing. For this technique, the mold is fabricated as described earlier, but the mold is a positive, rather than a negative, image of the desired design. PDMS is then polymerized in the mold to make channels where required. Like for microcontact printing, the PDMS form is then pressed against the substrate and a small amount of a solution containing the molecule of interest is injected or placed near the opening of a channel. Capillary action pulls liquid through all the channels and the areas of

**Figure 7.21**
For the microfluidics technique, (a) the mold is fabricated as described in microcontact printing, but the mold is a positive, rather than a negative, image of the desired design. (b) PDMS is then polymerized in the mold. (c) The formed PDMS is then removed from the mold and pressed against a glass slide. This setup is then plasma-treated to increase the hydrophilicity of inner areas of the channels only, while the regions between channels remain hydrophobic to maintain the integrity of each channel. Like for microcontact printing, (d) the PDMS form is then pressed against the substrate and a small amount of a solution containing the molecule of interest is injected or placed near the opening of a channel, where capillary action pulls the liquid throughout the channels. The areas of the substrate under the channels are appropriately modified. (e) After the molecule has reacted with the surface, the PDMS form is removed and the surface is rinsed [13, 16].

the substrate under the channels are appropriately modified. After the molecule has reacted with the surface, the PDMS form is removed and the surface is rinsed.

It may be possible to produce multi-functional surfaces using this method by including different surface-active molecules in different channels. Similar to micro-contact printing, this technique has been employed with a variety of both chemical and biological coating methods. A distinct advantage of this process is that it takes very little fluid volume, so it can be easily used with expensive or difficult-to-produce biologic reagents. Disadvantages include that, like other techniques based on photolithography, patterning is on the order of microns, and that, unless multiple microfluidic devices are employed simultaneously, this technique is relatively low throughput.

## 7.6  Techniques: Introduction to Surface Characterization

Surface characterization of biomaterials is important, both to determine the quality of the surface treatments described in this chapter and also to provide information about the extent of protein adsorption to a material. Because surfaces are chemically active, many surface techniques require special preparation equipment or conditions such as high vacuum to prevent contamination.

As depicted in Figure 7.22, there are surface characterization methods that record data from various depths. We begin our discussion in this section with the

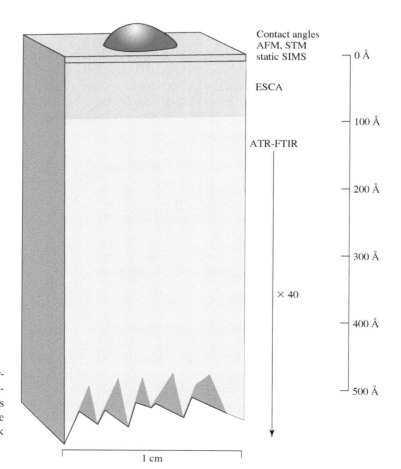

**Figure 7.22**
Surface penetration of various surface analysis methods. Some surface analysis techniques actually penetrate relatively deep into the bulk of the material [17].

TABLE 7.3

| Characterization Methods for Biomaterial Surfaces | | | | | |
|---|---|---|---|---|---|
| Method | Principle | Depth Analyzed | Spatial Resolution | Analytical Sensitivity | Cost[c] |
| Contact angles | Liquid wetting of surfaces is used to estimate the energy of surfaces | 3–20 Å | 1 mm | Low or high depending on the chemistry | $ |
| ESCA (XPS) | X-rays induce the emission of electrons of characteristic energy | 10–250 Å | 10–150 $\mu$m | 0.1 atom % | $$$ |
| Auger electron spectroscopy [a] | A focused electron beam stimulates the emission of Auger electrons | 50–100 Å | 100 Å | 0.1 atom % | $$$ |
| SIMS | Ion bombardment sputters secondary ions from the surface | 10 Å–1 $\mu$m[b] | 100 Å | Very high | $$$ |
| ATR-FTIR | IR radiation is adsorbed and excites molecular vibrations | 1–5 $\mu$m | 10 $\mu$m | 1 mol % | $$ |
| STM | Measurement of the quantum tunneling current between a metal tip and a conductive surface | 5 Å | 1 Å | Single atoms | $$ |
| SEM | Secondary electron emission induced by a focused electron beam is spatially imaged | 5 Å | 40 Å, typically | High, but not quantitative | $$ |

[a] Auger electron spectroscopy is damaging to organic materials and is best used for inorganics.
[b] Static SIMS ≈ 10Å, dynamic SIMS to 1 $\mu$m
[c] $, up to $5000; $$, $5000–$100,000; $$$, >100,000.
(Adapted with permission from [5].)

simplest, least expensive techniques for general surface analysis, including contact angle analysis and light microscopy. Surface spectroscopic techniques, which involve the absorption of electromagnetic radiation by the material, are then treated in order of descending energy (electron spectroscopy for chemical analysis and attenuated total internal reflectance-Fourier transform infrared spectroscopy). A modification of mass spectrometry for surface analysis (secondary ion mass spectrometry) and, finally, more advanced methods for obtaining topographical information (electron microscopy and scanning probe microscopy) are also described. A summary of each of these surface analysis methods is found in Table 7.3.

## 7.6.1 Contact Angle Analysis

**7.6.1.1 Basic Principles**   Contact angle analysis is often used to provide overall information about the hydrophobicity of a surface. The surface free energy or surface tension ($\gamma$) of a material can be defined thermodynamically as the work of making a unit area of new surface. In most contact angle experiments, a system with three interfaces (and corresponding $\gamma$ values) is created (Fig. 7.23)—the liquid–vapor surface ($\gamma_{LV}$), the solid–liquid surface ($\gamma_{SL}$), and the solid–vapor surface ($\gamma_{SV}$). In most cases, the liquid chosen for testing of biomedical materials is water. The energetics at each of the interfaces causes the water droplet to assume a particular shape (different degree of spreading). Therefore, by accurately measuring the angle between the drop and the solid surface (the **contact angle,** $\theta$), the surface tension can be calculated using the following equation, which represents a force balance between the horizontal components of three surface tensions (Young's equation, see Fig. 7.23):

$$\gamma_{SV} - \gamma_{SL} - \gamma_{LV}\cos\theta = 0 \qquad (7.1)$$

**Figure 7.23**
(a) Schematic of contact angle testing. Around the water droplet, there are three important interfaces: liquid–vapor ($\gamma_{LV}$), solid–liquid ($\gamma_{SL}$), and solid–vapor ($\gamma_{SV}$) [18]. (b) Change in wettability via surface modification. The water droplet spreads more on the modified surface because the modification decreases the surface tension of the liquid/solid interface, thus reducing the contact angle as calculated using Young's equation (7.1) [19].

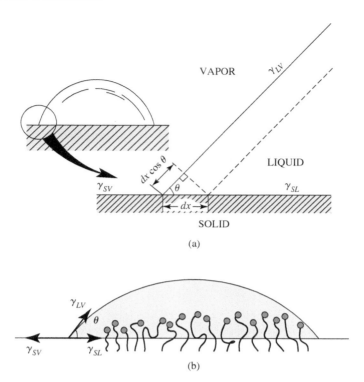

This equation contains two unknowns, $\gamma_{SV}$ and $\gamma_{SL}$. $\gamma_{SV}$ is often approximated using the critical surface tension ($\gamma_c$), as developed by Zisman. $\gamma_c$ is determined by testing the material using various liquids with a range of $\gamma_{LV}$ values. A plot of contact angle vs. $\gamma_{LV}$ is generated and extrapolated to $\theta = 0$ (complete spreading on the surface). The value of $\gamma_{LV}$ at this point is called $\gamma_c$. This is illustrated pictorially in Figure 7.24.

**Figure 7.24**
Diagram showing how the critical surface tension ($\gamma_c$) is determined. The contact angle of various liquids is measured for a specific material, and a plot of contact angle versus $\gamma_{LV}$ is generated. The extrapolated value of $\gamma_{LV}$ at $\theta = 0$ is $\gamma_c$ [5].

## EXAMPLE PROBLEM 7.4

Guided by the following image, derive Young's equation for surface tension:

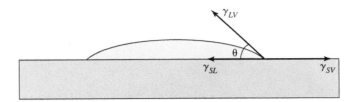

**Solution:** The forces in the diagram must balance in the plane of the solid material for the droplet to be in static equilibrium. As a result, the sum of $\gamma_{SL}$ and the projection of $\gamma_{LV}$ on the plane of the solid must equal $\gamma_{SV}$ for the net force in the plane of the material to be 0. The projection of $\gamma_{LV}$ on the plane of the solid can be determined by drawing a perpendicular line from the material surface to the end of the $\gamma_{LV}$ vector to form a right triangle. The projection ($p$) of $\gamma_{LV}$ on the plane of the material can then be calculated as follows:

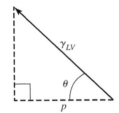

$$\cos = \frac{\text{adjacent}}{\text{hypotenuse}}$$

$$\cos \theta = \frac{p}{\gamma_{LV}}$$

$$p = \gamma_{LV} \cos \theta$$

Consequently, the vectors can be balanced as follows to yield Young's equation:

$$\gamma_{SL} + \gamma_{LV} \cos \theta = \gamma_{SV}$$

$$\underline{\gamma_{SV} - \gamma_{SL} - \gamma_{LV} \cos \theta = 0}$$

∎

**7.6.1.2 Instrumentation**   Unlike many other characterization techniques, the output of contact angle analysis is a single number ($\theta$ or $\gamma_c$), rather than a plot (see Fig. 7.25). The instrumentation for these measurements is fairly straightforward, but several experimental methods have been developed, as shown in Figure 7.26. Although the exact mechanisms behind each of these methods is beyond the scope of this text, all types of contact angle instrumentation have these components in common:

1. Holder for solid sample
2. Holder for liquid
3. Means to determine contact angle (may be automated)

For many of these experiments, a computer is not necessary, so the instrumentation is generally inexpensive. However, because the contact angle measurement is not always fully automated, user bias can have a substantial effect on the results.

**Figure 7.25**
Example of a contact angle measurement on a collagen-based surface [20].

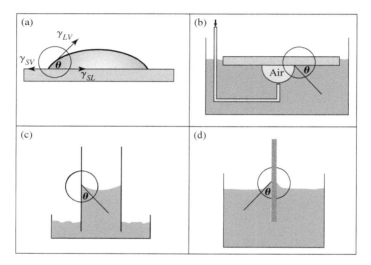

**Figure 7.26**
Different experimental setups for determining the contact angle: (a) sessile drop, (b) captive air bubble, (c) capillary rise method, and (d) Wilhelmy plate method. The circles indicate where the contact angle is measured [5].

### 7.6.1.3 Information Provided

Although contact angle data is widely available for most biomedical materials, this technique cannot provide detailed information about the chemical composition of the surface, so it is often used as a first step in surface characterization. **Dynamic contact angle measurements** are also used to measure **contact angle hysteresis**. In the most common of these measurements, water is slowly added to an area of the surface with a syringe and the **advancing contact angle** is measured. The water is then removed via the same mechanism and the **receding contact angle** is recorded. The difference between these two values represents the contact angle hysteresis for that material and describes how the surface tension of the material changes before and after it has been exposed to an aqueous environment. Hysteresis can occur for a variety of reasons. For example, hydrophilic domains within the material may become reorientated outward from the surface after contact with water, whereas they may be "hidden" within the bulk when exposed to hydrophobic environments such as air.

## 7.6.2 Light Microscopy

### 7.6.2.1 Basic Principles

Light microscopy is a relatively simple technique that is used as a first approach to gain primarily qualitative information about surface topography, or to view thin sections of a sample. In one type of light microscope, the **compound microscope**,

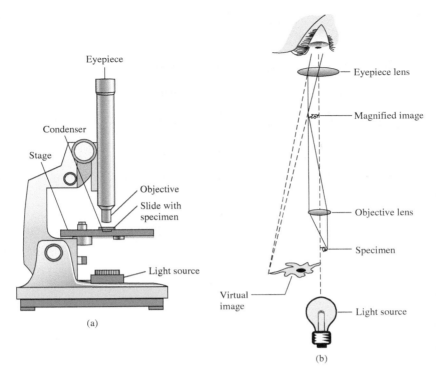

**Figure 7.27**
(a) Gross image of a compound microscope. On a compound microscope, the light source is placed below the specimen and the specimen is viewed from above. (b) Light path of a compound microscope. The objective forms a magnified image of the object that is larger than the original object. This image is then magnified many times by the eyepiece to form the large (inverted) virtual image.

a white light source is projected through the sample, where the combination of ocular (in the eyepiece) and objective lenses reflect the light in such a manner as to magnify the sample many times, providing a detailed image of features usually undetectable to the naked eye. A diagram of the light path in such a microscope is found in Figure 7.27.

For opaque samples, the light source can be located above rather than below the sample. The **resolution** of such instruments (distance under which two objects will appear as one) is limited by the wavelength of white light, and in most cases is around 0.2 $\mu$m. Therefore, features that are smaller than this, or that are more closely spaced than this, cannot be distinguished using this method.

**7.6.2.2 Instrumentation** Light microscopy images, like that found in Figure 7.28, are widespread and have a variety of uses. Of particular interest in this chapter, surface topographical features on the order of microns can be imaged via this technique (Fig. 7.29). As shown in Figure 7.30, there are four basic components to a light microscope:

1. Source—produces white light.
2. Lenses—glass lenses focus light beam and/or magnify image of sample.

**Figure 7.28**
Sample of a light microscopy image, in this case, fibroblasts attached to a poly(styrene) substrate. (Image courtesy of J. Guo and A.G. Mikos, Rice University.)

**Figure 7.29**
Surface topographical ridges as seen on a polymer surface. The sample is viewed via a particular type of light microscopy called *fluorescence microscopy*. Scale bar is 200 µm. (Reprinted with permission from [22].)

**Figure 7.30**
Block diagram of the components of a light microscope, which include the source, lenses, sample stage, and detector (camera or human eye).

3. Sample stage—holds sample securely.

4. Detector (camera or human eye)—views and captures resulting image.

If a camera is used as the detector, the image can be stored on a computer for further image analysis.

As illustrated in Figure 7.31, the sample surface (or a thin section from the bulk) is placed on the stage. The condenser lens focuses the light beam before it passes through the sample. After the light exits the specimen, the objective and ocular lenses act in concert to magnify the sample image. The image can then be either directed to a camera or viewed directly through the eyepiece.

**Figure 7.31**
Light path through a light microscope. The sample surface (or a thin section from the bulk) is placed on the stage. The condenser lens focuses the light beam before it passes through the sample. The objective and ocular lenses act in concert to magnify the sample image from the light that exits the specimen. The image can then be viewed directly through the eyepiece or directed to a camera.

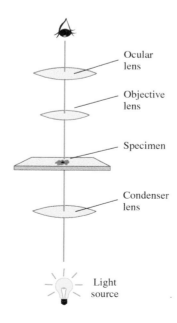

Ocular lens

Objective lens

Specimen

Condenser lens

Light source

**7.6.2.3 Information Provided**  Light microscopy is used exclusively for imaging, and provides in itself only qualitative assessment. Images can be further analyzed using specialized software to obtain semi-quantitative measures of certain colors or other user-defined parameters. In addition to imaging surface topography, this instrument is extremely important in histological analysis for biocompatibility assessment (discussed further in the second half of this textbook). Briefly, serial sections of a sample containing, for example, both the biomaterial and surrounding tissue after *in vivo* implantation, are taken, stained, and viewed through a light microscope to determine the extent of the inflammatory response to the implant.

While light microscopy has the advantage that vacuum is not required to view samples, it remains difficult to see thick or hydrated samples, so relating images directly to what would be seen *in vivo* is not possible. In addition, light microscopy remains a first approach to imaging, particularly for sample surface features, due to its limited spatial resolution.

## 7.6.3 Electron Spectroscopy for Chemical Analysis (ESCA) or X-ray Photoelectron Spectroscopy (XPS)

**7.6.3.1 Basic Principles**  As mentioned in Chapter 2, X-rays are a type of very high energy electromagnetic radiation used as a source in ESCA (also called XPS) analysis of material surfaces. In this type of spectroscopy, X-ray absorption causes the removal of an electron from one of the innermost atomic orbitals (not the valence shell). The kinetic energy of the emitted electron is then recorded. Measurement of the kinetic energy of this ejected electron separates this technique from other types of X-ray spectroscopy, such as X-ray fluorescence, which is discussed later in the section on electron microscopy, and Auger electron spectroscopy, which is beyond the scope of this book. Table 7.4 summarizes the distinctions between X-ray methods.

**TABLE 7.4**

| Summary of the Differences Between X-Ray Techniques | |
| --- | --- |
| *X-ray diffraction* | Interaction between X-rays and electrons of the sample material causes X-ray scattering. The angle of scattering gives information about the crystal structure of the material. |
| *Electron spectroscopy for chemical analysis (ESCA)* | Exposure of a sample to X-rays causes the removal of core electrons with a certain kinetic energy. From this, the binding energy, which gives information about the chemical composition of the material, can be calculated. The kinetic energy of ejected Auger electrons may be detected as an artifact. |
| *X-ray fluorescence* | Exposure of the sample to an electron beam or X-ray causes the removal of a core electron and formation of an ion. The ion can return to its ground state as one of the outer electrons falls into the vacancy, and, in the process, X-rays of a certain wavelength that is characteristic for that atom are emitted. It is often used in biomaterial analysis as an addition to electron microscopy to determine the composition of a sample that has been imaged. |
| *Auger electron spectroscopy* | Exposure of the sample to an electron beam or X-ray causes the removal of a core electron and formation of an ion. The ion can return to its ground state as one of the outer electrons falls into the vacancy, and, in the process, a second electron (Auger electron) with a kinetic energy characteristic for that atom is emitted. Auger emission and X-ray fluorescence are competing events, with atoms of higher atomic number favoring relaxation through X-ray fluorescence. |

**Figure 7.32**
(a) A typical ESCA spectrum of poly(dimethyl siloxane) (PDMS), plotted as electron count (*y*-axis) as a function of binding energy (*x*-axis). (b) Chemical structure of PDMS [17].

From the kinetic energy ($E_k$), the binding energy ($E_b$) of the electron can be calculated as

$$E_b = h\nu - E_k \tag{7.2}$$

where $\nu$ is the frequency and $h$ is the Planck's constant ($6.6 \times 10^{-34}$ J-s). Since the electrons are attracted to and held in place by the positively charged nucleus, the more they can feel the effects of the positive charge (either because they are located closer to the nucleus or because there are more positive charges in the nucleus (higher atomic number)), the larger their binding energy. Therefore, the binding energy gives an idea of how tightly bound the electron is to the nucleus, and it changes in accordance with the type of atom as well as interactions with the nuclei of neighboring atoms.

ESCA is often used to identify elements present at the surface of a material. Its analytical capabilities are limited to the uppermost ~100 Å of a sample because the energy of the emitted electrons allows escape from only the first few atomic layers.

**7.6.3.2 Instrumentation**    A typical ESCA spectrum of poly(dimethyl siloxane) (PDMS) is found in Figure 7.32. ESCA spectra are generally plotted as electron count (*y*-axis) as a function of binding energy (*x*-axis). As shown in Figure 7.33, there are four basic components to an electron spectrometer:

1. Source—produces X-rays with known wavelength.

2. Electron analyzer—uses an electrostatic field to separate electrons based on kinetic energy.[2]

**Figure 7.33**
Block diagram of the components of an ESCA instrument. The four main components are an X-ray source, an electron analyzer, a detector, and a processor (computer).

---

[2]Although there are other means to determine kinetic energy of electrons, this method, called a *dispersive analyzer*, is the most common and therefore is the focus of this discussion.

3. Detector—converts impact by separated electrons into an electrical signal.
4. Processor (computer)—translates the signal from the detector into the appropriate spectrum.

As illustrated in Figure 7.34, the sample is first bombarded with X-rays. The resulting emitted electrons then enter the analyzer chamber. Because of the geometry of the analyzer and the difference in voltage between the two walls, only electrons with a certain kinetic energy can be collected by the detector, while all the others strike non-detectable areas. (This is similar to the operation of mass analyzers in mass spectroscopy, as described in Chapter 2.) By altering the voltage difference between the walls in a controlled manner, the electrostatic field is altered to permit the detector to record the amount of electrons having various kinetic energies. At the end of the voltage sweep, the entire spectrum is plotted for that sample. As indicated in Figure 7.34, ESCA analysis is performed under vacuum to prevent unwanted interactions of emitted electrons with gas molecules in the air.

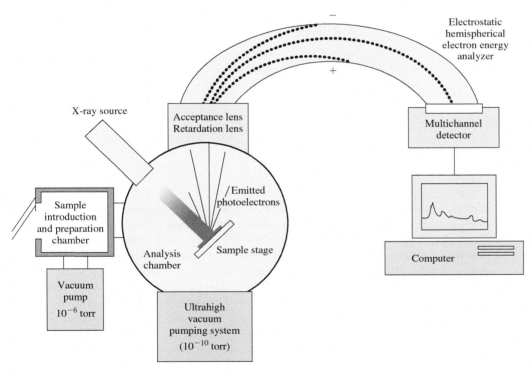

**Figure 7.34**

Schematic of ESCA equipment. First, the sample is bombarded with X-rays. The resulting emitted electrons then enter the analyzer chamber. Because of the difference in voltage between the two walls and the geometry of the analyzer, only electrons with a certain kinetic energy can be collected by the detector, with the remaining electrons striking non-detectable areas. By altering the voltage difference between the walls in a controlled manner, the electrostatic field is altered to permit the detector to record the amount of electrons having various kinetic energies. At the end of the voltage sweep, the entire spectrum is plotted for that sample [5].

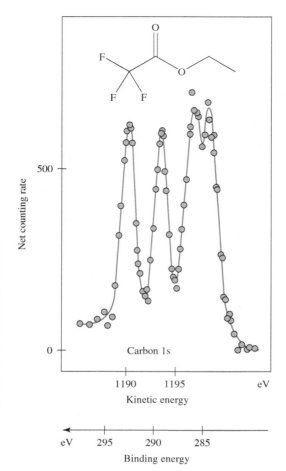

**Figure 7.35**
An ESCA spectrum for ethyl trifluoroacetate. As seen in the graph, binding energies can be distinguished for the various carbons in this molecule. Of the atoms depicted, fluorine has the most ability to withdraw valence electron density from carbon. Therefore, the positive nuclear charge is less shielded, and the core carbon electrons are held more tightly. This results in a higher binding energy for this carbon atom than for others in the molecule [23, 24].

**7.6.3.3 Information Provided**   ESCA methods are extremely sensitive and can detect all elements except hydrogen and helium in the outermost ~100 Å of an organic or inorganic material at concentrations down to 0.1 atomic percent. At the same time, the ESCA spectrum also provides information about neighboring atoms to which an element is bonded. For example, as shown in Figure 7.35 for ethyl trifluoroacetate, binding energies can be distinguished for the various carbons in this molecule. Of the atoms depicted, fluorine has the most ability to withdraw valence electron density from carbon (it is the most electronegative). Therefore, the positive nuclear charge is less shielded, and the core carbon electrons are held more tightly. This results in a higher binding energy for this carbon atom than for others in the molecule.

## 7.6.4 Attenuated Total Internal Reflectance-Fourier Transform Infrared Spectroscopy (ATR-FTIR)

**7.6.4.1 Basic Principles**   ATR-FTIR is an analysis technique that has developed through modification of a bulk characterization method to probe particular parameters at the material surface. The theory behind IR excitation of molecules has been described previously in Chapter 2. The major distinguishing characteristic of ATR-FTIR is the

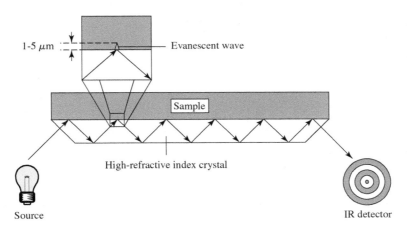

**Figure 7.36**
Schematic of the light path within an ATR-FTIR probe. In order to increase the level of absorption, the probe is designed so that, at certain angles of incident radiation, reflection of the IR beam is complete. Therefore, multiple reflection processes and multiple attenuations occur as the beam passes close to the sample, increasing the signal.

addition of a specialized probe made of a high-refractive index crystal that intimately contacts the sample surface and through which the IR beam is transmitted.

When a beam of electromagnetic radiation passes from a medium that is more dense to one that is less dense, reflection occurs. Upon reflection, the beam penetrates a small distance into the less dense medium and this penetrating radiation is called an **evanescent wave**. Like for other IR methods, the sample may absorb the evanescent beam due to the vibration frequency of bonds found within the material. Absorption of certain wavelengths causes their attenuation (thus giving the method its name) and provides information about the chemical structure of the material.

In order to increase the level of absorption to detectable values, the probe is designed so that, at certain angles of incident radiation, reflection of the IR beam is complete. Therefore, multiple reflection processes and multiple attenuations occur as the beam passes close to the sample (Fig. 7.36), thereby increasing the signal. By placing the probe in contact with the material, ATR-FTIR is thought to record only surface characteristics, but it should be noted that a signal can be obtained from relatively deep within the sample by surface analysis standards ($1 - 5 \, \mu$m).

**7.6.4.2 Instrumentation**  A typical IR spectrum of poly(dimethyl siloxane) is found in Figure 7.37. Like other IR spectra, ATR-FTIR data are generally plotted

Poly(dimethyl siloxane)

**Figure 7.37**
Typical ATR-FTIR spectrum of poly(dimethyl siloxane). Characteristic peaks include the C–H bond in Si-CH$_3$ at 800 cm$^{-1}$ (A), the Si-O-Si bonds at 1020 cm$^{-1}$ (B), and the C–H bond in Si-CH$_3$ at 1260 cm$^{-1}$ (C).

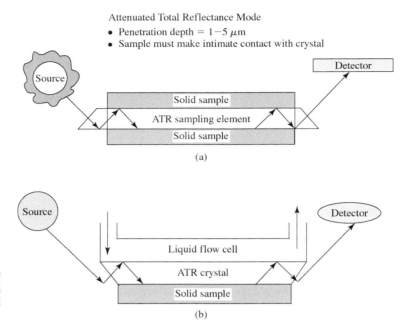

Attenuated Total Reflectance Mode
- Penetration depth = $1-5 \mu m$
- Sample must make intimate contact with crystal

(a)

(b)

**Figure 7.38**
Two types of ATR sample cells, (a) one for solids and (b) one for the solid/liquid interface [17, 5].

by transmittance (or absorbance) ($y$-axis) as a function of wavelength (or wavenumber) ($x$-axis). The basic instrumentation for ATR-FTIR spectroscopy is very similar to that described previously for other FTIR methods and includes an IR source, an interferometer, a detector, and a processor. Fourier-transform techniques are required for this application because they significantly increase the signal strength (signal to noise ratio), which, as mentioned previously, is weak due to the small mass at the material surface. Two types of ATR sample cells, one for solids and one for the solid/liquid interface, are shown in Figure 7.38. Cells allowing for the presence of liquid have particular application in the study of protein adsorption via ATR-FTIR techniques (see the following text).

**7.6.4.3 Information Provided** Although ATR-FTIR spectra are similar, they are not identical to regular IR spectra. While absorbance occurs at the same wavelengths, the intensity of the peak may be altered with respect to the spectra described in Chapter 2. Many of the applications for ATR-FTIR are identical to those of its bulk counterpart, including recording spectra to gain insight into chemical composition of the biomaterial surface.

Another common use for this technique is to follow the relative change over time of certain peaks that correspond to a specific type of bond. Examining the appearance of amide bonds, for example, allows the kinetics of protein adsorption to a biomaterial to be sensitively monitored. The development of sample cells that permit the introduction of a liquid/water interface (Fig. 7.38(b)) has greatly facilitated these types of experiments.

### 7.6.5 Secondary Ion Mass Spectrometry (SIMS)

**7.6.5.1 Basic Principles** Like ATR-FTIR, SIMS is a derivation of a bulk analytical technique: mass spectrometry. However, SIMS can be distinguished from spectroscopic techniques such as IR because it does not involve the absorption of electromagnetic radiation. The theory behind SIMS is identical to that described for mass spectrometry in Chapter 2 and centers on separation of ionic species by mass.

A minor difference in the surface version is the method of sample ionization, which involves the use of primary and secondary ions (thus giving SIMS its name).

Ionization begins when primary ions, such as $O_2^+$, $Ar^+$, $Xe^+$, or $Cs^+$, are ejected from an ion gun and strike the sample surface. This causes the surface layer of atoms to be stripped off, or **sputtered**, both as neutral species and as ions. (This is a similar process to the sputtering of atoms from the target in sputter coating or removal of atoms from the sample surface during ion beam implantation.) These emitted ions are called **secondary ions** and are drawn into the analyzer for separation by mass in a similar manner to bulk mass spectroscopy.

SIMS is considered a surface analysis technique since the energy of the incident ions generates collision cascades only in the surface region of the sample, and, of these collisions, only those that occur in the outermost layers produce secondary ions with sufficient energy to escape from the surface. Both static and dynamic SIMS methods have been developed. **Static SIMS** uses a relatively low ion dose (less than $10^{13}$ ions/cm$^2$) and induces minimal surface damage. In contrast, **dynamic SIMS** bombards the sample with a much larger ion dose. In this case, so much material is sputtered that the surface erodes while the experiment is being performed. This allows **depth profiling** of specimens (monitoring the intensity of a peak of interest as the surface erodes).

**7.6.5.2 Instrumentation** As demonstrated in Figure 7.39, like bulk mass spectra, SIMS spectra are plotted as relative intensity ($y$-axis) as a function of mass ($x$-axis). Figure 7.40 reveals that the instrumentation required for SIMS is very

**Figure 7.39**

A spectrum produced by a type of SIMS (Time of Flight SIMS recording only positive ions) for fibronectin adsorbed on a poly(styrene) surface. The various peaks correspond to different amino acids found in the fibronectin protein. By comparing the relative intensities of certain peaks as the protein is adsorbed on different surfaces, the biomaterialist can obtain information about the orientation of the protein on each surface [25].

**Figure 7.40**
Block diagram of instrumentation for SIMS, which includes four main components: an ionization chamber containing the sample and ion gun, a mass analyzer (mass filter), an ion detector, and a processor/computer to translate signals from the detector into the appropriate spectrum. SIMS analysis is conducted under ultra-high vacuum (UHV) [26, 27].

similar to that for bulk mass spectrometry, and includes the four main components: an ionization chamber containing the sample, a mass analyzer, an ion detector, and a processor/computer to translate signals from the detector into the appropriate spectrum. Like other types of mass spectroscopy, SIMS analysis is completed under vacuum.

**7.6.5.3 Information Provided**  SIMS provides information about the structure and composition of the outermost few Å of both inorganic and organic materials, although the accuracy of quantitative methods for this type of spectroscopy is limited. With dynamic SIMS, composition as a function of depth can also be recorded. For applications involving protein adsorption to surfaces, the spectra obtained can be compared to databases to identify the exact proteins attached to the surface.

## 7.6.6 Electron Microscopy: Transmission Electron Microscopy (TEM) and Scanning Electron Microscopy (SEM)

**7.6.6.1 Basic Principles**  The principles of quantum mechanics predict that accelerated electrons have wave-like properties. Electron microscopy techniques utilize this property of electrons to form images, much like light microscopy. The most direct corollary to light microscopy is the transmission electron microscope, which is designed very similarly to a compound microscope (Fig. 7.41) but using magnetic rather than glass lenses. Because the wavelength associated with electrons is shorter than that for white light, the resolving power of the TEM is greater, and much more detailed images can be obtained (Fig. 7.42).

However, TEM requires very thin samples (20–200 $\mu$m thick) because electron beams are completely absorbed by thicker samples and therefore are unavailable to create an image. Due to the stringent preparation techniques involved in making these thin sections, TEM is less often used in biomaterials research than SEM. In addition, because the sections can be taken from any portion of the sample, TEM is not strictly a surface analysis technique. Therefore, we will focus the remainder of this section on the principles and instrumentation of SEM.

SEM is based on a different mechanism of imaging. In this type of electron microscopy, the surface of a sample is scanned with an electron beam. The electrons from the beam undergo elastic and inelastic scattering as they collide with atoms in

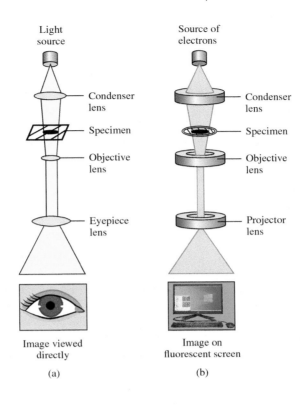

**Figure 7.41**
Comparison of energy path in (a) light microscopy and (b) transmission electron microscopy, which is designed very similarly to a compound microscope but uses magnetic lenses, as opposed to glass.

**Figure 7.42**
(a) Image of sperm cells under a white light microscope (scale bar is 10 μm). (b) Image of a sperm cell under transmission electron microscopy (scale bar 2 μm). Because the wavelength associated with electrons is shorter than that for white light, the resolving power of the TEM is greater, and much more detailed images can be obtained [21].

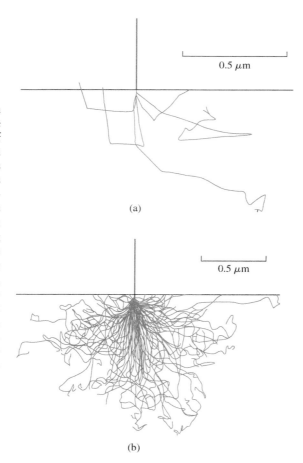

**Figure 7.43**
Examples of an electron beam hitting an iron surface in SEM. (a) shows the path of 5 electrons scattering within the sample and (b) shows 100 electrons. The electrons from the beam undergo elastic and inelastic scattering as they collide with atoms in the sample. Elastic scattering results in alteration of the trajectory of the electron, but not its energy. In many cases, after a number of elastic collisions, the electron will exit the sample as a backscattered electron. On the other hand, inelastic scattering occurs when the electron transfers part or all of its energy to a sample atom. The atom then emits secondary electrons, Auger electrons, or X-rays as a means to release this excess energy [28].

the sample (Fig. 7.43). **Elastic scattering** results in alteration of the trajectory of the electron, but not its energy. In many cases, after a number of elastic collisions, the electron will exit the sample as a **backscattered electron**. On the other hand, **inelastic scattering** occurs when the electron transfers part or all of its energy to a sample atom. The atom then emits secondary electrons, Auger electrons (see Table 7.4) or X-rays as a means to release this excess energy. SEM images are produced by recording the production of secondary electrons after an area is bombarded with the primary electron beam. Since the intensity of these electrons is dependent on the surface topography of the sample, SEM is considered a surface imaging technique.

SEM also provides the possibility of gaining information about the chemical composition of the imaged sample by analyzing the X-rays emitted, rather than the secondary electrons, after bombardment by the primary electron beam. As summarized in Table 7.4, X-ray fluorescence occurs if exposure to an electron beam causes removal of a core electron from an atom in the sample. To return to its ground state, one of the outer electrons falls into the vacancy, producing an X-ray of a certain wavelength that is characteristic for that atom. Therefore, recording the wavelength of the emitted X-rays provides an idea of the elemental composition of the sample. However, since the X-rays formed via this means can be produced from atoms deeper (1 μm or more) within the sample, this method does not provide information about the chemical nature of the surface. Finally, as mentioned previously in this chapter (Section 7.5), the SEM can be configured to use the electron beam for e-beam lithography in addition to imaging.

**Figure 7.44**
SEM image of osteoblasts cultured on a titanium mesh. The individual cells can be seen, particularly on the fiber in the back of the pore (in the center of the image). Scale bar is 100 μm. (Reprinted with permission from [29].)

**Figure 7.45**
Block diagram of the components of a SEM. There are five basic components to a SEM: the accelerated electron source, lenses, the sample holder, the detector, and a computer, which produces the final image.

**7.6.6.2 Instrumentation** A typical SEM image of osteoblasts on a titanium mesh is found in Figure 7.44. This image shows the interaction of cells and a biomaterial scaffold for bone tissue engineering. As shown in Figure 7.45, there are five basic components to a SEM:

1. Source—produces accelerated electrons.
2. Lenses—magnetic coils focus electron beam and reduce spot size.
3. Sample holder—holds sample securely.
4. Detector—records the spatial position of secondary electron impact and converts this information into an electrical signal.
5. Computer—translates the signal from the detector to produce an image.

For optimal imaging, nonconductive samples, such as polymers, must be precoated with a thin layer of conductive material (metal) to reduce charge build-up during scanning. This is accomplished via physical sputtering from a metallic target (see previous sections of this chapter) onto the sample before imaging. In reality, the secondary electrons are produced from the coating only, so a high-fidelity image of the surface topography is produced only if the coating is sufficiently thin and conformational.

As illustrated in Figure 7.46, the (coated) sample is placed into the holder and the electron beam is scanned over the surface in a raster motion. (The beam scans each line from side to side and all the lines from top to bottom.) The secondary electron detector is positioned so that the locations of the emitted electrons are recorded. The signal from the detector (indicating electron impact intensity and position) is then processed using appropriate software to produce a three-dimensional image. If emitted X-rays are also to be examined, a specialized detector system called **energy-dispersive X-ray analysis (EDXA)** is included to collect and analyze this radiation (Fig. 7.46). Because electrons readily interact with atoms in the air, all electron microscopy must be completed under vacuum.

**7.6.6.3 Information Provided** SEM is commonly used to visualize the surface topography of a biomaterial, or a biomaterial with attached tissue or cells. Although the requirement of imaging in vacuum prevents full analysis of biomaterials as they would be found *in vivo*, development of the environmental SEM allows imaging of

**Figure 7.46**
Schematic of a SEM. First, the specimen is placed into the sample chamber and the electron beam is scanned over the surface. The secondary electron detector is positioned so that the locations of the emitted electrons are recorded. The signal from the detector is then processed using appropriate software to produce a three-dimensional image. If emitted X-rays are also examined, a specialized detector system called energy-dispersive X-ray analysis (EDXA) is included to collect and analyze this radiation [23].

partially hydrated samples. The combination of SEM and EDXA provides information about chemical composition of the sample, although the ability to distinguish surface chemistry is limited.

### 7.6.7 Scanning Probe Microscopy (SPM): Atomic Force Microscopy (AFM)

**7.6.7.1 Basic Principles** **Scanning probe microscopy** is a general term that refers to any number of techniques producing a three-dimensional image due to the interactions between a small probe and atomic constituents of the sample surface. Of these, we will confine our discussion to *atomic force microscopy* (AFM). Like SEM, AFM can provide three-dimensional images of material surfaces with Å to nm spatial resolution. The analytical capabilities of AFM are limited to the uppermost atomic layer of a sample because its operation is based on interactions with the electron clouds of atoms at the surface.

As shown in Figure 7.47, in AFM, a small tip is attached to a cantilever. When the tip encounters the material surface, van der Waals and electrostatic interactions between atoms in the tip and those on the surface create a characteristic force profile and cause eventual attraction of the tip to the surface, thus bending the cantilever. To obtain an image, the cantilever/tip assembly is rastered across the material in

**Figure 7.47**
Tip used for atomic force microscopy. The tip is attached to the end of a cantilever beam [5].

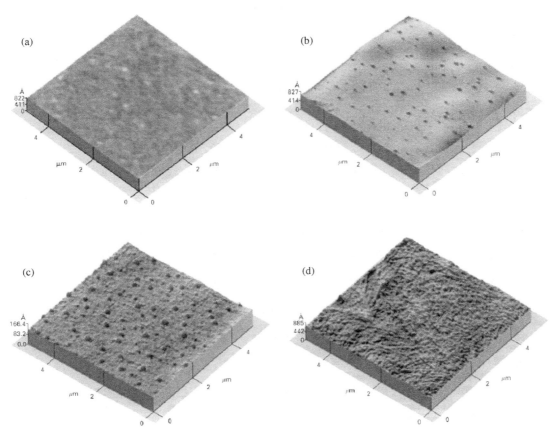

**Figure 7.48**
Surface topography (via AFM) of poly(DL-lactic acid-b-ethylene glycol)-monomethyl ether diblock copo-lymer (Me.PEG-PLAs—numbers indicate the weight of the corresponding polymer blocks in kDa) films compared to a PLA film: (a) PLA, (b) Me.PEG5-PLA45, (c) Me.PEG5-PLA20, (d) Me.PEG5-PLA10 as observed by AFM. The PLA film has an almost smooth, nonstructured surface. With increasing Me.PEG content of the polymers, the density of particulate structures (predominantly crystallized PEG) increases tremendously. (Reprinted with permission from [30].)

a controlled manner and the stage containing the sample is moved up or down in response to the bending of the cantilever so that the tip contacts the surface at all times. The record of the change in stage position required to achieve this constant contact forms the basis of the height data displayed in the three-dimensional image. As mentioned in Section 7.5, AFM tips can also be used for dip pen lithography to create nanoscale patterns on biomaterial surfaces.

**7.6.7.2 Instrumentation**  A typical AFM image is found in Figure 7.48. As demonstrated by this figure, AFM techniques can be utilized to image pure biomate-rial surfaces as well as those including adsorbed proteins. As shown in Figure 7.49, there are four basic components to an AFM:

1. Cantilever/tip—bends in response to forces between tip and sample.
2. Laser/detector—a laser beam is bounced off the cantilever and directed toward a photodiode detector to record the deflection of the cantilever in response to the surface.

**Figure 7.49**
Block diagram of an AFM setup.

3. Sample stage—holds sample securely. Uses a piezoelectric driver to alter position up or down to maintain contact between tip and sample.

4. Computer—translates the signal from the photodiode detector and provides feedback to control stage position. Records stage position and produces image.

AFM images are usually obtained via either contact or tapping mode. For ease of explanation, we will focus this discussion solely on contact mode. However, for proteins or polymeric samples, in contact mode, the pressure applied due to the small area at the tip may cause damage to the sample. Thus, tapping mode is more often employed for more delicate specimens. Both modes can be used with a specially designed fluid cell to allow imaging of biomaterials in aqueous conditions like those found *in vivo*.

As illustrated in Figure 7.50, imaging begins when the sample is placed on the stage and the tip is lowered until it contacts the surface. When this occurs, reflection of the laser off the cantilever indicates that the cantilever is bent toward the sample (Fig. 7.50). The tip/cantilever is then moved across the sample surface in a controlled manner and the cantilever deflection is monitored. In response to changes in deflection, the stage is moved up and down to maintain contact between the sample and the tip. Alterations in stage position are recorded and processed by the appropriate software to form a three-dimensional image.

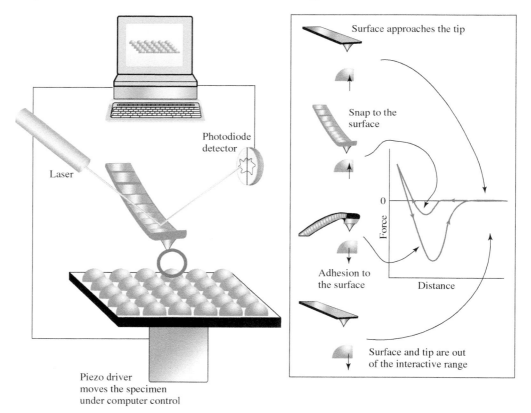

**Figure 7.50**

Schematic of AFM instrumentation. Imaging begins when the sample is placed on a stage and the tip is lowered until it contacts the surface. When this occurs, reflection of a laser off the cantilever indicates that the cantilever is bent toward the sample. The tip/cantilever is then moved across the sample surface and the cantilever deflection is monitored. In response to changes in defection, the stage is moved up and down to maintain contact between the sample and the tip. Alterations in stage position are recorded and processed by the appropriate software to form a three-dimensional image.

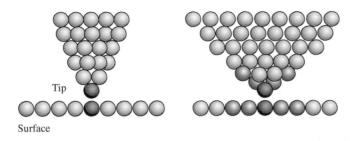

**Figure 7.51**
Two sample tips for use with AFM. The number of interacting atoms increases as the width of the tip increases, thus decreasing the spatial resolution. Due to this characteristic, it is desirable to have the width of the end of the tip smaller than the smallest feature to be imaged (a). If the tip is too wide, then artifacts in the imaging can occur (b).

**7.6.7.3 Information Provided** AFM is most often used to visualize surface topography, either of a biomaterial or a layer of adsorbed proteins. As illustrated in Figure 7.51, the number of interacting atoms increases as the width of the tip increases, thus decreasing the spatial resolution. Therefore, for optimal results, the width of the end of the tip should be smaller than the smallest feature to be imaged.

AFM can also be employed for quantitative force measurements using a variant of Hooke's law (see Chapter 4) to relate the deflection of the cantilever to the force between the tip and the surface (to do this, the spring constant of the cantilever, $E$, must be known). This modality has been exploited to determine binding forces between biological molecules. In these experiments, a molecule is covalently bonded to the tip and the adhesive force is recorded between the tip and a second molecule of interest that is attached to the sample surface.

## EXAMPLE PROBLEM 7.5

The following graph illustrates the roughness profile from the surface scan of a pyrolitic carbon artificial heart valve leaflet using an atomic force microscope. The graph represents the surface profile of a 5 μm stretch of the surface of the carbon material. The table gives the distances between several of the landmarks indicated on the graph. In the host environment, the leaflet could encounter bacteria (~10 μm in diameter when modeled as spheres), fibrils made of the protein fibrin (~1 μm in length), red blood cells (~2.5 μm across), platelets (~1 μm across and 1 μm tall when in blood) and other similar cells and molecules. Considering only the surface roughness information and the sizes of the listed blood elements, would the material be expected to result in much interaction with the blood elements listed? Why or why not?

| Points | Horizontal Distance (nm) | Vertical Distance (nm) |
|--------|--------------------------|------------------------|
| G&B    | 312.5                    | 0                      |
| B&D    | 0                        | 98.561                 |
| A&B    | 0                        | 55.423                 |
| H&F    | 0                        | 57.313                 |

Solution:   Although the surface appears to be quite rough upon initial visual examination of the AFM scan, the scale of these surface features must be compared with the size of the elements with which the surface could potentially interact. Examination of the data in the table reveals that the vertical distances between peaks is typically on the order of 100 nm or less. Considering that the listed elements of the blood with which the material could interact range from approximately 1 to 10 µm, these surface features are significantly smaller (one to two orders of magnitude smaller). Thus, the surface of the material appears rather smooth in this reference frame and minimal interactions between the material and the listed elements of the blood would be expected based on surface roughness. It should be noted that, in relation to the size of many proteins in the blood, the surface would be rough. It is possible that the surface roughness could promote protein adsorption that could, in turn, affect cell adhesion. However, the blood proteins were not included in the list of elements to be considered in this problem.

■

## EXAMPLE PROBLEM 7.6

As a biomaterials expert, you are asked to consult on surface modification for a new client. This company manufactures a neural conduit to promote contact-guided growth of neurites for restoration of function after nerve injury. This company wants to use its proprietary polymer, which is cytocompatible, but has less than optimal guidance properties. What type of surface modification technique would you recommend and why? What type of surface analysis would be most appropriate?

Solution:   Contact-guided neuron growth is generally achieved through the formation of channels in which the neurites will extend. Plasma treatment (or laser treatment) is the best option as it can result in etching, which will change the topography of the surface, a main concern in this case. Since atomic force microscopy (AFM) will characterize the 3D nature of the surface, this would be the best choice to analyze the depth and width of the features created.

■

# Summary

- The adsorption of proteins onto a biomaterial surface is governed by thermodynamic principles that are strongly influenced by two surface properties: surface hydrophobicity and surface charge. Other physical properties of the material surface, such as surface roughness and steric hindrance, influence protein adsorption as well.

- Controlling protein adsorption to the biomaterial surface is extremely important because it is to this coated surface, rather than the original implant, that the body reacts.

- Chemical surface treatments of biomaterials entail alteration of the surface composition of the material through use of physical principles or chemical reactions, but they do not involve the attachment of biological molecules to the material. Biological surface modification techniques, however, are used to attach biologically active molecules to a material surface.

- Chemical methods of surface modification can be based on covalent bonding to the surface, or other chemical interactions with the surface. Covalent surface coatings can be achieved through plasma discharge, chemical vapor deposition, physical vapor deposition, radiation grafting, or self-assembled monolayer deposition. Non-covalent surface coatings can be formed through solution coating, deposition of Langmuir-Blodgett films, layer-by-layer deposition, the use of surface-modifying additives, ion beam implantation, plasma treatment, conversion coatings, or the use of bioactive glasses.

- Biological surface modifications can be either covalent or non-covalent in nature. For covalent modifications, biomolecules may be attached to reactive material surfaces through a number of reaction schemes. Biomolecules can modify a material surface through forming non-covalent coatings by such mechanisms as hydrophobic or electrostatic interactions between the material and the biomolecules.

- Surface characteristics of a material can change with time. They are particularly susceptible to alteration caused by degradation, either of the surface coating itself or of the underlying substrate.

- Patterning techniques for altering the surface properties of biomaterials in a controlled manner, resulting in a geometric design of well-defined dimensions, generally fall into two categories: a form of direct writing on the surface (used for nanoscale and microscale features), or a type of pattern transfer technique, such as using molds or masks (for microscale features). Direct writing techniques include lithography with high-energy beams, dip-pen nanolithography, and ink-jet printing. Pattern transfer techniques include micro-contact printing and microfluidics.

- A number of techniques for the characterization of biomaterial surfaces exist. Contact angle analysis provides information related to the hydrophobicity of the material, and is typically an initial step in material surface characterization. Microscopy techniques, including light microscopy, electron microscopy, and scanning probe microscopy, primarily provide information about the appearance and topology of the biomaterial. Like for bulk materials, surface spectroscopic techniques, which involve the absorption of electromagnetic radiation by the material, include electron spectroscopy for chemical analysis (ESCA) and attenuated total internal reflectance-Fourier transform infrared spectroscopy (ATR-FTIR). These methods, along with a modification of mass spectrometry for surface analysis, secondary ion mass spectrometry (SIMS), record information about the structure and composition of the outermost few layers of both organic and inorganic materials.

## Problems

7.1   Explain why addition of long hydrocarbon chains to a biomaterial surface would be a poor modification to reduce protein attachment.

7.2   Explain the need for a spacer arm in biological modifications. Why is this not usually needed in other types of (nonbiological) surface modifications described in this chapter?

7.3   Three different surfaces (A, B, and C) were tested for their properties.

(a)   Reported below are the contact angles and the surface tension for the liquid–vapor surface ($\gamma_{LV}$) of four different solutions. Determine the critical surface tension ($\gamma_c$) for each material. Your answer should have two parts: (1) a graph on which you indicate the point that shows critical surface tension for each material and (2) the equation used to calculate exact critical surface tension for each material. Which of these is the most hydrophobic? Why?

| Solution | Surface Tension (dyn/cm$^2$) | Angle (Degrees) | | |
|---|---|---|---|---|
| | | Surface A | Surface B | Surface C |
| Water | 70 | 95 | 64 | 100 |
| Solution 1 | 60 | 76 | 43 | 82 |
| Solution 2 | 55 | 56 | 29 | 63 |
| Solution 3 | 50 | 39 | 19 | 45 |
| Solution 4 | 45 | 26 | 15 | 29 |

(b) Scientists are interested in coating the surface of one of these materials with an amphiphilic signaling lipid (like that shown in the figure). It is known that the phosphate-containing head group is responsible for signaling activation in target cells. Which material should you recommend for this application and why?

1-Stearoyl-2-oloeyl-3-phosphatidylcholine

(c) To further investigate the effect of surface chemical composition and behavior in aqueous solutions, you conduct dynamic contact angle analysis with water. Given the results in the following table, determine the contact angle hysteresis.

| Surface | Addition/Removal of Drops | Contact Angle (Degrees) | |
|---|---|---|---|
| | | Advancing | Receding |
| Surface A | 1 | 94.4 | 82.6 |
| | 2 | 93.9 | 82.2 |
| | 3 | 93.6 | 82.4 |
| | 4 | 94.3 | 82.7 |
| Surface B | 1 | 64.1 | 60.1 |
| | 2 | 64.3 | 59.8 |
| | 3 | 63.8 | 59.7 |
| | 4 | 64.0 | 60.0 |
| Surface C | 1 | 99.8 | 78.2 |
| | 2 | 100.3 | 78.5 |
| | 3 | 100.1 | 78.9 |
| | 4 | 99.7 | 78.4 |

(d) Based on the above dynamic contact angle measurements, would you select a different surface for your answer to part (b)? Explain your reasoning by describing what is occurring molecularly.

(e) Researchers know that all three surfaces are composed of different self-assembled monolayers (SAMs). The functional group for each SAM is shown below. *Note*: SAM 3 is a mixture of both SAMs 1 and 2. Given the results above, identify which of these SAMs is which surface and explain your reasoning from a molecular level.

SAM 1                          SAM 2                                      SAM 3

7.4 (a) In order to create a stable SAM coating, it has been found that you need chlorine in your polymer. Give a possible explanation of why chlorine would be needed—what part of the SAM would the chlorine likely interact with?

(b) A colleague would like to use your SAM to modify their polymer, which has no chlorine. Therefore, they decide to plasma treat their polymer in chlorine gas before SAM modification. Explain how this treatment could add chlorine to the polymer surface.

(c) Your colleague decides to perform Electron Spectroscopy for Chemical Analysis (ESCA) analysis on their plasma-treated polymer to confirm surface modification prior to using your SAM. Assuming that the plasma treatment worked, which of the peaks below would represent the modified polymer and which would represent the original polymer? (Assume this is a C1s spectrum.) Explain your answer based on the graph and also a detailed explanation of how the ESCA equipment works to generate data.

Binding Energy (eV)

7.5   How is it possible to achieve depth profiling with secondary ion mass spectroscopy (SIMS)? Be sure to discuss the instrumentation of SIMS and how the different parts of the instrumentation work together to produce plots of results.

7.6   The following images of two different material surfaces were obtained with atomic force microscopy (AFM). Which of the two surfaces below (a or b) would be likely to have more protein attached if placed in the body? Justify your answer.

(Adapted with permission from [6].)

7.7   Make a list of advantages and disadvantages of all of the surface patterning techniques described in this chapter.

7.8   As a biomaterials expert, you are asked to consult on surface modification for several companies. For the scenarios below, select the most appropriate type of surface modification and the *one* type of surface analysis technique that would be the most important to characterize this modification. Provide a rationale for your choices.

(a)   Company A manufactures metallic implants as replacements for the temporomandibular joint (TMJ, found in the jaw). However, they are concerned about the fatigue properties at the surface given the large loads experienced during chewing. They want to minimize changes to their current production process.

(b) Company B manufactures polymeric membranes to promote guided bone regeneration after tooth loss by encouraging bone cell attachment and migration. The company has discovered a new polymer that can easily be manufactured into a membrane and is cytocompatible and wants to find an appropriate modification. This new polymer can be synthesized by radical polymerization.

(c) Company C manufactures polymeric contact lenses. However, they have found that their current polymer is too hydrophobic, leading to discomfort when the lenses are worn for long periods. The company is therefore looking for a modification that would improve hydrophilicity, but does not want to add *any* post-processing steps.

# References

1. B. D. Ratner and A. S. Hoffman, "Physiochemical surface modification of materials used in medicine," in *Biomaterials science: an introduction to materials and medicine*, 2nd ed., B. D. Ratner, A. S. Hoffman, F. J. Schoen, and J. E. Lemons, Eds. San Diego: Elsevier Academic Press, 2004, pp. 201–218.
2. A. S. Hoffman and J. A. Hubbell, "Surface-immobilized biomolecules," in *Biomaterials science: an introduction to materials and medicine*, 2nd ed., B. D. Ratner, A. S. Hoffman, F. J. Schoen, and J. E. Lemons, Eds. San Diego: Elsevier Academic Press, 2004, pp. 225–233.
3. M. Geissler and Y. Xia, "Patterning: principles and some new developments," *Advanced Materials*, vol. 16, no. 15, pp. 1249–1269, Aug. 2004.
4. Z. Nie and E. Kumacheva, "Patterning surfaces with functional polymers," *Nature Materials*, vol. 7, no. 4, pp. 277–290, Apr. 2008.
5. B. D. Ratner, "Surface properties and surface characterization of materials," in *Biomaterials science: an introduction to materials and medicine*, 2nd ed., B. D. Ratner, A. S. Hoffman, F. J. Schoen, and J. E. Lemons, Eds. San Diego: Elsevier Academic Press, 2004, pp. 40–59.
6. J. P. Rosengren-Holmberg *et al.*, "Heparin molecularly imprinted surfaces for the attenuation of complement activation in blood," *Biomaterials Science*, vol. 3, no. 8, pp. 1208–1217, Aug. 2015.
7. R. Kossowsky, *Surface modification engineering: volume I: fundamental aspects*. Boca Raton: CRC Press, 1989.
8. J.-O. Jeong *et al.*, "Development and characterization of heparin-immobilized polycaprolactone nanofibrous scaffolds for tissue engineering using gamma-irradiation," *RSC Advances*, vol. 7, no. 15, pp. 8963–8972, Jan. 2017.
9. S. T. Picraux and L. E. Pope, "Tailored surface modification by ion implantation and laser treatment," *Science*, vol. 226, no. 4675, pp. 615–622, 1984.
10. L. L. Hench, "Ceramics, glasses, and glass-ceramics," in *Biomaterials science: an introduction to materials and medicine*, 1st ed., B. D. Ratner, A. S. Hoffman, F. J. Schoen, and J. E. Lemons, Eds. San Diego: Elsevier Academic Press, 1996, pp. 73–84.
11. S. W. Kim and J. Feijen, "Surface modification of polymers for improved blood compatibility," in *CRC Critical Reviews in Biocompatibility*, vol. 1, D. F. Williams, Ed. Boca Raton: CRC Press, 1985, pp. 229–260.
12. A. Folch and M. Toner, "Cellular micropatterns on biocompatible materials," *Biotechnology Progress*, vol. 14, no. 3, pp. 388–92, Jun. 1998.
13. L. M. Demers, D. S. Ginger, S.-J. Park, Z. Li, S.-W. Chung, and C. A. Mirkin, "Direct patterning of modified oligonucleotides on metals and insulators by Dip-Pen nanolithography," *Science*, vol. 296, no. 5574, pp. 1836–1838, Jun. 2002.
14. A. Doraiswamy, T. M. Dunaway, J. J. Wilker, and R. J. Narayan, "Inkjet printing of bio–adhesives," *Journal of Biomedical Materials Research Part B: Applied Biomaterials*, vol. 89B, no. 1, pp. 28–35, Apr. 2009.
15. R. T. Hill and A. Chilkoti, "Surface patterning," in *Biomaterials science: an introduction to materials and medicine*, 3rd ed., B. D. Ratner, A. S. Hoffman, F. J. Schoen, and J. E. Lemons, Eds. San Diego: Elsevier Academic Press, 2013, pp. 276–301.
16. N. Patel *et al.*, "Spatially controlled cell engineering on biodegradable polymer surfaces," *FASEB Journal*, vol. 12, no. 14, pp. 1447–1454, Nov. 1998.
17. B. D. Ratner, "Characterization of biomaterial surfaces," *Cardiovascular Pathology*, vol. 2, no. 3S, pp. 87S-100S, 1993.
18. J. D. Andrade, *Surface and interfacial aspects of biomedical polymers: volume 1: surface chemistry and physics*. New York: Plenum Press, 1985.
19. K. Tsujii, *Surface activity: principles, phenomena and applications*. San Diego: Academic Press, 1998.
20. W. Fu *et al.*, "Electrospun gelatin/PCL and collagen/PLCL scaffolds for vascular tissue engineering," *International Journal of Nanomedicine*, vol. 9, pp. 2335–2344, 2014.

21. Z. Lu *et al.*, "Evaluation of the Spermicidal and Contraceptive Activity of Platycodin D, a Saponin from Platycodon grandiflorum," *PLoS ONE*, vol. 8, no. 11, e82068, Nov, 2013.

22. J. S. Temenoff, E. S. Steinbis, and A. G. Mikos, "Effect of drying history on swelling properties and cell attachment to oligo(poly(ethylene glycol) fumarate) hydrogels for guided tissue regeneration applications," *Journal of Biomaterials Science, Polymer Edition*, vol. 14, no. 9, pp. 989–1004, 2003.

23. D. A. Skoog and J. J. Leary, *Principles of instrumental analysis*, 4th ed. Orlando: Saunders College Publishing, 1992.

24. K. Siegbahn, *ESCA, atomic, molecular and solid state structure studied by means of electron spectroscopy*. Uppsala: Almquist and Wiksells, 1967.

25. J. B. Lhoest, E. Detrait, P. van den Bosch de Aguilar, and P. Bertrand, "Fibronectin adsorption, conformation, and orientation on polystyrene substrates studied by radiolabeling, XPS, and ToF SIMS," *Journal of Biomedical Materials Research*, vol. 41, no. 1, pp. 95–103, Jul. 1998.

26. J. C. Vickerman, *Surface analysis: the principal techniques*. New York: John Wiley and Sons, 1997.

27. J. C. Vickerman, "Secondary ion mass spectroscopy," *Chemistry in Britain*, vol. 23, pp. 969–971, 973–974, 1987.

28. J. I. Goldstein, D. E. Newbury, P. Echlin, D. C. Joy, C. E. Fiori, and E. Lifshin, *Scanning electron microscopy and X-ray microanalysis: a text for biologists, scientists and geologists*. New York: Plenum Press, 1981.

29. G. N. Bancroft *et al.*, "Fluid flow increases mineralized matrix deposition in 3D perfusion culture of marrow stromal osteoblasts in a dose-dependent manner," *Proceedings of the National Academy of Sciences of the U S A*, vol. 99, no. 20, pp. 12600–5, Oct. 2002.

30. A. Lucke, J. Tessmar, E. Schnell, G. Schmeer, and A. Gopferich, "Biodegradable poly(D,L-lactic acid)-poly(ethylene glycol)-monomethyl ether diblock copolymers: structures and surface properties relevant to their use as biomaterials," *Biomaterials*, vol. 21, no. 23, pp. 2361–70, Dec. 2000.

31. K. C. Dee, D. A. Puleo, and R. Bizios, *An introduction to tissue-biomaterial interactions*. Hoboken: Wiley-Liss, 2002.

32. B. D. Ratner and A. S. Hoffman, "Physiochemical surface modification of materials used in medicine," in *Biomaterials science: an introduction to materials and medicine*, 3rd ed., B. D. Ratner, A. S. Hoffman, F. J. Schoen, and J. E. Lemons, Eds. San Diego: Elsevier Academic Press, 2013, pp. 259–276.

# Additional Reading

J.D. Andrade, *Surface and interfacial aspects of biomedical polymers: volume 2: protein adsorption*. New York: Plenum Press, 1985.

J.D. Andrade and V. Hlady, "Protein adsorption and materials biocompatibility: a tutorial review and suggested hypotheses," in *Biopolymers/non-Exclusion HPLC*, K. Dusek, C. G. Overberger, and G. Heublein, Eds. New York: Springer-Verlag, 1986, pp. 1–63.

J.D. Bronzino and J. B. Park, *Biomaterials: principles and applications*. Boca Raton: CRC Press, 2003.

J.A. Burdick, A. Khademhosseini, and R. Langer, "Fabrication of gradient hydrogels using a microfluidics/photopolymerization process," *Langmuir*, vol. 20, no. 13, pp. 5153–5156, Jun. 2004.

W.D. Callister, Jr, *Materials science and engineering: an introduction*, 7th ed. New York: John Wiley and Sons, 2006.

L.Cao, *Carrier bound immobilized enzymes: principles, application and design*. Weinheim: Wiley-VCH, 2006.

C.S. Chen, M. Mrksich, S. Huang, G. M. Whitesides, and D. E. Ingber, "Micropatterned surfaces for control of cell shape, position, and function," *Biotechnology Progress*, vol. 14, no. 3, pp. 356–363, Jun. 1998.

P.K. Chu, J. Y. Chen, L. P. Wang, and N. Huang, "Plasma-surface modification of biomaterials," *Materials Science and Engineering: R: Reports*, vol. 36, no. 5, pp. 143–206, Mar. 2002.

B.D. Cullity, *Elements of X-ray diffraction*, 2nd ed. Reading: Addison-Wesley, 1978.

J.Davies, *Surface analytical techniques for probing biomaterial processes*. New York: CRC Press, 1996.

G.W. Ewing, *Analytical instrumentation handbook*, 2nd ed. New York: Marcel Dekker, 1997.

T.A. Horbett, "Chapter 13 Principles underlying the role of adsorbed plasma proteins in blood interactions with foreign materials," *Cardiovascular pathology*, vol. 2, no. 3, Supplement, pp. 137–148, Jul. 1993.

J.A. Hubbell, "Matrix effects," in *Principles of tissue engineering*, 2nd ed., R. P. Lanza, R. Langer, and J. Vacanti, Eds. Austin: Academic Press, 2000, pp. 237–250.

K.J. Laidler, *Physical chemistry*, 4th ed. Princeton: Houghton Mifflin, 2003.

A.W. Lloyd, R. G. Faragher, and S. P. Denyer, "Ocular biomaterials and implants," *Biomaterials*, vol. 22, no. 8, pp. 769–785, Apr. 2001.

R.B. More, A. D. Haubold, and J. C. Bokros, "Pyrolytic carbon for long-term medical implants," in *Biomaterials science: an introduction to materials and medicine*, 2nd ed., B. D. Ratner, A. S. Hoffman, F. J. Schoen, and J. E. Lemons, Eds. San Diego: Elsevier Academic Press, 2004, pp. 170–181.

W.Norde and J. Lyklema, "Why proteins prefer interfaces," *Journal of Biomaterials Science Polymer Edition*, vol. 2, no. 3, pp. 183–202, 1991.

J.O'Connor, B. Sexton, and R. S. C. Smart, Eds., *Surface analysis methods in materials science*, 2nd ed. New York: Springer-Verlag, 2003.

F.Rouessac and A. Rouessac, *Chemical analysis: modern instrumental methods and techniques*. New York: John Wiley and Sons, 2000.

W.M. Saltzman, "Cell interactions with polymers," in *Principles of tissue engineering,* 2nd ed., R. P. Lanza, R. Langer, and J. Vacanti, Eds. Austin: Academic Press, 2000, pp. 221–235.

J.P. Schaffer, A. Saxena, S. D. Antolovich, J. Sanders, and S. B. Warner, *The science and design of engineering materials*, 2nd ed. Boston: McGraw-Hill, 1998.

T.S. Sudarshan, *Surface modification technologies*. New York: Marcel Dekker, 1989.

P.J. Tarcha and T. E. Rohr, "Diagnostics and biomaterials," in *Biomaterials science: an introduction to materials and medicine*, 2nd ed., B. D. Ratner, A. S. Hoffman, F. J. Schoen, and J. E. Lemons, Eds. San Diego: Elsevier Academic Press, 2004, pp. 684–697.

H.S. Tran et al., "Surface modifications of mechanical heart valves," in *Biomaterials engineering and devices: human applications*, vol. 1, D. L. Wise, J. D. Gresser, D. J. Trantolo, M. V. Cattaneo, K.-U. Lewandrowski, and M. J. Yaszemski, Eds. Totowa: Humana Press, 2000, pp. 137–144.

R.Vaidya, L. M. Tender, G. Bradley, M. J. O'Brien, M. Cone, and G. P. López, "Computer-controlled laser ablation: a convenient and versatile tool for micropatterning biofunctional synthetic surfaces for applications in biosensing and tissue engineering," *Biotechnology Progress*, vol. 14, no. 3, pp. 371–377, Jun. 1998.

D.Voet and J. G. Voet, *Biochemistry*, 3rd ed. Wiley, 2004.

G.M. Whitesides, "The 'right' size in nanobiotechnology," *Nature Biotechnology*, vol. 21, no. 10, pp. 1161–1165, Oct. 2003.

G.M. Whitesides, J. P. Mathias, and C. T. Seto, "Molecular self-assembly and nanochemistry: a chemical strategy for the synthesis of nanostructures," *Science*, vol. 254, no. 5036, pp. 1312–1319, Nov. 1991.

P.Yager, "Biomedical Sensors and Biosensors," in *Biomaterials science: an introduction to materials and medicine*, 2nd ed., B. D. Ratner, A. S. Hoffman, F. J. Schoen, and J. E. Lemons, Eds. San Diego: Elsevier Academic Press, 2004, pp. 669–684.

X.Yao, R. Peng, and J. Ding, "Cell-material interactions revealed via material techniques of surface patterning," *Advanced Materials*, vol. 25, no. 37, pp. 5257–5286, Oct. 2013.

# CHAPTER 8

# Protein Interactions with Biomaterials

**Main Objective**

To understand thermodynamic principles governing protein adsorption to biomaterial surfaces and relate protein structure and transport properties to kinetics and reversibility of adsorption.

**Specific Objectives**

1. To understand basic thermodynamic equations for protein-substrate systems.
2. To compare and contrast the three major factors that govern protein adsorption.
3. To understand basic protein chemistry and hierarchy of organization.
4. To understand how structure of proteins affects folding and adsorption.
5. To use equations to model protein transport to surfaces.
6. To compare and contrast reversible and irreversible protein binding, including molecular reasons behind these phenomena.
7. To understand how adsorption may be altered in solution with the presence of many protein types.
8. To understand the theory behind and possible limitations to the characterization techniques presented.

## 8.1 Introduction: Thermodynamics of Protein Adsorption

As discussed previously, since the body reacts to the layer of adsorbed proteins on a biomaterial surface rather than the surface itself, by changing the protein adsorption profile, one can affect the overall biological response to an implant. In Chapter 7, various means to modify biomaterial surfaces and the potential impact on protein adsorption were described. In this chapter, we will address the issue from a different perspective: the composition of proteins and how it affects their ability to bind to material surfaces.

Usually, protein attachment to biomaterials involves non-covalent interactions with the surface, and these types of interactions are the focus of this chapter. Occasionally, however, such as in the case of complement (see Chapter 12), covalent bonding to the biomaterial is possible. Further examples of protein-biomaterial interactions and their biological sequelae are found in later chapters of this text.

### 8.1.1 Gibbs Free Energy and Protein Adsorption

In order to understand the adsorption process, the system (protein, solvent, and surface) before and after the event must be analyzed to see if it is thermodynamically favorable for adsorption to occur. In order to do this, we must employ the basic thermodynamic quantity of **Gibbs free energy** ($G$).

The Gibbs free energy includes contributions from entropy ($S$), but there is also an enthalpic ($H$) component. Briefly, **enthalpy** is a measure of the amount of energy in a system available for mechanical work. **Entropy,** on the other hand, is a measure of the disorder of the system. The second law of thermodynamics states that spontaneous processes occur to increase the disorder of the universe (increase entropy). The Gibbs free energy,

$$G = H - TS \tag{8.1}$$

where $T$ is the temperature of the system, relates these two concepts and can be used to determine whether it is favorable for a given reaction to proceed.

In general, the Gibbs free energy cannot be measured, but changes in free energy ($\Delta G$) can be quantified for a system before and after a reaction. The previous equation then becomes (at constant temperature and pressure)

$$\Delta G = \Delta H - T \Delta S \tag{8.2}$$

where $\Delta$ in each case is the value for the products minus the value for the reactants. Due to the constraints imposed by the second law of thermodynamics, $\Delta G \leq 0$ indicates a spontaneous reaction and anything that lowers $\Delta G$ is energetically favorable.

These equations for a chemical reaction are applicable to adsorption processes since the adsorption of a protein ($P$) to an empty site on a surface ($*$) can be modeled as a reversible chemical reaction; that is,

$$P + {}^* \longleftrightarrow P^*$$

where $P^*$ denotes a surface site that has a protein adsorbed to it. Then, the change in $G$ for the entire adsorption process ($\Delta G_{ads}$) can be represented as

$$\Delta G_{ads} = \Delta H_{ads} - T \Delta S_{ads} \tag{8.3}$$

However, this equation is a generalization—it is important to remember that it includes calculation of $\Delta G$ for each component of the system before and after the adsorption event. These individual calculations include the following equations:

1. For the protein(s):

$$\Delta G_{prot} = \Delta H_{prot} - T \Delta S_{prot} \tag{8.4}$$

2. For the solvent (such as water and ions) near the adsorption surface:

$$\Delta G_{sol} = \Delta H_{sol} - T \Delta S_{sol} \tag{8.5}$$

3. For the biomaterial surface:

$$\Delta G_{surf} = \Delta H_{surf} - T \Delta S_{surf} \tag{8.6}$$

In each case, $\Delta$ is the value after adsorption minus the value before adsorption. These $\Delta G$ values are combined to get an overall $\Delta G$ for the adsorption reaction:

$$\Delta G_{ads} = \Delta G_{prot} + \Delta G_{sol} + \Delta G_{surf} \tag{8.7}$$

Therefore, if the adsorption event reduces $\Delta G$ for one or more components of the system with minimal concurrent increase in $\Delta G$ for another component, protein adsorption will be thermodynamically favored.

## EXAMPLE PROBLEM 8.1

Consider the equation for changes in Gibbs free energy in terms of the following cases of $\Delta H$ and $\Delta S$:

Case 1: $\Delta H < 0$ and $\Delta S < 0$
Case 2: $\Delta H > 0$ and $\Delta S < 0$
Case 3: $\Delta H < 0$ and $\Delta S > 0$
Case 4: $\Delta H > 0$ and $\Delta S > 0$

For each case, indicate what conditions would lead to positive values of $\Delta G$. Also, indicate the temperatures for which the process or reaction is spontaneous.

**Solution:**   Recall the equation for changes in Gibbs free energy:

$$\Delta G = \Delta H - T \Delta S$$

For Case 1, where $\Delta H < 0$ and $\Delta S < 0$, $\Delta G$ will be positive when $T \Delta S > \Delta H$. Recalling that reactions or processes are spontaneous when $\Delta G < 0$, it follows that the process for Case 1 is spontaneous when $T \Delta S < \Delta H$, or rearranged, $T < \Delta H/\Delta S$. For Case 2, where $\Delta H > 0$ and $\Delta S < 0$, $\Delta G$ will always be positive. Consequently, the process for Case 2 is nonspontaneous at all temperatures. For Case 3, where $\Delta H < 0$ and $\Delta S > 0$, $\Delta G$ will always be negative. As a result, the process for Case 3 is spontaneous at all temperatures. For Case 4, where $\Delta H > 0$ and $\Delta S > 0$, $\Delta G$ will be positive when $T \Delta S < \Delta H$. It follows that the process for Case 4 is spontaneous when $T \Delta S > \Delta H$, or rearranged, $T > \Delta H/\Delta S$.

**Summary of Cases:**

Case 1: $\Delta H < 0$ and $\Delta S < 0 \rightarrow \Delta G < 0$ when $T < \Delta H/\Delta S$
Case 2: $\Delta H > 0$ and $\Delta S < 0 \rightarrow \Delta G > 0$ for all $T$
Case 3: $\Delta H < 0$ and $\Delta S > 0 \rightarrow \Delta G < 0$ for all $T$
Case 4: $\Delta H > 0$ and $\Delta S > 0 \rightarrow \Delta G < 0$ when $T > \Delta H/\Delta S$   ∎

## 8.1.2 System Properties Governing Protein Adsorption

In the previous chapter, it was found that the following surface attributes most affect protein adsorption:

1. Surface hydrophobicity
2. Surface charge

When these concepts are generalized to the entire system, the factors that have the largest impact on protein adsorption are as follows:

1. Dehydration of the surface and protein (contribution of hydrophobicity)
2. Redistribution of charged groups (contribution of charge)
3. Structural rearrangement of the protein

When analyzing the system before and after adsorption, it is useful to think of interactions between domains on the biomaterial surface and the protein, rather than the entire surface or the protein as a whole. This concept is illustrated in Figure 8.1.

**Figure 8.1**
Schematic showing the interaction between a biomaterial surface and a protein. The surface of a protein can have multiple locations that interact with the material surface.

An overview of various properties of proteins and surfaces, and how they affect their interactions, is found in Tables 8.1 and 8.2.

Dehydration is a major driving force in protein adsorption. Water molecules become more ordered at hydrophobic surfaces (either biomaterial surfaces or protein surfaces). Therefore, if hydrophobic areas are able to come together through adsorption to reduce the overall hydrophobic surface area, disordering of the water (solvent) in the region and an increase in the entropy of the system results. From the second law of thermodynamics, this increase in entropy is highly desirable.

Charge can also play a significant role in determining if protein adsorption to a given surface is thermodynamically favorable. For example, if a protein and surface both have the same charge, a repulsive force will develop that reduces protein attachment. Since this process occurs in aqueous conditions, charge repulsion between the surface and the protein can be overcome through adsorption of ions with

**TABLE 8.1**

| Protein Properties That Affect Surface Interactions | |
|---|---|
| Property | Effect |
| Size | Larger molecules have more sites for surface contact. |
| Charge | Molecules near their isoelectric point* generally adsorb more readily. |
| Hydrophobicity | More hydrophobic molecules generally adsorb more readily on hydrophobic surfaces. |
| Structure: | |
| *Stability* | Less stable proteins (such as those with less intramolecular crosslinking) can unfold to a greater extent and form more surface contact points. |
| *Unfolding Rate* | Molecules that rapidly unfold can form surface contacts more quickly. |

*Isoelectric point: The pH at which the electrolyte concentration of an amphoteric substance such as protein is electrically zero because the concentration of its cation form equals the concentration of its anion form. (Adapted with permission from [1].)

**TABLE 8.2**

| Surface Properties That Affect Interactions With Proteins | |
|---|---|
| Feature | Effect |
| Topography | Greater texture exposes more surface area for interaction with proteins. |
| Composition | Chemical makeup of a surface will determine the types of intermolecular forces governing interaction with proteins. |
| Hydrophobicity | Hydrophobic surfaces tend to bind more protein. |
| Heterogeneity | Nonuniformity of surface characteristics results in domains that can interact differently with proteins. |
| Potential | Surface potential will influence the distribution of ions in solution and interaction with proteins. |

(Adapted with permission from [1].)

opposite charge from the media (Fig. 8.2). However, this involves an expenditure of energy to transfer the ions in the solvent to the adsorbed layer. Therefore, adsorption is preferred when many areas of the protein have opposite charge to regions of the biomaterial surface, because, in this instance, the transfer of fewer ions from the solvent is required.

Finally, structural rearrangement of the protein molecule during the adsorption process is extremely important to both the extent of the protein coat on the material surface and its resistance to delamination. If a protein is less structurally stable, it may preferentially adsorb to a biomaterial surface, since conformational rearrangement is easier. This rearrangement allows for an optimal conformation so that hydrophobic and charged regions of the protein can be placed to best fulfill the above two criteria.

**Figure 8.2**
Schematic of a protein adsorbed to surface. Charge can play a significant role in determining if protein adsorption to a given surface is thermodynamically favorable. For example, if the same charge is found on a protein and the surface, then a repulsive force will develop that reduces protein attachment. This repulsion between the surface and the protein can be overcome through adsorption of ions with opposite charge from the surrounding aqueous media (depicted here by charge signs). Shading indicates hydrophobic regions.

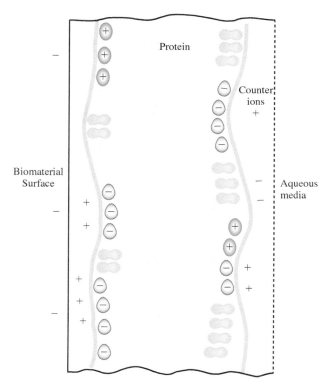

A protein's stability is primarily determined by intramolecular bonds, which are directly related to its chemical composition. The following sections describe the chemical subunits found in proteins and how they dictate protein structure and stability.

# 8.2 Protein Structure

## 8.2.1 Amino Acid Chemistry

Amino acids are the basic subunits of protein structure. As depicted in Figure 8.3, these molecules have a central carbon atom attached to a hydrogen atom, an amine group ($NH_2$), a carboxyl group (COOH), and an R group. Differences in R groups distinguish amino acids from one another. At physiological pH, the amino and carboxyl groups carry equal but opposite charges (Fig. 8.3) so amino acids are considered **zwitterions** and can act as either acids or bases.

There are 20 standard amino acids, as shown in Table 8.3. They are represented in shorthand form by either a three-letter or one-letter code. Each amino acid is designated genetically by a **codon,** a set of three sequential bases in the DNA strand. Each amino acid has one or more unique codons.

The properties of the individual amino acids vary greatly and are most affected by the size and composition of the R group. As illustrated in Figure 8.4, under physiological conditions, the R groups can be nonpolar, polar, positively charged, or negatively charged. Charge interactions between amino acids have a significant impact on the final protein structure, as discussed in the following sections.∎

Two noncharged amino acids that play a large role in determining the secondary, tertiary, and even quaternary structure of a protein (discussed next) are proline and cysteine. Proline, because it contains a ring structure as part of its backbone, has fewer degrees of rotational freedom than the other amino acids and therefore can limit protein folding in three dimensions. Cysteine contains a sulfide (SH) moiety in its R group and thus provides the possibility of forming disulfide (S-S) bonds with other cysteine residues (see the subsequent sections for further discussion).

## 8.2.2 Primary Structure

Using terminology introduced in Chapter 2 for polymer chemistry, amino acids are monomers that can be polymerized to form proteins. Since the bonds formed between the amino acids are called **peptide bonds**, proteins are also called **polypeptides.** Like other types of polymers, polypeptides are formed via condensation reactions (Fig. 8.5). However, these specific condensation reactions are catalyzed by enzymes inside the cells in response to the template provided by the codons found in the cellular DNA. Protein production is described further in Chapter 9.

A protein's **primary** structure is the linear order of its amino acids as dictated by the codons. The primary structure is extremely important as it directs all of the other levels of structure, and thus the final functionality of the protein. For example, substitution of a single amino acid (valine instead of glutamate) in the polypeptide chain that composes hemoglobin, the protein that carries oxygen in the blood, changes its overall folded shape and results in the disease known as sickle cell anemia (see Fig. 8.6).

## 8.2.3 Secondary Structure

As depicted in Figure 8.7, there are multiple levels of protein structure, which ultimately result in the final conformation, or three-dimensional arrangement, of the molecule. While the primary structure addresses only the linear order of the amino acids, the **secondary structure** is caused by localized interactions between these amino acid

(a)

(b)

**Figure 8.3**
(a) Amino acids have a central carbon atom attached to a hydrogen atom, a carboxyl group (COOH), an amine group ($NH_2$), and a R group. Differences in R groups are what distinguish amino acids from one another. (b) At physiological pH, the amino and carboxyl groups carry equal but opposite charges.

**TABLE 8.3**

| The Amino Acid Residues of Proteins | | | | | |
|---|---|---|---|---|---|
| Amino Acid Residue | Three-Letter Symbol | One-Letter Symbol | Mnemonic Help for One-Letter Symbol | Molecular Weight of Residue at pH 7.0 (daltons) | pK Value of Side Chain |
| Alanine | Ala | A | Alanine | 71 | |
| Glutamate | Glu | E | gluEtamic acid | 128 | 4.3 |
| Glutamine | Gln | Q | Q-tamine | 128 | |
| Aspartate | Asp | D | asparDic acid | 114 | 3.9 |
| Asparagine | Asn | N | asparagiNe | 114 | |
| Leucine | Leu | L | Leucine | 113 | |
| Glycine | Gly | G | Glycine | 57 | |
| Lysine | Lys | K | before L | 129 | 10.5 |
| Serine | Ser | S | Serine | 87 | |
| Valine | Val | V | Valine | 99 | |
| Arginine | Arg | R | aRginine | 157 | 12.5 |
| Threonine | Thr | T | Threonine | 101 | |
| Proline | Pro | P | Proline | 97 | |
| Isoleucine | Ile | I | Isoleucine | 113 | |
| Methionine | Met | M | Methionine | 131 | |
| Phenylalanine | Phe | F | Phenylalanine | 147 | |
| Tyrosine | Tyr | Y | tYrosine | 163 | 10.1 |
| Cysteine | Cys | C | Cysteine | 103 | |
| Tryptophan | Trp | W | tWo rings | 186 | |
| Histidine | His | H | Histidine | 137 | 6.0 |

[2] and [3]

residues. The formation of hydrogen bonds between the carboxyl and amino groups of amino acids lying closely together creates twists and folds in the polypeptide chain.

The two most common types of secondary structures (because they are the most thermodynamically favorable) are the $\alpha$-**helix** and the $\beta$-**pleated sheet**. Either left- or right-handed $\alpha$-helices can be formed, but right-handed are more stable. As shown in Figure 8.8, there are 3.6 amino acids per turn to allow for hydrogen bonding between an amino acid and one that lies four residues behind it. The amino acids are oriented with the side chains of their R groups toward the outside of the helix. An example of a protein with an $\alpha$-helical secondary structure is collagen (see Fig. 9.15), which is found in a number of human tissues. The collagen helix contains many proline residues. As mentioned in the previous section, there is less possibility for movement around the backbone of proline, which, in combination with the other amino acids in the primary structure of collagen, acts to stabilize the helical structure. However, in other cases (different primary structures), proline may disrupt the helix because it is difficult for sections of the chain containing this amino acid to twist and allow the correct positioning of the amino groups for the formation of stabilizing hydrogen bonds.

In contrast to the $\alpha$-helix, the $\beta$-pleated sheet structure is stabilized by hydrogen bonds between two chains or portions of a chain. In this case, each of the neighboring chains adopts an extended linear zigzag conformation, as illustrated

**Nonpolar Amino Acids**

Alanine

Valine

Leucine

Isoleucine

Phenylalanine

Tryptophan

Methionine

Proline

**Polar Amino Acids**

Glycine

Serine

Threonine

Cysteine

Tyrosine

Asparagine

Glutamine

**Negatively Charged Amino Acids**

Aspartic Acid

Glutamic Acid

**Positively Charged Amino Acids**

Lysine

Arginine

Histidine

**Figure 8.4**
The various R groups of amino acids, which can be nonpolar, polar, positively charged, or negatively charged.

**Figure 8.5**
Schematic of a condensation reaction. As shown here, this type of reaction can result in the formation of poly-peptides and always releases water.

in Figure 8.9. In this figure, the side chains project above and below the plane of the page. A **parallel β-pleatedsheet** contains chains that run in the same direction, while an **antiparallel β-pleatedsheet** consists of chains that extend in opposite directions. A natural polymer that contains this type of secondary structure is silk (see Fig. 8.10).

Hemoglobin

Sickle-cell Hemoglobin

Dimer of Sickle-cell Hemoglobin

**Figure 8.6**
Schematic of the structures of human hemoglobin (Protein Data Bank ID: 1o1n) and sickle-cell hemoglobin (Protein Data Bank ID: 2hbs). (*Note:* The Protein Data Bank (http://www.resb.org/pdb/home/home.do) is a freely accessible collection of structural data for proteins and nucleic acids derived from techniques such as NMR spectroscopy and X-ray crystallography and submitted by scientists.) The structure of the four chains of hemoglobin allows one hemoglobin molecule to carry four oxygen molecules. In sickle-cell hemoglobin, the oxygenated form is stable and functional, but residue 6 of chains B and D (normally glutamic acid) is mutated to valine (areas of mutation marked with black circles in the figure). The conformational change that occurs when the $O_2$ is released exposes the hydrophobic patch containing valine. To be more thermodynamically stable, the hydrophobic patches tend to aggregate, causing polymerization of the hemoglobin and the clinical presence of sickle-cell anemia (red blood cells containing the polymerized hemoglobin take on an elongated shape). (Image courtesy of N. Haspel and L.E. Kavraki, Rice University.)

## EXAMPLE PROBLEM 8.2

A research group has generated a synthetic oligopeptide with the following sequence:

FEFEFEFKFKFKFEFEFEFKFKFKF

Is the given structure the primary, secondary, tertiary, or quaternary structure of the oligopeptide? What is the net charge of this oligopeptide at pH 7.4? The research group would like to know if this oligopeptide will form an $\alpha$-helix or a $\beta$-sheet in aqueous solution. Make a prediction and rationalize your response. The research team has hypothesized that these oligopeptides will form dimers in physiological solution. Why would dimer formation be favorable? Predict the structural arrangement of the dimer and rationalize your prediction.

**Solution:** We are given the sequence of the amino acids; thus, we are given the primary structure of this oligopeptide. The given oligopeptide contains a total of 25 amino acids, with

6 negatively charged residues (glutamic acid, E), 6 positively charged residues (lysine, K), and 13 noncharged, nonpolar residues (phenylalanine, F) at pH 7.4. Thus, the net charge of the oligopeptide at pH 7.4 is zero. The oligopeptide would likely form a β-sheet in aqueous solution, as a result of the regular pattern between nonpolar residues and charged residues and consideration of the amino acids themselves. The regular repetition of the large aromatic R group of phenylalanine would likely present a steric barrier to the formation of an α-helix structure. Additionally, steric repulsion between the charged R groups of glutamic acid and lysine could strain an α-helix. A β-sheet structure, however, schematically indicated as follows, allows for the side groups of the phenylalanine to be on one side of the sheet, while the charged groups are on the other side of the sheet.

Primary Structure (E-helix)

SAQVKGHGKKVADALTNAV

Secondary Structure (E-helix)

Tertiary Structure (α subunit)

Quaternary Structure (Human hemoglobin)

**Figure 8.7**
An example of the multiple levels of protein structure, which ultimately result in the final conformation, or three-dimensional arrangement, of the molecule (in this case human hemoglobin). While the primary structure addresses only the linear order of the amino acids, the secondary structure is caused by localized interactions between these amino acid residues. The formation of hydrogen bonds between the carboxyl and amino groups of amino acids lying close together creates twists and folds in the polypeptide chain, as seen in the E-helix of this example. Further folding of these secondary structures in three dimensions forms the tertiary structure, as depicted in the α subunit of this example. Quaternary structure describes the orientation of multiple polypeptide chains and is caused by interactions between side groups belonging to different chains. In this example different subunits, such as α subunit, interact to form the quaternary structure of human hemoglobin. (Image courtesy of N. Haspel, L.E Kavraki, J.S. Olson, and J. Soman, Rice University.)

It is reasonable to hypothesize that the sheets would dimerize or form other assemblies of multiple sheets, as hydrogen bonding and charge interactions between the sheets stabilize the structures. The dimers would likely form as schematically illustrated in the following figure; however, the manner in which the sheets associate depends upon the conditions of the solution (ionic strength, temperature, presence, concentrations and charges of other solutes, etc.). The proposed dimerization shown here allows for interaction of the nonpolar phenylalanine

**Figure 8.8**
An α-helix structure. The amino acids are oriented with the side chains of their R groups toward the outside of the helix. There are 3.6 amino acids per turn to allow for hydrogen bonding between an amino acid and one that lies four residues behind it. Hydrogen bonds are depicted here as dashed lines [12].

(a) Antiparallel

(b) Parallel

**Figure 8.9**
The $\beta$-pleated sheet structure, which is stabilized by hydrogen bonds between portions within a chain or between chains. In this case, each of the neighboring chains adopts an extended linear zigzag conformation. The side chains project above and below the plane of the page. An antiparallel $\beta$-pleated sheet (a) consists of chains that extend in opposite directions, while a parallel $\beta$-pleated sheet (b) contains chains that run in the same direction. "H" indicates hydrogen, "N" indicates nitrogen, and "O" indicates oxygen in the figure. (Illustration, Irving Geis. Rights owned by Howard Hughes Medical Institute. Not to be used without permission.)

**Figure 8.10**
Schematic of the $\beta$-pleated sheet structure of silk. (Illustration, Irving Geis. Rights owned by Howard Hughes Medical Institute. Not to be used without permission.)

groups on the interior of the dimer, with the charged residues exposed to the aqueous solvent. From a thermodynamics point of view, it is favorable to have the charged groups exposed to the media, as exposure of the nonpolar groups would increase local order of the water molecules, and decrease entropy.

### 8.2.4 Tertiary Structure

The **tertiary structure** of a protein is the three-dimensional arrangement of an entire polypeptide chain (how the secondary structural elements are folded, see Fig. 8.7). This is caused by interactions between distant amino acids on the same chain. Unlike the secondary structure, which is mainly dictated by bonding between groups in the backbone of the chain, interactions between R group side chains play a large role in determining the tertiary structure of a protein. A common example of a unique tertiary structure is the so-called **TIM-barrel fold**, shown in Figure 8.11, named because it was first identified in triosephosphate isomerase (TIM), a protein involved in energy production in cells. This distinctive structure has eight parallel $\beta$-strands surrounded by eight $\alpha$-helices on the outside.

(a)

(b)

**Figure 8.11**
Schematic of the TIM-barrel fold structure viewed from (a) above and (b) the side. This distinctive structure has eight parallel $\beta$-strands surrounded by eight $\alpha$-helices on the outside. (Adapted with permission from [8].)

A number of types of interactions between side chains can occur to influence the folding of a protein in three dimensions, including the following:

1. Covalent bonding
2. Ionic interactions
3. Hydrogen bonding
4. Hydrophobic interactions

Covalent bonds are most commonly found between sulfur atoms on cysteine residues, as discussed earlier. Since covalent bonds are quite strong, disulfide bonds impart a great deal of stability to protein conformation. Although ionic interactions are weaker, they are also important in the final protein arrangement. These occur between positively and negatively charged side groups on the amino acids. Similarly, hydrogen bonds can be formed between polar amino acids. Folding due to hydrophobicity is caused by the mutual benefit of removing ordered water from near nonpolar residues through the interaction of the hydrophobic (nonpolar) residues with each other. This "hydrophobic effect" is based on the same entropic arguments as presented earlier for protein adsorption on hydrophobic biomaterial surfaces.

Because of thermodynamic concerns similar to those discussed previously for protein adsorption to surfaces, the most stable protein structures place most of the hydrophobic residues on the interior and most of the polar or charged residues on the exterior of the molecule to interact with the aqueous environment. In spite of these general rules, hydrophobic amino acids can occasionally be found on the external surface of a molecule and vice versa for charged residues. However, the energy cost in allowing this to occur indicates that there is a specific reason for such a structure. For example, external hydrophobic areas may provide binding sites for other proteins or cells. Similarly, charged residues found deep within the protein core may help stabilize a particular three-dimensional conformation.

### 8.2.5 Quaternary Structure

Most proteins are actually composed of several polypeptide chains, each with their own primary through tertiary structure. Each of these chains is referred to as a protein subunit, and the **quaternary structure** of a protein describes the three-dimensional arrangement of these subunits (Fig. 8.7). In this nomenclature, a single subunit is called a monomer, two subunits is a dimer, three is a trimer, etc.

As with tertiary structure, quaternary structure is a result of the interactions between side chains of the R groups of the amino acids, but in this case, the amino acids are on different peptide chains. The types of interactions that stabilize the structure are identical to those described earlier. Quaternary structure is usually very important to the overall activity of the protein. For example, it is the interactions of four separate polypeptide chains that allow the hemoglobin molecule to carry oxygen molecules in the blood (see Fig. 8.6).

Because the charge of both the peptide backbone and especially the side groups is pH dependent, pH changes may greatly affect both the tertiary and quaternary structures of proteins, which, in turn, could impact their adsorption profiles. The hierarchy presented here suggests that protein conformation is rigidly dictated by the order of amino acids and their subsequent interactions, but it is important to keep in mind that protein folding is a dynamic event. In reality, a protein's "structure" may refer to an equilibrium between several different conformations caused by thermodynamic fluctuations in bonds holding the protein in a certain arrangement. Although this dynamic folding and unfolding process is constantly occurring, the general idea holds that certain proteins are more stable than others (for example, because of a larger number of covalent or hydrogen bonds per volume), which, as described earlier, will affect their ability to adsorb to solid surfaces.

### EXAMPLE PROBLEM 8.3

Some individuals with naturally straight hair choose to "perm" their hair to add long-lasting waves. The permanent or perm procedure typically involves the wrapping of hair around curlers, followed by treatment of the hair with a reducing agent for a period of time and subsequent treatment with an oxidizing agent to set the form of the curl into the hair. Given the fact that a major structural component of human hair is keratin, a protein rich in the amino acid cysteine, explain in terms of protein chemistry how this method of curling hair works.

Solution:  The amino acid cysteine contains a sulfide moiety in its R residue. Disulfide bonds formed between cysteine residues in the keratin proteins contribute to the structural stability and elasticity of hair by serving as crosslinks between the protein chains. When hair that is naturally straight is wrapped around a curler, the protein components of the hair are subjected to tensile forces. The addition of a reducing agent results in the breaking of the naturally occurring disulfide bonds between and within the keratin proteins in the hair. The subsequent addition of an oxidizing agent to the hair facilitates the reformation of disulfide bonds. However, the bonds are now able to form in a configuration that stabilizes the curled structure that has been imparted to the hair by the curler. Thus, when the chemicals and the curlers are removed, the hair will have waves that are maintained by the new disulfide bonds between and within the keratin proteins of the hair.  ∎

## 8.3 Protein Transport and Adsorption Kinetics

The previous sections have revealed that hydrophobicity and charge of both the protein and surface, as well as the structural stability of the protein, can affect adsorption to biomaterials. For proteins, these characteristics are dictated by their primary through quaternary structure. However, before adsorption can occur, the proteins must be transported to the solid surface, and the rate of this transport can affect the kinetics of adsorption.

### 8.3.1 Transport to the Surface

Equations modeling protein transport generally include factors for the four main types of transport:

1. Diffusion
2. Thermal convection
3. Flow (also called convective transport)
4. Coupled transport (combinations of others, such as convection and diffusion)

Although an in-depth treatment of transport phenomena is beyond the scope of this text, a short discussion of basic transport principles as they relate to protein adsorption is included here. Of the types of transport listed earlier and depicted in Figure 8.12, we will focus on the effects of diffusion and flow on protein movement toward a solid surface.

Since transport properties are dependent on geometry, for the sake of the following discussion, we will define a system involving flow inside a cylinder as shown in Figure 8.13. This would be a simplified model of conditions that are found in blood vessels away from branch points, for example. In this case, the diagram would

**Figure 8.12**
Three types of transport phenomena seen in protein adsorption: flow, thermal convection, and diffusion. A concentration gradient drives diffusion, whereas a temperature gradient is responsible for thermal convection.

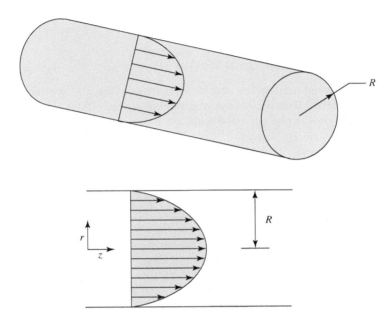

**Figure 8.13**
Velocity distribution for flow in a cylinder of radius $R$.

represent a cross-sectional view of the vessel and the fluid flowing through would be blood, with all its constituent proteins.

Due to interactions with the walls, liquids move more slowly near the sides of a channel, forming a parabolic velocity profile, as illustrated in Figure 8.13. For this type of geometry, the velocity profile can be represented by

$$V = \frac{2Q}{\pi R^2}\left[1 - \left(\frac{r}{R}\right)^2\right] \tag{8.8}$$

where $V$ is the velocity, $r$ and $R$ are defined in Figure 8.13, and $Q$ is the volumetric flow rate of liquid through the cylinder. An interesting characteristic of this equation is that at $r = R$ (the wall), $V = 0$. Because of the nature of this parabolic profile, there is no flow at the surface and therefore proteins cannot reach the interface by flow (convection) alone. Thus, diffusion plays a large role in protein transport to solid surfaces even in the presence of flow. In turn, however, the concentrations of proteins close to the surface, which affect the diffusion rate, are influenced by flow conditions.

In light of this, an equation is needed that considers both the convective and diffusional contributions to overall protein transport. This transport equation for the above-defined system is

$$\frac{\partial C}{\partial t} + V\frac{\partial C}{\partial z} = D\frac{1}{r}\frac{\partial}{\partial r}\left(r\frac{\partial C}{\partial r}\right) \tag{8.9}$$

where $C$ stands for the concentration of a protein at time $t$ and position $(z,r)$. In this equation, which considers radial but not axial diffusion, the term including $V$ represents the flow contribution, while the term including $D$ takes into account the diffusional contributions. Here, $D$ (diffusion coefficient) is a constant related to the size of the protein and its surrounding medium. The first term in the equation represents the unsteady state term: the change in the concentration with time.

The convective diffusion equation only describes the transport of the protein through a solution. Adsorption of the protein onto the surface can be incorporated using a boundary condition for the solution of this equation, which states that the rate of protein adsorption at the surface ($r = R$) is equal to the rate of transport of protein to the surface. Solutions of this and similar equations are left for more advanced texts on transport phenomena [4].

### 8.3.2 Adsorption Kinetics

As indicated earlier, due to their velocity profiles, all flowing fluids contain a layer of undisturbed solution (of varying thickness) near the walls of a vessel. Therefore, if a biomaterial is placed at the wall, the protein adsorption rate should be governed by diffusion alone. However, a number of experiments with blood proteins have found that there was a high initial adsorption rate correlating to diffusion-controlled mechanisms, but after some time, a plateau value was reached (Fig. 8.14). It is now believed that this plateau represents monolayer coverage of the entire surface by the proteins present in the system, as shown in Figure 8.15.

At longer times (near the plateau region), the rate of adsorption slows since, presumably, it is more difficult for the protein molecules to find a free space on the surface. At points during the adsorption process, there may be rearrangement of proteins on the surface to improve packing. This concept is illustrated in Figure 8.16. In this figure, the molecules change orientation in response to increasing surface concentration of protein, as would occur at later times in the adsorption process.

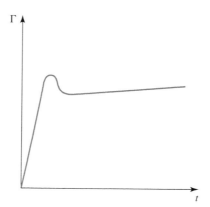

**Figure 8.14**
Diagram showing the total amount of adsorbed blood proteins ($\Gamma$) onto a surface as a function of time ($t$). There is a high initial adsorption rate correlating to diffusion-controlled mechanisms, and after some time, a plateau value is reached. The "overshoot", or "hump" in the adsorption curve has been explained in a variety of ways, including that during the rearrangement on the surface that occurs as more protein is absorbed, proteins that are less strongly bound may desorb. (Adapted with permission from [7].)

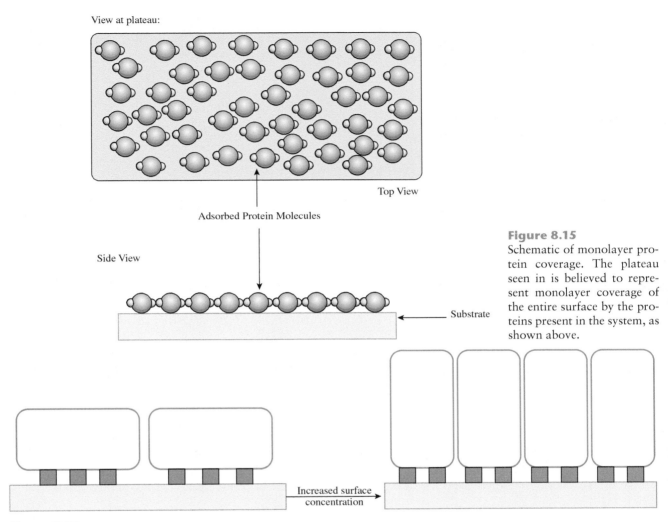

**Figure 8.15**
Schematic of monolayer protein coverage. The plateau seen in is believed to represent monolayer coverage of the entire surface by the proteins present in the system, as shown above.

**Figure 8.16**
Rearrangement of proteins on a surface. The rate of adsorption slows in the vicinity of the plateau region. Presumably, it is more difficult for protein molecules to find a free space on the surface at this point. Rearrangement of proteins (specifically change in their orientation) on the surface occurs to improve packing, thereby increasing the concentration of the protein on the surface.

## 8.4 Reversibility of Protein Adsorption

### 8.4.1 Reversible and Irreversible Binding

Whether the protein arrives early or near the plateau value in the adsorption process, there is always a short period of **reversible** binding before it attaches permanently to the surface. It is thought that the protein first makes a few contacts (a "handhold") for initial attachment. As its residence time on the biomaterial increases, the protein changes conformation to promote interactions with the surface. This may be a reaction to characteristics of the surface itself, or to neighboring proteins in the adsorbate (**lateral interactions**). This usually involves some degree of protein unfolding and spreading on the material.

After these conformational changes, eventually protein adsorption becomes **irreversible** (permanent). However, the time required for this to occur depends on the exact protein/surface combination. After this point, protein **desorption** is unlikely because all contacts between the surface and protein would have to be broken simultaneously (see following section).

**Figure 8.17**
Impact of protein adsorption on biological activity. (a) In this example, the red regions within the circles indicate biologically active regions of fibrinogen that promote platelet binding. (b) The final conformation of a protein on the surface, and hence where the active regions are located, has a strong impact on its activity. For example, in group 1 there are two biologically active surfaces opposite of the biomaterial surface, hence more activity is observed, whereas when the active regions are oriented toward the biomaterial surface (like in group 3) less activity is observed.

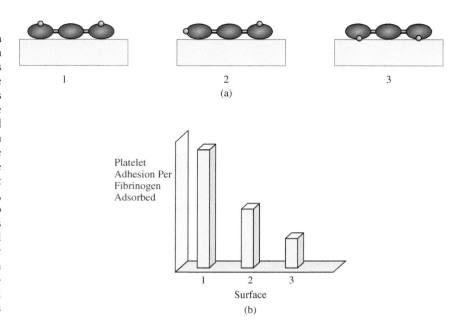

The final conformation of the protein on the surface has a strong impact on its activity, and, thus, usefulness after adsorption. For example, a series of studies indicates that the ability of fibrinogen (a protein found in the blood) to bind platelets (cell fragments important in blood clotting, see Chapter 13) is affected by the characteristics of the surface to which it is adsorbed [5]. As depicted in Figure 8.17, this can be due to alterations in the conformation of the adsorbed protein, which on some materials may be such that the platelet binding sites are oriented downward toward the surface and therefore cannot be recognized by the platelets.

## 8.4.2 Desorption and Exchange

While desorption is unlikely, exchange of adsorbed protein molecules does occur in systems like blood that contain multiple protein types. It is believed that this happens because of the dynamic nature of protein attachment to surfaces. It is possible that while a protein breaks contact for an instant due to fluctuations in bonds that govern its attachment to the surface, another protein could form an interaction in the vacated space. If the second protein can place enough "feet" on the surface in this manner, it will displace the first protein (Fig. 8.18).

Due to this phenomenon, the final protein composition on a surface not only depends on the concentration of protein in the solution, but also on its surface affinity. As discussed earlier in this chapter and summarized in Table 8.1, surface affinity can be influenced by the size, charge, hydrophobicity, structural stability, and unfolding rate of the protein. Since the diffusion rate is dependent on concentration, it follows that proteins with higher concentration will arrive and adsorb first, but they will eventually be replaced by those with greater surface affinity. This exchange is known as the **Vroman effect**. A summary of the Vroman effect with selected plasma proteins on glass and metal oxide surfaces is found in Figure 8.19.

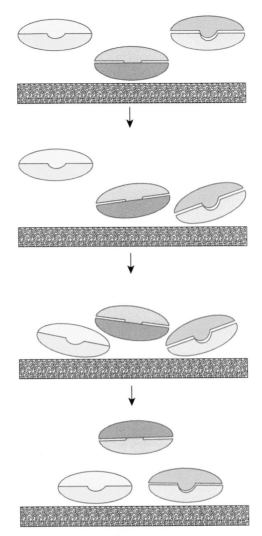

**Figure 8.18**
A schematic of proteins exchanged on a material surface. The initial protein (purple) is wedged out of the way by the newer proteins (orange and yellow), which have a greater affinity for the material.

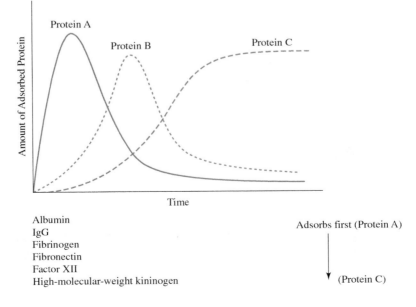

Albumin
IgG
Fibrinogen
Fibronectin
Factor XII
High-molecular-weight kininogen

Adsorbs first (Protein A)

(Protein C)

**Figure 8.19**
A diagram of the Vroman effect. Proteins with higher concentration (such as albumin in the case of blood) will rapidly attach, and then be replaced over time by proteins with greater surface affinity [1].

## EXAMPLE PROBLEM 8.4

An experimental biomaterial is placed into an aqueous solution containing protein A (10 kDa) at an initial solution concentration of [A] and protein B (100 Da) at an initial solution concentration of [B]. It can be assumed for this exercise that the protein adsorption rate is governed by diffusion alone. Consider the results of the following experiments:

In experiment 1, the initial concentration of protein A in solution was four times the initial concentration of protein B in solution. The following profiles of protein concentration at the surface of the biomaterial with time were obtained.

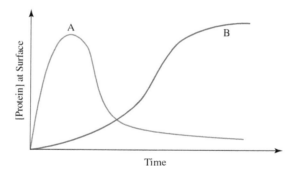

In experiment 2, the initial concentrations of protein A and B in solution were equal. The following profiles of protein concentrations at the surface of the biomaterial with time were obtained. However, the computer did not label each profile with the corresponding protein.

Using information deduced from the first experiment, indicate which profile corresponds to each protein (A and B) and support your answer.

**Solution:**   In experiment 1, [A] = 4[B]. Protein adsorption profiles for experiment 1 showed A adsorbing initially at a much higher concentration than B. However, with time, B was present at high concentrations at the material surface and A was scarcely present. Considering that the initial concentration of A was high relative to B, the high initial adsorption of A relative to B can be explained in terms of the availability of many more molecules of A than B to interact with the surface. However, as time progressed, protein B adsorbed to the surface at a much higher concentration than A, despite the lower initial solution concentration. Thus, B exhibited a higher affinity for the material surface and displaced the lower affinity A molecules from the surface with time. This is an example of the Vroman effect. In experiment 2, [A] = [B]. Considering that protein B demonstrated a higher affinity for the material surface than A in experiment 1, one would expect that it would be present on the material surface at higher concentrations than A with time. However, A might be expected to show an initial rate of adsorption higher than B due to the relatively smaller molecular size, which could facilitate initial diffusion of A to the material surface. Thus, the profiles should be labeled as follows:

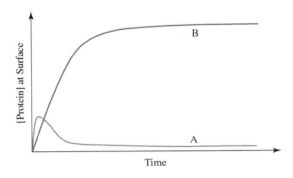

## 8.5   Techniques: Assays for Protein Type and Amount

Although many methods exist to identify and quantify proteins in solution, determination of protein conformation on surfaces (a main subject of this chapter) is more difficult. Information about molecular arrangement after adsorption can be obtained using a number of the surface analysis techniques described in Chapter 7. ATR-FTIR and other more advanced surface analysis methods have been employed to probe protein coatings on materials.

Therefore, rather than surface analysis, the focus of this section is on established techniques to identify specific proteins and determine their amount in a given sample. Although these methods are most commonly used to assess a liquid sample containing proteins, some, especially those using antibodies (see following text), may be modified for applications involving surface-adsorbed proteins. Alternatively, these techniques can provide information about the protein constitution of the liquid phase over the surface before and after adsorption and, thus, give an indication of the composition of the adsorbate.

This section first discusses affinity chromatography, which achieves quantification and protein purification through the use of the thermodynamic parameters discussed earlier in this chapter. The remainder of the section describes general characterization techniques to determine protein type and quantity, including colorimetric and fluorescent assays, enzyme-linked immunosorbent assays (ELISAs), and Western blotting. It should be noted that a combination of methods are often required to identify/quantify the amount of a particular protein in a sample. For example, a sample that has been fractionated via affinity chromatography (see Section 8.5.1) can then be subjected to an ELISA to confirm that a certain protein is found in that portion of the sample.

## 8.5.1 High-Performance Liquid Chromatography (HPLC): Affinity Chromatography

As shown in Figure 2.57, there are many different types of liquid chromatography. Size exclusion chromatography (SEC) was described in Chapter 2. We will focus in this section on one type of **affinity chromatography** known as adsorption chromatography. **Ion exchange chromatography** is another important kind of affinity chromatography that separates compounds based on charge, but discussion of this technique is beyond the scope of this book.

### 8.5.1.1 Basic Principles
**Adsorption chromatography** employs the concept of separation by preferential adsorption of the analyte (often proteins) based on hydrophobic and polar interactions. Like SEC, the system contains both a mobile and a stationary phase. The mobile phase is a liquid solvent into which the dissolved sample is injected. The stationary phase is composed of small (diameter $3 - 10 \mu m$) porous silica or polymer beads. However, unlike SEC, in affinity chromatography, there is no physical entrapment of the analyte in the porous beads. For adsorption chromatography, the beads are coated with either a very hydrophobic (nonpolar) or very hydrophilic (polar) polymer that is covalently bonded to their surface. The analyte molecules then adsorb to the beads in differing degrees, depending on their own hydrophobicity.

Retention time is highly affected by the chemical composition of the analyte. The first species to exit the stationary phase is the molecule with the least affinity for the column, and that with the most affinity is eluted last (Fig. 8.20). In between, molecules are retained for varying amounts of time depending on the extent of their interaction with the beads. However, what constitutes "least" and "most" affinity depends on the configuration of the HPLC system.

**Normal-phase chromatography** employs a polar stationary phase, and a nonpolar mobile phase, such as hexane. In contrast, **reversed-phase chromatography** generally uses a nonpolar stationary phase and a polar (often aqueous) mobile phase. Therefore, in normal-phase chromatography, more hydrophilic molecules are eluted later since they have more affinity for the stationary than the mobile phase. However, in reversed-phase chromatography, more hydrophilic species are eluted first, as they have more affinity for the mobile than for the stationary phase (Fig. 8.21).

### 8.5.1.2 Instrumentation
As depicted in Figure 8.22, the instrumentation required for affinity chromatography is identical to that used for SEC, and includes five basic components: a pump, an injector, a column to separate samples based on hydrophobicity, a detector, and a processor/computer to translate signals from the detector into the appropriate plot. As for SEC, there are a wide variety of detectors used in affinity chromatography, including those based on UV, refractive index, or fluorescence.

### 8.5.1.3 Information Provided
An advantage of affinity chromatography is that it can be used quantitatively to determine the amount of a certain separated species present in the original sample. This is accomplished by first integrating the area under the peak for that species. In a similar manner, a standard curve can be generated by

1. Methylparaben (R = —CH$_3$)
2. Ethylparaben (R = —CH$_2$CH$_3$)
3. Isopropylparaben (R = —CH(CH$_3$)$_2$)
4. n-Propylparaben (R = —CH$_2$CH$_2$CH$_3$)
5. sec.-Butylparaben (R = —CHCH$_3$C$_2$H$_5$)
6. Isobutylparaben (R = —CH$_2$CH(CH$_3$)$_2$)
7. n-Butylparaben (R = —CH$_2$CH$_2$CH$_2$CH$_3$)

**Figure 8.20**
HPLC trace of a mixture of parabens (p-hydroxybenzoic acid esters—parabens are widely used antimicrobial agents) on a reversed phase column using a water-methanol (50:50) mixture as the mobile phase. Overall, parabens with increasing hydrophobicity (longer hydrocarbon chains in the R group) demonstrate greater retention time due to increased interactions between the molecule and the column [9].

integrating the area under the peaks representing increasing amounts of the substance of interest (Fig. 8.23). By comparing the area from the unknown to that recorded on the standard curve, the amount of the unknown species can be quantified. Unlike SEC, where time to elution is used to assign molecular weight, in affinity chromatography, the area under the peak is of most importance for quantification.

However, elution time is a key element in **fractionation**, another application of affinity chromatography. Such procedures are commonly used for purification of proteins (Fig. 8.24). For example, if the elution time of a pure protein is determined, fractions of the mobile phase can be collected around this time. Because this chromatographic method is nondestructive, these fractions can be reconstituted and used for further studies as a source of uncontaminated sample material.

## EXAMPLE PROBLEM 8.5

Five standard samples of known concentrations of protein X were run through a reversed-phase HPLC system. The data that follow were obtained. After running the standards, three samples (A, B, and C) of protein X of unknown concentration were run through the system. Calculate the concentrations of each of the unknown protein solutions, given that the area under the absorbance curve of sample A was $0.87 \times 10^7$, of sample B was $1.32 \times 10^7$, and of sample C was $0.21 \times 10^7$. What would you predict the area under the curve to be for a sample of protein X of concentration 29.0 ng/mL? A sample of a second protein (protein Y) was run on the sample column under the same conditions and eluted approximately 2 minutes after protein X. Based on this observation, which protein has the largest molecular weight? Which protein has greater hydrophilic character?

**Figure 8.21**
Normal-phase chromatogram (mobile phase: hexane–amyl alcohol (99.5:0.5)) of a mixture of $\alpha$-, $\beta$-, $\gamma$-, and $\delta$-Tocopherol (four isoforms of vitamin E). In this case, the most hydrophilic substance ($\delta$-Tocopherol) exits the column last because it has a relatively low affinity for the hydrophobic mobile phase. (b) Reversed-phase chromatogram (mobile phase: methanol-water (9:1)) of a mixture of $\alpha$-, $\beta$-, $\gamma$-, and $\delta$-Tocopherol. Here the most hydrophilic substance ($\delta$-Tocopherol) exits the column first because it has a relatively high affinity for the hydrophilic mobile phase [10].

| Compound | $R_1$ | $R_2$ | $R_3$ |
|---|---|---|---|
| $\alpha$-Tocopherol | —$CH_3$ | —$CH_3$ | —$CH_3$ |
| $\beta$-Tocopherol | —$CH_3$ | —H | —$CH_3$ |
| $\gamma$-Tocopherol | —H | —$CH_3$ | —$CH_3$ |
| $\delta$-Tocopherol | —H | —H | —$CH_3$ ← **Most hydrophilic** |

**Figure 8.22**
Block diagram of affinity chromatography instrumentation. Five basic components are included: a pump, an injector, a column to separate samples based on hydrophobicity, a detector, and a processor/ computer to translate signals from the detector into the appropriate plot.

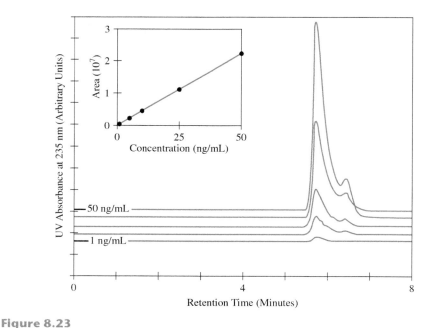

**Figure 8.23**
Reversed-phase HPLC chromatographs of N-vinyl pyrrolidone standards (1, 5, 10, 25, and 50 ng/mL). Inset graph: Calibration curve generated from the areas under the peaks.

Relative protein hydrophilicty

Mixture of molecules

Affinity column

Proteins elute based on differences in hydrophobicity

Proteins with a high hydrophilicty (blue) will elute early due to high affinity for the mobile phase

Proteins with more hydrophobicity (purple and red) will be retained on the column due to favorable interactions with the hydrophobic beads.

Proteins with the greatest hydrophobicity (red) elute later due to stronger attractive interactions with the beads.

**Affinity chromatogram:**          Load column

**Figure 8.24**
Fractionation of a protein mixture using affinity chromatography. By placing vials under the column at different times, proteins with differing levels of hydrophobicity can be separated.    In this case (reverse-phase chromatography), the most hydrophilic molecules will elute first [11].

| [X] (ng/mL) | Area Under the Absorbance Curve (Arbitrary Units) |
|---|---|
| 1.0 | $0.05 \times 10^7$ |
| 5.0 | $0.25 \times 10^7$ |
| 10.0 | $0.50 \times 10^7$ |
| 25.0 | $1.25 \times 10^7$ |
| 50.0 | $2.50 \times 10^7$ |

**Solution:**   Given the information for the standards, a standard curve can be generated from a linear regression of the data, with the concentration being the variable "$x$" and the area under the absorbance curve being the variable "$y$" in the linear equation $y = mx + b$, where "$m$" is the slope and "$b$" is the $y$-intercept.

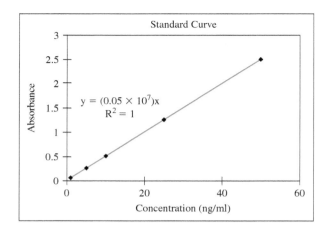

In this case, the slope is $0.05 \times 10^7$ mL/ng and the $y$-intercept is 0, with a correlation coefficient of 1. The equation can be verified for each data point as illustrated here for the first data point:

$$y = mx + b$$

$$0.05 \times 10^7 = m \cdot (1.0\,\text{ng/mL}) + b$$

$$0.05 \times 10^7 = 0.05 \times 10^7\,\text{mL/ng} \cdot (1.0\,\text{ng/mL}) + 0$$

$$0.05 \times 10^7 = 0.05 \times 10^7$$

Thus, the linear equation for the calibration curve is as follows:

$$(\text{Area Under the Absorbance Curve}) = (0.05 \times 10^7\,\text{mL/ng}) * [X]$$

$$[X] = (\text{Area Under the Absorbance Curve})/(0.05 \times 10^7\,\text{mL/ng})$$

The unknown concentration of each sample can be calculated by substituting into this equation the corresponding area under the absorbance curve.

For sample A,

$$[X] = 0.87 \times 10^7/(0.05 \times 10^7\,\text{mL/ng}) = \underline{17.4\ \text{ng/mL}}$$

For sample B,

$$[X] = 1.32 \times 10^7/(0.05 \times 10^7\,\text{mL/ng}) = \underline{26.4\ \text{ng/mL}}$$

For sample C,

$$[X] = 0.21 \times 10^7/(0.05 \times 10^7\,\text{mL/ng}) = \underline{4.2\ \text{ng/mL}}$$

The area under the absorbance curve for a 29.0 ng/mL sample of protein X would be predicted to be

$$\text{Area Under the Absorbance Curve} = (0.05 \times 10^7\,\text{mL/ng}) \cdot 29.0\ \text{ng/mL}$$

$$\text{Area Under the Absorbance Curve} = \underline{1.45 \times 10^7\ \text{arbitrary units}}$$

The elution times of various proteins do not give any indication of the molecular weight of the proteins in HPLC, as it is an affinity-based assay and not a size-exclusion assay. Thus, no determination can be made with respect to the relative sizes of proteins X and Y based upon the HPLC information given. However, there is sufficient information to comment on the relative hydrophilicity of the proteins. Since this is reversed-phase HPLC, it can be assumed that a nonpolar stationary phase and polar mobile phase were used. Therefore, hydrophilic species are eluted first, as they have greater affinity for the mobile phase than the stationary phase. As protein X eluted before protein Y, protein X is more hydrophilic than protein Y based upon the given results. ■

### 8.5.2 Colorimetric Assays

The following techniques are examples of assays for the presence of a certain protein, based on changes in an observable quantity such as color. Many of these are robust enough to be used to quantify one protein from a mixture. These assays provide similar information to affinity chromatography, but the HPLC technique is usually more sensitive to small amounts of protein. Also, these assays have not been developed for all types of proteins, so certain samples may still be best detected via HPLC.

**8.5.2.1 Basic Principles and Instrumentation**   The simplest test for the presence of a given protein involves direct reaction of the component with a marker chemical to cause a specific color change. The molecule causing this specific color (**chromophore**) will absorb UV-VIS radiation in a manner similar to that described in Chapter 2. Therefore, a UV-VIS spectrophotometer (or, often, an automated plate reader with an attached spectrophotometer) can be used to read the absorbance of the sample at a known wavelength. Beer-Lambert's law is then employed to determine the concentration of the protein in the sample as compared to a standard curve (see Chapter 2).

Colorimetric assays have been designed for proteins that are either enzymes or nonenzymes, although the mechanism of color formation varies slightly. Since the job of an **enzyme** is to cleave substrate materials (see Chapter 9 for more information), this can be exploited to form the basis of the colorimetric assay. If a substrate can be added, that, when cleaved, alters color dramatically (or changes from colorless to colored), the color change can easily be quantified. Since the amount of substrate cleaved is directly proportional to the amount of enzyme present, there is usually a linear correlation between the degree of color change and the amount of enzyme of interest.

Detection of nonenzymatic components may involve a reaction that attaches a chromophore directly to the protein of interest. Alternatively, a portion of the protein to be quantified may react to change the conformation or other chemical characteristics of a dye, thus producing a color change.

## EXAMPLE PROBLEM 8.6

You are trying to quantify the amount of total protein [P] in three different samples using a colorimetric assay. You have run the assay using nine protein standards in addition to your three samples and the results are found below. What is the protein content in each of your samples?

| [P] (µg/mL) | Absorbance (arbitrary units) |
|---|---|
| 0 | 0.09 |
| 2 | 0.103 |
| 4 | 0.126 |
| 8 | 0.158 |
| 12 | 0.206 |
| 16 | 0.233 |
| 20 | 0.270 |
| 25 | 0.309 |
| 30 | 0.366 |
| Sample 1 | 0.285 |
| Sample 2 | 0.241 |
| Sample 3 | 0.237 |

**Solution:**   Given the information for the standards, a standard curve can be created from a linear regression of the data, with the concentration being the variable "$x$" and the area under the absorbance curve being the variable "$y$" in the linear equation where "$m$" is the slope and "$b$" is the $y$-intercept.

In this case, the slope is 0.0091 mL/µg and the $y$-intercept is 0.0884, with a correlation coefficient of 0.998.

Using the general format of the equation $y = mx + b$, the linear equation for the calibration curve is as follows:

$$(Absorbance) = (0.0091 \text{ mL}/\mu g)^*[A] + 0.0884$$

$$[P] = (Absorbance - 0.0884)/(0.0091 \text{ mL}/\mu g)$$

The unknown concentration of each sample can be calculated by substituting into this equation the corresponding absorbance value.
For sample 1,

$$[P] = (0.285 - 0.0884)/(0.0091 \text{ mL}/\mu g) = \underline{21.6 \ \mu g/mL \ protein}$$

For sample 2,

$$[P] = (0.241 - 0.0884)/(0.0091 \text{ mL}/\mu g) = \underline{16.8 \ \mu g/mL \ protein}$$

For sample 3,

$$[P] = (0.237 - 0.0884)/(0.0091 \text{ mL}/\mu g) = \underline{16.3 \ \mu g/mL \ protein} \quad \blacksquare$$

### 8.5.3 Fluorescent Assays

**8.5.3.1 Basic Principles** Fluorescent assays for proteins are similar in concept to colorimetric assays, but there are key differences in instrumentation. In this case, the reaction causes the attachment of a fluorescing molecule (**fluorophore**) to the protein of interest. Visible light fluorescence (like X-ray fluorescence discussed in Chapter 7) involves excitation of the fluorophore molecule through absorption of a specific amount of energy (visible light of a given wavelength). On a molecular level, for visible light fluorescence, the excitation often involves the transition of electrons from the $\pi$ bonding to antibonding orbital. The excited molecule undergoes collisions and interactions with surrounding molecules, which causes **radiationless decay** (loss of energy) until the lowest excited energy state is reached. The molecule then returns to the ground state (see Chapter 2), and, in so doing, emits energy of the same order of magnitude as that absorbed (in this case, a slightly different wavelength of visible light due to the loss of energy via radiationless decay).

**8.5.3.2 Instrumentation** The instrumentation for a fluorometer is similar to that for the UV-VIS spectrophotometer described in Chapter 2. Like a spectrophotometer, a fluorometer includes four main components: a source of visible light, a filter to select the appropriate wavelength, a detector, and a processor/computer to translate signals from the detector into the appropriate values. However, as seen in Figure 8.25, the light source sample and detector are not collinear, in order to minimize the effect of emission beam scattering. Also in contrast to UV-VIS spectrophotometers, the instrumentation is configured to analyze light intensity from

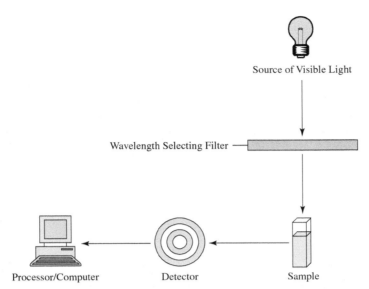

**Figure 8.25**
Schematic of a fluorometer. A fluorometer includes four main components: a source of visible light, a filter to select the appropriate wavelength, a detector, and a processor/computer to translate signals from the detector into the appropriate values. However, in contrast to UV-VIS spectrophotometers, the instrumentation is configured to analyze light intensity from the sample near a certain wavelength (the expected emission wavelength) only, instead of providing values for the entire spectrum.

the sample near a certain wavelength (the expected emission wavelength) only, instead of providing values for the entire spectrum. Because fluorescent phenomena are short-lived, the fluorometer must be able to provide the excitation wavelength and detect at the emission wavelength simultaneously.

**8.5.3.3 Information Provided** A derivative of Beer-Lambert's law can be used with fluorescence intensity values, thus allowing the quantification of fluorescently labeled protein molecules, given appropriate standards. Advantages of fluorescent assays include that fluorescent phenomena are detectable at one to three orders of magnitude lower concentration than that observable with traditional colorimetric (absorbance) techniques. Additionally, certain amino acids, such as tryptophan or tyrosine, are intrinsic fluorophores. Therefore, if the protein of interest contains enough of these amino acids, an additional reaction to label the protein is unnecessary.

## 8.5.4 Enzyme-Linked Immunosorbent Assay (ELISA)

For very specific identification of a protein, the enzyme-detection approach described above can be combined with the use of antibodies in an **enzyme-linked immunosorbent assay** (**ELISA**). The most common type of ELISA is the **sandwich ELISA**. Antibodies, discussed further in Chapter 12, have a unique structure designed to recognize specific portions of proteins and bind tightly to them. Therefore, in the sandwich ELISA, well plates are first coated with an antibody[1] (called the **primary antibody**) designed to attach to the protein of interest. The following steps are then performed (Fig. 8.26):

1. The sample (containing the possible protein of interest) is added.
2. A second antibody (the **secondary antibody**) that is conjugated to an enzyme is added. The secondary antibody will bind to another specific site on the protein of interest. (The enzymes most commonly used for these assays include alkaline phosphatase, horseradish peroxidase, and *p*-nitrophenol phosphatase.)
3. The substrate for the enzyme is added and the color change is quantified on a plate reader/spectrophotometer.

---

[1]This method assumes that adsorption of the antibodies to the surface of the well plates does not cause structural rearrangement to such a degree that they are no longer able to bind their target molecules. This is confirmed by running standards of the pure protein along with unknown samples in each experiment to ascertain that the standard curves are linear with respect to protein concentration.

**Figure 8.26**
Process used in a sandwich ELISA. First, the primary antibody is attached to a well, after which the sample is added. The proteins of interest will then attach to the primary antibody. A secondary antibody is then added, which will attach to the protein of interest. A substrate is added. The well is rinsed after each step, and color change produced by the secondary antibody is measured on a spectrophotometer. This measurement corresponds to the amount of protein of interest in the initial solution.

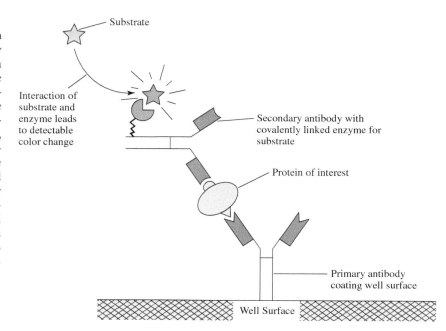

Similar to colorimetric assays, the color change is proportional to the amount of protein present. Quantification occurs as the color change for the sample is compared to that which occurs in the presence of different concentrations of the pure protein of interest (standards) after the standards are subjected to the same procedure as described earlier. It is also common to fluorescently label or radio-label the secondary antibody in this procedure, rather than conjugating it to an enzyme. In these cases, the amount of the protein of interest is quantified by fluorometric-based methods as described previously or by using a radiation detector (such as a gamma counter).

A modification of this technique, in which soluble antibodies are added to a protein adsorbed on a biomaterial surface, can be used to probe the conformation of the adsorbed protein. If the antibodies do not bind to the same degree as they would if the protein were in solution, this is an indication that the protein has unfolded or the regions recognized by the antibody are masked by the surface.

ELISAs are generally used to quantify the amount of a particular protein in a solution or on a biomaterial surface. While this is a sensitive assay (general range 0.01 ng to 0.1 ng [6]), there must be an antibody available to the protein of interest to utilize this technique.

### 8.5.5 Western Blotting

Antibodies can also be used to identify a certain protein after separation of the many proteins contained in a sample through the use of gel electrophoresis. This procedure is called **Western blotting**. In this case, the sample is first treated with sodium dodecyl sulfate (SDS) (Fig. 8.27), an **amphiphilic** molecule (one that has both hydrophilic and hydrophobic regions). SDS binds to the hydrophobic regions of proteins and causes them to unfold. The SDS-treated sample is then loaded on a poly(acrylamide) gel and exposed to an electric field. SDS is highly negatively charged and effectively masks any charge on the protein, so in the presence of an electric field, the SDS protein will migrate toward the positive pole. Larger molecules will experience more drag while moving through the pores of the gel, and thus will migrate more slowly. The result is discrete bands in the gel, representing proteins with different molecular weights. This procedure, called **SDS-poly(acrylamide)-gel electrophoresis (SDS-PAGE)**, is a means to separate proteins based solely on molecular weight, and is often used to purify a protein of interest.

**Figure 8.27**
Structure of sodium dodecyl sulfate (SDS).

**Figure 8.28**
Process used in a Western blot assay. The sample is run on a poly(acrylamide) gel, and then transferred to a nitrocellulose sheet. This sheet is then reacted with antibodies (in this case antibodies for proteins A and B) to determine what proteins were present in the initial sample.

To confirm that a certain band contains the target protein, a Western blot can then be performed (Fig. 8.28). This involves the following steps:

1. The bands are transferred to nitrocellulose paper by pressing the gel firmly against the paper. Since nitrocellulose binds proteins nonspecifically, the bands are transferred and appear in the same order as on the original gel.

2. A primary antibody in solution is added on top of the blotted paper.

3. A labeled secondary antibody is added that binds the primary antibody.

4. If the secondary antibody is enzyme-conjugated, the substrate is then added.

Color change, fluorescence, or radioactivity is recorded via camera or other means.

Western blots, like ELISAs, are generally used to quantify the amount of a particular protein in a solution. Depending on the antibody, this assay may be less sensitive than the ELISA, but the ability to identify multiple proteins on a single blot is an advantage when the amount of sample is limited. Like ELISAs, an antibody to the protein of interest must be available in order to use this technique.

## EXAMPLE PROBLEM 8.7

You are trying to quantify protein X adsorption to a biomaterial, but there are no known antibodies for protein X. In addition, it is known that pre-labeling the protein with a chromo-/fluorophore will affect its affinity for your surface. Assuming protein X is not an enzyme, of the protein assays described in this chapter, which one would be most appropriate and why?

**Solution:** Since protein X is not an enzyme and cannot be pre-labeled, colorimetric assays will be difficult. Since there are no antibodies to this protein, Western blotting and ELISAs cannot be performed. Thus, the best two options would be affinity chromatography or fluorescent assays. Fluorescent assays would only be appropriate if there are sufficient tryptophan or tyrosine amino acids in the protein that labeling would be unnecessary, and this assay could be done while the protein is still attached to the biomaterial surface.

Affinity chromatography could be used if there are not sufficient number of fluorescent amino acids in the protein, but can only be done in solution, so this technique would require desorbing the proteins from the surface before quantification. ◾

## Summary

- Protein adsorption involves a system composed of the protein, solvent, and surface. In order to assess the likelihood of a specific adsorption event, the thermodynamics of the event are evaluated in terms of the total change in Gibbs free energy $(G)$ from before to after the event. An adsorption event is deemed energetically favorable if it results in a negative $\Delta G$.

- The factors of the entire protein adsorption system that have the greatest impact on adsorption are dehydration of the surface and protein, redistribution of charged groups, and structural rearrangement of the protein.

- The primary structures of proteins are dictated by the linear order of their constituent amino acids. The secondary structure can result in the formation of $\alpha$-helices and $\beta$-pleated sheets. The tertiary structure depends upon how the secondary structural elements are folded, and it entails the three-dimensional arrangement of the entire polypeptide chain. Many proteins are composed of several polypeptide chains, each with its own primary through tertiary structures. The quaternary structure of a protein is determined by the interactions between the side groups of amino acids on different polypeptide subunits, and it describes the three-dimensional arrangement of the polypeptide chains.

- The structural arrangement of a protein can depend on environmental factors such as pH and can result in the presentation of varying regions of hydrophobicity or charge, each of which can affect its adsorption to a material. The ability of proteins to rearrange structurally allows the protein to obtain the optimal conformation for hydrophobic and charged domains to best fulfill the thermodynamic requirements of adsorption.

- Equations modeling protein transport generally include factors for diffusion, thermal convection, flow, and coupled transport. In the case of flow in a cylinder, a parabolic velocity profile can be modeled.

- A short period of reversible binding of a protein to a surface occurs before the protein permanently attaches. During the period of initial binding, a protein can make conformational changes to promote interactions with the surface. With time, the protein becomes irreversibly bound to the surface. The final protein composition on a material surface depends upon the concentration of the protein in solution as well as its affinity for the material surface.

- Affinity chromatography techniques such as adsorption chromatography and ion exchange chromatography allow for protein quantification and purification/fractionation through the application of thermodynamic principles.

- Colorimetric and fluorescent assays can be used to determine and quantify the presence of a certain protein based upon observable changes in the color or fluorescence of the assay solution, respectively. ELISA techniques provide for very specific identification of a protein through the interaction and subsequent detection (colorimetric, fluorescent, or radiographic) of antibodies specific for the protein of interest.

- Western blotting provides a means for separation of proteins through electrophoresis and identification of the protein of interest through use of a detectable antibody specific for the protein of interest.

# Problems

8.1  Explain how each of the levels of protein structure (primary-secondary-tertiary-quaternary) may affect a protein's level of adsorption to a hydrophobic biomaterial.

8.2  You are concerned with protein adsorption to a vascular graft material. Assume that it is known that Protein H, which is rich in histidine, is important in initiating the blood clotting cascade. You have the following choices for your graft material:

(1) Poly(ethylene) (contact angle ~90°)

(2) Poly(ethylene) that has been plasma treated to possess + surface charge

(3) Poly(ethylene) that has been plasma treated to possess − surface charge

(4) Poly(ethylene) with covalently attached PEG chains on the surface

  (a) Briefly explain the difference between adsorption and absorption.
  (b) Based on the above information and what you know regarding protein adsorption, on which surface (1, 2, 3, or 4) would you be most likely to observe clotting? Explain why you chose the surface you did as well as why you think that there would be less clotting on the other surfaces.
  (c) Assume that new experiments have revealed that there are actually two types of Protein H, which is comprised of a total of 40 amino acids:
       Protein H1 has 7 His and 10 Cys residues
       Protein H2 has 15 His and 5 Cys residues

Protein H1 is dominant and therefore has a higher concentration in the blood. Draw the expected profile of H1 and H2 adsorption to the surface you chose for (b) over time. Explain why your diagram appears as it does based on principles of protein-surface interactions.

8.3  A neutral, hydrophobic biomaterial surface was incubated with a mixture of Protein X (20%) and Protein Y (80%) OR a mixture of Protein Z (20%) and Protein Y (80%) and the protein compositions at the surface were measured over time.

  (a) Given the information about the proteins listed below and the graphs of the protein composition at the surface, explain why, in the mixture with Protein Y, Protein X binds to the material and forms a relatively pure monolayer at early timepoints while Protein Z does not.

| Protein | MW (total) | # Cysteines | Isoelectric Point (pI) |
|---------|-----------|-------------|------------------------|
| Protein X | 11.6 kD | 2 | 9.6 |
| Protein Y | 67 kD | 3 | 6.9 |
| Protein Z | 64.5 kD | 10 | 5.8 |

  (b) Why does Protein Y displace Protein X from the surface of the material?
  (c) Why does Protein Y displace Protein Z from the surface of the material?

8.4 You have a mixture of two proteins that you are trying to separate via affinity chromatography.

X – contains many serine residues

Y – contains many phenylalanine residues

(a) You are using a reversed phase system with water as the mobile phase. Which protein would you expect to elute first? Explain based on molecular interactions with the column.

(b) If you switch to using methanol as the mobile phase, will this make it easier or harder to separate the two proteins? Explain based on the table here and molecular interaction with the column.

| Solvent List | Relative Polarity |
|---|---|
| Methanol | 2 |
| Water | 1 |
| Acetone | 0.5 |

(c) After optimizing your reversed-phased HPLC system, you run standard samples of protein X. After running the standards, three samples (A, B, and C) of protein X of unknown concentration were run through the system as noted here:

| Protein [X] (ng/mL) | Area Under the Curve (Arbitrary Units) |
|---|---|
| 1.0 | 0.10 |
| 7.0 | 0.75 |
| 15.0 | 1.60 |
| 25.0 | 2.76 |
| 50.0 | 5.00 |

| Unknown Samples | Area Under the Curve (Arbitrary Units) |
|---|---|
| A | 0.5 |
| B | 1.2 |
| C | 3.2 |

Calculate the concentrations of each of the unknown protein samples. Make all steps explicit in the generation of your answer, including where in the process the Beer-Lambert law is used.

8.5 (a) What can you learn about adsorbed protein using an ELISA assay?

(b) How do you modify a sandwich ELISA to provide information about a protein adsorbed on a biomaterial surface?

(c) You have two antibodies that are specific for two different regions of the protein that you are studying—one binds to the red region of the protein, the other to the green region. You test the adsorption of your protein to a biomaterial surface using a modified ELISA. In each of the cases illustrated here, would the red antibody bind to the protein, the green antibody bind to the protein, both bind to the protein, or neither bind to the protein? Briefly justify each of your answers.

The protein in solution:

The protein on the surfaces:

A    B    C    D

8.6 Make a list of advantages and disadvantages of all of the protein characterization techniques described in this chapter.

# References

1. K. C. Dee, D. A. Puleo, and R. Bizios, *An introduction to tissue-biomaterial interactions*. Hoboken: Wiley-Liss, 2002.
2. J. D. Andrade, *Surface and interfacial aspects of biomedical polymers: volume 2: protein adsorption*. New York: Plenum Press, 1985.
3. G. E. Schulz and R. H. Schirmer, *Principles of protein structure*. New York: Springer-Verlag, 1985.
4. R. B. Bird, W. E. Stewart, and E. N. Lightfoot, *Transport phenomena*, 2nd ed. New York: John Wiley and Sons, 2002.
5. T. A. Horbett, "Principles underlying the role of adsorbed plasma proteins in blood interactions with foreign materials," *Cardiovascular Pathology*, vol. 2, no. 3S, pp. 137S–148S, 1993.
6. "ELISA Results – Quantitative, Qualitative & Sensitivity," *Bio-Rad*. (Online). Available: https://www.bio-rad-antibodies.com/elisa-results-quantitative-semi-qualitative.html.
7. J. D. Andrade and V. Hlady, "Protein adsorption and materials biocompatibility: a tutorial review and suggested hypotheses," in *Biopolymers/Non-exclusion HPLC*, K. Dusek, C. G. Overberger, and G. Heublein, Eds. New York: Springer-Verlag, 1986, pp. 1–63.
8. R. K. Wierenga, "The TIM-barrel fold: a versatile framework for efficient enzymes," *FEBS Letters*, vol. 492, no. 3, pp. 193–8, Mar. 2001.
9. Y. Maeda et al., "High-performance liquid chromatographic determination of six p-hydroxybenzoic acid esters in cosmetics using Sep-Pak florisil cartridges for sample pre-treatment," *Journal of Chromatography*, vol. 410, no. 2, pp. 413–8, Dec. 1987.
10. A. Pyka and J. Sliwiok, "Chromatographic separation of tocopherols," *Journal of Chromatography A*, vol. 935, no. 1–2, pp. 71–6, Nov. 2001.
11. D. R. Appling, S. J. Anthony and C. K. Mathews, *Biochemistry: Concepts and Connections*, 2nd ed. Pearson Education Inc, 2019.
12. R. S. Vieira-Pires and J. H. Morais-Cabral, "3₁₀ helices in channels and other membrane proteins. *The Journal of General Physiology*, vol. 136, no. 6, pp. 585–592, 2010.

# Additional Reading

B. Alberts, A. Johnson, J. Lewis, M. Raff, K. Roberts, and P. Walter, *Molecular biology of the cell*, 4th ed. New York: Garland Publishing, 2002.

P. Atkins and J. de Paula, *Physical chemistry*, 8th ed. New York: W. H. Freeman, 2006.

T. A. Horbett, "Principles underlying the role of adsorbed plasma proteins in blood interactions with foreign materials," *Cardiovascular Pathology*, vol. 2, no. 3S, pp. 137S–148S, 1993.

J. A. Hubbell, "Matrix effects," in *Principles of tissue engineering*, 2nd ed., R. P. Lanza, R. Langer, and J. Vacanti, Eds. Austin: Academic Press, 2000, pp. 237–250.

J. Kuby, *Immunology*, 3rd ed. New York: W. H. Freeman, 1997.

F. Rouessac and A. Rouessac, *Chemical analysis: modern instrumental methods and techniques*. New York: John Wiley and Sons, 2000.

D. A. Skoog and J. J. Leary, *Principles of instrumental analysis*, 4th ed. Orlando: Saunders College Publishing, 1992.

D. Voet and J. G. Voet, *Biochemistry*, 2nd ed. New York: John Wiley and Sons, 1995.

# 9

# Cell Interactions with Biomaterials

**Main Objective**

To understand the components and important functions of eukaryotic cells, as well as methods to quantify how cells interact with the biomaterial environment.

**Specific Objectives**

1. To understand the basic components of a eukaryotic cell.
2. To understand the types of receptor–ligand interactions.
3. To compare and contrast properties of the major components of the extracellular matrix.
4. To understand how receptor signaling can result in changes in gene expression, which in turn can alter important cellular functions.
5. To distinguish among four major cellular functions.
6. To understand and use DLVO theory to model nonspecific interactions between cells and surfaces.
7. To understand and use basic equations describing receptor–ligand interactions to model specific interactions involved in cell adhesion.
8. To understand important parameters in models of cell migration.
9. To identify components that may affect cytotoxicity of a biomaterial.
10. To understand the theory behind and possible limitations to the cytotoxicity and cellular function assays/techniques presented.

## 9.1 Introduction: Cell-Surface Interactions and Cellular Functions

As discussed at length in the previous two chapters, biomaterial surface properties affect protein attachment and, in turn, the composition of the adsorbed layer dictates cell recruitment and attachment. Therefore, surface characteristics play a large role in the overall biological response to a material. In this chapter, we will explore cellular responses to surfaces and/or attached proteins. It is important to keep in mind that, while protein–surface interactions are often nonspecific, protein–cell interactions are, in many instances, specific, and usually occur via receptor–ligand interactions (see Section 9.2).

Regardless of the type of interaction, it is imperative to the success of the implant that the chosen biomaterial (and adsorbed proteins) support all the required functions of the attached (or neighboring) cells. Among these functions are the following:

1. Viability (all cell types, often associated with adhesion/spreading on a substrate)
2. Communication (all cell types)
3. Protein synthesis (all cell types)
4. Proliferation (some cell types)
5. Migration (some cell types)
6. Activation/differentiation (some cell types)
7. Programmed cell death (some cell types)

However, before we discuss in more detail how cell–substrate interactions can influence each of the above functions, we will first review the basic components of a cell and how these allow for communication with the extracellular environment.

## 9.2 Cellular Structure

There exists a wide variety of cell types in human tissues, with each type having different functions. Some cells' main action is secretion of soluble factors, others are electrically active, and still others act to destroy invading pathogens. Both **differentiated (committed)** and **non-differentiated (progenitor)** cells can be found in the body. Differentiated cells are those that have attained tissue-specific functions, while progenitor cells remain uncommitted and can **differentiate** (undergo a controlled series of changes, usually involving alterations in gene expression and protein synthesis) into a variety of cell types. Further discussion of the process of differentiation is found in Section 9.4.3.

All of these cells, however, have certain functions, and thus certain structural parameters, in common. The basic cellular components found in mammalian cells are described in this section and are summarized in Figure 9.1. A key aspect to maintaining cell viability is that each of the main cellular tasks is compartmentalized in a different **organelle**, which is usually bounded by a selectively permeable membrane. In many cases, several organelles work together to perform one of the functions found on the previous list (e.g., the nucleus, the endoplasmic reticulum/Golgi apparatus, and cellular vesicles all play a role in protein synthesis).

### 9.2.1 Cell Membrane

The cell is divided from its external environment by the **cell membrane,** a bilayered structure (Fig. 9.1) composed primarily of phospholipids. **Phospholipids** are molecules possessing a polar (hydrophilic) head group and a nonpolar (hydrophobic) tail composed of fatty acids. Figure 9.2 depicts both the chemical structure and the three-dimensional conformation of one of the phospholipids commonly found in the cell membrane. Because of the differences in polarity between the regions of the molecule, when exposed to an aqueous environment, the most thermodynamically stable structure for phospholipids is a bilayer wherein the hydrophobic tails are effectively "hidden" from the water and the polar head groups interact with the environment. (This is based on the same principles as self-assembly techniques described for surface modification in Chapter 7.)

As shown in Figure 9.1, the cell membrane also contains a number of proteins. Some of these have both hydrophilic and hydrophobic domains and thus can span the entire membrane (called **transmembrane proteins**), while others are anchored in

**Figure 9.1**
A mammalian cell showing the main cellular components: (a) the plasma cell membrane, (b) mitochondria, (c) Golgi apparatus, (d) cytoplasm, (e) lysosome, (f) cytoskeleton, (g) nucleus, (h) smooth endoplasmic reticulum, and (i) rough endoplasmic reticulum. The nucleus contains the nucleolus, an area where ribosomes are assembled. [Source: (a) Panaiotidi/ Shutterstock, (b) Aldona Griskeviciene/Shutterstock, (c) Sciencepics/Shutterstock, (f) Soleil Nordic/Shutterstock]

the cell membrane, but project primarily either into the extracellular or intracellular space. Many transmembrane proteins act as channels or pumps for specific molecules to maintain a well-defined chemistry within the cell. Transmembrane **channel proteins** do not bind to the transported molecules, but form small pores in the phospholipid bilayer to allow (usually) inorganic ions such as $Na^+$, $K^+$, $Ca^{2+}$, or $Cl^-$ to pass down their concentration gradients into or out of the cell. In contrast, transmembrane **carrier proteins** such as ion pumps physically bind to the molecule to be transported and often require an expenditure of energy to cause transport opposite the concentration gradient. A common example of this is the $Na^+/K^+$ pump that is required to maintain osmotic pressure and regulate cell volume.

Proteins projecting into the extracellular space are often receptors for specific extracellular molecules, and will be discussed later in this section (9.2.7). In addition, there are a number of carbohydrate-derived molecules covalently attached to

1-Stearoyl-2-oloeyl-3-phosphatidylcholine

(a)

(b)

**Figure 9.2**
(a) The chemical structure and (b) the three-dimensional conformation of one of the phospholipids commonly found in the cell membrane. (Image in (b) courtesy of Richard Pastor, NIH, Bethesda, MD.)

the cell surface to form the cell **glycocalyx**. The importance of this coating to the prevention of unwanted blood clotting is addressed in Chapter 13. The positions of the molecules within the membrane are not fixed, but, rather, are quite fluid, and the locations of specific molecules on the cell surface can easily be rearranged in response to external stimuli.

Maintenance of the integrity of the cell membrane is extremely important because it divides the aqueous environment outside the cell (extracellular space) from that within the cell (the **cytoplasm**). The cytoplasm has a unique chemical composition, which can be very different from that found outside the cell and which is crucial to cell survival. Additionally, the cell membrane is the point of contact between the extracellular and intracellular environments and therefore represents the main mechanism by which a cell communicates with other cells and its surroundings.

## 9.2.2 Cytoskeleton

A brief overview of cytoskeletal elements is given in this section, but the reader may consult resources at the end of the chapter for more extensive information. There are three general types of cytoskeletal elements: 6–8-nm-diameter **actin filaments**, 10-nm-diameter **intermediate filaments**, and 25-nm-diameter **microtubules** (Fig. 9.1). They are all protein-based structures that can be lengthened or shortened in response to cellular needs. Like the skeleton of the body, they impart shape to the cell and play a large role in cell motility. For example, they allow the extension of finger-like portions of the cell membrane called **pseudopodia** in response to external stimuli or as the first step in cell locomotion (see later sections of this chapter).

In addition to their contribution to cell structure, microtubules play a significant role in separation of duplicated DNA before cell division (see Section 9.4.2 for more on cell proliferation). Intermediate filaments also attach to a number of receptor proteins that project into the extracellular space and are therefore an important means for the cell to "translate" external signals (see Section 9.2.7).

### 9.2.3 Mitochondria

Several **mitochondria**, which produce energy for cellular functions via a process called oxidative phosphorylation, are usually found in each cell. They have a unique structure that involves two phospholipid membranes (Fig. 9.1). The **inner membrane** is highly folded to increase its surface area, and surrounds the **matrix space**. The matrix contains a mixture of enzymes to break down molecules such as glucose, while the final generation of energy through redox reactions culminating in oxidative phosphorylation occurs at the inner membrane. The **outer membrane** serves to separate the matrix and inner membrane from the rest of the cytoplasm.

The end product of oxidative phosphorylation is **adenosine triphosphate (ATP)**. This molecule is often called the "energy currency" of the cell since it can be transported to the area needed and then hydrolyzed to **adenosine diphosphate (ADP)**. This reaction is very exothermic, and the energy produced can be used to drive required cellular processes (such as pumping ions against a concentration gradient to maintain the proper chemistry in the cytoplasm). The ADP is then recycled back to the mitochondria, where it once again undergoes phosphorylation to ATP.

### 9.2.4 Nucleus

#### 9.2.4.1 Structure and Function of the Nucleus
The **nucleus** can be considered the control center for the cell, and it contains genetic information in the form of **deoxyribonucleic acid (DNA)** that is condensed into **chromatin**. The nucleus is separated from the rest of the cell by the **nuclear envelope**, which consists of two phospholipid membranes (Fig. 9.1). The outer membrane is contiguous with the endoplasmic reticulum (see Section 9.2.5) and is connected with the inner membrane at specific locations called **nuclear pores**. The pores are composed of proteins that form gates to allow only specific molecules in and out of the nucleus.

As shown in Figure 9.1, the nucleus also contains an area called the **nucleolus**, where ribosomes are assembled. Ribosomes are important to the process of protein assembly in the endoplasmic reticulum and are discussed further later in this chapter.

#### 9.2.4.2 Structure of DNA
Due to its particular structure, DNA carries thousands of information-containing elements called **genes**. In essence, DNA forms a template for all proteins synthesized by the cell. When a gene is **expressed**, the cell is actively producing the protein encoded by the gene. DNA remains in its condensed (or **supercoiled**) form in the nucleus, except in the areas where genes are being expressed to produce proteins. Additionally, before a cell divides, the DNA opens up to a less tightly coiled form so that it can be replicated.

**Figure 9.3**
A nucleic acid is composed of a phosphate group, a sugar and a base. Nucleic acids can be combined to create structures like DNA [5].

As mentioned in Chapter 8, genes contain **codons** that code for specific amino acids and thus determine the primary structure of a protein (see Section 9.4.4 for a more detailed description of how protein synthesis occurs). This is possible due to the unique structure of the DNA double helix. DNA is a polymer of **nucleic acid** subunits. As shown in Figure 9.3, each nucleic acid is composed of a phosphate

**BASES**

The bases are nitrogen-containing ring compounds, either pyrimidines or purines.

**Figure 9.4**
Schematic of the bases of DNA/RNA. These bases can be either single-ring structures (pyrimidines) or double-ring structures (purines). The two pyrimidine bases in DNA are thymine (T) and cytosine (C), while the two purine bases are adenine (A) and guanine (G). Uracil (U) replaces thymine in RNA [5].

group, a sugar and a base. In DNA, the bases can be either double-ring structures (the **purines**) or single-ring structures (the **pyrimidines**). As depicted in Figure 9.4, the two purine bases found in DNA are **adenine** (**A**) and **guanine** (**G**), while the two pyrimidine bases are **thymine** (**T**) and **cytosine** (**C**).

The nucleic acids are polymerized using a phosphodiester linkage to form the molecule seen in Figure 9.5. The 3′ and 5′ designate the carbon on each sugar that participates in the bonding and are used to indicate the orientation of the chain. As noted in the figure, the type of sugar present in DNA is the *deoxyribose sugar*, thus giving the molecule its name.

As discovered in the 1950s, the three-dimensional structure of DNA is a double helix in which the sugar and phosphate groups form a backbone, while the bases from each chain are directed toward the interior. This is very important, because it allows for hydrogen bonding between bases on opposite chains, with A bonding to T and G bonding to C (Fig. 9.6). To maximize base pairing, the two strands in DNA are antiparallel, so that one is aligned in the 3′ to 5′ direction, while its complementary strand is aligned in the 5′ to 3′ direction (Fig. 9.6).

A three-dimensional illustration of the structure of DNA is found in Figure 9.7. The right-handed double helix has approximately 10 base pairs per turn and is held

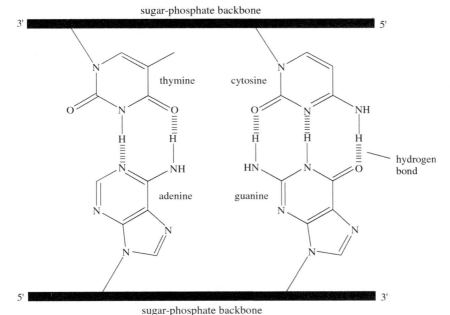

**Figure 9.5**
Sugar backbone of DNA. For DNA, the nucleic acids are polymerized using a phosphodiester linkage to form the molecule. The 3′ and 5′ designate the carbon on each sugar that participates in the bonding and indicates the orientation of the chain. The type of sugar is the deoxyribose sugar, thus giving the molecule its name [5].

**Figure 9.6**
Base–base interactions in DNA. The three-dimensional structure of DNA is a double helix in which the sugar and phosphate groups form a backbone, while the bases from each chain are directed toward the interior. This orientation is very important, because it allows for hydrogen bonding between bases on opposite chains (A bonds to T and G bonds to C). To maximize base pairing, the two strands in DNA are antiparallel, so that one is aligned in the 3′ to 5′ direction, while its complementary strand is aligned in the 5′ to 3′ direction [5].

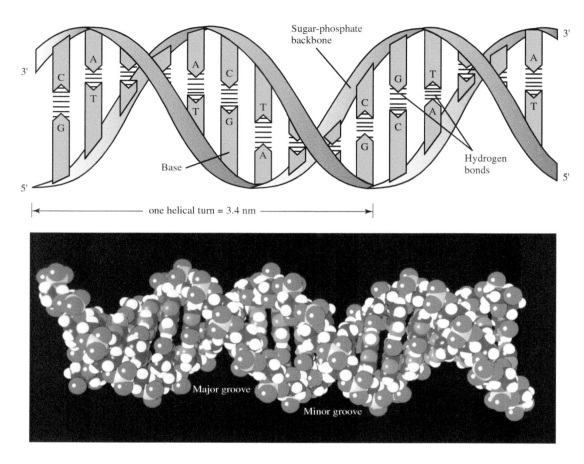

**Figure 9.7**
The chemical structure and three-dimensional conformation of DNA. ((a)[5] (b) Photo Researchers/Science History Images/Alamy Stock Photo.)

together predominately by hydrophobic interactions. Besides imparting additional structural stability through hydrogen bonds, the bases are the key to the genetic information found within DNA. A set of three bases comprises a codon for a specific amino acid and thus can be directly related to protein structure if the proper transcription and translation machinery is in place (see Section 9.4.4).

**9.2.4.3 Structure of RNA** In addition to DNA, some types of **ribonucleic acid (RNA)** are found in the nucleus. Although both molecules are polymers of nucleic acids and thus share many structural characteristics, there are several points in which RNA differs from DNA. From a chemical standpoint, the sugar in the backbone of RNA contains an additional oxygen (the ribose sugar, see Fig. 9.8), and the pyrimidine base thymine found in DNA has been replaced by **uracil (U)** in RNA (Fig. 9.4). However, probably the most striking difference between DNA and RNA is that, as depicted in Figure 9.9, RNA is single-stranded and therefore does not form a regular helical structure.

The purpose of RNA is to act as an intermediate for the genetic code found in DNA and direct protein synthesis. Three main types of RNA have been identified: **messenger RNA (mRNA)**, **transfer RNA (tRNA)**, and **ribosomal RNA (rRNA)**. Of these, mRNA is commonly found in the nucleus near expressed genes and rRNA

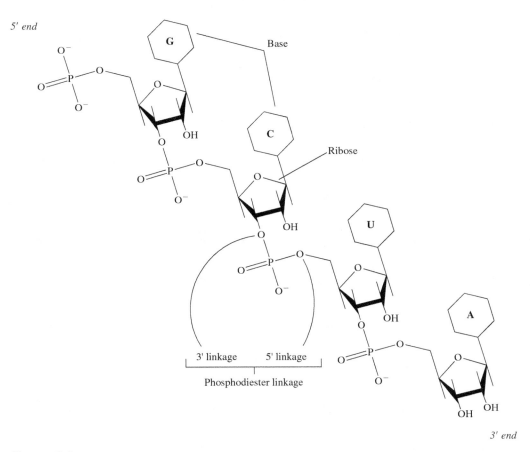

**Figure 9.8**
Sugar backbone of RNA. For RNA, the nucleic acids are polymerized using a phosphodiester linkage to form the molecule, just like in DNA. However, the type of sugar present in the backbone of RNA is ribose. (Adapted with permission from [5].)

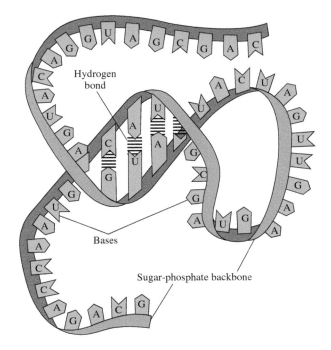

**Figure 9.9**
Structure of RNA. RNA is single-stranded and therefore does not form a regular helical structure [5].

may be temporarily located in the nucleolus as a part of ribosome synthesis. Each type of RNA and its contribution to protein production will be discussed further in subsequent sections of this chapter.

### 9.2.5 Endoplasmic Reticulum

As mentioned earlier, the outer membrane of the nuclear envelope is connected to the **endoplasmic reticulum** (**ER**) of the cell (Fig. 9.10). These long, flattened sheets made of phospholipid membranes are where protein synthesis occurs. The ER is generally divided into two separate but connected domains: the **rough ER**, which contains a large number of ribosomes on its external surface, and the **smooth ER**, which is more tubular in structure and includes no ribosomes.

**Ribosomes** are composed of two subunits containing rRNA and associated proteins, each of which is assembled in the nucleolus. In their final form, they are globular structures that catalyze the reaction in which mRNA, possessing the information derived from DNA, is used as a template to synthesize a particular protein (see Section 9.4.4 for more details).

After the protein is formed, it is released into the interior (**lumen**) of the rough ER where it is directed to the smooth ER and packaged into small phospholipid vesicles (see Section 9.2.6) for transport to the **Golgi apparatus** (Fig. 9.10). In the Golgi apparatus, the different proteins are further modified, sorted, and packaged for transport to their final destinations. In this manner, proteins can either be targeted to a certain organelle within the cell, or can be tagged for release into the extracellular space.

### 9.2.6 Vesicles

**Vesicles** containing proteins encased in a phospholipid bilayer are found throughout the cytoplasm, trafficking proteins from the ER to the Golgi, or from the Golgi to a target destination. If the proteins are to be secreted, the vesicles will join the cell membrane and release their contents in a process known as **exocytosis**. Vesicles are

**Figure 9.10**
Schematic of the endoplasmic reticulum (ER), which is responsible for protein synthesis. The rough ER, which contains a large number of ribosomes, is attached to the nuclear envelope. The rough ER transforms into the smooth ER away from the nucleus. Pieces of the ER will then split off and transfer to the Golgi apparatus, where the proteins created in the ER are further modified and transported to their final destinations [6].

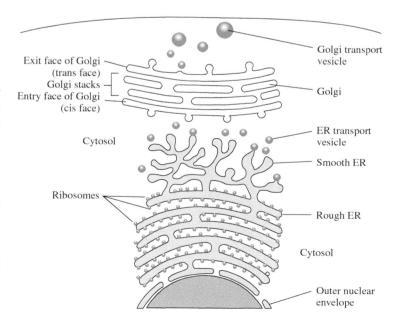

also important to the opposite process, **endocytosis**, where particles from the extra-cellular environment are taken in via infolding of the cell membrane. During endo-cytosis, specialized vesicles with digestive enzymes (**lysosomes**, see Fig. 9.1) may join with the newly formed endocytotic vesicle. Lysosomes are designed to help break down the ingested particles and are particularly important to the actions of granulo-cytes and neutrophils in the acute inflammatory response (see Chapter 10).

### 9.2.7 Membrane Receptors and Cell Contacts

Interactions between a cell and other cells or its extracellular environment can result in alterations in functions such as cell spreading, migration, communication, dif-ferentiation, and/or activation (Fig. 9.11). This is often referred to as *"outside-in"* signaling. Conversely, for a variety of reasons, the cell may secrete different mol-ecules or rearrange its contacts and thus change its extracellular environment (*"inside-out"* signaling). In either case, these cell–cell and cell–**extracellular matrix** (**ECM**) interactions are enabled by protein-based receptors on the cell membrane. In this section, we describe several categories of cell contacts as well as the receptors that facilitate them.

**9.2.7.1 Types of Cell Contacts**   As shown in Figure 9.12, cells can form various contacts with other cells. These include tight junctions, gap junctions, and desmo-somes. **Tight junctions** form when adjacent cell membranes adhere to each other, preventing even small molecules from passing between the cells. **Gap junctions** are small, hydrophilic channels created by a plaque-like structure that connects two dif-ferent cell membranes. **Desmosomes** are mechanical attachments of two cells, either in broad bands (**belt desmosomes**) or in specific spots (**spot desmosomes**). They are caused by the association of cadherin receptors on each cell.

Similarly, cells can be attached in various ways to the ECM. The most com-mon contacts are **hemidesmosomes** and **focal adhesions**. Both hemidesmosomes and focal adhesions have structures similar to the desmosome, but, here, the receptor

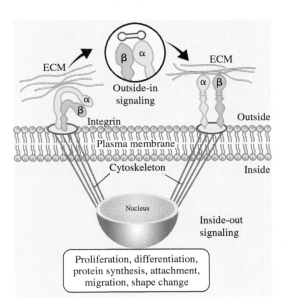

**Figure 9.11**
Cell interactions with the external environment can result in an alteration of cellu-lar function ("outside-in" sig-naling). Conversely, because of changes in cellular func-tions such as differentia-tion and migration, the cell may change its extracellular environment ("inside-out" signaling). All of these inter-actions are enabled by pro-tein-based receptors on the cell membrane, such as the integrins.

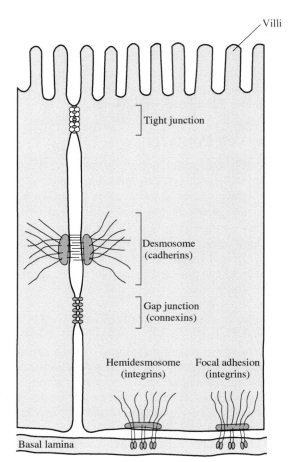

**Figure 9.12**
Schematic showing the different types of cell contacts in epithelial cells. Tight junctions, desmosomes, and gap junctions form as a part of cell–cell contacts, whereas hemidesmosomes and focal adhesions occur during cell-ECM contacts [5].

mediating the adhesion is of the integrin class (see Section 9.2.7.2). These interactions are indicative of strong adhesion to the ECM.

### 9.2.7.2 Types of Membrane Receptors and Ligands

The varied cellular interactions described earlier are facilitated by different cell membrane receptors, each of which is specific for a small range of target molecules (**ligands**). Some of the most common receptor molecules are grouped into the following categories:

1. Cadherins
2. Selectins
3. Mucins
4. Integrins
5. Other cell adhesion molecules (CAMs)

As mentioned previously, the transmembrane **cadherins** are responsible for cell–cell contacts in the form of desmosomes (Fig. 9.13). They undergo calcium-dependent **homophilic** binding (a cadherin molecule on one cell binds to a cadherin molecule on a second cell), while their cytoplasmic regions attach to intermediate filaments, thus linking the extracellular and intracellular environments.

Like cadherins, the **selectins** are involved in cell–cell binding, but selectins take part in **heterophilic** binding. Instead of binding to other selectins, these receptors are specific for certain carbohydrate groups present on target cell membranes. An illustration of selectin structure is found in Figure 9.14.

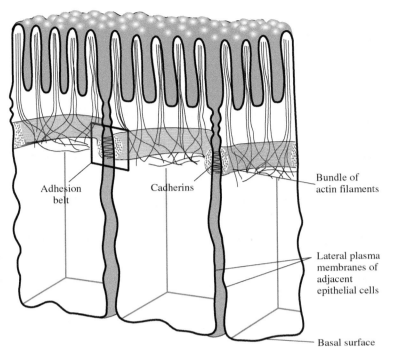

**Figure 9.13**
Location of cadherins in epithelial cells. Transmembrane cadherins are responsible for cell-cell contacts in the form of desmosomes. They undergo calcium-dependent homophilic binding (cadherin molecules on the two cells bind to each other), while their cytoplasmic regions attach to intermediate filaments, thus linking the extracellular and intracellular environments [5].

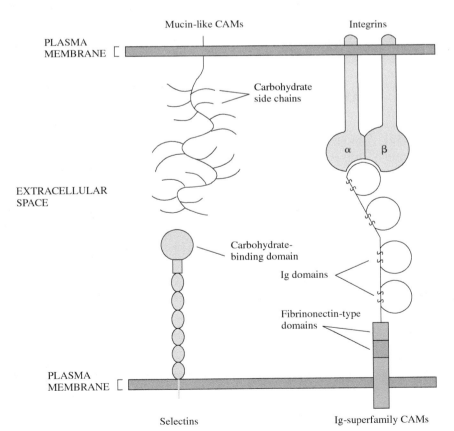

**Figure 9.14**
Various types of cell membrane receptors: mucins, integrins, selectins, and Ig-cell adhesion molecules (Ig-CAMs) [7].

**Mucins** are protein-based molecules that contain covalently bound carbohydrate moieties and, thus, present ligands for binding to selectins. As such, they are also involved in heterophilic cell–cell interactions. Mucin–selectin interactions (depicted in Fig. 9.14) play a large role in the early stages of white blood cell migration to sites of injury (see Chapter 10).

**Integrins** are transmembrane proteins involved in both cell–cell and cell–matrix contacts. These receptors are linked intracellularly to the intermediate filaments, thereby directly coupling extracellular binding events to cellular structure. As shown in Figure 9.14, these proteins are **heterodimers**, possessing two distinct subunits ($\alpha$ and $\beta$). There are variations in the composition of both the $\alpha$ and $\beta$ chains, and, therefore, different subunit combinations result in adhesion to different ligands. For example, some integrin receptors bind ECM proteins like collagen and thus form an important mediator of focal adhesions, as described previously. Other combinations of subunits lead to specificity for the cell adhesion molecules described in the following paragraph.

Other **cell adhesion molecules (CAMs)** comprise a large group of membrane proteins that mediate cell–cell interactions via both hetero- and homophilic binding. Many of these are considered part of the immunoglobulin (Ig) superfamily, based on the structure of the molecule. As indicated in Figure 9.14, CAMs interact with integrin receptors on neighboring cells. Like the mucin-selectin interactions, CAM–integrin binding is important in cell migration that occurs early in the inflammatory response (see Chapter 10).

While the receptors described earlier consist mainly of protein with a small amount of attached carbohydrate (sugar), other receptors contain only a small protein core and extensive amounts of attached carbohydrates. These molecules are called **proteoglycans** and their structure is described further in the following section. Proteoglycan receptors are important to a wide range of cell functions. An important one in cardiovascular tissues is the thrombomodulin receptor, which is expressed on cells that line blood vessels and aids in blood clotting (see Chapter 13).

## 9.3 Extracellular Environment

Contacts between a cell and the surrounding ECM are dynamic and crucial to cell survival. Alterations to the ECM, such as may occur during biomaterial implantation, can result in changes to the shape and/or function of neighboring cells. In addition, as key cell-matrix interactions are further understood, it may be possible to select important aspects of the ECM to include in new biomaterials in order to better direct the tissue response to the implant. This section describes in more detail the most common components of the ECM.

The ECM can be conceptualized as a fiber-reinforced matrix, with fiber-forming elements (collagen and elastin) surrounded by various space-filling molecules (glycoproteins and proteoglycans). This matrix also contains both free and sequestered soluble mediators, such as growth factors. We begin our discussion with the contributions of the fibrous proteins to the structure of the ECM.

### 9.3.1 Collagen

**Collagen** is the most abundant protein in mammals and is primarily responsible for tissue tensile strength. As shown in Figure 9.15, collagen is formed from a triple helix of polypeptide chains called $\alpha$ **chains**. Combinations of different $\alpha$ chains form the nearly 20 different collagen types now identified. The most common are the fibrillar collagens (Types I, II, and III), and, of these, Type I is the most abundant.

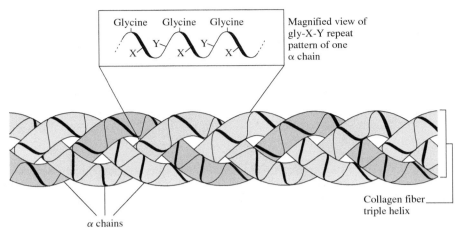

**Figure 9.15**
Schematic representation of three collagen α chains combining to form a collagen fiber triple helix. Each α chain has a unique color in this figure to facilitate visualization. It can be seen in the magnified view that each α chain is composed of alternating amino acids in a Gly-X-Y pattern.

Other collagens, such as Types IX and XII, are nonfibrillar but play an important role in the assembly of the fibers formed from Types I–III.

Examining Figure 9.15 in more detail, it can be seen that each α chain is composed of alternating amino acids in a Gly-X-Y pattern. Because glycine is the smallest amino acid, its position at every third residue allows for tight packing of the three chains in a helical conformation. Although X and Y can be any amino acids, they are often proline and hydroxyproline, respectively. As discussed in Chapter 8, the unique ring structure of proline causes kinks in the polypeptide chain, which, in this instance, is used to stabilize the helical structure.

Because the final collagen fibers are usually too large to be completely assembled within the cell, **procollagen** molecules are secreted into the extracellular space, where they undergo self-assembly into mature fibers. As illustrated in Figure 9.16,

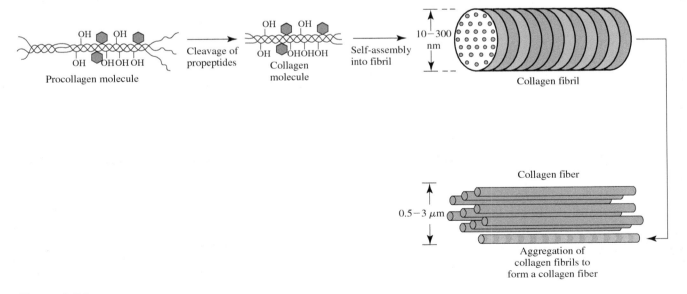

**Figure 9.16**
Assembly of collagen fibers. Because the final collagen fibers are usually too large to be completely assembled within the cell, the process occurs in stages both in the intracellular and extracellular environment. Procollagen molecules, which are created in the intracellular space, are secreted into the extracellular space, where they undergo self-assembly into mature fibers. Upon exiting the cell, small peptide sequences of the procollagen molecule are cleaved to allow for more efficient packing of the collagen molecules into fibrils (diameter 10–300 nm). Individual fibrils then further assemble into larger fibers (final diameter 0.5–3 μm) [5].

**Figure 9.17**
Diagram of elastin showing the relaxed and stressed states. Tensile forces cause the individual elastin molecules to unfold and align in the direction of loading. The network is held together by the crosslinks between the elastin molecules.

upon exiting the cell, small peptide sequences of the procollagen molecule are cleaved to allow for more efficient packing of the collagen molecules into **fibrils** (diameter 10–300 nm). Individual fibrils then further assemble into larger **fibers** (final diameter 0.5–3 μm). Fibrils and fibers are stabilized by the formation of lysine-lysine covalent crosslinks via the actions of the protein **lysyl oxidase.** Further information about the formation of collagen molecules can be found in Section 9.4.4.

Collagen molecules, particularly the fibrillar collagens, possess many of the same physical properties as other polymeric materials (discussed in Chapters 3–4). For example, if the crosslinking of collagen is prevented, the tensile strength of the material is significantly reduced because the fibers are allowed to slide past one another, much like the blocks of a semi-crystalline polymer undergoing tensile testing (see Fig. 4.17). Therefore, methods are currently being explored to increase the crosslinking of collagen to improve mechanical properties and handling characteristics for such applications as tissue engineering scaffolds and wound dressings.

## 9.3.2 Elastin

As mentioned in Chapter 4, **elastin** forms fibers that allow large elastic deformation at low stresses and that are responsible for the resiliency and extensibility of the ECM (Fig. 9.17). Elastin consists of a large number of hydrophobic amino acids (~85%), particularly valine (~15%). **Elastic fibers** consist of elastin as well as auxiliary (nonelastin) proteins, including lysyl oxidase, which creates a complex three-dimensional network by crosslinking lysine residues both within and between chains. Like with other rubbery materials, these covalent crosslinks are key to the elasticity of the fibers. As discussed in Chapter 4, thermodynamic considerations drive the return of elastin to its unstretched state and result in the unique mechanical properties of this ECM element.

### 9.3.3 Proteoglycans

Other (amorphous) components of the ECM include proteoglycans and glycoproteins. These molecules are important to the matrix structure due to their extensive interactions with water and other ECM elements. Although their names are similar, and both contain protein and carbohydrate constituents, **proteoglycans** can be considered mainly carbohydrate (glycan) with small amounts of attached protein, while **glycoproteins** are polypeptides having attached carbohydrate chains. (Glycoproteins are discussed further in the next section.)

Another major difference between glycoproteins and proteoglycans is that while the carbohydrates in glycoproteins are highly branched, the carbohydrates in proteoglycans take the form of long chains of polysaccharides (sugars) called **glycosaminoglycans (GAGs)**. The chemical structure of the polysaccharide component of the most common GAGs, including **hyaluronic acid (HA)**, **keratan sulfate (KS)**, **chondroitin/ dermatan sulfate (CS or DS)**, **heparan sulfate (HS)**, and heparin are found in Figure 9.18. Because of the large amount of negative charge present, especially on sulfated GAGs (KS, CS, and HS), these molecules attract and interact strongly with water. Therefore, in aqueous environments, they quickly form extended hydrated chains with hydrogel-like properties, which allows GAGs to be used *in vivo* for space filling and lubrication.

A proteoglycan molecule is composed of several GAGs attached to a single protein core. A typical proteoglycan is **aggrecan**, which is found in cartilage tissue. In aggrecan, as in other proteoglycans, KS and CS GAGs are attached to a protein core via specialized linkages with serine or threonine residues in the polypeptide chain. As depicted in Figure 9.19, this forms a bottle-brush structure, with each GAG molecule projecting away from the protein core.

Like KS and CS, proteoglycans containing heparan sulfate GAGs are also found in the ECM, where they are often used to interact with and retain soluble bioactive molecules (see Section 9.3.5). In addition, heparan sulfate is found on the surface of many mammalian cells. Heparan sulfate and its cousin heparin, which has a similar chemical structure (see Fig. 9.18), are best known for their anticoagulant properties (see Chapter 13). Thus, as discussed in Chapter 7, heparin-based surface coatings have been widely explored to improve blood compatibility of cardiovascular devices.

### 9.3.4 Glycoproteins

Although a variety of glycoproteins are found in the ECM, this section will focus on two representative molecules, fibronectin and laminin. Both of these, like many other glycoproteins, contain several repeating motifs as well as binding domains for cells or a number of ECM constituents. Glycoproteins are therefore often considered a type of "glue" to link various tissue components.

**Fibronectin** is composed of two peptide subunits held together by disulfide bonds (Fig. 9.20). Three distinct repeat motifs have been identified, as shown in the figure. Each subunit also possesses multiple binding sites for various ECM molecules, including collagen and CS. Fibronectin is particularly important because it contains a ligand for binding to certain integrin receptors on cells, thus facilitating formation of hemidesmosomes and focal adhesions. This glycoprotein also plays a role in blood coagulation since it possesses binding domains for both fibrin and heparin (see Chapter 13).

Like fibronectin, **laminin** also has multiple subunits. In this case, there are three disulfide-linked peptide chains (A, $B_1$, and $B_2$) that are arranged in a loosely woven, cross-like structure (Fig. 9.20). Also like fibronectin, a number of repeating motifs have been observed in laminin, as well as sites for binding to integrin receptors on the cell membrane and ECM molecules such as Type IV collagen.

(a) Hyaluronic Acid

(b) Keratan Sulfate

(c) Chondroitin/Dermatan Sulfate

(d) Heparin Sulfate

(e) Heparin

**Figure 9.18**

The chemical structure of (a) hyaluronic acid, (b) keratan sulfate, (c) chondroitin/dermatan sulfate, (d) heparan sulfate, and (e) heparin. For (a)–(c), "glcUA" denotes D-glucuronic acid, "glcNAc" denotes N-acetyl glucosamine, "gal" denotes D-galactose, and "idoUA" denotes L-iduronic acid. The dashed lines and asterisk in (c) denote the positions of the indicated elements for $-1,4-$ $idoUA-\alpha-1,3-$galNAc$-\beta-$ [8] and [9].

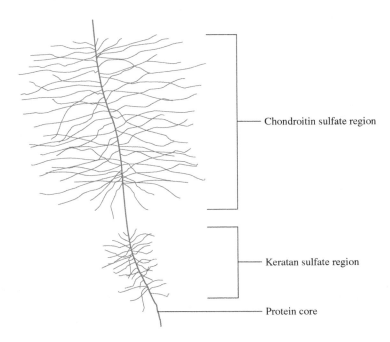

Chondroitin sulfate region

Keratan sulfate region

Protein core

**Figure 9.19**
Example of the bottle-brush structure of a large proteoglycan including areas of keratan sulfate and chondroitin sulfate that are attached to a protein core.

## EXAMPLE PROBLEM 9.1

As discussed in previous chapters, proteins often adsorb to biomaterial surfaces when implanted *in vivo* or exposed to serum-containing media *in vitro*. Many biomaterials do not support cell adhesion prior to the adsorption of a protein layer. How might proteins facilitate adhesion of cells to a biomaterial?

**Solution:** In the natural physiological environment, cells attach to other cells and elements of the extracellular environment. Many of these cell–cell and cell–extracellular matrix contacts are enabled by protein-based receptors on the cell membrane. These receptors are specific for binding with a limited range of target molecules. As many biomaterials are not native to the body, especially synthetic biomaterials, receptors specific for binding to these biomaterials generally do not occur naturally. However, receptors are naturally present for a large number of proteins. Thus, protein adsorption to a biomaterial can facilitate adhesion of cells that have receptors specific for the adherent proteins, and/or regions of the adherent proteins, assuming that the process of adsorption did not distort or sterically occlude the binding region of the protein. In this manner, cells that might not naturally adhere to a biomaterial may adhere by binding to a protein that is adsorbed to the material. ■

## 9.3.5 Other ECM Components

In particular cases, such as bone and teeth, there is deposition of *mineral crystals* between the collagen fibers in the ECM, imparting a significantly higher modulus to these tissues than others in the body. The localized deposition of these crystals, made from combinations of Ca and P ions, is tightly regulated by the cells inhabiting the region. Although the full regulation mechanism is not yet known, it has been discovered that both membrane vesicles and certain negatively charged ECM proteins, such as osteopontin and bone sialoprotein, among others, play important roles in this process.

Additionally, many tissues contain ECM proteins with motifs that interact specifically with key soluble mediators, such as growth factors. The result of these interactions is to *sequester* the soluble factor and store it until it is needed to stimulate a specific cellular function through binding to the proper cell membrane receptor.

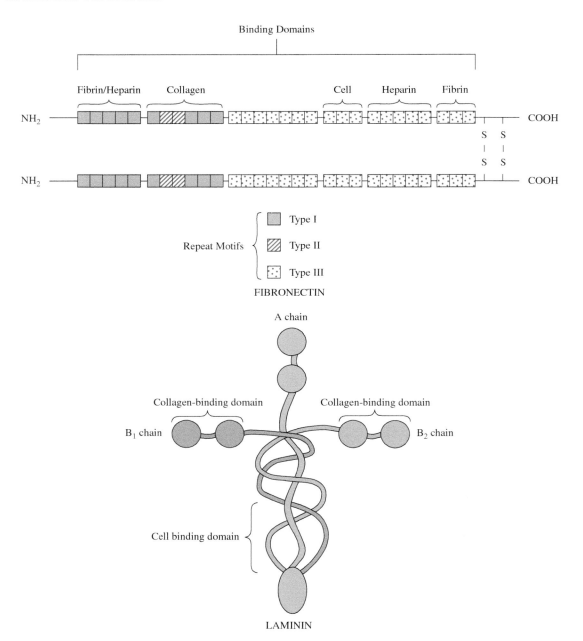

**Figure 9.20**
Structure of fibronectin and laminin. Fibronectin is composed of two peptide subunits held together by disulfide bonds. Three distinct repeat motifs (indicated by Type I, Type II, and Type III in the figure) have been identified in fibronectin. Laminin also has multiple subunits: three disulfide-linked peptide chains (A, $B_1$, and $B_2$) are arranged in a loosely woven, cross-like structure. Although not depicted here, within the laminin subunits repeat motifs can be observed, as in fibronectin.

Release of these soluble factors often occurs during matrix remodeling (see Section 9.3.6), when the cells digest part of the protein binding the bioactive molecule or as a part of matrix injury. In this way, cells can be directed to alter their functions in response to localized changes in their environment.

One specific example of this is the interaction of fibroblast growth factor (FGF) with heparan sulfate. In this case, not only does the HS retain the growth factor in the ECM, but for some cells, the presence of HS seems to be required to promote the actions of FGF, which, after binding to specific cell membrane receptors, usually causes cell proliferation. The high affinity of FGF for HS has been exploited in the design of biomaterials (often hydrogels) containing heparin or heparan sulfate. After loading these materials with FGF, they can be used as controlled delivery devices because the bound growth factor is only delivered upon degradation of the material and release of the heparin/HS fragments or via disruption of the ionic interactions between the HS and FGF.

### 9.3.6 Matrix Remodeling

The extracellular matrix is continually being **remodeled**. During this process, older components are digested and the amino acids recycled back into the cells for later use. Simultaneously, the cells synthesize new matrix molecules, which are further modified after being deposited extracellularly. The molecules responsible for most of these actions are a subset of proteins called enzymes, which catalyze specific reactions, either within the cell, or in the ECM. As mentioned earlier, the enzyme lysyl oxidase catalyzes crosslinking of collagen and elastin. Like other catalysts, enzymes act to promote certain reactions by lowering the required activation energy. In particular, these molecules function by bringing the reactants physically closer, and potentially weakening existing interactions, thus facilitating the formation of new bonds, or the breakage of bonds at specific points.

Enzymes are globular proteins with complex tertiary and quaternary structures. As shown in Figure 9.21, folding of the polypeptide chains results in a small pocket into which the molecule that is acted upon by the enzyme (the **substrate**) can insert. This cleft is called the **active site**, and is specific for a certain portion of the substrate. After the appropriate reaction has been catalyzed, the substrate or pieces of

**Figure 9.21**
The structure of an enzyme, in this case Q1999R *Bacillus subtilis* adenylate kinase (gray ribbons). The folding of the polypeptide chains results in a small pocket into which the molecule that is acted upon by the enzyme (the substrate, in this case bis-(adenosine)-5′-pentaphosphate, shown in the blue spheres) can insert. This pocket, called the active site, is specific for a certain portion of the substrate. After the appropriate reaction has been catalyzed, the substrate is released and the enzyme can bind to additional molecules to begin the process again. (Image courtesy of R. Couñago, J.S. Olson, Y. Shamoo, and J. Soman, Rice University.)

cleaved substrate are released and the enzyme can bind to additional molecules to begin the process again.

Matrix degradation in humans is primarily the result of the enzyme family called the **matrix metalloproteinases (MMPs)**. These molecules catalyze the cleavage of collagens and proteoglycans, among others. In healthy tissue, matrix remodeling is strictly regulated so that matrix degradation does not occur at a higher rate than the synthesis of new ECM molecules. One of the means to do this is through alterations in the localized concentrations of inhibitors of the MMPs, called **tissue inhibitors of metalloproteinases (TIMPs)**. Therefore, the relative concentrations of MMPs and TIMPs in a particular region will determine to what extent the ECM is degraded in that area.

### 9.3.7 ECM Molecules as Biomaterials

As mentioned in Chapter 1, many ECM molecules have been employed as biomaterials, particularly collagen and certain types of proteoglycans. These molecules, either with or without further chemical modification, have been used in a wide variety of tissues. It is also possible to utilize the entire intact ECM, rather than just one specific ECM molecule, to replace damaged tissue. Although unwanted immune responses are a potential problem with ECM-derived materials, decellularization and fixation procedures have been developed to reduce the risk of material "rejection." Examples of this type of biomaterial currently used in clinical procedures include decellularized bone grafts and decellularized heart valve replacements (see Chapter 14 for more about the problem of pathologic calcification of naturally derived tissue replacements).

### EXAMPLE PROBLEM 9.2

A researcher developed a synthetic hydrogel material for cartilage tissue engineering applications, but discovered that the material takes 200 years to degrade under physiological conditions *in vitro*. The researcher then developed a method to add a chemically reactive group to each end of gelatin (a type of denatured collagen), such that it can serve as a crosslinker in the hydrogel. The researcher subsequently showed that the gelatin crosslinker could be incorporated into the hydrogels at high weight percentages.

(a) A study was conducted to characterize the degradation of the hydrogel material *in vivo*. In one group (Group A), hydrogels containing the gelatin crosslinker were implanted for 12 weeks. Control hydrogels containing a nongelatin, nondegradable crosslinker were implanted for 12 weeks in Group B. The hydrogels from one group degraded completely over the course of the study, whereas the samples from the other group did not degrade at all. From which group do you suppose the samples degraded? Why?

(b) It was found that the concentration of tissue inhibitors of metalloproteinases (TIMPs) at the implantation site for one subject in Group A was an order of magnitude higher than that of the other subjects. Also, it was found that the degradation profile of the sample in this subject was different from the other samples in Group A. Did the sample in this subject degrade more rapidly or more slowly than the others from this group? Support your answer.

Solution:

(a) The samples from Group A likely degraded as they contained gelatin crosslinkers at high weight percentages. Thus, the majority of the hydrogel for samples in Group A was gelatin by weight. Recalling that gelatin is processed collagen and that collagen can be enzymatically degraded through the action of matrix metalloproteinases (specifically, collagenases), it follows that the gelatin crosslinkers can be degraded by the collagenases normally present in the physiological environment *in vivo*. Thus, the hydrogel likely degraded through the enzymatic cleavage of the gelatin crosslinkers, which were not present in samples from Group B.

(b) TIMPs inhibit the action of matrix metalloproteinases and are a natural regulator of remodeling of the extracellular matrix. It follows that the hydrogel sample from the subject in which high levels of TIMPs were detected degraded more slowly than the samples from the other subjects in Group A, as the enzymatic degradation of the gelatin crosslinkers in the hydrogel was impeded by the higher concentration of TIMPs.   ■

## 9.4 Cell–Environment Interactions That Affect Cellular Functions

A cell's microenvironment, including localized cell–cell and cell–ECM contacts, is extremely important because these interactions can result in alterations of cellular functions via complex intracellular pathways. Examining a more detailed picture of cell–environment interactions (Fig. 9.11), the binding of ECM molecules to integrin receptors to form focal adhesions causes changes in the cytoskeleton that ultimately affect gene expression in the nucleus. Similarly, cells also possess receptors for soluble mediators, such as growth factors, that can act through a cascade of intracellular factors (**secondary messengers**) to alter gene expression. The effects of soluble factors are particularly important in the immune and inflammatory responses to biomaterials, as described in Chapters 10–12.

Alterations in gene expression can affect the four major cellular functions—cell viability, proliferation, differentiation, and protein synthesis—as well as other functions like communication. The pathways involved in these cellular functions that may be regulated by cell–environment interactions are described in this section, while cell migration is addressed in the following section. Specific examples of how these processes may be altered by changes in the extracellular environment due to biomaterials implantation are found in subsequent chapters.

### 9.4.1 Cell Survival

In extreme cases, changes in the extracellular environment can result in cell death, either through the more traditional necrosis, or via a type of programmed cell death termed **apoptosis**. This can occur due to general changes in the chemistry of the surroundings (e.g., decrease in pH), or due to the presence of a specific factor that binds to the cell membrane to expressly direct cell death (more common for apoptosis).

**Necrosis** is a series of changes in cell structure, including increased permeability of the membrane and a leakage of important intracellular enzymes, eventually resulting in cell lysis (disintegration). Microscopically, this type of cell death is characterized by cell swelling and a disintegration of organelles. The area is cleared when expired cells are phagocytosed (consumed) by inflammatory cells (see Chapter 10).

In contrast, apoptosis involves a series of more controlled changes that can also be observed microscopically. Important characteristics include cell shrinkage, the formation of cytoplasmic buds and finally, fragmentation into **apoptotic bodies** comprised of vesicles containing small groups of organelles. These vesicles are then phagocytosed by neighboring cells, and, unlike necrosis, no inflammatory response is initiated. This type of cell death is particularly important in embryogenesis and development, as well as in the deletion of autoreactive immune cells, discussed further in Chapter 12.

### 9.4.2 Cell Proliferation

Although the events governing the cell cycle are not completely understood, the presence of the proper extracellular environment (e.g., enough "space") is an important factor in determining whether a cell will divide at a given time. Cells can be classified as labile, permanent, or stable, depending on their propensity for proliferation.

**Labile** cells replicate continuously, while **permanent** cell types are terminally differentiated (see next section) and have lost the ability to divide. **Stable** cells fall somewhere between these two extremes. After one division, they take on a specific function, but they can be induced by cues, such as the loss of nearby cells, to reenter the cell cycle and proliferate.

**9.4.2.1 Cell Cycle: Interphase**   Each of these cell types and their relation to the cell cycle is depicted in Figure 9.22. The cell cycle is divided into **mitosis (M phase)**, when the cell divides, and **interphase** (phases $G_1$, S and $G_2$), in which cellular DNA and organelles are replicated in preparation for mitosis. The $G_1$ **phase** is considered a time of general cell growth and fabrication of additional organelles, including an increase in the size of the cell membrane. During the **S phase**, the nuclear DNA is replicated. This is followed by the $G_2$ **phase**, in which proteins and structures enabling cell division are assembled.

Instead of $G_1$, stable cells may enter a $G_0$ **phase** and be considered **quiescent** (resting). During this period, these cells do not increase in size or replicate their organelles, but, rather, perform a specific function within a tissue. As discussed above, particular stimuli may encourage them to return to the cycle at $G_1$ and continue replication.

**9.4.2.2 Cell Cycle: Mitosis**   After the $G_2$ phase is completed, the cell is ready to begin mitosis (M phase). Mitosis is subdivided into several characteristic periods, illustrated in Figure 9.23(a):

1. Prophase
2. Metaphase
3. Anaphase
4. Telophase

**Figure 9.22**
Diagram of the typical cell cycle. The cell cycle is divided into mitosis (M phase), when the cell divides, and interphase (phases $G_1$, S, and $G_2$), in which cellular DNA and organelles are replicated in preparation for mitosis. The $G_1$ phase is a time of general cell growth and fabrication of additional organelles. During the S phase, the nuclear DNA is replicated. In the $G_2$ phase the proteins and structures enabling cell division are assembled. Instead of $G_1$, stable cells may enter a $G_0$ phase and be considered quiescent (resting). During this period, these cells do not increase in size or replicate their organelles, but, rather, perform a specific function within a tissue.

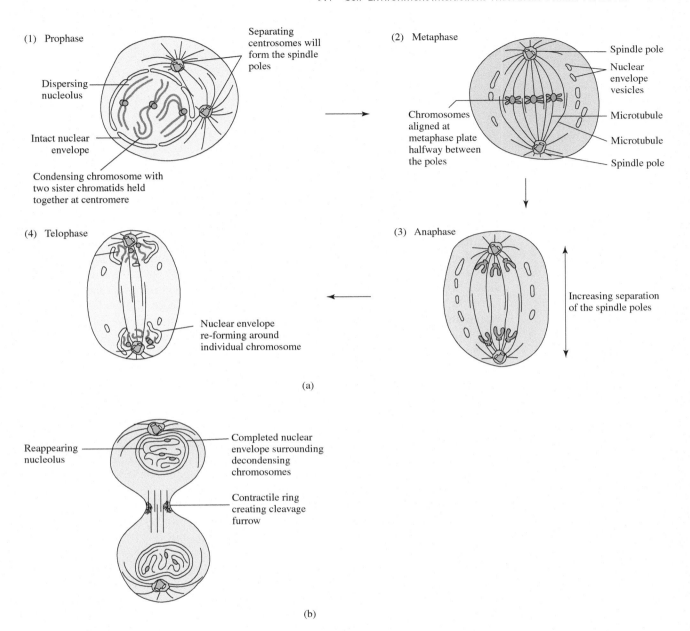

(1)  Prophase

Dispersing nucleolus

Intact nuclear envelope

Condensing chromosome with two sister chromatids held together at centromere

Separating centrosomes will form the spindle poles

(2)  Metaphase

Chromosomes aligned at metaphase plate halfway between the poles

Spindle pole

Nuclear envelope vesicles

Microtubule

Microtubule

Spindle pole

(4)  Telophase

Nuclear envelope re-forming around individual chromosome

(3)  Anaphase

Increasing separation of the spindle poles

(a)

Reappearing nucleolus

Completed nuclear envelope surrounding decondensing chromosomes

Contractile ring creating cleavage furrow

(b)

**Figure 9.23**
(a) Mitosis is subdivided into four main characteristic periods: prophase, metaphase, anaphase, and telophase. Prophase is marked by the dissipation of the nucleolus and formation of the mitotic spindles. During metaphase, the chromosomes are aligned between the two mitotic spindles. Anaphase is the period when the chromosomes are pulled apart by the spindle microtubules and arrange themselves at the spindle poles. Telophase is the period of time when the nuclear envelope begins to reform and the cell starts to undergo cytokinesis. (b) Cytokinesis, the division of the cytoplasm, occurs after mitosis and consists of the development of a cleavage furrow and eventual separation into the two daughter cells [5].

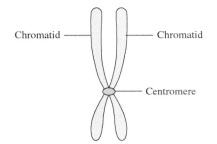

**Figure 9.24**
Schematic of a chromosome, which consists of two chromatids and a centromere [10].

Chromatid — — Chromatid

Centromere

The transition from $G_2$ to **prophase** is marked by the dissipation of the nucleolus and condensation of chromatin in the nucleus into **chromosomes** (Fig. 9.24). After replication in the S phase, each chromosome contains two identical sister **chromatids**. After mitosis, one chromatid of each chromosome will be found in the nucleus of one of the daughter cells. The separation of two pairs of centrosomes with their attached microtubules is also observed outside the nuclear envelope. These will form the **mitotic spindle**, necessary for equally dividing the chromosomes in later phases of mitosis.

As the cell moves into the next stage of mitosis, **metaphase**, the nuclear envelope disintegrates and the spindle microtubules can now attach directly to the chromosomes. This portion of mitosis is sometimes called **prometaphase**. After attachment to the mitotic spindle, the chromosomes are tugged back and forth in the cell until they align near the equator of the cell (Fig. 9.23(a)). This alignment marks the end of metaphase.

**Anaphase** begins abruptly when the sister chromatids are pulled apart by the spindle microtubules and visibly separate (Fig. 9.23(a)). Each chromatid (now called a chromosome) then travels toward the closest spindle pole (centrosome). Simultaneously, the cell begins to elongate, producing more distance between poles.

In the last stage of mitosis, **telophase**, the divided chromosomes have reached their respective poles and the spindle microtubules begin to disassemble (Fig. 9.23(a)). The nuclear envelope reforms and the nucleolus reappears. **Cytokinesis**, or division of the cytoplasm, usually begins in anaphase and ends after telophase (Fig. 9.23(b)). This process is characterized by a slow infolding of the plasma membrane around the center of the cell (the cleavage furrow) and results in two separate daughter cells with cytoplasmic constituents identical to that of the parent cell.

### 9.4.3 Cell Differentiation

As mentioned earlier in the chapter, in many tissues, there exists a type of **stem cell**. The definition of a stem cell is that it must possess the capability to self-renew as well as produce differentiated cells. **Differentiated** or **committed** cells usually perform a particular function within a tissue. They may be labile, stable, or permanent, but can only reproduce their own cell type. Stem cells can be categorized as **unipotent** (producing only one type of differentiated cell), **multipotent** (producing several differentiated cell types), or **toti-potent** (producing all cell types found in the body).

**Embryonic stem cells (ESCs)**, derived from the inner cell mass of the blastocyst stage of embryos, have not yet been committed to a certain type of tissue. Thus, ESCs are generally considered totipotent or **pluripotent** (producing most cell types found in the body). In the past decade, another type of pluripotent cell, the **induced pluripotent stem cell (iPSC)** has been developed, in which committed cells have been genetically reprogrammed to become pluripotent. While there are now a number of ways in which this process is done, often involving delivery of DNA, RNA, or protein into the cell, it is thought that reactivation of particular genes (Oct4, Sox2, etc.) that are normally silenced during development is key to formation of iPSCs.

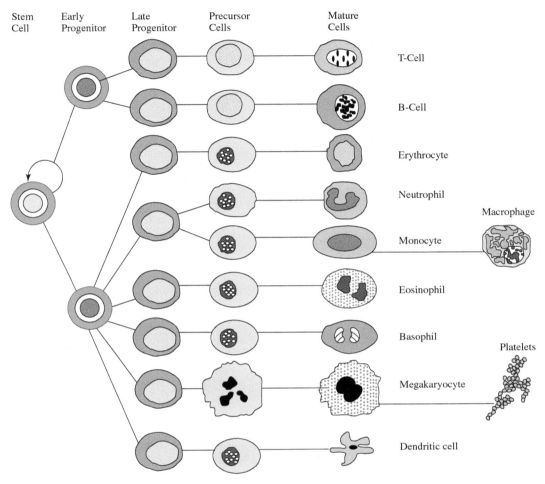

**Figure 9.25**
Production of blood cells from a hematopoietic stem cell. The stem cell can either replicate itself (curved arrow), or differentiate into various cell types [11].

In contrast, **adult stem cells** are isolated from the adult and are generally considered to be either multi- or unipotent, depending on the source. Two common examples of multipotent adult stem cells are found in the bone marrow: **hematopoietic stem cells** form both red and white blood cells (Fig. 9.25), while **mesenchymal stem/stromal cells** may differentiate into cells from various connective tissues (such as bone, cartilage and tendon/ligament) (Fig. 9.26).

When stem cells (either pluripotent or totipotent) are required to differentiate (such as to regenerate tissue that has been lost due to injury), they undergo a controlled set of changes, usually involving alterations in gene expression and levels of protein synthesis, which result in transformation of their **phenotype**. A cell's phenotype refers to its observable characteristics, including its **morphology**, or cell shape, as well as quantifiable parameters, such as production of a specific protein.

It has been found that these differentiation stages can be initiated and controlled by soluble and insoluble elements from the extracellular environment, including both chemical and mechanical factors, through binding to transmembrane receptors on the cell surface. Understanding these stimuli and incorporating them into the design of novel biomaterials is a focus of much current research, especially in the field of tissue engineering.

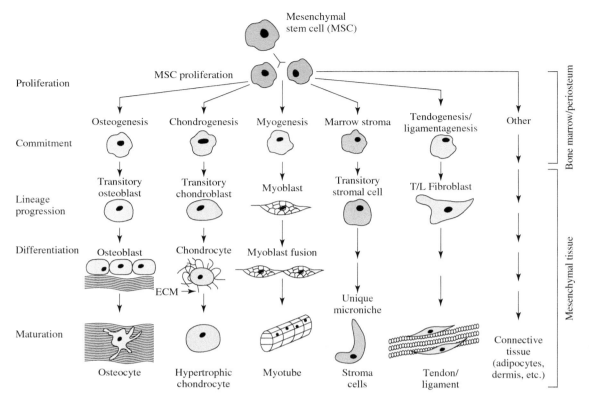

**Figure 9.26**
Mesenchymal stem/stromal cells (MSCs) have the potential to differentiate through a number of different pathways (as shown) to form mesenchymal tissues such as bone, cartilage, muscle, tendon, ligament, and adipose tissue. The MSCs can proliferate to produce additional MSCs, or they can commit to a specific lineage for tissue-specific differentiation. The commitment and progression of an MSC to and through a specific lineage involves the action of bioactive molecules, such as growth factors and cytokines. In the process of differentiation and maturation the cell increases its production of tissue-specific molecules. Terminally differentiated cells, such as osteocytes, may alter their levels of synthesis of matrix molecules to play an increased role in tissue maintenance or homeostasis. (Adapted with permission from [12].)

### 9.4.4 Protein Synthesis

In addition to affecting cellular differentiation, receptor-ligand binding can cause changes in the function of committed cells, which, like differentiation, is usually associated with alterations in the amount or type of protein synthesized. For example, protein production is important in cellular functions such as communication and activation, as well as in the creation and remodeling of the ECM surrounding the cell.

The general steps that are required to create and secrete a protein starting from its genetic code are described in this section. As an example, we will focus on the production of an important extracellular matrix protein, collagen (see Section 9.3.1). An overview of this process is given in Figures 9.27 and 9.28.

**9.4.4.1 Collagen Synthesis: Transcription**   Collagen synthesis begins when the portion of chromatin coding for collagen becomes less compact, allowing enzymes that "unzip" the double helix to separate the DNA strands. These enzymes, called **RNA polymerases**, then synthesize linear mRNA strands that are complementary to the collagen gene on the DNA using the base-pairing technique described previously (Fig. 9.29). This process is **transcription**. (A similar process occurs during replication of the chromatin before cell division, but in this case the new molecules generated

**Figure 9.27**
Block diagram of the steps for the creation and modification of proteins.

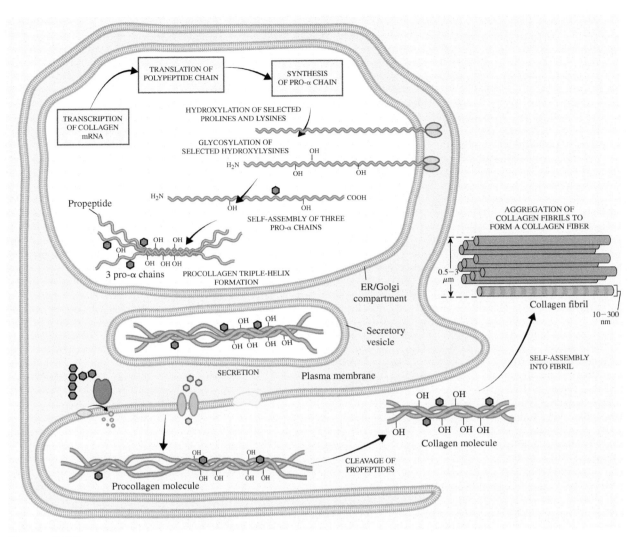

**Figure 9.28**
Summary of the steps of collagen synthesis. Transcription, translation, synthesis to create the $\alpha$-chain, and the joining of three of these chains to create the collagen triple helix occur within the cell. The procollagen molecule is then secreted and assembled into fibrils and finally fibers.

are complementary DNA strands and the enzymes that form them are **DNA polymerases**.) The rate of this transcription can be controlled by DNA-binding proteins collectively called **transcription factors** that can act as promotors (by helping to recruit RNA polymerases) or repressors (by reducing RNA polymerase binding).

The linear, single-stranded mRNA molecules can be 1,000 to 10,000 bases long and contain the complement to the DNA code. For example, if a base sequence in DNA was CCAGGA, the corresponding mRNA bases would be GGUCCU. Since three bases form the codon for a specific amino acid, in this example, this section of mRNA (and thus DNA) would code for glycine (GGU codon on mRNA) and proline (CCU codon on mRNA). The entire list of mRNA codons is found in Figure 9.30. After fabrication, the mRNA strand moves out of the nucleus through nuclear pores and into the ER.

### 9.4.4.2 Collagen Synthesis: Translation and Post-Translational Modification
Once in the ER, another type of RNA, tRNA, is required in addition to the mRNA. tRNA is also single-stranded, but it is folded into a complex "hairpin" structure that is stabilized by base pairings within the molecule (Fig. 9.31). tRNAs act as adaptor

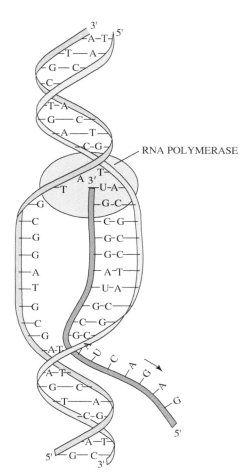

**Figure 9.29**
Schematic showing the transcription process on a separated DNA stand. RNA polymerase (shaded region) is responsible for "unzipping" the strand and synthesizing the linear mRNA strand [10].

| 1st position (5' end) ↓ | 2nd position | | | | 3rd position (3' end) ↓ |
| --- | --- | --- | --- | --- | --- |
| | **U** | **C** | **A** | **G** | |
| **U** | Phe | Ser | Tyr | Cys | U |
| | Phe | Ser | Tyr | Cys | C |
| | Leu | Ser | STOP | STOP | A |
| | Leu | Ser | STOP | Trp | G |
| **C** | Leu | Pro | His | Arg | U |
| | Leu | Pro | His | Arg | C |
| | Leu | Pro | Gln | Arg | A |
| | Leu | Pro | Gln | Arg | G |
| **A** | Ile | Thr | Asn | Ser | U |
| | Ile | Thr | Asn | Ser | C |
| | Ile | Thr | Lys | Arg | A |
| | Met | Thr | Lys | Arg | G |
| **G** | Val | Ala | Asp | Gly | U |
| | Val | Ala | Asp | Gly | C |
| | Val | Ala | Glu | Gly | A |
| | Val | Ala | Glu | Gly | G |

**Figure 9.30**
List of mRNA codons [5].

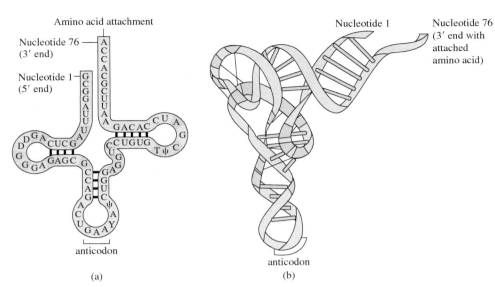

Amino acid attachment

Nucleotide 76 (3′ end)

Nucleotide 1 (5′ end)

anticodon

(a)

Nucleotide 1

Nucleotide 76 (3′ end with attached amino acid)

anticodon

(b)

**Figure 9.31**
(a) Schematic representation of the "hairpin" structure of tRNA. (b) Actual three-dimensional conformation of tRNA. The anticodon consists of three bases that act as binding sites for the mRNA, while the opposite end serves as an attachment point for the amino acid that matches the anticodon [5].

molecules and possess binding sites for a specific amino acid on one end and the mRNA molecule on the other. The binding site for the mRNA is a series of three bases known as the **anticodon**. The anticodon is complementary to the mRNA code for that particular amino acid. In the above example, a tRNA containing glycine and the anticodon CCA could bind to the first part of the mRNA molecule, followed by a second tRNA containing proline and the anticodon GGA (Fig. 9.32). Note that the anticodons are similar to the original DNA sequence, except for the use of U instead of T.

The actual process of protein assembly has three stages: initiation, elongation, and termination. It requires the presence of ribosomes located on the external surface of the rough ER (Fig. 9.33). In the **initiation** stage, the smaller ribosomal subunit binds to a specific codon (a **start codon**) on the mRNA and this promotes the attachment of the second, larger ribosomal subunit. As shown in Figure 9.34(a), there are two distinct domains on the ribosome: the **P site** binds the growing peptide, while the **A site** contains the next amino acid to be added to the chain.

During the **elongation** phase, two tRNA molecules, one in the P site and one in the A site on the ribosome, are bound to the mRNA (Fig. 9.34(b)). The ribosome catalyzes the formation of a peptide bond between the amino acids and the tRNA

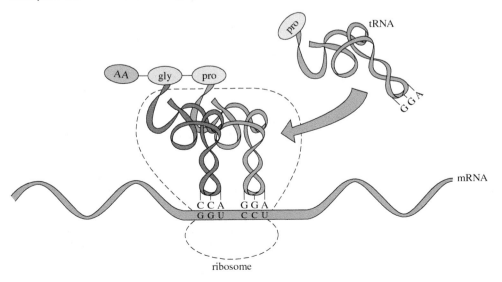

pro

tRNA

AA   gly   pro

GGA

mRNA

CCA   GGA
GGU   CCU

ribosome

**Figure 9.32**
Addition of proline to a growing peptide chain. The tRNA carrying the proline and exhibiting an appropriate anticodon (GGA) is able to bind to the codon (CCU) of the mRNA. The proline is then attached to the glycine residue via a peptide bond.

**Figure 9.33**
Diagram of collagen pro α-chain synthesis. The ribosomes bind to the mRNA, and the pro α-chain is formed and then released into the ER lumen after translation [6].

in the P site is released. The tRNA previously in the A site moves to the P site and a third tRNA molecule attaches in the newly open A site. A peptide bond again forms and the process is repeated.

When the ribosome reaches particular codons on the mRNA (**termination codons**) that are recognized by release factors, protein synthesis is **terminated**. The polypeptide chain is cleaved from the last tRNA and the tRNA is released (Fig. 9.34(c)). The release factor then initiates the dissociation of the ribosomal subunits. The entire process of converting the codons from the mRNA to a polypeptide chain is called **translation**.

After translation is completed, the protein, now a fully formed collagen pro-α chain, moves into the ER lumen (Fig. 9.33). Further **post-translational processing** in the ER and Golgi, illustrated in Figure 9.28, results in the association of three pro-α chains to form a procollagen molecule. As discussed in Section 9.3.1, additional reactions occur after procollagen secretion into the ECM to further stabilize the triple-helical structure, and eventually, fibril and fiber assembly.

## EXAMPLE PROBLEM 9.3

Some approaches for tissue regeneration involve the application of a biomaterial to deliver bioactive factors to promote a specific biological response. For instance, some strategies involve the delivery of the protein Bone Morphogenetic Protein-2 (BMP-2) to promote local bone formation. Several researchers, however, are developing methods to deliver DNA specifically engineered to contain the gene encoding BMP-2 in addition to sequences that promote expression of the gene. One approach to deliver the DNA to the cell is to complex it with a polycationic polymer, such as poly(ethylenimine). Another approach is to encapsulate the DNA within phospholipid microspheres.

(a) In terms of structural stability and duration of bioactive effect, what are the potential advantages of delivering DNA that encodes a therapeutic protein, rather than delivering the protein directly?
(b) Discuss the mechanism of complexation of DNA with a polycationic polymer. If the complex carries a net positive charge, how might this facilitate cellular entry of the DNA?
(c) Discuss a possible mechanism of cellular entry of lipid-encapsulated DNA.
(d) Is cellular entry of the DNA alone sufficient for protein expression, or must the DNA enter a specific part of the cell for expression? If it must reach a specific part of the cell, name that part.

Solution:

(a) Proteins generally require maintenance of a complex three-dimensional structure to retain biological activity. As discussed in previous chapters, this overall structure includes the primary, secondary, tertiary, and quarternary structure of the protein. The structure of the protein is highly susceptible to environmental factors, such as the pH of the solution

(a) Initiation

(b) Elongation

(c) Termination

**Figure 9.34**

Diagram of the translation process. There are three main stages: initiation, elongation, and termination. (a) In the initiation stage, the smaller ribosomal subunit binds to a specific codon (a start codon) on the mRNA and this promotes the attachment of the second, larger ribosomal subunit. (b) During the elongation phase, two tRNA molecules, one in the P site (which binds the growing peptide) and one in the A site (which contains tRNA with the next amino acid to be added to the chain), are bound to the mRNA. The ribosome catalyzes the formation of a peptide bond between the amino acids and the tRNA in the P site is released. The tRNA previously in the A site moves to the P site and a third tRNA molecule attaches in the newly open A site. This process then repeats. (c) When the ribosome reaches particular codons on the mRNA (termination codons) that are recognized by release factors, protein synthesis is terminated. The polypeptide chain is cleaved from the last tRNA and the tRNA is released. The release factor then initiates the dissociation of the ribosomal subunits [10].

and the presence of enzymes. In the extracellular environment, proteins can be degraded by the action of enzymes and the effects of pH, such as the acidic pH of the wound-healing environment. DNA is generally more stable than proteins, and it depends, primarily, on its sequence of bases, for maintenance of function. The double-stranded structure of DNA is driven by the hydrophobic effect to have the negatively charged phosphate backbone exposed to the (aqueous) solution, while the ring structures of the nucleotides form stabilizing hydrogen bonds in the interior of the double helix. Thus, DNA is generally more structurally stable than proteins in the aqueous physiological environment, and consequently, it is generally better able to maintain bioactivity than proteins can. In terms of duration of bioactive effect, proteins are only effective as long as they are present in a bioactive form. As therapeutic proteins are degraded and cleared from the target site, additional proteins must be delivered to maintain the desired biological effect with time. DNA, however, can be expressed to form the protein of interest. As it is essentially a blueprint for protein production, many copies of a protein can be produced from one gene. The protein expression can potentially continue in a cell as long as the cell and the DNA are viable. Thus, plasmid DNA presents the potential for a sustained bioavailability of the desired therapeutic protein when compared to delivery of the protein itself.

(b) DNA is a polyanionic macromolecule due to the negative charges of the phosphate groups along the backbone of the DNA. As a result, polycationic polymers can form electrostatic complexes with plasmid DNA in proper conditions through charge–charge interaction of the negative DNA and the positive polymer. If the complex carries a net positive charge, the positive charge can potentially interact with the negatively charged cell membrane through electrostatic attraction. This electrostatic interaction of the complex with the cell membrane may facilitate cellular entry of the DNA, as DNA alone would likely be repelled by the cell membrane (due to negative charges repelling each other).

(c) The cell membrane is composed of a dynamic and fluid phospholipid bilayer. If DNA is encapsulated in microspheres composed of comparable phospholipids, the phospholipids of the microsphere could potentially approach and fuse with the cell membrane, thereby transferring the DNA cargo into the interior of the cell.

(d) Cellular entry of DNA alone is not sufficient for gene expression. The DNA must enter the nucleus to be expressed. DNA in the nucleus of a cell can be transcribed to messenger RNA (mRNA). Translation of the mRNA to the encoded protein subsequently occurs outside the nucleus with the assistance of ribosomal RNA (rRNA) and transfer RNA (tRNA). ∎

# 9.5 Models of Adhesion, Spreading, and Migration

Besides affecting cell viability, proliferation, differentiation, and protein synthesis, cell-ECM interactions have a large impact on the degree of cell adhesion and migration across/through a substrate. These aspects of cell function must be considered in biomaterial design in order to ensure implant integration and prevent unwanted scarring around the device.

The steps involved in cellular adhesion and migration have been extensively studied for a variety of cell types. These experiments have given us a better understanding of the role of membrane receptors and the cytoskeleton in these processes, and have allowed for the development of a number of increasingly complex mathematical models for adhesion, spreading, and migration. Key aspects of simple models for these processes are reviewed here.

## 9.5.1 Basic Adhesion Models: DLVO Theory

A basic model for cell adhesion to a surface is centered on **DLVO theory,** based on work from **D**erjaguin, **L**andau, **V**erway, and **O**verbeek. First developed to explain coagulation of charged colloidal particles, this theory is based on thermodynamic

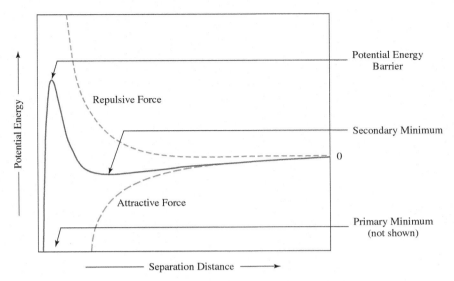

**Figure 9.35**
Particle adhesion modeled with DLVO theory. The graph depicts the free energy of interaction as a function of separation distance. As a particle approaches a surface, there is a drop in potential energy, which represents a balance between long-range electrostatic interactions (repulsive) and long-range van der Waals interactions (attractive). The particle (cell) may remain loosely attached to the surface as a result of this secondary minimum; however, it will never become firmly adherent unless it can overcome the potential energy barrier (shown in the figure by the peak) and move into the primary minimum (not shown).

arguments, like those explained in Chapter 8 for protein adsorption. This is a highly simplified model for contact between a cell and a surface, since it does not take into account any specific receptor–ligand interactions between molecules on the cell membrane and those on the substrate. Therefore, it may be used only as a first approximation to understand how cells react to a biomaterial. Similarly, it may also be employed to model bacterial adhesion to biomedical implants (see Chapter 14).

Figure 9.35 depicts the free energy of interaction, $G(z)$, between a particle and the surface as determined by DLVO theory as a function of separation distance ($z$). Similar to force-distance curves for atomic bonding (Chapter 1), this curve is the result of several competing forces, two of which are shown as dashed lines in the graph. As a particle approaches a surface, there is a drop in potential energy (called the **secondary minimum**), which represents a balance between long-range electrostatic interactions (repulsive) and long-range van der Waals interactions (attractive). As discussed previously, overall electrostatic interactions are influenced by the charge of the surface, charge of the cell, and composition of the surrounding media, while van der Waals forces are caused by dipolar interactions between the cell and the substrate. Hydrophobic (dehydration) effects are not considered in DLVO theory since they exist over much shorter ranges than electrostatic and van der Waals forces and thus do not significantly contribute to the energy of interaction between the particle and the surface.

The particle (cell) may remain loosely attached to the surface as a result of this secondary minimum; however, it will never become firmly adherent unless it can overcome the potential energy barrier (shown in Fig. 9.35) and move into the **primary minimum** (not shown in Fig. 9.35). The primary minimum is caused by the balance of short-range electrostatic and van der Waals forces at the point of contact. The energy needed to overcome the barrier is provided by random motion of the particle and is dependent on the temperature of the system (Brownian motion).

## 9.5.2  DLVO Theory Limitations and Further Models

While the DLVO theory provides an estimate of cell-surface binding, it does not take into account several important factors, including steric repulsion. Much like proteins, cells are not able to attach to surfaces with bulky, hydrophilic groups that extend into the environment and are in constant motion near the surface. In addition, the role of surface topography is not addressed in this model. Also, similar to protein adsorption, rough surfaces may physically trap cells in grooves on the surface. It is important to note, however, that cells are several orders of magnitude larger than proteins, so what is "rough" from the perspective of proteins may be relatively smooth at the size that would be sensed by the cell.

Also, as discussed earlier, DLVO theory does not consider specific ligand–receptor interactions, which are extremely important in cell adhesion. Thus, additional models have been developed to address this topic, many of which include terms involving the kinetics of receptor–ligand binding. Although the details of these models are beyond the scope of this book, equations have been formulated to provide information about the number of ligand–receptor complexes formed over time in a variety of situations if the total number of receptor molecules and original ligand amounts are known. For example, the receptor–ligand binding can be modeled as a reversible chemical reaction:

$$R + L \underset{k_f}{\overset{k_r}{\rightleftarrows}} C$$

In this reaction, $R$ is the free receptor, $L$ is the free ligand, $C$ is the receptor–ligand complex, and $k_f$ and $k_r$ are the reaction rates of complex formation and dissociation, respectively. $k_f$ and $k_r$ can be related to the thermodynamic principles of binding discussed previously and in Chapter 1. Therefore, it is possible to model the change in receptor–ligand complex concentration over time as

$$\frac{dC}{dt} = k_f R L - k_r C \tag{9.1}$$

where $R$, $L$, and $C$ represent the concentrations of the free receptor, free ligand, and receptor–ligand complex, respectively. However, it is possible to combine these models with the DLVO theory to make a more accurate prediction of cell–substrate adhesion, taking into account both specific and nonspecific interactions.

### 9.5.3 Models of Cell Spreading and Migration

**9.5.3.1 Cell Spreading** After attachment, cells may extend finger-like pseudopodia along the substrate surface. At this point, integrin receptors in the cell membrane may interact with ligands on the material surface to firmly anchor the cell in place. This process is known as **cell spreading** and occurs to a greater or lesser degree with all cell types. Since this is a complex phenomenon involving internal cytoskeletal rearrangement as well as production and/or adsorption of adhesive proteins on the substrate, simple models of cell spreading have not yet been developed.

However, there is experimental evidence that, at least for certain cell types, there is a correlation between degree of spreading and the free energy of the surface. The existence of such a correlation is logical since surface free energy affects protein adsorption (see Chapter 8), and it is the interaction between the protein coating and membrane receptors that results in cell spreading.

**9.5.3.2 Cell Migration** Cell migration begins with similar events as those involved in cell spreading. As depicted in Figure 9.36, extension of the cell membrane in long pseudopodia is directed by polymerization of actin filaments near the leading edge of the cell. This is followed by attachment of membrane integrin receptors to the substrate. After the pseudopodia are firmly adhered, there is generation of a contractile force and a concomitant release of rear receptors, leading to forward

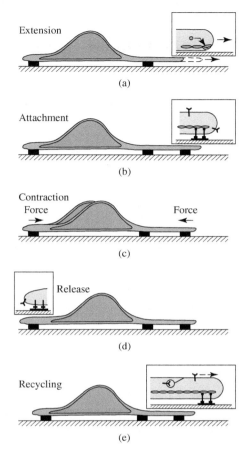

Extension

(a)

Attachment

(b)

Contraction
Force                                           Force

(c)

Release

(d)

Recycling

(e)

**Figure 9.36**
Diagram of cell migration. (a) First, extension of the cell membrane in long pseudopodia is directed by polymerization of actin filaments near the leading edge of the cell. (b) The membrane then attaches to the substrate via integrin receptors. (c, d) After the pseudopodia are firmly adhered, there is generation of a contractile force and a concomitant release of rear receptors, leading to forward cellular motion. (e) Finally, the integrin receptors are recycled to the leading edge so that they may be used again as the process continues. (Adapted with permission from [13].)

cellular motion. Finally, the integrin receptors are recycled to the leading edge so that they may be used again as the process continues.

Because this is an extremely complicated process, models of cell migration that describe events at various levels of detail have been developed, and parameters calculated in one model can be used to determine constants in larger-scale models. The diagram in Figure 9.37 demonstrates that information about detailed intracellular events may eventually be used to predict the movement of entire cell populations.

At the top of the hierarchy, mathematical models have been designed to provide information about the migration of a population of cells. As introduced in Chapter 2 for diffusion of atoms in a metallic biomaterial, the number of cells migrating across a particular location can also be modeled using a flux equation. In the simplest case, cell migration is the result of a combination of random cell motility and directed movement in response to soluble chemical signals (**chemotaxis**). Therefore, the flux of cells $M$ (cells/distance/time) for a two-dimensional system can be represented as

$$M = random\ motility + chemotaxis \tag{9.2}$$

or

$$M = -\sigma \frac{dN}{dx} + \chi N \frac{dC}{dx} \tag{9.3}$$

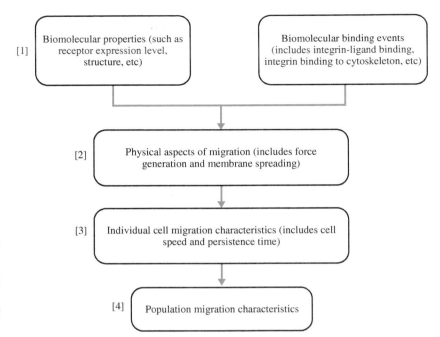

**Figure 9.37**
A diagram demonstrating the relationship between different levels of modeling of cellular movement. Information about detailed intracellular events may eventually be used to predict the movement of entire cell populations.

where $\sigma$ is the random motility coefficient, $N$ is the cell number, $\chi$ is the chemotactic coefficient, $C$ is the concentration of the chemical signal, and $x$ is the distance coordinate.

The random motility term, as the name suggests, models the random nature of nondirected cell movement. If no chemical factor is present to induce cell movement in a particular direction, the second term is 0, and it is assumed that the cells move in a random-walk pattern. If a soluble agent is present, migration depends on the concentration of the substance at the location of interest, which is included in the second term.

On a more detailed level, the migration of individual cells can be modeled. The paths of individual cells are tracked and plotted in Figure 9.38. From these plots, two main parameters, **translocation speed** ($s$) and **persistence time** ($p$) are determined. Translocation speed is the speed of cell movement over any straight-line portion of the graph, between changes in direction. Persistence time is the length of time that the cell moves along the substrate without a drastic change in direction. At times much longer than $p$, these parameters can be related to the random motility coefficient in the population model (assuming a two-dimensional system) by the formula

$$\sigma = \frac{1}{2}s^2p \tag{9.4}$$

Models of increasingly detailed intracellular events, such as actin polymerization and integrin binding, are also possible, but their descriptions are beyond the scope of this text. Experimental means of tracking movements of both individual cells and cell populations are discussed in the following section.

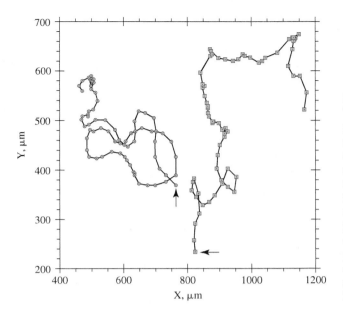

**Figure 9.38**
Typical trajectories for bovine pulmonary artery endothelial cells migrating in a uniform environment. Symbols represent the location of the centroid of each cell at 30-minute intervals. The arrows indicate the starting point for each trajectory. Two main parameters can be determined from these plots: translocation speed and persistence time. (Image courtesy of Y. Lee and K. Zygourakis, Rice University.)

## EXAMPLE PROBLEM 9.4

Some tissue engineering strategies use synthetic polymer hydrogel scaffolds to promote and direct tissue regeneration. However, many hydrogel materials, such as those based upon poly(ethylene glycol) (PEG), do not readily support cell adhesion unless modified to do so. One method of modification of hydrogels is the covalent attachment of a specific peptide sequence or sequences promoting cell attachment. The peptide sequence RGD (arginine-glycine-aspartic acid) is a motif found in a number of extracellular matrix proteins. Recognition of the RGD sequence by integrins can lead to cell binding. Consider a tissue engineering hydrogel scaffold composed from a poly(ethylene glycol)-*co*-poly(α-hydroxy acid) diacrylate macromer [1]. The acrylate moieties allow for the covalent crosslinking of the macromers upon proper initiation to form a hydrogel, while the ester groups allow for hydrolytic degradation of the resulting hydrogels. Assume that the hydrogels have been modified through the covalent inclusion of another macromer chain of poly(ethylene glycol) acrylate modified with a terminal RGD sequence.

(a) Given that poly(ethylene glycol)-*co*-poly(α-hydroxy acid) diacrylate hydrogels are biodegradable, should the peptide modification be limited to the surface of the material or should it occur throughout the bulk of the material to promote long-term cell adhesion? Justify your answer.

(b) The peptide sequence will be chemically coupled to a reactive acrylate group that will allow for covalent incorporation of the peptide moiety into the hydrogel network. You are given the choice between having (a) a PEG spacer (molecular weight of 3,400 Da) between the acrylate group and the peptide or (b) no spacer between the acrylate group and the peptide. Which method will yield the highest cell attachment per given number of peptides? Why? Assume that the PEG-*co*-poly(α-hydroxy acid) diacrylate used to fabricate the hydrogels has a molecular weight of 8,000 Da.

(c) Assume now that a sheet of the peptide modified PEG-*co*-poly(α-hydroxy acid) diacrylate hydrogel will be tested for cell adhesion to the surface of the material in a tissue culture experiment. Three groups are examined. The surface concentration of the RGD peptide is $0.001$ pmol/cm$^2$ in Group A, $0.1$ pmol/cm$^2$ in Group B, and $1$ pmol/cm$^2$ in Group C. Which group will likely result in the highest cell adhesion? Which group will likely result in the highest degree of cell spreading on the material? How is cell migration affected by the concentration of the ligand (in this case, the peptide) on the material surface?

Solution:

(a) Given that the hydrogel is intended for tissue engineering applications in which long-term cell adhesion to the material is desirable, the peptide modification should be present in the bulk of the material, rather than limited to the surface of the material. If the modification is limited to the surface of the material, the cell adhesive properties of the material will be greatly diminished when the modified surface is lost to degradation. However, if the bulk of the material is modified with the peptide sequence, the peptide will be present in the material throughout the course of degradation of the material, be it through surface erosion or a bulk degradation mechanism. Thus, cell adhesion will be promoted throughout the course of material degradation through bulk incorporation of the peptide sequence.

(b) Use of the peptide moiety with the PEG spacer will likely result in greater cell attachment per given number of peptides. The hydrogel surface will present free ends and exposed sections of the constituent PEG-*co*-poly(α-hydroxy acid) diacrylate polymer chains. These free ends and sections of the polymer chains will have some mobility. In the case of a peptide moiety with no spacer, the peptide sequence will likely be sterically blocked from exposure to cells due to the presence of the PEG-*co*-poly(α-hydroxy acid) diacrylate chain segments and ends at the hydrogel surface. However, a PEG spacer will likely allow for the peptide sequence to be tethered from the bulk of the material. The 3,400-Da molecular weight of the spacer is nearly half that of the PEG-*co*-poly(α-hydroxy acid) diacrylate chains and will likely be sufficient to allow for presentation of the peptide sequence with minimal steric hindrance from the free chain ends at the surface. Thus, it will promote cell adhesion.

(c) The group with the highest surface concentration of the peptide (Group C) will generally result in the highest degree of cell adhesion and the highest degree of cell spreading. As the number of ligands on the material surface increases, the number of ligands available for cell attachment generally increases, so the degree of cell adhesion increases. As adherent cells become capable of making increasing numbers of contacts, the degree of cell spreading increases. Cells require interactions with the ligands on the surface for adhesion. Increasing concentrations of ligands on the surface will allow for increasing cell motility up to a point, beyond which the motility decreases with increasing surface concentrations of ligands. This is due to the fact that, at higher concentrations of ligands on the surface, the cells will be highly spread upon the surface and will have many points of contact that must be broken to allow for motility. ∎

# 9.6   Techniques: Assays to Determine Effects of Cell–Material Interactions

In this chapter, we have examined the basic constituents of the cell and the ECM and discussed how their interactions affect various cell functions. In this section, assays to determine to what extent certain functions have been altered are described. These include measurements of **cytotoxicity** (cell death), cell adhesion and spreading, cell migration, and changes in gene expression (DNA/RNA assays). As mentioned previously, the production of proteins is also important to cellular differentiation and function, and can be quantified using the same methods described in Chapter 8 (colorimetric or fluorescent assays, ELISAs, or Western blotting). The location of various proteins in the ECM may be detected through immunostaining, which is described later in this section.

## 9.6.1 Cytotoxicity Assays

At the most basic level, cell–environment interactions affect the viability of the cell. Therefore, cytotoxicity is a large concern in developing new substrates for cells, and *in vitro* assays for cytotoxicity are often a required first step in biocompatibility testing for novel biomaterials. A number of regulatory boards, including the ASTM (mentioned in Chapter 4 for mechanical testing protocols) and the International Organization of Standardization (ISO) have developed standard procedures for cytotoxicity experiments and analysis of the resulting data.

A number of accepted cytotoxicity assays have been developed, including direct contact, agar diffusion, and elution tests. One of the reasons that alternative testing procedures exist is that there are several characteristics of a biomaterial that can affect its overall cytotoxicity. Often, the aspects of the material that determine its cytotoxicity are different from those that determine its interactions with the cell surface. Therefore, a particular material may promote cell adhesion and spreading, while at the same time be deleterious to viability over days or weeks. Anything present in a biomaterial (on the surface or in the bulk) that interferes with cellular metabolism or protein synthesis machinery is considered cytotoxic. This includes the material itself, any additives or processing agents used in fabrication, and potential degradation products.

It is important to note that both the type and differentiation state of the surrounding cells, as well as the final use of the product, must be taken into account when selecting which combinations of cytotoxicity tests are most appropriate. An example of this is found with zinc eugenol cements in dentistry, which produce cell death in elution assays, but have been used in dental procedures where the material is separated from surrounding cells by a thick layer of calcified tissue called dentin.

**9.6.1.1 Direct Contact Assay**  The conceptually simplest cytotoxicity test is the **direct contact assay**. Here, the test material is fabricated to specific dimensions and placed on top of a layer of cells cultured in a cell culture plate (see Fig. 9.39). After a minimum of 24 hours in a culture incubator, the cells in the area around the sample are examined microscopically to evaluate the extent of swelling and lysis. Those cells that are no longer living will often lift up from the surface and float in the media, resulting in a cell-less ring around the material. In some protocols, the size of this ring (including both dead and damaged cells) is measured. Because this assay is primarily qualitative, the inclusion of positive (non-cytotoxic) and negative (completely cytotoxic) controls is crucial so that the relative degree of cytotoxicity for the sample material can be estimated.

**Figure 9.39**
Schematic of the direct contact assay, used to determine cytotoxicity of a material sample. This diagram depicts results of a cytotoxic sample. The test specimen is placed directly on top of cells that are attached to a well plate. The cells are kept in culture for a minimum of 24 hours. The plate is then visualized via light microscopy to determine if cells have lifted off around the sample, indicating cell death. In some cases, the width of the cell-less ring around the material is quantified.

In the more recent versions of the relevant ISO standard (ISO 10993-5), more quantitative tests to determine cytotoxicity are recommended. Examples include quantifying cell death by using dyes that change color only in the presence of viable cells. In many cases, the color change can then be read at a specified wavelength on a microplate reader equipped with a spectrophotometer, similar to the method that was described for protein assays in Chapter 8. The amount of viable cells is then represented as a fraction based on the ratio of color generation in the sample wells to the color found in wells with no treatment (positive control). Common compound recommended for such measurements are (3-(4,5-dimethylthiazolyl-2)-2, 5-diphenyltetrazolium bromide) (MTT), which produces a purple color in the presence of living cells, or neutral red, which stains living cells red.

### 9.6.1.2 Indirect Contact Assays

These tests are similar to the direct contact assay; except in this case, the cells are allowed to adhere to culture dishes and are then covered with agar (**agar diffusion assay**) or cellulose-based filter paper (**filter diffusion test**) before exposure to the sample material. Agar is a natural polymer derived from red algae and will not harm the cells below it. However, the agar or filter paper does provide a physical barrier to keep the sample from crushing or disturbing the cell layer, as may occur in direct contact testing.

Testing is carried out in cell culture media to ensure the survival of the cells. However, soluble products from the sample may diffuse across the agar/filter paper and result in cell death in localized regions under the material. The cells are then divided into zones, depending on their distance from the sample, and viability is examined 1–3 days after exposure (Fig. 9.40). The greater the number of affected zones and/or the farther away from the specimen effects are observed, the greater the cytotoxicity of the sample. As in the direct contact assay, cellular dyes indicating viability may be included in the media to provide a better estimate of the number of dead cells in each zone. Positive and negative controls are often included to aid in comparison of results.

### 9.6.1.3 Elution Assay

**Elution or extract assays** are performed to determine the cytotoxicity of leachable molecules found in biomaterials, such as nonreacted monomers or degradation products. The most common version of this procedure is completed by eluting any soluble molecules in aqueous media, since this is closest to the biological environment.

In these assays, cells are plated and allowed to adhere to cell culture wells for at least 24 hours. Simultaneously, extract media is prepared by placing a known amount of material in a given amount of fresh cell culture media and allowing any soluble products to diffuse into the media for 1–72 hours at 37°C (time depends on final application

**Figure 9.40**
Schematic of the agar diffusion assay, used to determine cytotoxicity of a material sample. Cells adhered to a well plate are covered with agar. The test specimen is then placed on top of the agar and the cells are kept in culture for 1–3 days. The cells are then divided into zones, depending on their distance from the sample, and viability is examined. The greater the number of affected zones and/or the farther away from the specimen the effects are observed, the greater the cytotoxicity of the sample.

**Figure 9.41**
Image showing results from a colony forming assay using cells derived from a cancerous tumor of the pancreas. Colonies are stained with a dye called crystal violet to make them easier to visualize. In this experiment, the sample on the right was treated with a peptide that promotes cell death, resulting in fewer colonies observed [14].

of the material). After this period, the extract media is added to the wells containing cells and viability is monitored over 1–3 days using the techniques described previously.

### 9.6.1.4 Colony-Forming Assays

In addition to the cytotoxicity tests described earlier, ISO standards also suggest a colony formation assay. In this case, cells are allowed to attach to cell culture dishes and incubated with test materials for several days, during which time the number of colonies, or small groups of cells growing from the originally plated cells, are observed, counted, and compared with untreated controls (see Fig. 9.41). As in the other cytotoxicity assays, dyes are often used to stain the cells to assist in counting colonies.

### EXAMPLE PROBLEM 9.5

You are interested in screening the toxicity of a new woven biomaterial (the actual material, not any degradation products from the material), but you are concerned that the rough edges on the side of the woven material will touch and disrupt (scrape off) the cells you are using in your assay. Of the cytotoxicity assays described in this chapter, which one would be most appropriate and why?

**Solution:**  If you are concerned that the material will disrupt a layer of cells plated on a dish, neither the direct contact nor the colony forming assay would be appropriate, since if the material mechanically scrapes off the cells, that could be seen as a cytotoxic effect, when there really was no cytotoxicity. Since you are interested in the cytotoxicity of the material itself, an elution assay is not appropriate. Therefore, the best would be the agar diffusion assay, where the layer of agar would protect the cells from the edges of the biomaterial.  ∎

## 9.6.2 Adhesion/Spreading Assays

Cell adhesion to various surfaces is often quantified by allowing cells to attach to the sample material for a set amount of time and then rinsing away nonadhered cells in a controlled manner. The amount of cell adhesion is then measured by recording either the number of cells that remain on the surface, or the number of cells washed away. For the latter case,

$$\begin{pmatrix} \text{Number of} \\ \text{cells on surface} \end{pmatrix} = \begin{pmatrix} \text{Total number} \\ \text{of seeded cells} \end{pmatrix} - \begin{pmatrix} \text{Number of cells in} \\ \text{washing media} \end{pmatrix}$$

In either instance, the number of cells can be determined by staining the cells with a dye, radioactively labeling them, or lysing them and assaying for intracellular enzymes.

Examination of cell spreading is more qualitative and usually involves staining the cells and looking at representative fields via light microscopy. In some cases, analysis software can be used with images obtained by the microscope to determine the surface area of cells under different conditions, thus providing a more quantitative assessment of spreading.

**Figure 9.42**
Schematic of a parallel plate flow chamber, which can be used to control shearing forces imparted on cells during adhesion/spreading assays. The parameter $h$ indicates the distance between the plates, $w$ indicates the width of the plates in the test setup and $V_m$ denotes the velocity of the flow of the solution. As shown in (a), $V_m$ changes with time upon initiation of fluid flow until a parabolic steady-state $V_m$ profile is reached.

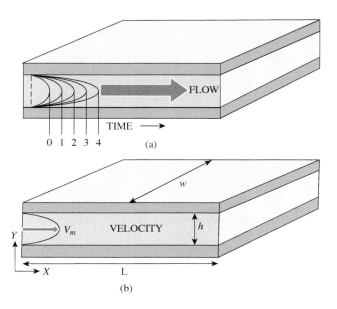

A major disadvantage to these adhesion assays is that it is difficult to reproduce the force exerted in the washing step, which can cause high experimental error between samples. To overcome this limitation, a number of means to provide controlled flow during the washing step have been developed. One of these is to place the specimen in a parallel plate flow chamber (Fig. 9.42). For such a system, the shear stress ($\tau$) at the wall (where the sample is inserted) is proportional to the volumetric flow rate ($Q$) as well as the viscosity ($\mu$) of the solution ($h$ and $w$ are dimensional parameters defined in Fig. 9.42):

$$\tau = \mu \frac{6Q}{h^2 w} \tag{9.5}$$

Therefore, the force imparted on the specimen can be controlled by altering either of these parameters in the washing step. Other methods of producing controlled shear during sample rinsing include the use of radial flow chambers or centrifugation techniques.

### 9.6.3 Migration Assays

Several procedures for assessing cell migration have been developed and may be used in combination with the mathematical models described previously to characterize cell movement on various surfaces. In particular, a number of means to examine the migration of cell populations can be used, including those that record the average distance migrated, the time it takes for cells to migrate and close a gap, or the number of cells that have moved away from the point of origin. Examples of assays that measure distance of migration include the **capillary tube** test. The capillary tube method was one of the first developed and involves confinement of cell populations in a small tube (a capillary tube). The opening of the tube is then placed against a surface (often a cell culture well), allowing the cells to migrate out of the tube in a fan-like shape (Fig. 9.43). After 2–4 days, the area of the fan shape is measured to provide a quantitative assessment of distance migrated. In a modification of this technique, the cells may be confined within a physical barrier (such as a ring),

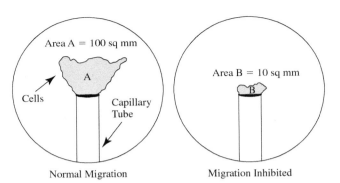

**Figure 9.43**
Schematic of the capillary tube test, a type of migration assay. In this instance, cells are originally contained in the capillary tube, which is then placed on a cell culture surface. The migration of the cells is then monitored microscopically over 2–4 days. (Adapted with permission from [15].)

and then the barrier lifted (Fig. 9.44). The increase in the radius of the cell population over several days can be monitored and measured using a light microscope and appropriate image analysis software.

Assays that measure the time required for cells to migrate and close a gap are called **scratch tests**. In this type of assay, cells are plated in culture dishes and allowed to adhere for several hours. Subsequently, a pipette tip or other sharp object is used to lift a line of cells from the middle of the well, leaving a gap or scratch (see Fig. 9.45). Over several hours-days, light microscopy can be used to follow migration of cells into the gap, and the time it takes for the gap to become completely repopulated with cells is recorded. The main drawback to these two assays, as well as other population migration assays, is that it is difficult to distinguish what portion of the increase in area is attributable to migration, and what portion is caused by cell proliferation. This is a particular problem if the experiment is performed over several days, when cell proliferation may have a significant effect.

The number of cells in a population migrating away from a given area can be quantified using the **Boyden chamber assay**. This assay is most often employed to determine the effects of soluble factors on migration, rather than examining the impact of the substrate. In the Boyden chamber (or transwell chamber) test, a porous filter separates the cells from the soluble agent to be tested. As seen in Figure 9.46, the cells are originally seeded in the top layer, and the test substance placed in the bottom chamber, where it can diffuse through the filter and interact with the cells. After a specified period of time, the number of cells that have migrated through the filter and are found in the bottom chamber are quantified via light microscopy. Further refinements of this technique (Zigmond chamber, Dunn chamber) allow for more direct microscopic visualization of the cells as they migrate through the barrier in response to the attractive agent.

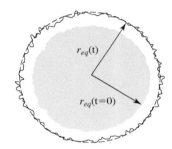

**Figure 9.44**
Schematic of an alternative migration assay. The cells are seeded in the bottom of a cell culture dish surrounded by a ring of known diameter (gray area in diagram). The ring is removed, and the radius of the cell colony $r_{eq}$ is monitored over time to determine the extent of migration [16].

**Figure 9.45**
Image of time-lapse light microscropy images indicating the migration of epithelial cells into a cell-free gap area created in a standard scratch test. Scale bar = 200 $\mu$m. (Adapted with permission from [17].)

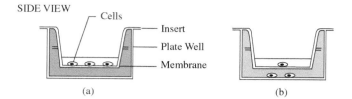

**Figure 9.46**

Schematic of the Boyden chamber assay, a migration assay that can quantify the number of cells in a population moving away from a given area. In the Boyden chamber test, a porous filter separates the cells and the soluble agent to be tested. The pores are large enough to allow cells to migrate through (~3–8 μm), but small enough to prevent cells from dropping through due to gravity (<12–20 μm). (a) The cells are originally seeded in the top layer, and the test substance is placed in the bottom chamber. This setup allows the soluble agent to diffuse through the filter (membrane) and interact with the cells. (b) After a specified period of time, the number of cells that have migrated through the membrane and that are found in the bottom chamber are quantified via light microscopy. (Adapted with permission from [13].)

Test methods examining movement of individual cells usually involve an apparatus that allows the incubation of the cells with the test surface on top of a microscope stage. Images of cell locations at given time intervals up to several hours are then captured and processed to determine the precise location of the cell centers at each time point, thus forming a "cell track" over the culture period. Using mathematical models like those described above and comparing cell positions between time points, parameters such as cell speed ($s$) and persistence time ($p$) can be calculated.

### 9.6.4 DNA and RNA Assays

DNA and RNA assays can be used to determine if there is direct damage to a cell's DNA caused by a biomaterial (this is a test for mutagenicity, discussed further in Chapter 14), but, they are most often employed to see how the biomaterial environment affects gene expression, and thus cellular function. Dramatic changes in gene expression may not be desired, because this may result in altered protein production, which could cause problems in the surrounding tissue. However, in diseased tissues, alteration of gene expression to increase or decrease production of a certain protein may be desired. (This forms the basis of gene therapy/genome editing techniques, which are beyond the scope of this text.) Both down- and up-regulation of specific genes can be detected using the following techniques.

9.6.4.1 Polymerase Chain Reaction (PCR) and Reverse-Transcription Polymerase Chain Reaction (RT-PCR)    Before the presence of a certain gene can be confirmed or quantified, it is first necessary to expand the amount of DNA or RNA for that gene to detectable levels. For DNA, this procedure uses the **polymerase chain reaction (PCR)** and for RNA, the **reverse-transcription polymerase chain reaction (RT-PCR)**. For these techniques to be useful, the DNA base sequences on each end of the gene of interest must be known, so that a set of DNA-binding **primers** (short oligonucleotide sequences) can be synthesized. For PCR, the following steps are then performed (Fig. 9.47):

1.  The double-stranded genomic DNA (dsDNA) is denatured via heat treatment to produce two single strands of DNA (ssDNA).

2. The ssDNA is cooled with an excess of primers to promote primer-DNA **hybridization** (binding).

3. A heat-stable DNA polymerase (Taq polymerase) and the four deoxyribonucleotide triphosphates (bases) are added.

4. The DNA polymerase then replicates each strand, starting at the primers.

5. The newly formed dsDNA is then heated to separate the strands and the reaction continues.

This procedure can be repeated for many cycles to produce a large number of copies of the gene of interest in a relatively short time.

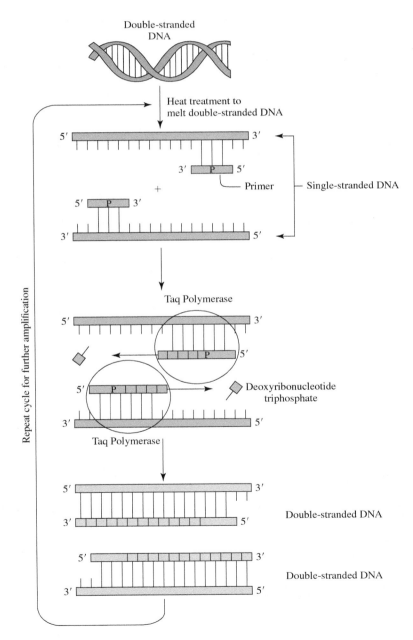

**Figure 9.47**
Diagram of the steps for PCR processing. First, the double-stranded genomic DNA is denatured via heat treatment to produce two single strands of DNA. A heat-stable DNA polymerase (Taq polymerase) and the four deoxyribonucleotide triphosphates (bases or dNTPs) are subsequently added and the DNA polymerase replicates each strand, starting at the primers. The newly formed dsDNA is then heated to separate the strands and the reaction continues for a second cycle. This procedure can be repeated for many cycles, resulting in a large number of copies of the gene of interest in a relatively short time.

RT-PCR follows the same steps as described above, with one additional step at the beginning of the procedure. In this case, the starting material is mRNA, so it must first be transcribed into DNA before PCR can proceed. This is done with an enzyme, reverse transcriptase, derived from viruses. Here, the enzyme generates ssDNA complementary to the mRNA present in the sample. This ssDNA is then placed into the PCR reaction starting at step 2, where the specific gene of interest can be expanded.

To obtain more quantitative estimates of mRNA content in a sample, researchers now often use **real-time RT-PCR**, which operates using similar principles to RT-PCR, but tracks the fold expansion of the DNA using a fluorescent probe (see Fig. 9.48). In this case, a sample is placed in a thermal cycler that will heat and cool the sample many times rapidly, allowing for easy amplification of the sequence (gene) of interest. The dyes used in the process either intercalate within double stranded DNA or will only fluoresce when hybridized to the target sequence. In either case, tracking the increase in fluorescence after each cycle provides quantitative assessment of the degree of amplification of that specific DNA sequence. Computational software can then use this data to determine the amount of the target gene expressed in the original sample.

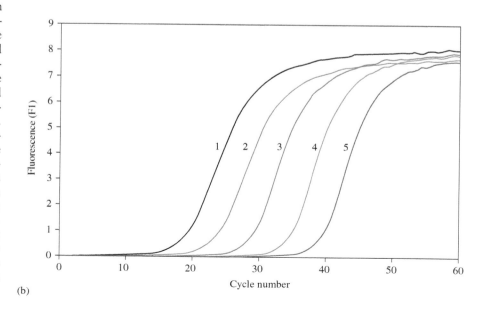

**Figure 9.48**
Overview diagram of the steps for real-time RT-PCR. (a) First the RNA is reverse transcribed to form complementary DNA (cDNA). Then the sample is placed in a thermal cycler and through many cycles the gene of interest is amplified. In this example, each time the gene is replicated, the dye can attach to the resulting double stranded portion of the DNA and the equipment will record the resulting fluorescence. The original sample can be divided into several tubes, with primers for different genes in each tube. (b) Processing software produces a graph of fluorescence versus the cycle of amplification for each gene. In this example, five different genes are plotted. Gene 5 had the lowest expression in the original sample because it took the most cycles to amplify (lower original copy number required more cycles to expand) [18].

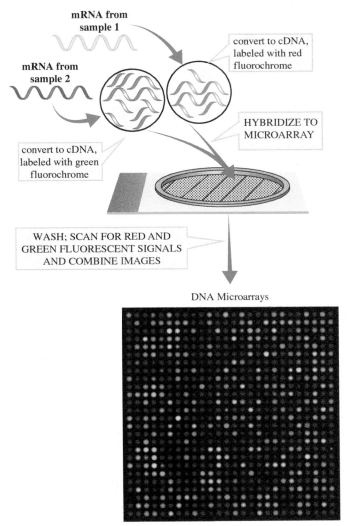

**Figure 9.49**
Overview diagram of the steps for use of DNA microarrays for determining gene expression in a sample. Short DNA oligonucleotide probes are spotted in an array on a solid surface. In this example, RNA is extracted from two samples and reverse transcribed to DNA, which is then fluorescently labeled with two different colors (red and green). When DNA is placed on this array, probe-DNA hybridization in a particular location causes that spot to become fluorescent. The lighted spots are then captured by a camera. Image analysis can determine which fragments of DNA (and thus which genes) were present in each sample, as each spot fluoresences either red, green, or yellow (indicating DNA from both samples hybridized to this spot) [Alila Medical Media/ Shutterstock].

### 9.6.4.2 DNA Microarrays

More recently, in order to increase the throughput of DNA analysis, gene chips, or microarrays, have been developed. In this case, short DNA oligonucleotide probes are fixed, or "spotted," in an array on a solid surface, such as glass (often using surface patterning techniques described in Chapter 7). In the simplest form of the assay, the DNA extracted from the sample is fluorescently labeled, so when DNA is placed on this array, probe-DNA hybridization in a particular location causes that spot to become fluorescent (see Fig. 9.49). The lighted spots are then captured by a camera. Knowing which probe was in each spot allows determination of which fragments of DNA were in the original sample. This method can be used to detect the presence of thousands of DNA fragments simultaneously, allowing comparisons of genomes between cells. It can also be employed to determine gene expression of thousands of genes, by first extracting the RNA and reverse transcribing it using methods described above to produce a DNA library, which can be introduced to the chip. In this case, "hits" indicate that a particular gene was being actively transcribed in the sample.

### 9.6.4.3 DNA/RNA Sequencing (Next-Generation Sequencing)

Traditional DNA sequencing techniques, like Sanger sequencing, were used in the 1990s and 2000s to sequence the entire human genome. Since that time, a number of improvements, called next-generation sequencing techniques, have reduced cost, improved automation, and increased throughput so that this technology is now available to a wider range of researchers, including biomaterialists. **Whole genome sequencing (WGS)** of cells exposed to a particular treatment or biomaterial is now possible within individual laboratories. In this technique, DNA is first extracted from a sample and cut into fragments. While there are several types of next generation sequencing (called **next-gen sequencing** or **DNA-Seq**), each with their own detailed chemistries, generally, the methods involve the following:

1. *Capturing DNA.* First, fragments are exposed to a set of thousands of oligonucleotides that will hybridize and capture the DNA on a surface, bead, etc.

2. *Amplifying DNA.* A modified version of PCR is then used to generate multiple copies of the captured DNA sequence, all of which are spatially grouped. This will create enough of each fragment to produce a readable signal during sequencing.

3. *Sequencing DNA.* While many different chemistries and approaches have been developed for this step, the point is to use PCR-like methods to make complementary strands, one nucleotide at a time, to those DNA fragments captured. Each of the four nucleotides are labeled (such as with different fluorophores) before introduction into the sample so that it is obvious which base has been added to the end of each new strand. Much like microarrays, an image is captured after each step and is used to register which base was added to each strand. The reagents are then washed away and the process is repeated until the entire complementary strand is formed, using the images recorded to determine the sequences of bases in that strand. See Figure 9.50 for more details.

It is possible to use this method for **transcriptomics** by first reverse transcribing RNA extracted from a sample to DNA and then sequencing DNA using methods described above. This gives the exact sequence of mRNAs found in the sample, and is termed **RNA-Seq**. In both genomic and transcriptomic analysis, results are then compared to databases in which particular sequences have been annotated to have an assigned function, such as coding of a certain protein. (Of course, many sequences yet remain to be annotated.) Such experiments result in large amounts of data that

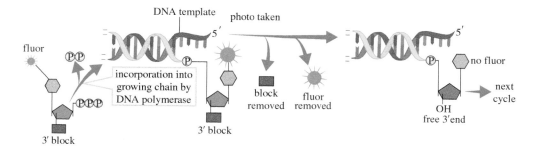

**Figure 9.50**

Overview diagram of the steps for one type of next generation DNA sequencing (Illumina system). After the DNA fragment has been captured by a probe and amplified, the series of bases that comprise the DNA fragment are sequenced using PCR-like methods to make complementary strands, one nucleotide at a time. In the Illumina technology, each of the four nucleotides are labeled with different fluorophores and also have a blocking agent so only one nucleotide can be added at a time. An image is captured after each step and is used to register which base was added to each strand. The blocking agent and fluorophore are then washed away and the process is repeated until the entire complementary strand is formed, using the images recorded to determine the sequences of bases in that strand.

can give global insight into classes of genes (cell metabolism, cell cycle, cell-matrix interactions, etc.) that are up- or down-regulated due to a particular cellular environment, or a particular disease state. Such information can lead, for example, to additional insight about the mechanism of action behind changes in phenotypes seen in cells or tissues, and thus further refinement of a treatment strategy.

### 9.6.4.4 Chromatin Immunoprecipitation (ChIP)

In order to better understand how gene transcription is regulated, it may be necessary to explore binding between proteins (such as transcription factors or histones) and DNA. For example, learning which portions of the DNA can be bound by specific proteins may provide insight into how various DNA sequences in the genome can influence expression of various genes. In order to do this, the DNA of a sample can be chemically crosslinked to its binding proteins and then the complex can be extracted from the cell. A bead with an antibody to the binding protein is then introduced to pull out that protein and its associated DNA fragment from the sample mixture (see Fig. 9.51).

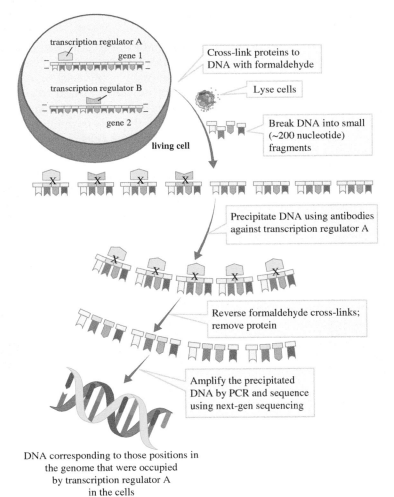

**Figure 9.51**
Block diagram of the steps for chromatin immunoprecipitation (ChIP) for a specific transcription factor. After crosslinking DNA proteins to their corresponding DNA binding partners, the cells are lysed and DNA fragmented. Subsequently, antibodies for factor A are used to separate only those DNA fragments that are bound to that transcription factor. The DNA is released, amplified, and then can be sequenced using DNA-seq methods.

**Figure 9.52**

Example of the advantages of analysis of single cells versus an entire cell population. Analysis of a biological outcome of a population of cells will result in an average value (shown as $\mu_1$ on these graphs). However, looking at only an average can result in missing a small population of cells that are behaving differently to the treatment (high responders shown in brown on figure i), which may be of interest therapeutically. Alternatively, the average value may actually be the result of two distinct sub-populations (figures ii and iii) that would be missed by only analyzing the full population [19].

This process is called chromatin immunoprecipitation (**ChIP**). The crosslinking is then reversed, releasing the DNA fragment, which can then be sequenced using the methods described above (called **ChIP-Seq**).

**9.6.4.5 Single-Cell Analysis**   It is important to note that all of the high through-put DNA/RNA assays (microarray, DNA/RNA seq, ChIP seq) can be performed either on tissue-derived samples containing many cells or on samples containing single cells. Single-cell analysis is very powerful in that it allows for detection of heterogeneity in biological responses between cells in a population, rather than simply providing the average response of all the cells in the population (see Fig. 9.52). Such analysis may allow classification of some cells as "responders" and others as "non-responders." Further biological assays on each of these sub-populations can then lead to more precise understanding about the mechanism of action of a treatment or disease, for example.

Single-cell analysis occurs using identical protocols as those described previously, but provides two additional challenging requirements: (1) separation of samples into single cells, and (2) amplification of the genetic material to sufficient quantities for use in the assays. A number of methods and devices have been employed to separate samples into individual cells in an automated manner, including fluorescence-activated cell sorting, described in Chapter 10, or it can be accomplished more traditionally by using a micropipette to manually separate cells under a microscope. Subsequently, the individual cells are lysed and the genetic material extracted. However, the DNA produced/recovered from the samples must be amplified using PCR-based methods to a greater degree than traditional, multicellular samples so that enough signal is produced to be "read" in microarrays or by next-generation sequencing equipment.

## EXAMPLE PROBLEM 9.6

You are designing a material for pancreatic islet encapsulation and would like to understand if the global inflammatory response to your biomaterial will be different in healthy versus diabetic rats.

(a) Design an experiment to determine the response using the DNA/RNA assays listed in this chapter.
(b) What would single-cell analysis be appropriate for this test? Why or why not?

Solution:

(a) A number of answers are possible; however, in any case, you would need to first excise the tissue around the biomaterial to examine inflammatory response. You would want to compare the data from the tissue around the biomaterial in diabetic versus healthy animals to see if there was a large difference in what was expressed. Since inflammation is a process that involves upregulation of various proteins, which are regulated by the genes that are being transcribed, an RNA assay would be most appropriate, rather than a DNA assay that captures only genomic changes. Finally, you would want to select an assay that captures many genes (microarray or RNA-Seq), since you are interested in the global inflammatory response, rather than simply looking at the response of one or two genes.

(b) Single-cell analysis may be useful, but may not be required. Based on the question, the general inflammatory state of the entire tissue is what is of interest, so knowing how individual cells in the tissue respond may not be necessary. However, if cells can be extracted from the tissue and single-cell analysis performed, this can provide additional information as to which subtypes of cells are responding to the implanted material, and if these are the same subtypes that are responding in the diabetic versus healthy animal. Such additional information may help to design an improved material that would target these particular cells and reduce the inflammatory response to the biomaterial.  ■

### 9.6.5 Protein Production Assays

**9.6.5.1 Proteomics**   Generally, the term **proteomics** refers to analysis of a large set of proteins within a sample (much like genomics for DNA or transcriptomics for RNA). This technique can be used for analysis of proteins in any sort of sample, such as to understand what types of proteins are adsorbed on a biomaterials surface, but it is included here since it is often utilized with samples containing cells to determine how general classes of proteins (DNA-binding, metabolism, cell-matrix interaction, etc.) are up- or down-regulated in response to a particular treatment. Like the nucleic acid analysis techniques described previously, this technique can be performed on single cells or populations of cells. In this sort of analysis, after extraction of all proteins from the sample, the proteins are digested by enzymes into fragments, which are usually characterized via mass spectroscopy (see Chapter 2) and the resulting peaks are compared to those in a database of known proteins to determine which proteins were present in the sample.

**9.6.5.2 Immunostaining**   There are a number of means to quantify protein synthesis, including those described in Chapter 8, such as colorimetric and fluorescent assays. These methods, based on changes in color or fluorescence of a marker molecule once it has bound to the protein of interest, have been developed to detect both enzymes and non-enzymatic molecules. In addition, they may be readily used for ECM components with low amino acid contents, such as proteoglycans. Additional techniques described in the previous chapter that are common for protein detection are antibody-based methods like ELISAs and Western blotting.

In a method similar to those described for ELISAs and Western blots, antibodies can be used to identify the location of proteins in tissues, particularly in thin sections taken and visualized via light microscopy. This technique is called **immunohisto-chemistry**, and the sections are said to be **immunostained**. The process is depicted in Figure 9.53.

1. A primary antibody is added to the section, which then binds to the protein of interest.

2. A labeled secondary antibody is then added that can bind to a portion of the primary antibody. The secondary antibody can be linked to an enzyme, or can be tagged directly with a **chromophore** (colored molecule).

**Figure 9.53**
Diagram of the technique used in immunohistochemistry. First, a primary antibody is added to the sample section, which then binds to the protein of interest. A labeled secondary antibody is then added that can bind to a portion of the primary antibody. The secondary antibody can be monitored via a variety of means.

3. The enzyme's substrate is added, if necessary, and then the section is imaged under visible light to detect areas of the sample where the protein is present (should demonstrate a characteristic color).

This is the **indirect method** of immunostaining. It is the most commonly used, since there is the possibility of signal amplification, depending on the design of the primary and secondary antibodies. *Amplification* occurs if many tagged secondary molecules bind to the primary antibody, thus giving a strong localized color, even in the presence of only a small amount of protein. Similar techniques can be used to fluorescently label proteins in a section and visualize them with a fluorescent microscope. As with other antibody-based techniques, antibodies specific to the target biomolecule must be available in order to carry out this staining technique.

### 9.6.6 Laser Confocal Scanning Microscopy

**9.6.6.1 Basic Principles** Specialized light microscopy techniques have been developed to penetrate deeper into biological samples, allowing visualization of tissues or tissue-based constructs that are over 100 microns thick. One of the most common of these, **laser confocal scanning microscopy** (**LCSM**), uses fluorescent probes like those described in the previous section. The fluorophore on the tagged samples will be excited at one specific wavelength and emit at another, longer wavelength. Thus, fluorescent microscopes generally contain a dichroic mirror, which allows reflection of the shorter (excitation) wavelengths, but allows longer (emission) wavelengths to pass back (through an additional filter) to a detector (see Fig. 9.54). The problem with this set-up is that all emitted light is collected, some of which comes from the part of the sample that is out of the focal plane, thus limiting the depth that can be clearly visualized. In confocal microscopy, a laser is used for illumination, and physical pinholes are placed so that only in-plane light is allowed to pass to the detector (see Fig. 9.55), forming a crisp image of only that plane. To create a 2D image, the laser is scanned across the sample left to right (XY dimensions). By repeating this

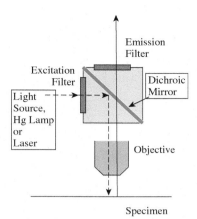

**Figure 9.54**
Light path through a traditional fluorescence microscope. The shorter, excitation wavelength is reflected to the specimen through the dichroic mirror. Excited fluorophores in the sample then emit a longer wavelength that can pass through the mirror to the detector, producing an image [20].

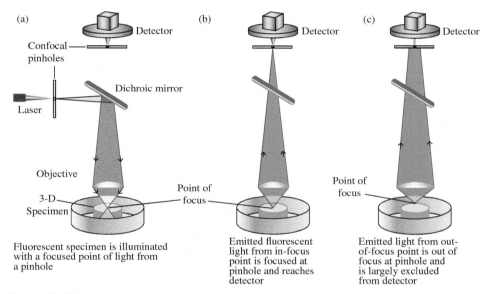

**Figure 9.55**
Light path through a laser scanning confocal fluorescence microscope. (a) The shorter, excitation wavelength produced by the laser moves through a pinhole before it is reflected to the specimen through the dichroic mirror. (b and c) Excited fluorophores in the sample then emit a longer wavelength that can pass through the mirror and then through another pinhole before reaching the detector. As shown, the second pinhole physically blocks out-of-plane light from hitting the detector, resulting in a clear image of only the focal plane.

scan at different focal planes (Z dimension), a clear 3D image of the entire specimen can be created.

**9.6.6.2 Instrumentation**   As shown in Figure 9.56, there are six basic components to a confocal microscope:

1. Laser source— produces appropriate excitation wavelength of light.
2. Pinhole/dichroic mirror—directs excitation light to sample.
3. Sample stage—holds sample securely.

**Figure 9.56**
Block diagram of the components of a laser confocal scanning microscope, which include the source, pinholes, dichroic mirrors, sample stage and detector (camera or human eye).

**Figure 9.57**
Confocal microscopy image of polymer microparticles (stained here with a fluorescent red dye) embedded in rat muscle tissue. Nuclei of muscle cells that are stained with a fluorescent blue dye (4′,6-diamidino-2-phenylindole or DAPI) can be seen on top of, around, and, in some cases, below the microspheres, demonstrating the 3D information that can be visualized with confocal microscopy. (Photo courtesy of J.S. Temenoff laboratory, Georgia Tech.)

4. Pinhole/dichroic mirror—directs emitted light to detector.

5. Detector (camera or human eye)—views and captures resulting image.

6. Processor—controls scanning of laser across sample, compiles 2D images to form 3D image.

More specifically, as depicted in Figure 9.55, the excitation light beam from the laser moves through the pinhole and is reflected onto the sample. After excitation, fluorophores produce emission light that is allowed to pass through the dichroic mirror. Only the in-plane light reaches the detector through a second pinhole. The image can be viewed immediately or captured with a camera. The excitation light is scanned across the sample in a controlled manner using mirrors to produce a 2D image of the entire sample, which can be repeated at different focal planes to recreate a 3D image of the specimen.

**9.6.6.3 Information Provided**   LCSM is primarily used for 3D reconstructions of samples or visualization of what is occurring in the interior of a thick specimen. Figure 9.57 shows a confocal microscopy image of polymer microparticles (stained with a fluorescent red dye) embedded in rat muscle tissue. Nuclei of muscle cells that are stained with a fluorescent blue dye (4′,6-diamidino-2-phenylindole or DAPI) can be seen on top of, around, and, in some cases, below the microspheres. Like other types of light microscopy, it is primarily used for qualitative assessments, but specialized software can be employed to provide quantitative measures of brightness, amount of color found per image, or other parameters. Although LCSM is better than traditional fluorescent microscopy at imaging thick samples, it is still limited to ~150 microns in depth for most fluorophores, so extremely thick samples or tissues cannot be visualized.

# Summary

- Eukaryotic cells contain a number of specialized components. The cell membrane is a bilayered phospholipid barrier that divides the cytoplasm of the cell from the extracellular environment. The cytoskeleton generally consists of dynamic protein-based structures, including actin filaments, intermediate filaments, and microtubules. Mitochondria have a highly folded inner membrane and produce energy for the cell through oxidative phosphorylation of ADP to ATP. The nucleus holds the cellular DNA and is separated from the remainder of the cell by the nuclear envelope. The outer membrane of the nuclear envelope is connected to the endoplasmic reticulum, where protein synthesis occurs. Ribosomes on the rough endoplasmic reticulum catalyze the synthesis of proteins. Specialized vesicles called lysosomes contain digestive enzymes used to break down ingested particles.

- Cells can form a number of different types of contacts with one another as well as a variety of attachments to the extracellular matrix. These connections occur through interaction of cell membrane receptors.

- General categories of membrane receptors include cadherins, selectins, mucins, integrins, and other cell adhesion molecules (CAMs). Cadherins undergo calcium-dependent homophilic binding to form desmosomes. Selectins take part in cell-cell binding through heterophilic interaction with carbohydrate groups on target cell membranes, such as mucins. Different combinations of the two distinct subunits of membrane-spanning integrins can lead to interactions to form either cell-cell or cell-matrix contacts. CAMs mediate cell-cell interactions through both heterophilic and homophilic binding.

- Glycoproteins are mainly proteins with small amounts of attached carbohydrates, whereas proteoglycans are largely carbohydrates with small protein components. The carbohydrates attached to the polypeptide in a proteoglycan are called glycosaminoglycans and can include hyaluronic acid, keratin sulfate, and chondroitin/dermatan sulfate.

- The binding of extracellular matrix molecules to integrins, which are linked intracellularly to intermediate filaments, can cause changes in the cytoskeleton that can affect gene expression in the cell. Also, soluble mediators can interact with receptors on the cell membrane and lead to alterations in gene expression through secondary messenger cascades.

- Four major cellular functions are viability, proliferation, differentiation, and protein synthesis.

- Cell death can occur by one of two general mechanisms: necrosis, which involves swelling and lysis of the cell and clearance of the debris by inflammatory cells, and apoptosis (programmed cell death), in which the cell fragments in a controlled manner to form apoptotic bodies that are phagocytosed by surrounding cells without inducing an inflammatory response.

- Cellular proliferation proceeds through a number of steps, which include mitosis (M phase) and interphase (phases $G_1$, S, and $G_2$). Cells that are not proliferating are in phase $G_0$.

- Stem cells can be categorized as unipotent (producing only one type of differentiated cell), multipotent (producing several differentiated cell types), or totipotent (or pluripotent) (producing all (or most) cell types found in the body). Induced pluripotent stem cells (iPSCs) have been developed, in which committed cells have been genetically reprogrammed to become pluripotent.

- Protein synthesis involves RNA polymerase transiently separating the strands of DNA in the region encoding the protein of interest and subsequent transcription to form the respective mRNA. The mRNA moves to the ER, and specific tRNA molecules and ribosomes interact with it to translate the protein of interest. Post-translational processing then occurs in the ER and the Golgi apparatus.

- DLVO theory entails a basic model for cell adhesion to a surface through nonspecific hydrostatic and van der Waals interactions. Models have also been developed to describe specific receptor–ligand interactions based upon thermodynamic principles and concentrations of ligands and receptors. It is possible to combine these models with DLVO theory to result in a more accurate model of cell–substrate adhesion, which considers both specific and nonspecific interactions.

- Migration of a population of cells on a surface can be random or in response to specific stimuli, such as soluble chemical signals (chemotaxis). Cell population motility can be modeled in terms of the flux of cells across a particular location on a surface, with separate terms included for random motility and chemotaxis.

- The migration of individual cells can be modeled with the inclusion of the translocation speed (speed of cell movement between changes in direction) and persistence time (length of time that the cell moves along the substrate without changing direction).

- Biomaterial cytotoxicity is a complex topic that involves consideration of the cytotoxicity of the material, its leachable products, and its degradation products.

- A variety of cytotoxicity assays exist, including direct contact assays, agar diffusion assays, elution assays, and colony forming assays, and involve the quantification of either the number of dead cells, the number of living cells, or both.

- Cell adhesion assays entail counting the number of adherent cells on a material with respect to the number of seeded cells, either visually through microscopic examination, or through the use of wash and cytometry techniques. Cell spreading assays involve staining and, with the aid of a microscope, counting the cells that have spread on a material.

- Migration assays can include characterization of the migration of cell populations with techniques such as the capillary tube test, the scratch test, and the Boyden chamber assay, or the movement of individual cells through the use of complex imaging systems capable of tracking individual cells over time in culture.

- Changes in gene expression in a sample can be followed by real-time reverse-transcription polymerase chain reaction (RT-PCR), or in a more high-throughput manner using microarrays.

- Whole genome sequencing (WGS) of cells can also be used in biomaterials assessment using methods collectively called next generation sequencing (called next-gen sequencing or DNA-Seq). It is also possible to use this method for transcriptomics by first reverse transcribing RNA extracted from a sample to DNA and then sequencing the DNA (RNA-Seq).

- Chromatin immunoprecipitation (ChIP) is used to explore binding between proteins (such as transcription factors or histones) and DNA. The exact protein-binding sequence can be identified using next-gen sequencing methods described in the previous bullet (ChIP-Seq).

- Proteomics can be used to examine global changes in all the proteins in one sample compared to another.
- Immunostaining provides a method for qualitatively visualizing protein expression. Often this method is combined with the light microscopy technique called laser confocal scanning microscopy, which allows visualization of the location of proteins in tissue sections that are over 100 microns thick.

## Problems

9.1  Assume that in response to a signal, a cell eventually will secrete protein A. Explain each step that would lead to secretion of protein A, starting in the cell nucleus, and explain in what part of the cell each step occurs. Which single-cell analysis technique is appropriate for each step?

9.2  (a) Yes-associated protein (YAP) is a transcription factor that is part of a signal transduction pathway that allows cells to respond to changes in their mechanical environment. Below are images of cells on two different surfaces ((i) and (ii)). YAP is shown in green and the nucleus is shown in blue. Based on the actions of transcription factors, which surface has activated this pathway? (Reprinted with permission from [2])

(b) Would confocal microscopy be appropriate for this study? What additional information, if any, would it provide?

(c) Would ChiP-Seq be appropriate for this study? What additional information, if any, would it provide?

9.3 You have developed a new ceramic coating to be used on hip implants and test it in a series of *in vitro* assays. For each of the parameters listed here, describe (1) how you would measure the characteristic and (2) what outcome you would hope for in that particular assay to demonstrate that you have the ideal biomaterial for bone tissue engineering.

   (a) Cell cytotoxicity
   (b) Cell proliferation
   (c) Cell migration
   (d) Cell differentiation

9.4 You are now investigating a polymer coating that inhibits leukocyte (pro-inflammatory cell) migration with the intent of minimizing inflammation for the stem of your hip implant. You choose to do a capillary tube test to observe leukocyte migration over 4 days.

   (a) Explain how a capillary tube test is used to measure cell migration.
   (b) The capillary tube test gave the following results over 4 days for leukocytes on coated and uncoated surfaces. Would you recommend using the polymeric coating to inhibit leukocyte migration?

| | Inhibitory Coating: | Uncoated Control Surfaces: |
|---|---|---|
| Time (d) | Area of Cells (mm²) | Area of Cells (mm²) |
| 0 | 0 | 0 |
| 1 | 2 | 3 |
| 2 | 3 | 7 |
| 3 | 7 | 35 |
| 4 | 10 | 52 |

   (c) What is the major drawback to this study as a measure of cell migration over 4 days?
   (d) To determine the effect of the coating on other cell types, migration of leukocytes, endothelial cells (to form blood vessels), and osteoblasts (bone-forming cells) were compared on polymer-coated surfaces by capillary tube tests. Do these results support the use of this coating for the stem of a hip implant? Justify your answer using the results in the table found here.

| | Leukocytes on Coated Surfaces: | Endothelial Cells on Coated Surfaces: | Osteoblasts on Coated Surfaces: |
|---|---|---|---|
| Time (d) | Area of Cells (mm²) | Area of Cells (mm²) | Area of Cells (mm²) |
| 0 | 0 | 0 | 0 |
| 1 | 2 | 2 | 1 |
| 2 | 3 | 2 | 3 |
| 3 | 7 | 5 | 6 |
| 4 | 10 | 7 | 9 |

9.5 After the hip implant, you have now decided to develop a different polymer for use as a ligament replacement. Your new material is synthesized by polymerizing monomer X. However, after testing, you found that this polymer has very poor ligament fibroblast cell adhesion. Since you know that fibroblasts like to attach to the extracellular matrix protein collagen, you decide to make a copolymer of X and a monomer Y. Monomer Y has a pendant group that you believe will interact electrostatically with collagen after (co)polymerization and processing.

(a) You first tested the contact angle of the copolymers and obtained the results in the following table. Based on these data, what are the relative hydrophophilicity of monomer X and monomer Y? Why?

| Polymer Composition (%Y by weight) | Water Contact Angle (degree) |
|:---:|:---:|
| 5 | 120 |
| 10 | 100 |
| 25 | 80 |
| 50 | 60 |
| 75 | 50 |
| 100 | 45 |

(b) You then immerse each of these materials in a collagen solution and rinse gently in water. You then test the contact angle again and obtain the following results. Explain why the water contact angle decreases for all compositions after exposure to collagen. Why is a plateau in contact angle seen?

| Polymer Composition (%Y) | Water Contact Angle (degree) | % Spread Fibroblasts* |
|:---:|:---:|:---:|
| 5 | 100 | |
| 10 | 80 | 30 |
| 25 | 60 | |
| 50 | 31 | |
| 75 | 35 | |
| 100 | 33 | |

*This refers to the % of spread cells (e.g., % cells on surface that have a surface area above a threshold value).

(c) It was found that 30% fibroblasts spread on the copolymer with 10% monomer Y after treatment with the collagen solution. Using the table given under part (b), estimate the value of % spread cells on the other surfaces after treatment with the collagen solution. Briefly justify your answer.

(d) Explain what is happening within the cell to cause cell spreading after the cells are placed on the 100% Y surface.

(e) Finally, you decide to take the collagen-treated materials and rinse them with a mixed protein solution, rather than water (better representing what would be found in the body), before repeating the experiments above. You obtain the following new results. Fill in your predictions for the rest of the % spread cells column and justify your predictions. What is different versus the case for 5(c)?

| Polymer Composition (%Y) | Water Contact Angle (degree) | % Spread Fibroblasts* |
|:---:|:---:|:---:|
| 5 | 100 | |
| 10 | 82 | |
| 25 | 59 | |
| 50 | 30 | |
| 75 | 36 | |
| 100 | 33 | 5 |

(f) Based on all this data, would you recommend copolymer XY for use as a ligament replacement? If yes, justify your answer. If no, suggest a means to modify this material so it is more suitable for this application.

9.6 Below is a summary of data from a RNA-Seq experiment in which hepatocytes (liver cells) were cultured in 2D (on surfaces), in 3D as cell aggregates (SP-3D), or in 3D on a porous scaffold (ST-3D). In this graph, genes that were upregulated are shown in red, those that were downregulated are shown in green, and those that did not change are shown in gray. Which samples are the most different based on this data? Give a possible explanation based on impact of culture conditions on cell function. (Graph reprinted with permission from [3]).

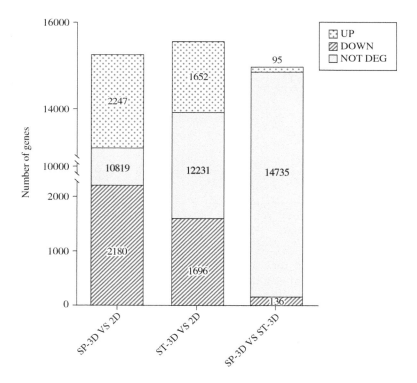

9.7 This study was conducted with different surface modifications to poly(methyl methacrylate) (PMMA), which is used as a bone cement, among other things.

(a) Based on the following images, on which surface do epithelial cells prefer to adhere? Cells are stained green. Reprinted with permission from [4].

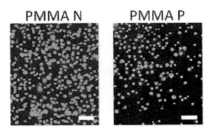

PMMA N      PMMA P

(b) Subsequently, the cell-laden surfaces were characterized by proteomics. Based on the following results, what is one possible explanation as to why more cells are seen on the surface you chose for 7a)?.

# References

1. A. S. Sawhney, C. P. Pathak, and J. A. Hubbell, "Bioerodible hydrogels based on photopolymerized poly (ethylene glycol)-co-poly(alpha-hydroxy acid) diacrylate macromers," *Macromolecules*, vol. 26, no. 4, pp. 581–587, 1993.

2. C. Yang *et al.*, "Spatially patterned matrix elasticity directs stem cell fate," *Proceedings of the National Academy of Sciences*, vol. 113, no. 31, pp. E4439–E4445, 2016.

3. J. Wang *et al.*, "Engineering EMT using 3D micro-scaffold to promote hepatic functions for drug hepatotoxicity evaluation," *Biomaterials*, vol. 91, pp. 11–22, 2016.

4. M.-N. Abdallah *et al.*, "Biomaterial surface proteomic signature determines interaction with epithelial cells," *Acta biomaterialia*, vol. 54, pp. 150–163, 2017.

5. B. Alberts, D. Bray, J. Lewis, M. Raff, K. Roberts, and J. Watson, *Molecular biology of the cell*, 3rd ed. New York: Garland Publishing, 1994.

6. R. A. Bergman, A. K. Afifi, and P. M. Heidger, *Histology*. Philadelphia: W.B. Saunders Company, 1996.

7. J. Kuby, *Immunology*, 3rd ed. New York: W.H. Freeman, 1997.

8. E. D. Hay, *Cell biology of extracellular matrix*, 2nd ed. New York: Plenum Press, 1991.

9. S. V. Bhat, *Biomaterials*, 2nd ed. Alpha Science Int'l Ltd., 2005.

10. H. Curtis, *Biology*, 4th ed. New York: Worth Publishers, 1983.

11. M. R. Koller and B. O. Palsson, "Tissue engineering: reconstitution of human hematopoiesis ex vivo," *Biotechnology and Bioengineering*, vol. 42, no. 8, pp. 909–930, 1993.

12. S. P. Bruder and A. I. Caplan, "Bone regeneration through cellular engineering," in *Principles of tissue engineering*, 2nd ed., R. P. Lanza, R. Langer, and J. Vacanti, Eds. Austin: Academic Press, 2000, pp. 683–696.

13. B. O. Palsson and S. N. Bhatia, *Tissue engineering*. Upper Saddle River: Pearson Prentice Hall, 2004.

14. P. Pamonsinlapatham *et al.*, "A RasGAP SH3 peptide aptamer inhibits RasGAP-Aurora interaction and induces caspase-independent tumor cell death," *PLoS one*, vol. 3, no. 8, p. e2902, 2008.

15. N. Hallab, J. J. Jacobs, and J. Black, "Hypersensitivity to metallic biomaterials: a review of leukocyte migration inhibition assays," *Biomaterials*, vol. 21, no. 13, pp. 1301–14, Jul. 2000.

16. H. Shin, K. Zygourakis, M. C. Farach-Carson, M. J. Yaszemski, and A. G. Mikos, "Attachment, proliferation, and migration of marrow stromal osteoblasts cultured on biomimetic hydrogels modified with an osteopontin-derived peptide," *Biomaterials*, vol. 25, no. 5, pp. 895–906, Feb. 2004.

17. Y. Matsubayashi, W. Razzell, and P. Martin, "'White wave' analysis of epithelial scratch wound healing reveals how cells mobilise back from the leading edge in a myosin-II-dependent fashion," *Journal of Cell Science*, vol. 124, no. 7, pp. 1017–1021, 2011.

18. K. Müller and M. Wirth, "Real-time RT-PCR detection of retroviral contaminations of cells and cell lines," *Cytotechnology*, vol. 38, no. 1–3, pp. 147–153, 2002.

19. S. J. Altschuler and L. F. Wu, "Cellular heterogeneity: do differences make a difference?," *Cell*, vol. 141, no. 4, pp. 559–563, 2010.

20. K. Hauch and B.D. Ratner, "Microscopy for Biomaterials Science," in *Biomaterials science: an introduction to materials in medicine*, 3rd ed., B.D. Ratner, A.S. Hoffman, F.J. Schoen, and J.E. Lemons, Eds. San Diego: Elsevier Academic Press, 2013, pp. 677–692.

# Additional Reading

A. R. Asthagiri and D. A. Lauffenburger, "Bioengineering models of cell signaling," *Annual Review of Biomedical Engineering*, vol. 2, no. 1, pp. 31–53, 2000.

S. D. Bruck, *Properties of biomaterials in the physiological environment*. Boca Raton: CRC Press, 1980.

S. Cai, Y. Liu, X. Z. Shu, and G. D. Prestwich, "Injectable glycosaminoglycan hydrogels for controlled release of human basic fibroblast growth factor," *Biomaterials*, vol. 26, no. 30, pp. 6054–6067, 2005.

R. L. Carpendo and T. C. McDevitt, "Stem cells: key concepts," in *Biomaterials science: an introduction to materials and medicine*, 3rd ed., B. D. Ratner, A. S. Hoffman, F. J. Schoen, and J. E. Lemons, Eds. San Diego: Elsevier Academic Press, 2013, pp. 487–495.

B. P. Chan and K.-F. So, "Photochemical crosslinking improves the physicochemical properties of collagen scaffolds," *Journal of Biomedical Materials Research Part A*: vol. 75, no. 3, pp. 689–701, 2005.

V. Charulatha and A. Rajaram, "Influence of different cross-linking treatments on the physical properties of collagen membranes," *Biomaterials*, vol. 24, no. 5, pp. 759–767, 2003.

R. Couñago, S. Chen, and Y. Shamoo, "In vivo molecular evolution reveals biophysical origins of organismal fitness," *Molecular cell*, vol. 22, no. 4, pp. 441–449, 2006.

K. C. Dee, D. A. Puleo, and R. Bizios, *An introduction to tissue-biomaterial interactions*. Hoboken: Wiley-Liss, 2002.

R. B. Dickinson, A. G. Ruta, and S. E. Truesdail, "Physiochemical basis of bacterial adhesion to biomaterial surfaces," in *Antimicrobial/anti-infective materials: principles, applications, and devices*, S. P. Sawan and G. Manivannan, Eds. Lancaster: Technomic Publishing, 2000, pp. 67–93.

E. R. Edelman, E. Mathiowitz, R. Langer, and M. Klagsbrun, "Controlled and modulated release of basic fibroblast growth factor," *Biomaterials*, vol. 12, no. 7, pp. 619–626, 1991.

R. Fujisawa and Y. Kuboki, "Preferential adsorption of dentin and bone acidic proteins on the (100) face of hydroxyapatite crystals," *Biochimica et Biophysica Acta (BBA)-General Subjects*, vol. 1075, no. 1, pp. 56–60, 1991.

S. C. Gad and S. Gad-McDonald, *Biomaterials, medical devices, and combination products: biocompatibility testing and safety assessment*. CRC Press, 2015.

A. Guyton and J. Hall, *Textbook of medical physiology*, 11th ed. Philadelphia: W.B. Saunders Company, 2006.

J. D. Hartgerink, E. Beniash, and S. I. Stupp, "Self-assembly and mineralization of peptide-amphiphile nanofibers," *Science*, vol. 294, no. 5547, pp. 1684–1688, 2001.

M. J. Heller, "DNA microarray technology: devices, systems, and applications," *Annual Review of Biomedical Engineering*, vol. 4, no. 1, pp. 129–153, 2002.

A. A. Horbett, "Principles underlying the role of adsorbed plasma proteins in blood interactions with foreign materials," *Cardiovascular Pathology*, vol. 2, no. 3S, pp. 137S-148S, 1993.

T. A. Horbett, "The role of adsorbed proteins in tissue response to biomaterials," in *Biomaterials science: an introduction to materials and medicine*, 2nd ed., B. D. Ratner, A. S. Hoffman, F. J. Schoen, and J. E. Lemons, Eds. San Diego: Elsevier Academic Press, 2004, pp. 237–246.

F.-M. Huang, K.-W. Tai, M.-Y. Chou, and Y.-C. Chang, "Cytotoxicity of resin-, zinc oxide-eugenol-, and calcium hydroxide-based root canal sealers on human periodontal ligament cells and permanent V79 cells,"

*International Endodontic Journal*, vol. 35, no. 2, pp. 153–158, 2002.

J. A. Hubbell, "Matrix Effects," in *Principles of Tissue Engineering*, 2nd ed., R. P. Lanza, R. Langer, and J. Vacanti, Eds. Austin: Academic Press, 2000, pp. 237–250.

G. K. Hunter and H. A. Goldberg, "Modulation of crystal formation by bone phosphoproteins: role of glutamic acid-rich sequences in the nucleation of hydroxyapatite by bone sialoprotein," *Biochemical Journal*, vol. 302, no. 1, pp. 175–179, 1994.

A. A. Kolodziejczyk, J. K. Kim, V. Svensson, J. C. Marioni, and S. A. Teichmann, "The technology and biology of single-cell RNA sequencing," *Molecular Cell*, vol. 58, no. 4, pp. 610–620, 2015.

C.-C. Liang, A. Y. Park, and J.-L. Guan, "In vitro scratch assay: a convenient and inexpensive method for analysis of cell migration in vitro," *Nature Protocols*, vol. 2, no. 2, p. 329, 2007.

X. Lin, "Functions of heparan sulfate proteoglycans in cell signaling during development," *Development*, vol. 131, no. 24, pp. 6009–6021, 2004.

M. Martins-Green, "Dynamics of cell-ECM interactions," in *Principles of tissue engineering*, 2nd ed., R. P. Lanza, R. Langer, and J. Vacanti, Eds. Austin: Academic Press, 2000, pp. 33–55.

R. N. Mitchell and F. J. Schoen, "Cells and cell injury," in *Biomaterials science: an introduction to materials and medicine*, 2nd ed., B. D. Ratner, A. S. Hoffman, F. J. Schoen, and J. E. Lemons, Eds. San Diego: Elsevier Academic Press, 2004, pp. 246–260.

P. J. Park, "ChIP–seq: advantages and challenges of a maturing technology," *Nature Reviews Genetics*, vol. 10, no. 10, p. 669, 2009.

E. Salih, S. Ashkar, L. C. Gerstenfeld, and M. J. Glimcher, "Identification of the phosphorylated sites of metabolically 32P-labeled osteopontin from cultured chicken osteoblasts," *Journal of Biological Chemistry*, vol. 272, no. 21, pp. 13966–13973, 1997.

W. M. Saltzman, "Cell interactions with polymers," in *Principles of tissue engineering*, 2nd ed., R. P. Lanza, R. Langer, and J. Vacanti, Eds. Austin: Academic Press, 2000, pp. 221–235.

J. M. Schakenraad, "Cells: their surfaces and interactions with materials," in *Biomaterials science: an introduction to materials and medicine*, 1st ed., B. D. Ratner, A. S. Hoffman, F. J. Schoen, and J. E. Lemons, Eds. San Diego: Elsevier Academic Press, 1996, pp. 141–147.

F. J. Schoen and R. N. Mitchell, "Tissues, the extracellular matrix, and cell-biomaterial interactions," in *Biomaterials science: an introduction to materials and medicine*, 2nd ed., B. D. Ratner, A. S. Hoffman, F. J. Schoen, and J. E. Lemons, Eds. San Diego: Elsevier Academic Press, 2004, pp. 260–281.

T. Scott-Burden, "Extracellular matrix: the cellular environment," *News in Physiological Science*, vol. 9, no. 3, pp. 110–115, 1994.

J. Shendure and H. Ji, "Next-generation DNA sequencing," *Nature biotechnology*, vol. 26, no. 10, p. 1135, 2008.

J. Shendure and E. L. Aiden, "The expanding scope of DNA sequencing," *Nature Biotechnology*, vol. 30, no. 11, p. 1084, 2012.

Y. Shi, H. Inoue, J. C. Wu, and S. Yamanaka, "Induced pluripotent stem cell technology: a decade of progress," *Nature Reviews Drug Discovery*, vol. 16, no. 2, p. 115, 2017.

D. Voet and J. G. Voet, *Biochemistry*, 3rd ed. Wiley, 2004.

A. Watts and R. C. Paterson, "Pulpal response to a zinc oxide–eugenol cement," *International Endodontic Journal*, vol. 20, no. 2, pp. 82–86, 1987.

M. F. Wolf, K. P. Coleman, and G. M. Lewerenz, "In vitro assessment of cell and tissue compatibility," in *Biomaterials science: an introduction to materials and medicine*, 3rd ed., B. D. Ratner, A. S. Hoffman, F. J. Schoen, and J. E. Lemons, Eds. San Diego: Elsevier Academic Press, 2013, pp. 593–608.

K. Zygourakis, "Quantification and regulation of cell migration," *Tissue Engineering*, vol. 2, no. 1, pp. 1–16, 1996.

# 10

# Biomaterial Implantation and Acute Inflammation

## Main Objective

To become familiar with the cells involved in the various stages of the acute inflammatory response and to understand the interplay of inflammation with the acquired immune response.

## Specific Objectives

1. To distinguish between innate and acquired immunity.
2. To compare and contrast the formation and actions of the four types of leukocytes.
3. To understand the physiological response of acute inflammation.
4. To learn the clinical signs of inflammation and their physiologic causes.
5. To understand the steps and signals involved in migration of neutrophils and their action in neutralizing foreign invaders.
6. To understand the role of macrophages in tissue inflammation and repair, as well as their interaction with the acquired immune system.
7. To understand the concepts behind and possible limitations to the *in vitro* techniques presented.

## 10.1 Introduction: Overview of Innate and Acquired Immunity

In the next few chapters, we will examine the specific protein and cellular inter-actions with biomaterials involved in various common responses, such as inflammation, immunity, and blood clotting. An example of the biological response to a material implanted for several weeks is found in Figure 10.1. Implantation of a bio-material is regarded as an assault on the body's status quo, or **homeostasis**. The body has developed several defense mechanisms against invasion in an attempt to return to homeostasis. Although originally intended to protect against assault from pathogens, many of the same cells and signaling molecules also respond to biomaterials.

One is born with **innate (nonspecific) immunity** and this is the first line of de-fense. If the invading organism is not cleared by the innate immune response, then

**Figure 10.1**

Sequence of images of *in vivo* response to a biodegradable, polymeric biomaterial (poly(propylene fumarate-co-ethylene glycol)) implanted subcutaneously in a rat for up to 12 weeks: (a) four days post-implantation, (b) three weeks post-implantation, (c) 12 weeks post-implantation. Hemotoxylin and eosin stain. The letter P indicates polymer or space left by polymer, N represents neutrophils, FC denotes fibrous capsule, M designates macrophages, and PF signifies polymer fragments embedded in the fibrous capsule. A typical wound-healing response is shown in this example. Within the first few days, infiltration of neutrophils into the implantation area is seen (acute inflammation), followed by the slower development of a fibrous capsule surrounding the implant (fibrous encapsulation/healing). Because this material is biodegradable, evidence of polymer fragmentation is also present at the later time points. (Reprinted with permission from [5].)

the body engages the **acquired (specific) immune response,**[1] which involves the activation of a type of white blood cell called the lymphocyte. In contrast to innate immunity, which resides in an individual at birth, the acquired immune response is activated when children are given vaccinations for specific diseases or develop immunity following exposure to particular pathogens.

If the organism persists after exposure to both the innate and acquired immune response, **infection** may develop. However, it is important to recognize that aspects of the innate response, such as inflammation, can occur without the presence of infection, as is often the case with biomaterial implantation. The two types of immune responses are highly intertwined, often sharing signaling molecules, as discussed later in the chapter. Both responses also depend, in large part, on the activity of various white blood cells (**leukocytes**).

---

[1]Innate and acquired immunity are terms developed by immunologists to describe these two different responses to foreign organisms. In a clinical setting, inflammation is often used as a synonym for innate immunity, and the "immune response" to a pathogen refers to the acquired immune response only.

### 10.1.1 Characteristics of Leukocytes

**10.1.1.1 Leukocyte Types**    There are four main types of leukocytes usually encountered in blood, each performing a unique function:

1. *Granulocytes.* These cells, so named because of their granular appearance under light microscopy, can be subdivided into neutrophils, eosinophils, and basophils. Their nuclei have multiple lobes (making them appear to have several nuclei) and their main function is to phagocytose ("eat") foreign invaders and aid in the inflammatory response.

2. *Monocytes.* Unlike the granulocytes, these cells do not have nuclei divided into lobes. They have a large phagocytic capability and play a central role in the inflammatory response.

3. *Lymphocytes/plasma cells.* These cells, including T and B cells, function as a part of the acquired immune response, and will be discussed further in Chapter 12. Lymphocytes can be divided into memory cells, which are responsible for a more rapid response if one is exposed to the same pathogen for a second time, and effector cells, which produce antibodies or take other actions to remove foreign invaders.

4. *Megakaryocytes.* This cell type is found only in the bone marrow, where it fragments to produce **platelets**. These nonnucleated fragments circulate in the blood and aid in blood clotting (discussed in Chapter 13).

**10.1.1.2 Leukocyte Formation**    The genesis of leukocytes begins with the pluripotent hematopoetic stem cell, which forms two different types of early precursor cells: one that eventually differentiates into red blood cells (erythrocytes), granulocytes, monocytes, and megakaryocytes, and one that differentiates into lymphocytes (Fig. 9.25). Granulocytes, monocytes, and megakaryocytes are formed in the bone marrow. Lymphocytes are created in the bone marrow and mature in the lymphoid tissue (lymph glands, spleen, thymus, and tonsils). Granulocytes are usually stored in the bone marrow until needed by the body. Lymphocytes are often stored in lymphoid tissue, but a fraction of them circulate in the blood at all times.

**10.1.1.3 Life Span of Leukocytes**    Generally, leukocytes are only present in the blood to be transported to a tissue where they are needed. Granulocytes, for example, usually spend 4–8 hours in the blood and 4–5 days in the target tissue, unless they die while combating an invading organism. Monocytes are present for 10–20 hours in the blood, and then migrate into the tissues, where they become **tissue macrophages**. Macrophages are larger than monocytes, possess more killing potential, and can live months to years. These cells provide a continual, resident defense against infection.

Lymphocytes enter the circulation with drainage of lymph fluid, stay in the blood for only a few hours, and then reenter the lymphoid tissue. Here, the cells can remain for some time or can almost immediately return to the bloodstream through the lymph drainage. This cycle is repeated again and again, so there is continual circulation of lymphocytes throughout the body. The life span of a single lymphocyte is weeks to years, depending on the body's need.

### 10.1.2 Sources of Innate Immunity

While the details of acquired immunity are discussed further in Chapter 12, the remainder of this chapter will focus on innate immunity. There are four main components of the defense provided by innate immunity:

1. Anatomic barriers (skin and mucous membranes)
2. Physiologic barriers (temperature of body, low pH in stomach)

**3.** Phagocytic cells (granulocytes)

**4.** Inflammation

It is important to note that a typical innate immune response will use a combination of these defenses to reduce the number of invading organisms, such as with the recruitment of phagocytic cells (number 3 on the list ) during the inflammatory process (number 4).

# 10.2   Clinical Signs of Inflammation and Their Causes

Clinically, inflammation is characterized by certain symptoms, called the four **cardinal signs**. These signs have Latin names, indicating that they have been observed for centuries as a part of the inflammatory process. Inflamed tissue often exhibits

**1.** Rubor (redness)

**2.** Tumor (swelling)

**3.** Calore (tissue heating)

**4.** Dolore (pain)

As medical knowledge has progressed, the causes of these particular symptoms have been determined. They are a result of physiological changes that help to define **acute inflammation**. Acute inflammation, a part of innate immunity, is an immediate response to tissue injury. The associated physiological changes occur in the first hours to days after the assault, so acute can be distinguished from **chronic inflammation**, in which changes persist over weeks to months. Both acute and chronic inflammation can be observed in the response to the implanted material in Figure 10.1. Chronic inflammation will be discussed further in Chapter 11.

Acute inflammation is mediated via substances released from the cells/proteins involved in innate immunity, from T-type lymphocytes (discussed further in Chapter 12), or via by-products of the blood-clotting cascade (see Chapter 13). Examples of these soluble substances, which cause a variety of responses, are listed in Table 10.1.

After injury, blood vessels in nearby regions will **vasodilate**, or expand. This is one of the reasons for both the development of redness and tissue heating during inflammation. There is also an increase in the permeability of nearby capillaries, leading to leakage of fluid into the surrounding (**interstitial**) space. Certain blood

**TABLE 10.1**

| Selected Mediators of Inflammatory Effects | |
| --- | --- |
| Inflammatory Effect | Mediators |
| Vasodilation of local blood vessels | Kinins, fibrinopeptides, histamine, prostaglandins |
| Increased permeability of capillaries | Bradykinin, fibrinopeptides, prostaglandins |
| Clotting in the interstitial spaces | Fibrinogen and other plasma proteins |
| Migration of neutrophils into tissue | IL-8, platelet activating factor (PAF), complement split products C3a, C5a, C5b67, fibrinopeptides, prostaglandins, leukotrienes |
| Migration of macrophages into tissue | IL-1, tumor necrosis factor-$\alpha$ (TNF-$\alpha$) |

proteins, such as fibrinogen, that have found their way to this interstitial space then encourage clotting to wall off the injured area and form an anatomical barrier to invading organisms. Other soluble factors act to attract large numbers of granulocytes and monocytes into the tissue to begin to phagocytose debris and foreign organisms. Individual tissue cells can also swell at this time. This combination of events is a main cause of the observed tumor, or tissue swelling, during inflammation. The pain associated with the inflammatory response is a by-product of the release of certain substances called **kinins** from the blood clotting cascade (see Chapter 13).

## 10.3 Role of Tissue Macrophages and Neutrophils

A key portion of the defense mechanism presented by the inflammatory response is the influx of phagocytic cells to combat foreign invaders. The body's first line of cellular defense is the actions of the tissue macrophages residing in the area. This response occurs within an hour after injury. Also during this time, there is an invasion of granulocytes, especially neutrophils, from the bloodstream in response to soluble factors in the inflamed tissue. The movement of the neutrophils out of the blood vessels and into the tissue is called **extravasation**.

### 10.3.1 Migration of Neutrophils

To extravasate, neutrophils must first bind to vascular endothelium, then penetrate the endothelial layer lining the blood vessel, and finally, migrate to the area of inflammation. This involves four major steps: **rolling, activation, arrest and adhesion**, and **migration** (Fig. 10.2). Rolling occurs because, as the neutrophils are carried along by the blood, they can bind briefly to the vascular endothelium through low-affinity selectin–carbohydrate interactions. As discussed in Chapter 9, selectins are receptors found on endothelial cells that have a carbohydrate-like portion to interact with proteoglycans (mucins) on the surface of the neutrophils. Selectins are upregulated on inflamed endothelium, facilitating the binding of neutrophils. However, since these are not strong interactions, the cells are tethered briefly to the endothelium, and then the flowing blood dislodges them. This is repeated over and over, giving the appearance that the cells are rolling along the surface of the blood vessel.

As the neutrophils are rolling, they can be activated by **chemoattractants**, substances that cause the migration of neutrophils toward the damaged tissue. Movement of cells in response to chemical stimuli is called **chemotaxis**, and extravasation is the first part of this process for neutrophils. Certain chemoattractant molecules can bind to specific receptors on the neutrophil's surface and activate intracellular pathways that induce a conformational change in integrin molecules in the cell membrane. The integrins now have a higher affinity for the immunoglobulin superfamily of cell adhesion molecules (CAMs) found on the surface of the endothelium.

The strong interaction between integrin receptors on the neutrophil and CAMs presented by endothelial cells leads to the cessation of cellular rolling and a firm adhesion to the endothelium (arrest and adhesion). The final stage of extravasation occurs as the neutrophil undergoes **transendothelial migration** into the inflamed tissue. The cell accomplishes this through **diapedesis**, or by squeezing parts of the cell at a time though small spaces between endothelial cells (Fig. 10.2). Although the

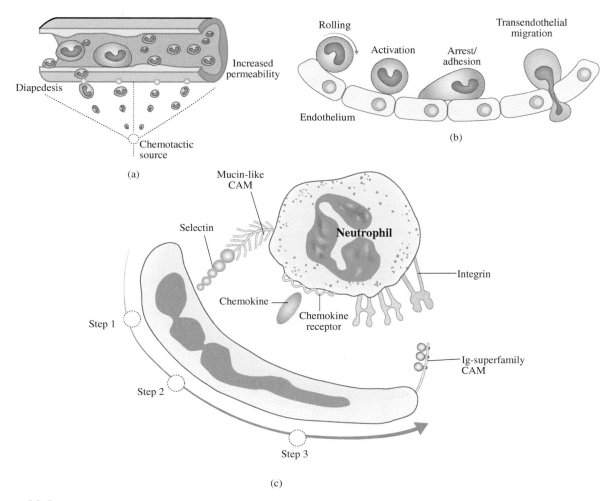

**Figure 10.2**
Extravasation of neutrophils. (a) To extravasate, neutrophils must bind to vascular endothelium, penetrate the endothelial layer lining the blood vessel, and migrate to the area of inflammation. (b) This involves four major steps: rolling, activation, arrest/adhesion, and migration. (c) Rolling occurs because, as the neutrophils are carried along by the blood, they can bind briefly to the vascular endothelium through low-affinity selectin–carbohydrate interactions (step 1 in diagram). Neutrophils can then be activated by chemoattractants. Chemoattractants (such as IL-8 and MIP-1b) bind to specific receptors on the neutrophil's surface and activate intracellular pathways that induce a conformational change in integrin molecules in the cell membrane (step 2). The integrins now have a higher affinity for the immunoglobulin superfamily of cell adhesion molecules (CAMs) found on the surface of the endothelium, which results in the cessation of rolling and a firm adhesion to the endothelium (arrest and adhesion, step 3) [8].

precise stimulus for transendothelial migration is unknown, once in the target tissue, neutrophils express high levels of receptors for further chemoattractants, allowing them to home to the area where they are needed.

## 10.3.2 Actions of Neutrophils

Once at the site of injury, neutrophils can perform several functions to deter invasion of foreign organisms and aid in the wound-healing response. These functions include killing mechanisms based on phagocytosis, a respiratory burst, or secretion of signaling molecules (see the following sections). These responses occur when neutrophils encounter particular molecular structures on the foreign cell surface. These **pathogen-associated molecular patterns** (PAMPs) are unique to invading organisms and do not occur in mammalian cells. Examples of PAMPs include oligosaccharides rich in mannose (found on bacterial and fungal cell walls) and lipopolysaccharide (LPS; from bacterial cell walls).

**10.3.2.1 Phagocytosis** The main task of neutrophils is to phagocytose foreign agents. In addition to the normal steps of endocytosis, as outlined in Chapter 9, neutrophils contain granules containing bactericidal agents and enzymes that join with the phagosome (a large vesicle through which large particles are ingested) to digest foreign matter. Activated neutrophils also express a greater number of receptors for antibody- and complement-coated foreign particles to help in their removal from the area. These coatings, to be discussed further in later chapters, are used specifically to speed the elimination of foreign substances. In this case, the activating chemical that upregulates the receptors for the coatings is a by-product of the complement cascade (see Chapter 12).

**10.3.2.2 Respiratory Burst** Activated neutrophils also exhibit a respiratory burst, in which glucose metabolism increases up to tenfold and oxygen consumption increases two- to threefold. This leads to the formation of reactive oxygen and nitrogen species (radicals and strong oxidizers) in intracellular granules. These can be released as another means to kill foreign organisms, and are also the compounds that promote corrosion and oxidative degradation of biomaterials in the body (see Chapter 5). However, such reactive species may also cause unwanted tissue damage, so it is important to contain the inflammatory response to localized areas. Means of inflammation control are discussed later in this chapter.

**10.3.2.3 Secretion of Chemical Mediators** In addition to their role in eliminating foreign invaders, neutrophils secrete a number of factors, called **cytokines**, that have specific effects on several cell types. The general actions of selected cytokines are listed in Table 10.2; however, the effects of specific cytokines on the inflammatory response will depend on the local concentration and the specific target cell, as well as interactions of the multiple cytokines that are present in the injured tissue. The complexities of cytokine signaling in the overall immune response are beyond the scope of this introductory text, so please see [1] for more details on classes of cytokines and their actions.

**TABLE 10.2**

| Actions of Cytokines | |
|---|---|
| Interleukin-1 (IL-1) | Promotes granulocyte migration, activates lymphocytes, promotes release of tissue factor |
| Interferon $\gamma$ | Activates macrophages |
| Interleukin-12 (IL-12) | Activates NK cells and lymphocytes |
| Transforming growth factor-$\beta$ (TGF-$\beta$) | Limits inflammatory response |
| Tumor necrosis factor-$\alpha$ (TNF-$\alpha$) | Promotes granulocyte migration, promotes release of tissue factor |

In general, activated neutrophils in tissues can release mediators to recruit monocytes to the area, as well as more neutrophils, thus enhancing the inflammatory response. Many of these factors are also chemotactic for lymphocytes, which provides a point of communication, or crossover, between the innate and acquired immune response.

## EXAMPLE PROBLEM 10.1

A company developed a new synthetic material for use in small diameter vascular graft applications. Initial studies conducted *in vitro* to examine the potential inflammatory response to the material involved the culture of cells isolated from whole blood in the presence of the material for 48 hours. The media was analyzed with the use of an ELISA following the culture period. It was found that the expression levels of IL-1 and TNF-α were approximately four times the normal physiological levels. A control material cultured in the same manner in the presence of the cells did not present an increase in IL-1 and TNF-α expression. Based on these results, will the material be expected to induce a stronger inflammatory response than the control material when implanted as a vascular graft *in vivo*? Why or why not? Does the material seem well suited for use in long-term vascular graft applications from an inflammation standpoint?

Solution:   An inflammatory response is to be expected with any surgical implantation of a material, as tissue disruption is a necessary part of the implantation procedure. However, some factors can instigate a more severe inflammatory response than would normally occur. In this case, it is stated that the experimental material invokes heightened expression of IL-1 and TNF-α, relative to a control material. Recalling that IL-1 and TNF-α are strong chemoattractants for granulocytes, it follows that heightened expression of these chemokines by leukocytes in the presence of the material will likely result in increased granulocyte activation and adhesion close to the implant and thus probably produce a greater inflammatory response *in vivo* than the control material. The problem does not give adequate information to comment on the expected time frame of the inflammatory response. However, a large initial inflammatory response could decrease the long-term viability of the implant, as it may be exposed to low pH, oxidizing species, and radical species that could potentially damage and/or alter the material. ■

# 10.4   Role of Other Leukocytes

Like neutrophils, the remainder of the leukocytes involved in innate immunity will also respond to recognition of PAMPs on foreign cells. The specific response for each cell type is outlined in the following sections.

## 10.4.1 Monocytes/Macrophages

Partially due to the signals released by the neutrophils, about five to six hours after the inflammatory response begins, monocytes arrive at the injury site. They then start to enlarge to form tissue macrophages. Macrophage maturation can take up to eight hours and involves swelling of the cell and formation of a large quantity of lysosomes. Over days to weeks, the macrophage will become the dominant cell type. The functions of the macrophage are similar to that of the neutrophil, although macrophages have greater and more sustainable killing capacities.

## 10.4.2 Actions of Macrophages

Like neutrophils, macrophages act to phagocytose foreign agents, as well as secrete chemical mediators to coordinate the responses from a number of body systems. However, the macrophage is also essential in the interaction of the innate and acquired immune response through its role as an antigen-presenting cell, as discussed in section 10.4.2.3. Finally, it should be noted that recent work has distinguished a range of sub-types of macrophages with different functions within the wound healing response, which are discussed in more detail at the end of this section.

**10.4.2.1 Phagocytosis and Biomaterials**  Although phagocytosis proceeds in the same way as for neutrophils, an individual macrophage can engulf many more bacteria or particles than a neutrophil. However, because macrophages remain at the site of injury longer, a number of events can occur that interfere with their phagocytic processes, especially if the injury is associated with implantation of a biomaterial. For example, if phagocytosed biomaterial particles resist degradation, they can remain sequestered in the macrophage until it dies and lyses, when they are re-released into the environment. If the number of these indigestible particles is small, this process may be repeated over a long period of time, with several cycles of macrophages recruited to the area in an attempt to eliminate the particles.

However, if there are a large number of indigestible particles, a clinical condition can develop due to the many macrophages continually dying and being replaced in a localized region. **Silicosis** is an example of such a condition caused by inhaled silica particles that remain in the lung tissue. These small crystals can activate a set of proteins in macrophages and neutrophils known as the *inflammasome*, which results in the secretion of the pro-inflammatory cytokine IL-1. Moreover, as the macrophages lyse after being unable to digest the silica, not only are the particles returned to the tissue, but other cellular contents, such as cytokines, are also released. One of the actions of these cytokines is to stimulate fibroblasts to form fibrous tissue in the afflicted areas. These fibrotic regions in the lungs reduce the surface area available for oxygen transfer, thus severely impairing oxygen intake by the patient. Similar mechanisms may be at play during loosening of metallic joint implants, so this is currently an area of significant research interest for biomaterialists.

In contrast, if the size of the nondegradable material is much larger than that of the cell, another event, **frustrated phagocytosis**, may be observed. This can occur either with neutrophils or macrophages, and involves the release of lysosomal enzymes and other products into the environment around the foreign material, as the particle is too large to be taken into the cell and degraded intracellularly. This usually occurs if the particle is greater than $5\mu$m along its largest dimension. The amount of enzymes released during this process has been linked to the size of the particle, suggesting that larger implants may induce a greater response.

**10.4.2.2 Secretion of Chemical Mediators**  Like other granulocytes, activated macrophages secrete many chemical mediators, depending on their sub-type (see section 10.4.3). Some or all of these factors have the following effects, in three general areas:

1. Effects on the inflammatory response
2. Effects on the acquired immune response
3. Systemic effects

Examining these responses in more detail, in inflammation, secretion of both IL-1 and TNF-$\alpha$ act to promote cell migration by increasing the expression of adhesion molecules on the vascular endothelium. They are also implicated in increasing the expression of CAMs that bind integrins on the granulocyte surface. In addition, TNF-$\alpha$ can directly activate both neutrophils and macrophages. Secretion of these cytokines also provides communication with the acquired immune response (see Chapter 12) as some cytokines released by macrophages, such as IL-1, have been found to activate and/or promote migration of lymphocytes. Secretion of anti-inflammatory proteins, such as TGF-$\beta$, can also occur (see sections 10.4.3–10.4.4 for more details).

Systemic effects are also possible. These cytokines induce production of acute-phase proteins by the liver, which results in a rise in body temperature (fever) to reduce the viability of an invading pathogen. IL-1 and TNF-α also promote synthesis and release of a molecule called *tissue factor* from endothelial cells and macrophages, which causes activation of the blood-clotting cascade (see Chapter 13).

**10.4.2.3 Role as Antigen-Presenting Cells**   A key function of the macrophage is its role as an **antigen-presenting cell (APC)**, which provides a direct connection between the innate and acquired immune responses. Activated macrophages exhibit increased expression of a certain receptor (major histocompatibility complex class II) that allows the presentation of foreign proteins (antigens) to lymphocytes. The interaction of certain lymphocytes with a macrophage having the protein attached to this receptor triggers the activation of the acquired immune response (discussed further in Chapter 12).

## EXAMPLE PROBLEM 10.2

Several patients who had undergone spinal fusion surgeries in the past three months were complaining to their orthopedic surgeon of excessive swelling and heat in the area of the surgery. After review of the patients' charts, it was discovered that titanium pedicle screws and rods were implanted in each case. The surgeon hypothesized that motion between the screws and the rods could have led to the formation of debris particles [2] immediately surrounding the implants. Upon further investigation, it was found that the amount of debris particles was proportional to the degree of motion between the pedicle screws and the rods. Also, the presence of macrophages was noted to be directly proportional to the amount of debris particles present. How would the expected tissue response to the wear debris particles from the implants differ from the expected response to the bulk implants?

**Solution:**   An inflammatory response ensues upon the tissue injury induced by any surgical implantation of a biomaterial. In the ideal case, the inflammatory response is resolved in a number of days. However, many biomaterials are recognized as foreign objects and result in a prolonged inflammatory response, as phagocytic cells such as macrophages attempt to remove the material. Materials much larger than macrophages in size, such as a pedicle screw, are too large to be phagocytosed. As a result, macrophages surround the material and release lysosomal enzymes into the extracellular environment in an attempt to degrade the material in a process called frustrated phagocytosis. On the other hand, micrometer scale wear debris particles from the implants are capable of being endocytosed by the macrophages. As titanium is not biodegradable, the particles will remain in the macrophages in this case until cell death and lysis, at which time the particles will be reintroduced into the environment, where they can be endocytosed by other macrophages. Additionally, the creation of wear debris increases the total amount of surface area of the implant material being presented, thereby increasing the degree of biological response. ■

## 10.4.3 Macrophage Subtypes

In the past decade, increasing attention has been paid to distinguishing sub-types of macrophages that play distinct roles in acute inflammation and wound healing. Originally, two general sub-types were distinguished based on surface markers and the type of cytokines secreted. M1 (or classically activated) macrophages are implicated in many of the actions described in Section 10.4.2, including pathogen clearance and release of reactive oxygen radials, as well as secretion of more pro-inflammatory cytokines. In contrast, M2 (or alternatively activated) macrophages are associated with extracellular matrix deposition, vascular remodeling, and secretion of more anti-inflammatory cytokines (see section 10.5).

Subsequent studies have determined that there is a large degree of plasticity between these sub-types and that rather than simply two, there are likely a gamut of phenotypes (or **polarization states**) between M1 and M2, depending on the local environment for the specific cell. However, for biomaterials, the polarization state of the macrophage can lead to differences in level of fibrosis around an implant, so characterization of the local cellular composition around an implant may be needed in *in vivo* studies to predict long-term performance.

### 10.4.4 Other Granulocytes

Although the cellular events of inflammation are associated primarily with the actions of neutrophils and macrophages, other granulocytes are also involved to a lesser degree. Eosinophils respond to chemoattractants in a similar manner as neutrophils/macrophages, but their phagocytic capacities are relatively small. They are important, however, in that they can attach to and destroy parasites. In addition, they may detoxify some of the inflammation-inducing agents, thus preventing the spread of inflammation outside a localized area.

Basophils are found in the blood, and are similar in function to mast cells found in various tissues. These cells can be activated to release heparin, histamine, bradykinin, and serotonin, which are soluble mediators of inflammation (some of the actions of these substances can be found in Table 10.1). Basophils and mast cells also play a large role in the allergic reaction, discussed further in Chapter 12.

## 10.5  Termination of Acute Inflammation

The acute inflammatory response is well designed to help in recovering homeostasis and preventing the invasion of foreign organisms after injury. However, several of the physiological changes associated with this response would prove detrimental to the function of the tissue if they were widespread or continued for a long period of time. Therefore, several means to reduce or end acute inflammation are found in all tissues.

Throughout the inflammatory process, the interaction of a variety of chemical mediators provides a system of checks and balances to ensure that the effects are localized. One example of this is the production of IL-1 receptor agonist (IL-1Ra) by the same cells that produce IL-1 (macrophages, among others). This molecule has a similar chemical structure to IL-1 and thus binds to the same receptors on target cells, but, unlike IL-1, does not stimulate them. In this way, target cells' activation can be inhibited by binding IL-1Ra (Fig. 10.3). Therefore, the relative amount of IL-1 and IL-1Ra produced by macrophages aids in determining how severe the inflammatory response becomes.

**Figure 10.3**
Schematic showing a cell's response to IL-1 receptor agonist (IL-1Ra) and IL-1. IL-1Ra has a similar chemical structure to IL-1 and thus binds to the same receptors on target cells. However, unlike IL-1, IL-1Ra does not stimulate the cells. In this way, binding IL-1Ra can inhibit a target cell's activation. The severity of the inflammatory response is determined by the relative amounts of IL-1 and IL-1Ra.

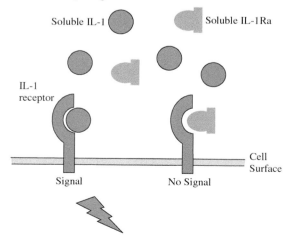

An alternative means of controlling the extent of inflammation is production of a substance that limits the inflammatory response. In some cases, transforming growth factor-$\beta$ (TGF-$\beta$), produced by both macrophages (particularly M2-like macrophages) and lymphocytes, has been known to have this effect by inhibiting activation of certain cell types involved in the inflammatory response. Finally, it is important to note that the chemical mediators involved in inflammation are quickly inactivated or destroyed in solution, meaning they must act within a small radius from where they were produced. This further promotes a localized response to injury.

As the stimulus for acute inflammation is removed, the response may terminate in several ways. Acute inflammation may progress to chronic inflammation, which, as discussed in Chapter 11, is characterized by the presence of lymphocytes and other mononuclear cells. Alternatively, it may be more successfully resolved by the formation of granulation tissue and a foreign body reaction. This reaction, described in detail in the next chapter, is considered to be a normal wound-healing response in the presence of a nondegradable biomaterial.

# 10.6 Techniques: *In Vitro* Assays for Inflammatory Response

Many of the *in vitro* assays performed to gain information about how or to what extent biomaterials provoke an inflammatory response fall into the categories described in Chapter 9. In most cases, cells are isolated from human blood and cultured in the presence of the sample material for hours to days before testing for cellular activation. It is expected that with a greater level of activation, the biomaterial will be more pro-inflammatory *in vivo*. These experiments can be performed on a variety of cells involved in the inflammatory response, including endothelial cells and several types of leukocytes.

## 10.6.1 Leukocyte Assays

*In vitro* techniques involving leukocytes (most commonly neutrophils or macrophages) generally examine one or more of the following as indicators of cell activation:

1. Cell adhesion and spreading
2. Cell death
3. Cell migration
4. Cytokine release
5. Cell surface marker expression

Cell adhesion can be quantified in a number of ways, as discussed in the previous chapter. These means include radioactively or fluorescently labeling the cells or lysing the cells and then measuring the release of a particular intracellular molecule. Also as mentioned in Chapter 9, judging the extent of cell spreading is more qualitative and involves staining and then imaging the adherent cells with a light microscope.

Assays for migration of inflammatory cells, both in response to degradation products from biomaterials and along biomaterial surfaces in response to other stimuli, are extremely important since movement to areas of need is a key function of this cell type. Versions of all of the migration assays described in Chapter 9 have been employed to study cell movement. Direct observation of individual cells over time may provide information about the effect of material properties on cell motility. Alternatively, a population assay may be used to examine the migration of a group of monocytes or granulocytes after culture with and without exposure to the sample biomaterial.

Release into the media of pro-inflammatory cytokines, such as TNF-α, is another distinctive marker of cell activation. Detection is usually accomplished via the use of an ELISA (see Chapter 8) for the cytokine of interest.

A final assay for monocyte or granulocyte activation requires the identification of cells expressing certain cell surface markers, usually specific receptors that will eventually interact with the ligands presented by endothelial cells. Since these receptors are upregulated in response to certain stimuli, including those discussed earlier, the number of cells in a population expressing these markers after exposure to a biomaterial provides a means of quantifying the ability of the material to induce activation. Cell counting is accomplished using a **fluorescence-activated cell sorter** (**FACS**) or **flow cytometry** techniques.

FACS machines and flow cytometry operate on similar principles and are based on immunostaining techniques (see Chapter 9). After a fluorescently tagged antibody to the receptor of interest has been incubated with the inflammatory cells, the entire population is then placed in the FACS (Fig. 10.4). The cells are passed one at a time from a vibrating nozzle past a laser that is set to emit a wavelength of light that will excite the fluorophore. The intensity of the fluorescence for each leukocyte (number of antibody molecules attached to the cell) is monitored and sent as output to a computer, enabling quantification of relative amounts of fluorescing (activated) and nonfluorescing (nonactivated) cells. Modern machines use several lasers, each with different emission wavelengths, and thus can detect cells stained with multiple antibodies simultaneously.

Physical separation of the activated and nonactivated cells is also possible via FACS. Detection of fluorescence causes the equipment to induce a charge on the droplet containing that cell. Droplets (cells) can therefore be deflected from electrically charged plates and directed to different containers. Depending on the configuration of these plates, cells can be separated into two or more groups displaying varying degrees of fluorescence (Fig. 10.4). Since this process is nondestructive, after separation, if desired, individual cells can be subjected to single cell genomics, transcriptomics, or proteomics, as described in Chapter 9.

## 10.6.2 Other Assays

A further *in vitro* assay for the inflammatory potential of biomaterials tests the response of endothelial cells. The upregulation of cell surface receptors (e.g., selectins) or ligands (e.g., CAMs) on endothelial cells promotes the migration of neutrophils and macrophages and thus is a key step in the inflammatory response. Therefore, after exposure to a biomaterial, the presence of these cell surface markers is examined using similar methods (FACS or flow cytometry) as described for leukocytes.

A recent development in *in vitro* assays utilizes model systems derived from tissue-engineered constructs to examine the inflammatory response. For example, a tissue-engineered skin replacement can be cocultured with a potential skin-contacting biomaterial and the release of inflammatory cytokines by the cells in the construct may be monitored via ELISA or other means [3]. These three-dimensional constructs, which may include a variety of cell types and are usually called *organ-on-a-chip* models, could be a future means to obtain information that would help to correlate *in vitro* and *in vivo* responses.

**Figure 10.4**
Cell characterization via fluorescence-activated cell sorting (FACS). First, fluorescently tagged cells are placed in the FACS. The cells are passed one at a time from a vibrating nozzle past a laser that is set to emit a wavelength of light that will excite the fluorophore. The intensity of the fluorescence for each cell (number of antibody molecules attached to the cell) is monitored and sent as output to a computer, enabling quantification of relative amounts of fluorescing (expressing receptor) and nonfluorescing cells (not expressing receptor). Physical separation of the two cell populations is also possible. The laser excitation causes a cell to possess a negative charge in proportion to the intensity of the fluorescence. Cells can therefore be deflected from electrically charged plates. Depending on the configuration of these plates, cells can be separated into two or more groups displaying varying degrees of fluorescence.

## EXAMPLE PROBLEM 10.3

The following FACS data was collected from mice hearts that were either healthy or had undergone myocardial infarction (MI or heart attack) to determine the role of inflammation in tissue damage after a heart attack. In both cases, the hearts were removed after 7 days and cells were isolated and treated with an antibody to CD11b, which is a cell surface marker for macrophages, prior to FACS analysis. (Note: SSC in the following graph is side scatter data used to make sure the machine is registering cells and not tissue debris. Low SSC indicates cells in this case.) Does it appear that inflammation may play a role in myocardial infarction [4]?.

**Solution:** Yes, the data suggests that inflammation may play a role in tissue damage after a myocardial infarction. While the data would still need to be normalized to take into account the total cell number in each sample, it does appear that there are more CD11b positive cells in the myocardial infarction sample, suggesting that inflammation occurs in the tissue after a heart attack. (This finding has been corroborated in many studies, and it is thought that this early inflammatory response leads to "scarring" in the heart, which is why the muscle does not pump as effectively after myocardial infarction—see Chapter 11 for the details of how scar formation occurs after inflammation.)  ∎

## Summary

- The first line of defense of the body to foreign materials and organisms is innate or nonspecific immunity. If the innate immune response is not sufficient to neutralize the invasion, an acquired immune response can be invoked. Innate immunity depends in part on the actions of white blood cells like granulocytes and monocytes. Acquired immunity involves the action of white blood cells called lymphocytes.

- Granulocytes and lymphocytes are both derived from hematopoetic stem cells. Granulocytes, monocytes, and megakaryocytes are formed in the bone marrow, while lymphocytes are created in the lymphoid tissue. Granulocytes commonly remain in the bone marrow until needed. Their main function is to assist in the inflammatory response and to phagocytose foreign material. Lymphocytes, however, are generally stored in the lymphoid tissues, but a certain number of them circulate in the blood at all times.

- The clinical signs of inflammation are rubor (redness), tumor (swelling), calore (tissue heating), and dolore (pain). Vasodilation of blood vessels in the vicinity of an injury results in redness and tissue heating. The leaking of fluid into the interstitial space caused by an increase in the permeability of surrounding capillaries in response to an injury contributes to swelling, as does the swelling of individual cells. A blood clotting cascade ensues to segregate the injured area and to create a barrier to invading organisms. This cascade involves the release of kinins, which can result in pain. This immediate response (in the range of hours to days) is considered acute inflammation.

- Low affinity interactions between circulating neutrophils and the vascular endothelium result in an apparent rolling of the neutrophils along the surface of the blood vessel. Chemoattractants can activate neutrophils, resulting in a higher affinity of the integrins on the neutrophils for the CAMs on the vascular endothelial cells. The stronger interactions result in the arrest and adhesion of the neutrophils to the vascular endothelial cells. Once adhered, the neutrophils undergo transendothelial migration by a process of diapedesis to enter the extravascular space, where they encounter further chemoattractants to direct them to the site of injury.

- Once activated by pathogen-associated molecular patterns (PAMPs), neutrophils can deter invasion of foreign organisms through phagocytosis, a respiratory burst, or secretion of chemical mediators. Phagocytosis involves the engulfment and ingestion of the insulting material by the cell, where it can be digested by enzymes and bactericidal agents. Activated neutrophils can form granules containing highly reactive nitrogen and oxygen species as a result of the respiratory burst, which can be released to kill foreign organisms. Additionally, activated neutrophils secrete a number of cytokines to recruit monocytes and other neutrophils to the area of insult.

- Macrophages phagocytose materials as neutrophils do; however, macrophages can engulf many more bacteria or particles than a neutrophil. Macrophages and neutrophils both can be involved in frustrated phagocytosis in response to a nondegradable material much larger than the cell. Activated macrophages secrete cytokines that can have systemic effects as well as effects on the inflammatory and/or acquired immune responses. A key function of the activated macrophage is its role as an antigen-presenting cell, which provides a direct connection between the innate and acquired immune responses. Macrophages can be polarized between the M1 (or classically activated/pro-inflammatory) and M2 (or alternatively activated/pro-regenerative) states.

- A variety of *in vitro* techniques can be employed to gain information regarding the inflammatory response that a biomaterial may invoke. *In vitro* techniques involving leukocytes generally examine cell adhesion and spreading, cell death, cell migration, cytokine release, and/or cell surface markers as indicators of cell activation. Fluorescence-activated cell sorting and flow cytometry techniques provide a means for quantifying the number of cells (leukocytes or endothelial cells) expressing certain surface markers. Additional *in vitro* assays for inflammatory potential include the use of model systems derived from tissue engineering constructs.

# Problems

10.1  List the four cardinal signs of inflammation and explain their cellular and molecular causes.

10.2  Explain the main functions of each of the four main types of leukocytes.

10.3  Explain the role of integrin receptors in transendothelial migration.

10.4  (a) Complete the following table to explain the differences between monocytes and macrophages. Specifically address differences in cell origin/formation, location where these cells appear in the body, time of occurrence in the inflammatory process (hours/days/weeks ), and cell function.

| | Monocytes | Macrophages |
|---|---|---|
| Cell origin/formation | | |
| Location in the body | | |
| Time of occurrence in the inflammatory process | | |
| Cell function | | |

(b) What is the main difference in M1-like and M2-like macrophages?

10.5   List three parameters that can be tested as indicators of neutrophil activation and describe why each of these things are important for the overall function of neutrophils in the inflammatory response.

10.6   You are developing a coating for a vascular stent. You decide to test the inflammatory potential of your material by culturing with macrophages. After 48 hours of culture, the culture media was collected to measure the expression levels of various cytokines using ELISA. The following table shows the absorbance data of several Interferon $\gamma$ standards of known concentrations, the media from cells cultured on the new polymeric coating, and the media from cells cultured on the stent without coating (control).

(a) Calculate the concentration of Interferon $\gamma$ in the media from cells on the polymeric coating and control. (Standard curve should be used to calculate exact concentrations.)

| Sample | Concentration (pg/ml) | Absorbance |
|---|---|---|
| Standard 1 | 5 | 0.322 |
| Standard 2 | 10 | 0.345 |
| Standard 3 | 25 | 0.411 |
| Standard 4 | 50 | 0.542 |
| Standard 5 | 100 | 0.767 |
| Standard 6 | 200 | 1.253 |
| Polymer coating | | 0.575 |
| Control | | 0.675 |

(b) You also completed ELISAs in the same manner to test the level of other inflammatory cytokines, as shown in the following table. From the point of view of the inflammatory response, would you recommend continuing to develop this material for a vascular stent? Justify your answer based on all of the ELISA data collected.

| | Polymer coating (pg/ml) | Control (pg/ml) |
|---|---|---|
| IL-12 | 30 | 28 |
| TNF-$\alpha$ | 390 | 400 |
| IL-1 | 250 | 260 |

# References

1. J. A. Owen, J. Punt, S. A. Stranford, and P. P. Jones, *Kuby immunology*, 7th ed. New York: W. H. Freeman, 2013.
2. J. C. Wang, W. D. Yu, H. S. Sandhu, F. Betts, S. Bhuta, and R. B. Delamarter, "Metal debris from titanium spinal implants," *Spine*, vol. 24, no. 9, pp. 899–903, May 1999.
3. S. Trasciatti, A. Podesta, S. Bonaretti, V. Mazzoncini, and S. Rosini, "In vitro effects of different formulations of bovine collagen on cultured human skin," *Biomaterials*, vol. 19, no. 10, pp. 897–903, May 1998.
4. M. Shiraishi *et al.*, "Alternatively activated macrophages determine repair of the infarcted adult murine heart," *The Journal of Clinical Investigation*, vol. 126, no. 6, pp. 2151–2166, 2016.
5. L. J. Suggs, R. S. Krishnan, C. A. Garcia, S. J. Peter, J. M. Anderson, and A. G. Mikos, "In vitro and in vivo degradation of poly(propylene fumarate-co-ethylene glycol) hydrogels," *Journal of Biomedical Materials Research*, vol. 42, no. 2, pp. 312–20, Nov. 1998.
6. A. C. Guyton and J. E. Hall, *Textbook of medical physiology*, 9th ed. Philadelphia: W.B. Saunders, 1996.
7. J. Kuby, *Immunology*, 3rd ed. New York: W.H. Freeman, 1997.
8. B. D. Ratner, in *Biomaterials science: an introduction to materials in medicine*, 3rd ed., B. D. Ratner, A. S. Hoffman, F. J. Schoen, and J. E. Lemons, Eds. San Diego: Elsevier Academic Press, 2012.

# Additional Reading

B. Alberts, A. Johnson, J. Lewis, M. Raff, K. Roberts, and P. Walter, *Molecular biology of the cell*, 4th ed. New York: Garland Publishing, 2002.

J. M. Anderson, "Mechanisms of inflammation and infection with implanted devices," in *Cardiovascular Pathology*, vol. 2, 1993, pp. 33–41.

J. Black, *Biological performance of materials: fundamentals of biocompatibility*, 4th ed. New York: CRC Press, 2005.

R. W. Colman, J. Hirsh, V. J. Marder, A. W. Clowes, and J. N. George, *Hemostasis and thrombosis: basic principles and clinical practice*. Lippincott, Williams, and Wilkins, 2001.

K. C. Dee, D. A. Puleo, and R. Bizios, *An introduction to tissue-biomaterial interactions*. Hoboken: Wiley-Liss, 2002.

D. Granchi *et al.*, "Flow-cytometric analysis of leukocyte activation induced by polyethylene-terephthalate with and without pyrolytic carbon coating," *Journal of Biomedical Materials Research*: vol. 39, no. 4, pp. 549–553, 1998.

C. Gretzer, K. Gisselfält, E. Liljensten, L. Ryden, and P. Thomsen, "Adhesion, apoptosis and cytokine release of human mononuclear cells cultured on degradable poly (urethane urea), polystyrene and titanium in vitro," *Biomaterials*, vol. 24, no. 17, pp. 2843–2852, 2003.

N. Hallab, J. J. Jacobs, and J. Black, "Hypersensitivity to metallic biomaterials: a review of leukocyte migration inhibition assays," *Biomaterials*, vol. 21, no. 13, pp. 1301–14, Jul. 2000.

C. R. Jenney, K. M. DeFife, E. Colton, and J. M. Anderson, "Human monocyte/macrophage adhesion, macrophage motility, and IL-4-induced foreign body giant cell formation on silane-modified surfaces in vitro," *Journal of Biomedical Materials Research*: vol. 41, no. 2, pp. 171–184, 1998.

M. E. Ogle, C. E. Segar, S. Sridhar, and E. A. Botchwey, "Monocytes and macrophages in tissue repair: Implications for immunoregenerative biomaterial design," *Experimental Biology and Medicine*, vol. 241, no. 10, pp. 1084–1097, 2016.

J. A. Owen, J. Punt, S. A. Stranford, and P. P. Jones, *Kuby immunology*, 7th ed. New York: W. H. Freeman, 2013.

F. O. Martinez and S. Gordon, "The M1 and M2 paradigm of macrophage activation: time for reassessment," *F1000prime Reports*, vol. 6, 2014.

R. N. Mitchell, "Innate and adaptive immunity: the immune response to foreign materials," in *Biomaterials science: an introduction to materials and medicine*, 3rd ed., B. D. Ratner, A. S. Hoffman, F. J. Schoen, and J. E. Lemons, Eds. San Diego: Academic Press, 2013, pp. 512–532.

B. O. Palsson and S. N. Bhatia, *Tissue engineering*. Upper Saddle River: Pearson Prentice Hall, 2004.

F. R. Pu, R. L. Williams, T. K. Markkula, and J. A. Hunt, "Expression of leukocyte–endothelial cell adhesion molecules on monocyte adhesion to human endothelial cells on plasma treated PET and PTFE in vitro," *Biomaterials*, vol. 23, no. 24, pp. 4705–4718, 2002.

M. Shen and T. A. Horbett, "The effects of surface chemistry and adsorbed proteins on monocyte/macrophage adhesion to chemically modified polystyrene surfaces," *Journal of Biomedical Materials Research*: vol. 57, no. 3, pp. 336–345, 2001.

R. Sridharan, A. R. Cameron, D. J. Kelly, C. J. Kearney, and F. J. O'Brien, "Biomaterial based modulation of macrophage polarization: a review and suggested design principles," *Materials Today*, vol. 18, no. 6, pp. 313–325, Jul. 2015.

F. H. Silver and D. L. Christiansen, *Biomaterials science and biocompatibility*. New York: Springer Science & Business Media, 1999.

M. C. Trindade, M. Lind, D. Sun, D. J. Schurman, S. B. Goodman, and R. Lane Smith, "In vitro reaction to orthopaedic biomaterials by macrophages and lymphocytes isolated from patients undergoing revision surgery," *Biomaterials*, vol. 22, no. 3, pp. 253–259, Feb. 2001.

# 11

# Wound Healing and the Presence of Biomaterials

**Main Objective**

To understand the stages and types of resolution after biomaterial implantation and how this differs from wound healing without the presence of an implant.

**Specific Objectives**

1. To identify the characteristics of granulation tissue.
2. To understand how implant properties affect the foreign body response.
3. To compare and contrast fibrous encapsulation and chronic inflammation.
4. To distinguish among four different types of resolution and characterize them as successful or unsuccessful outcomes.
5. To compare and contrast wound repair and regeneration.
6. To compare and contrast the stages of normal wound healing with the stages after biomaterial implantation.
7. To understand the concerns and possible limitations associated with *in vivo* (animal) models for assessment of inflammatory response and biocompatibility.

## 11.1 Introduction: Formation of Granulation Tissue

In this chapter, we will continue to examine the body's response to an implanted biomaterial with a focus on events that occur starting approximately 24 hours after implantation. (Acute response to implantation was discussed in Chapter 10.) As early as one day postimplantation (or injury), macrophages and other cells involved in the inflammatory process provide chemoattractive signals to promote migration of fibroblasts and vascular endothelial cells into the area (Fig. 11.1). Within three to five days, microscopic observation of the beginning of granulation tissue formation is possible.

**Granulation tissue** is characterized histologically by a pebbly, granular appearance (thus its name) (Fig. 11.2). This is caused by the creation of many vascular buds sprouting from existing blood vessels. This process is called **neovascularization** or **angiogenesis**. At its peak, granulation tissue has more capillaries per volume than any other tissue type.

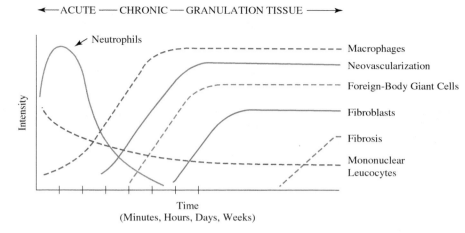

**Figure 11.1**
Wound-healing response of the body after injury or biomaterial implantation [7].

This stage of wound healing is also characterized by the proliferation of **fibroblasts**. Fibroblasts, mentioned briefly in the previous chapter, are a committed cell type found in many tissues. One of their main functions is to synthesize and maintain connective tissues by producing an extracellular matrix rich in collagen and proteoglycans. In granulation tissue, some of these fibroblasts may take on features of smooth muscle cells and are termed **myofibroblasts**. Myofibroblasts are responsible for wound contraction, which results in faster healing due to a decrease in the overall defect size.

## EXAMPLE PROBLEM 11.1

Blood vessels can be formed *de novo* during development in a process termed **vasculogenesis**. In this process, vascular progenitor cells migrate and differentiate to form blood vessels in response to cues presented through the extracellular matrix and cytokines. How does angiogenesis differ from vasculogenesis? Why is blood supply important for developing and regenerating tissue?

**Solution:**   Angiogenesis involves the creation of new blood vessels through a process of budding or sprouting from existing blood vessels. Thus, angiogenesis is not a *de novo*

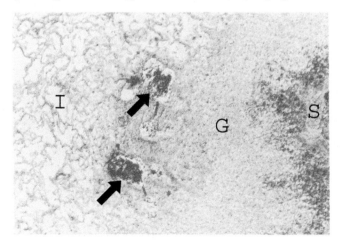

**Figure 11.2**
Granulation tissue formation at the tissue/material interface. Large surface wounds in the spleen were treated with a porous sodium amylose succinate material in a canine model. A well-developed zone of granulation tissue (G) separates the spleen (S) and the polymer (I). Blood-vessel-like areas are at the leading edge of the granulation tissue (arrows). The sample is stained with hematoxylin and eosin, which highlights the nuclei of the cells (black dots). Original magnification 60× [8].

process. Vasculogenesis, however, does not involve sprouting or budding of new blood vessels from existing ones. Rather, it entails the creation of new vessels from vascular progenitor cells guided by cellular and extracellular matrix signals. Blood vessels are necessary in developing and/or regenerating tissue to provide cells with nutrients and to remove cellular waste products. ∎

## 11.2 Foreign Body Reaction

Granulation tissue may form part of the **foreign body reaction**. This reaction involves **foreign body giant cells** (**FBGCs**) and the elements of granulation tissue discussed previously. Foreign body giant cells are multinucleated cells formed by the fusion of monocytes/macrophages in an attempt to phagocytose the biomaterial, which is much larger than a single cell.

The relative composition of the foreign body reaction is dependent on several factors associated with the implant. One of these is the surface properties of the material. This includes the topography (roughness) and surface chemistry of the implant. For example, for smooth implants, such as silicone breast prostheses, layers of macrophages one to two cells in thickness can be observed. However, for rough implants, such as the outer surfaces of degrading biomaterials, a mixture of macrophages and FBGCs is seen (Fig. 11.3 and 11.4).

The shape of the implanted material (in particular, its surface area to volume ratio) can also have an effect on the foreign body reaction. Implants with a high surface area to volume ratio (e.g., fabrics or porous materials) have higher amounts of macrophages and FBGCs at the tissue–material interface, while implants with a lower surface area to volume ratio show more fibrous (granulation) tissue production. FBGCs and/or macrophages may remain surrounding a biomaterial for the lifetime of the implant, but it is not clear if these cells are actively secreting bioactive factors, such as degradative enzymes or chemotactic agents, during this entire period.

**Figure 11.3**
Scanning electron micrograph demonstrating a foreign body reaction to poly(propylene fumarate-co-ethylene glycol) implanted subcutaneously in a rat model. Both macrophages (smaller cells) and foreign body giant cells (larger cells) can be seen in the image. Scale bar 100 μm. (Reprinted with permission from [9].)

**Figure 11.4**
Histological sections from a rabbit wound chamber. (a) Foreign-body reaction to particulate PMMA (round voids) with numerous macrophages (small arrow) identified in the tissue. (b) Foreign-body reaction to large particles of UHMWPE (irregular voids) with macrophages and foreign-body giant cells (large arrow). Basic Oil Red O Stain, original magnification 60×. (Reprinted with permission from [10].)

# 11.3 Fibrous Encapsulation

The final stage of healing for implants made from nondegradable materials is fibrous encapsulation (Fig. 11.1). This involves granulation tissue maturation, which is marked by the presence of larger blood vessels and alignment of collagen fibers in response to local mechanical forces. In this case, the presence of the biomaterial prevents both the collapse of the capsule surrounding the implant and the subsequent formation of a scar, as would occur in normal wound healing (see later in this chapter for an in-depth discussion of scar formation). Fibrous encapsulation is considered an acceptable result after implantation of many biomaterials.

The degree of long-term (four weeks postimplantation and later) capsule formation depends on several factors:

1. Degree of original injury during implantation
2. Amount of subsequent cell death
3. Location of implant site
4. Degradation time of implant (if degradable)

More specifically, the thickness of the capsule may be affected by the following factors:

1. Amount and composition of small particulates produced
2. Mechanical factors at implant site
3. Shape of implant
4. Electrical currents (if produced)

The size of the fibrous capsule increases in proportion to the rate of shedding of small particulates, which can be caused by corrosion, degradation, and wear. The chemical composition of these fragments, particularly their cytotoxicity, is also a large factor in capsule formation. In addition, the capsule becomes thicker in response to mechanical factors like motion between the implant and the surrounding tissue.

Thicker capsules have been observed over edges and distinct changes in surface features of the material and, thus, are affected by the shape of the implant. Finally, in implants producing electrical currents, such as stimulating electrodes, capsule thickness corresponds to current density. In this case, functioning electrodes can mediate changes in local pH and $O_2$ concentrations and encourage corrosion, so capsule formation may be caused by these indirect effects as well as the presence of the electric current.

### EXAMPLE PROBLEM 11.2

A pharmaceutical laboratory developed a nondegradable synthetic polymer implant for controlled drug delivery. The researchers envision subcutaneous implantation of the delivery device, with the release of the drug being controlled by diffusion. They determined the release kinetics of the drug from the carrier in studies conducted *in vitro*, but have found that the release kinetics differ when the device is implanted *in vivo*. Specifically, the drug is found to release more slowly *in vivo*. What are some possible factors that could contribute to the differences in the observed release kinetics? Would a cube-shaped form of the implant or a spherical form of the implant of the same volume likely result in a thicker fibrous capsule formation? Why?

**Solution:** The complex environment encountered *in vivo* is difficult to replicate in experiments conducted *in vitro*. Consequently, it is common for experimental results obtained from *in vitro* studies to differ from studies conducted *in vivo*. The final stage of the tissue response to the implantation of the nondegradable synthetic polymer drug delivery device will be fibrous encapsulation of the device. The fibrous capsule could potentially serve as a barrier to the diffusion of the drug out of the device, thereby slowing the release. Fibrous encapsulation would be very difficult to replicate *in vitro*; thus, the observed release *in vitro* likely did not entail a diffusional barrier presented by a tissue element. Additionally, the presence and concentrations of enzymes could differ between the cases studied *in vitro* and *in vivo*, and could affect the release kinetics. A cube-shaped implant would probably result in a thicker fibrous capsule formation than a spherical implant of the same volume, as the distinct edges and corners of the cubic implant could promote a greater fibrous tissue formation response to isolate the implant. Additionally, the surface area presented by a cube is greater than the surface area presented by a sphere of the same volume; thus, the presentation of more surface area of a foreign material with sharp corners could elicit a more pronounced fibrous encapsulation and possibly an increased presence of macrophages and foreign body giant cells. ∎

## 11.4 Chronic Inflammation

**Chronic inflammation** is less uniform histologically than acute inflammation (Fig. 11.5). It is characterized by the presence of mononuclear cells, including lymphocytes and plasma cells, which may also indicate that the material has triggered an acquired immune response (discussed further in the following chapter). Although it is common to see a short-lived chronic inflammatory response between the end of acute inflammation and the full development of granulation tissue (Fig 11.1), persistence of chronic inflammation beyond this point is considered pathologic.

In some cases, chronic inflammation can include the presence of **granulomas**. Granulomas consist of a layer of FBGCs surrounding a nonphagocytosable particle. The FBGCs are themselves contained within a ring of large modified macrophages called **epitheloid cells**. This cell mass is then surrounded by a layer of lymphocytes. Chronic inflammation can be a result of the chemical or physical properties of the biomaterial, or can be caused by motion at the implant site.

**Figure 11.5**
Example of chronic inflammation in the form of a granuloma surrounding a nondegradable debris particle from a hip implant. The dark-staining cells towards the outside of the ring are primarily epithelioid macrophages. Light portion in the center is the debris particle. Hematoxylin and eosin stain. Original magnification 200×, inset 400× [16].

## 11.5 Four Types of Resolution

As mentioned in the previous chapter, the overall goal of the inflammation and wound healing response is to restore the body's status quo after injury. Therefore, the formation of a new equilibrium state can be considered a **resolution** of this response. There are four main types of possible resolutions, some of which were discussed previously:

1. Extrusion
2. Resorption
3. Integration
4. Encapsulation

In extrusion, if the implant is in contact with epithelial tissue (the top layer of the skin), a pouch contiguous with this tissue can be formed and the material can be forced out of the body. This is how a splinter "works itself out."

If an implant is biodegradable (resorbable), it is possible that no fibrous capsule will form, depending on the rate of degradation. Alternatively, if a capsule does form, after implant resorption, the capsule can either collapse and remain this way or can be replaced with appropriate tissue.

Integration occurs in limited cases, such as the implantation of pure titanium in bone. This resolution type is characterized by a close approximation of host tissue to the implant, with no intervening fibrous capsule.

Encapsulation is the traditional response to nonresorbable materials, as described previously. Chronic inflammation/granuloma generation is not included in this category, since in this case there is not a return to the status quo (no resolution has occurred).

Each of the resolution types described above can be considered a failure or a success, depending on the reason for biomaterial implantation. For example, resorption and integration are the two most ideal resolutions for tissue engineering applications, whereas encapsulation, normally considered an acceptable outcome for biomaterial implantation, would represent failure of the tissue-engineered product. This is due to the nature of tissue engineering, a field in which the overriding goal is to create a fully functional tissue, rather than to replace damaged tissue with synthetic materials.

## 11.6    Repair versus Regeneration: Wound Healing in Skin

As mentioned above, tissue engineering uses biomaterials to create functional tissue. Two processes can form functional tissue: **repair** and **regeneration**. Either can have a successful result, depending on the goal of the tissue engineering treatment. In tissue repair, the defect is replaced by scar tissue, which may have a different structure, biochemical composition, and/or mechanical properties from native tissue. In tissue regeneration, the defect is replaced by tissue identical to that which was there before the wound occurred. In this case, the normal tissue structure, composition, and properties are completely restored. In this section, we will use wound healing in the skin as an example to illustrate differences in repair versus regeneration and to highlight how normal wound healing differs from healing near a nondegradable biomaterial.

### 11.6.1  Skin Repair

Skin is composed of two regions, the internal **dermal layer**, and the outer **epidermal layer**, as shown in Figure 11.6. If injury involves only the epidermal layer, defect regeneration is possible (see the following section). However, many cuts and burns extend into the dermal layer, where the primary means of wound healing is repair.

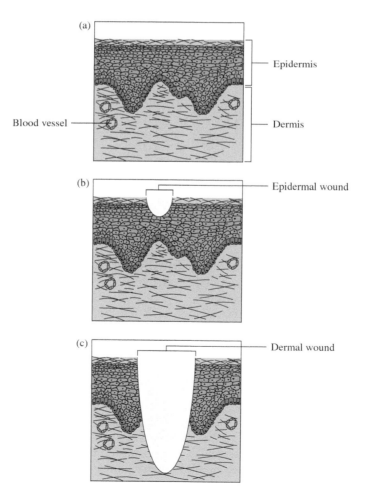

**Figure 11.6**
(a) Schematic of skin representing the internal dermal layer and the outer epidermal layer. If injury involves only the epidermal layer, as shown in (b), defect regeneration is possible. However, if cuts or burns extend into the dermal layer, as shown in (c), the primary means of wound healing is repair.

After injury, the first response is blood clotting and the formation of a fibrin network to prevent fluid loss (see Chapter 13 for a more in-depth discussion). This is followed by acute inflammation, including the same sequence of localized response and cellular migration as described previously for biomaterial implantation (Chapter 10). This stage is characterized by removal of tissue debris and deposition of hyaluronic acid, a glycosaminoglycan, in the extracellular matrix.

The inflammatory response triggers an influx of fibroblasts, which proliferate and deposit extracellular matrix, and mark the beginning of granulation tissue formation. As described previously, a large number of new blood vessels are also formed during this time. A particular characteristic of the tissue at this stage is that the collagen fibers (type III) deposited in the extracellular matrix are thin and randomly oriented. As new extracellular matrix is deposited, the fibrin clot is dissolved via release of specific enzymes and phagocytosis from the remaining macrophages.

The final stage of skin wound repair is *remodeling*, or scar formation. Starting approximately one week after injury, there is turnover of collagen molecules in the extracellular matrix, characterized by degradation of collagen type III via enzymes and/or phagocytosis and its eventual replacement by collagen type I. The new collagen bundles are larger and oriented along the principal lines of stress in the tissue. Similarly, there is an increase in the ratio of glycosaminoglycans such as chondroitin and dermatan sulfate to hyaluronic acid.

Collagen accumulation in scar tissue can continue for two to three months after injury. Additionally, the mechanical properties of the neotissue continue to increase over several months due to further crosslinking of the collagen fibers. During this time, blood vessels that have not formed connections are resorbed, and the scar becomes pale and avascular.

This represents the completion of skin repair: a functional tissue replacement has been generated, that, in many cases, may be entirely adequate. It should be noted that this stage cannot be fully completed in the presence of a nondegradable material since the capsule around the material remains and is never remodeled into scar tissue. As the defect in the dermis is being filled, the wound may concurrently be reepithelialized, as described in the next section. This does not represent regeneration of the defect, however, due to the presence of the scar tissue in the dermal layer.

## 11.6.2 Skin Regeneration

For smaller skin wounds that are contained in the epidermal layer (termed erosions), full regeneration of the defect is possible via **reepithelialization**. As in the case of complete repair, this process cannot take place with the continued presence of a nondegradable implant in the epidermis.

As shown in Figure 11.7, reepithelialization begins as the cells at the edge of defect change shape (flatten) to cover more of the wound. Dissolution of attachments to extracellular matrix at the wound edge allows migration of these cells into the defect site. Simultaneously, there is proliferation of epithelial cells behind the advancing front to gradually form a thin covering over the entire wound site.

Once the cells at the leading migratory edge come in contact with other epithelial cells (when the defect has been completely covered), they recover their more cuboid morphology and reattach to the extracellular matrix. Further proliferation and matrix production then occurs to restore the original thickness of tissue. This completes tissue regeneration in the epithelial layer. The resulting neotissue has the same structure and properties as the tissue before the injury.

**Figure 11.7**
Regeneration of skin wounds contained in the epidermal layer. (a) Reepithelialization begins as the cells at the edge of the defect change shape (flatten) to cover more of the wound. (b) These cells then migrate into the defect site. (c) Once the cells at the leading migratory edge come in contact with other epithelial cells (when the defect has been completely covered), they recover their more cuboid morphology and reattach to the extracellular matrix. (d) Further proliferation and matrix production then occurs to restore the original thickness of the tissue.

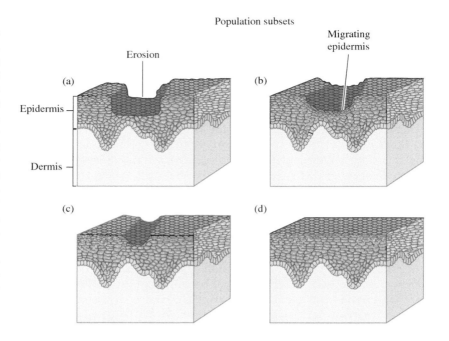

## 11.7   Techniques: *In Vivo* Assays for Inflammatory Response

While *in vitro* evaluation of the inflammatory response (see previous chapter) can be useful as an indicator of material biocompatibility, it cannot replace *in vivo* testing due to the complex interplay of cell types and signaling molecules that comprise the inflammatory response. Table 11.1 lists factors related to a biomedical implant that may affect the *in vivo* response. The items on this list may cause a specific biological response through a variety of means:

1. Interactions of biological molecules (such as proteins and ions) or cells with the implant (this includes both the topography and chemistry of the material).
2. Interactions of biological molecules or cells with soluble agents leached from the implant (leaching may occur due to the original chemical properties, additives, or degradation of the material).

**TABLE 11.1**

| Relevant Factors of *In Vivo* Tissue Compatibility Evaluation |
| --- |
| The material(s) of manufacture |
| Intended additives, process contaminants, and residues |
| Leachable substances |
| Degradation products |
| Other components and their interactions in the final product |
| The properties and characteristics of the final product |

[1]

3. Interactions of biological molecules or cells with insoluble particulates (usually caused by implant degradation).

4. Alterations in load or strain in the area around the implant (can be caused by material properties, but is also affected by geometry and final properties of the device).

Given the complexity of these interactions and the importance of biocompatibility testing, a number of organizations (U.S. Food and Drug Administration, ASTM, ISO) have proposed guidelines and procedures for *in vivo* biocompatibility assessment (ISO standards include 10993 and 14971, while ASTM standards include F895, E1397, E1398, F748, F749, F750, F813, F981, F1027, F1983, F1877, F1904, among others). According to these standards, **biocompatibility** can be considered "the ability of a medical device to perform with an appropriate host response in a specific application" and thus, **biocompatibility assessment** is "a measurement of the magnitude and duration of the adverse alterations in homeostatic mechanisms that determine the host response" [3].

A wide variety of tests fall under this broad definition of biocompatibility assessment, which includes examination of carcinogenicity, hemocompatibility, immune response, and the inflammatory response (see Table 11.2). Whether or not each of these tests is recommended depends on the final application of the device and the length of time it will be in contact with the body (see Table 11.2). Many of these studies will be discussed in later chapters. In this section, we will focus on *in vivo* examinations most directly assessing toxicity and inflammatory response. As per the ISO standards, this involves tests for localized reactivity and toxicity, as well as systemic toxicity (acute, subacute, and chronic). Additionally, it is recommended that these effects be determined both after injection of extracts of the biomaterial and after implantation.

The subsequent discussion follows after Spector and Lalor [4] and is intended to point out some of the major concerns in devising *in vivo* studies for biomedical devices, particularly those involving implantation of a biomaterial into a specific tissue. Although these parameters should be considered for relatively "inert" implants as well as tissue engineered products, it should be noted that biocompatibility testing of devices including active molecules, such as cells and growth factors, further complicates the screening procedure, so additional *in vitro* and *in vivo* tests may be required for tissue-engineered products. Of course, as with all animal studies, *in vivo* biocompatibility examinations must follow proper animal care guidelines for concerns such as sterility and mitigation of pain both during and after surgery.

## 11.7.1 Considerations in Development of Animal Models

**11.7.1.1 Choice of Animal**   To study the inflammatory response *in vivo*, the animal species should be selected based on a similarity in physiology and healing response to that which would occur in humans for a given application. Of course, there is often no animal that will completely match the course of healing in humans, so it may be impossible to entirely predict human responses to a biomaterial based on animal experiments. For the development of new materials, investigators usually start with a small animal model (rat, rabbit) and then move to a larger model (goat, dog, sheep, cow) if results from the first study show an acceptable amount of localized inflammation. Table 11.3 shows common animal models for testing various medical devices.

# TABLE 11.2

## FDA Device Categories and Suggested Biological Testing

| Device Categories | Body Contact | Contact Duration | Cytotoxicity | Sensitization | Irritation or Intracutaneous Reactivity | Systemic Toxicity (Acute/Pyrogenicity) | Subchronic Toxicity | Genotoxicity | Implantation | Hemocompatibility | Chronic Toxicity | Carcinogenicity |
|---|---|---|---|---|---|---|---|---|---|---|---|---|
| | | | | | | Initial Evaluation | | | | | Supplemental Evaluation | |
| Surface Devices | Skin | A | • | • | • | | | | | | | |
| | | B | • | • | • | | | | | | | |
| | | C | • | • | • | | | | | | | |
| | Mucosal membrane | A | • | • | • | 0 | 0 | • | 0 | | 0 | |
| | | B | • | • | • | 0 | | • | 0 | | | |
| | | C | • | • | • | | | | | | | |
| | Breached/compromised surface | A | • | • | • | 0 | 0 | • | 0 | | 0 | |
| | | B | • | • | • | 0 | | • | 0 | | | |
| | | C | • | • | • | 0 | | | | | | |
| External Communicating Devices | Blood path indirect | A | • | • | • | • | 0 | • | 0 | • | • | • |
| | | B | • | • | • | • | • | | | • | | |
| | | C | • | • | 0 | • | | | | • | | |
| | Tissue/bone dentin communicating | A | • | • | • | 0 | 0 | • | • | | 0 | • |
| | | B | • | • | 0 | 0 | 0 | • | • | | | |
| | | C | • | • | 0 | 0 | | | | | | |
| | Circulating blood | A | • | • | • | • | 0 | 0 | 0 | • | • | • |
| | | B | • | • | • | • | • | • | 0 | • | | |
| | | C | • | • | • | • | | • | | • | | |
| Implant Devices | Bone/tissue | A | • | • | • | 0 | 0 | • | • | | • | • |
| | | B | • | • | 0 | 0 | 0 | • | • | | | |
| | | C | • | • | 0 | 0 | | | | | | |
| | Blood | A | • | • | • | • | 0 | • | • | • | • | • |
| | | B | • | • | • | • | • | | • | • | | |
| | | C | • | • | • | • | | | • | • | | |

A, limited exposure (≤24 hours); B, prolonged exposure (24 hours–30 days); C, permanent contact (>30 days); •, FDA and ISO evaluation tests; 0, additional tests for FDA [2].

**11.7.1.2 Choice of Implant Site**   For the majority of studies, the implant site should be as close as possible to that which will be used in the final application. Sometimes a more accessible site, such as a subcutaneous pouch, is used for a first screening of the inflammatory response to a new material. In any case, the implant site should be assessed for several parameters that may affect the amount of inflammation perceived. For example, if there is a reduction in the number of

**TABLE 11.3**

| Medical Devices and the Corresponding Animal Models Used for *In Vivo* Testing | |
|---|---|
| Device Classification | Animal |
| Ophthalmological | |
|     Contact lens | Rabbit |
|     Intraocular lens | Rabbit, monkey |
| Neurological | |
|     Peripheral nerve regeneration | Rat, cat, nonhuman primate |
|     Electrical stimulation | Rat, cat, nonhuman primate |
| Cardiovascular | |
|     Heart valves | Sheep |
|     Vascular grafts | Dog, pig |
|     Stents | Pig, rabbit, dog |
|     Ventricular assist devices | Calf |
|     *Ex vivo* shunts | Baboon, dog |
|     Artificial hearts | Calf |
| Orthopedic | |
|     Bone regeneration/substitutes | Rabbit, dog, pig, mouse, rat |
|     Total joints–hips, knees | Dog, goat, nonhuman primate |
|     Vertebral implants | Sheep, goat, baboon |
|     Craniofacial implants | Rabbit, pig, dog, nonhuman primate |
|     Cartilage | Rabbit, dog |
|     Tendon and ligament substitutes | Dog, sheep |

[5]

macrophages and other inflammatory cells observed at a site that is not well vascularized, this may represent a lack of access to these cells, rather than anti-inflammatory properties of the material. Other important factors are the surrounding cells' ability to proliferate and migrate, and the effect of alterations in mechanical factors on the behavior of the surrounding cells.

**11.7.1.3 Length of Study**   As per ISO standards, several types of toxicity should be addressed if appropriate for the final application of the material. **Acute toxicity** refers to negative effects appearing up to 24 hours after administration, while **subacute toxicity** involves effects occurring 14–28 days after administration. **Subchronic toxicity** refers to responses occurring usually within the first 90 days (or less than 10% of the lifetime of the animal), while **chronic toxicity** involves effects appearing after this time. These studies can be performed using extracts of the biomaterial, or direct implantation at an appropriate location, depending on the final device design.

In addition to toxicity tests, ISO standards have also been developed for localized tissue response around an implant. In this case, materials are implanted and retrieved at several timepoints corresponding to various stages of the foreign body reaction, and then the response is monitored by histological analysis (see Section 11.7.2.1). For these implantation tests, the response measured is actually a combination of responses to surgery, inflammation, and finally tissue remodeling around the implant (resolution). Often, these implantations occur beneath the skin or in muscle.

**11.7.1.4 Biomaterial Considerations: Dose and Administration**   Because the form of an implant affects the biological response, it is important to test not only new materials, but materials in the same shape as will be used in the final device. In essence, the shape of the material affects its "dose" as seen by the body. It should be noted that biocompatibility testing may be carried out for two primary reasons: either to screen novel materials to gain insight into the degree and type of inflammatory response (in which case the shape of the material is of little concern) or to assess the inflammatory response to the material in a form very similar to that which will be implanted (in which case shape is more important).

For experiments that involve direct implantation of a material into a specific location, the following factors in addition to overall shape can affect the dose of the material received by the animal:

1. Implant weight and/or bulk size
2. Implant surface area
3. Implant topography
4. Number of implants per animal

As explained previously, biomaterial samples can be administered to an animal via direct implantation. Alternatively, extracts of the material may be injected into the animal to assess the response to soluble products. In this case, the extraction media as well as the site of injection may affect the inflammatory response.

A method falling between these two means of administration is the cage implant model. Here, the biomaterial is placed in a stainless steel cage, which is then implanted (Fig. 11.8). This enables investigators to examine the inflammatory response without providing direct contact between the material and the surrounding tissue. The method is particularly suited to assessing the reaction to the soluble (extractable) fraction of the biomaterial. A possible drawback is that the addition of the cage material may alter the inflammatory response in the localized area around the cage.

**11.7.1.5 Inclusion of Proper Controls**   In many cases, the addition of appropriate controls can provide useful information about the relative response to the test sample. Depending on the application and comparison desired, controls may include intact contralateral tissue (from the opposite limb) or an unfilled surgical implant site. At other times, material and device controls (comparison of the new implant with a standard material or a previous version of the device) may be recommended.

## 11.7.2 Methods of Assessment

The method of assessment for biological response to biomaterials should be selected to provide the most pertinent information possible and should be included as a

**Figure 11.8**
Image of a stainless steel cage implant model. The cage implant system was developed by James M. Anderson and his associates at Case Western Reserve University [12] and involves the placement of an experimental biomaterial in a stainless steel cage, which is then implanted. This system allows investigators to examine the inflammatory response without direct contact between the implanted experimental biomaterial and the surrounding tissue. (Reprinted with permission from [13].)

**Figure 11.9**
Histological image of the inflammatory response to a nylon mesh implanted subcutaneously for four weeks. This section was stained with hematoxilin and eosin stain and clearly shows inflammatory cells in close contact with the nylon fibers (cell nuclei stained blue/black; fibers shown in cross section so appear as circles). Inset shows higher magnification of one fiber. Scale bar 20 μm. (Adapted with permission from [11].)

part of the design of the experiment. For biocompatibility studies involving direct implantation of a material, there are a number of assessment methods, described in the following text. The use of several methods concurrently is encouraged in order to obtain a full picture of the degree and nature of the inflammatory response to the implant.

**11.7.2.1 Histology/Immunohistochemistry** After explantation, the tissue containing the implant can be sectioned and stained, either with conventional dyes or antibodies, as described in Chapter 9. This technique is very common and allows for visualization of the tissue reaction at various stages through the identification of specific cell types and/or extracellular matrix molecules (see example in Fig. 11.9). The types of biological responses that are normally assessed through histology can be found in Table 11.4. However, due to variation between samples or suboptimal staining protocols, quantification of the amount or intensity of stain can be difficult using this technique. This has improved with the addition of computer-aided analysis of stained sections.

**11.7.2.2 Electron Microscopy** Both transmission electron microscopy (TEM) and scanning electron microscopy (SEM) can be employed to examine the tissue response to an implant at higher magnifications than light microscopy. The principles

**TABLE 11.4**

| Biological Response Parameters as Determined by Histological Assessment of Implants |
| --- |
| Number and distribution of inflammatory cells as a function of distance from the material/ tissue interface |
| Thickness and vascularity of fibrous capsule |
| Quality and quantity of tissue ingrowth (for porous materials) |
| Presence of necrosis |
| Other parameters such as material debris, fatty infiltration, granuloma, dystrophic calcification, apoptosis, proliferation rate, biodegradation, thrombus formation, endothelialization, migration of biomaterials or degradation products |

(Adapted with permission from [5].)

**Figure 11.10**
Transmission electron microscopy image of inflammatory response to a xenograft tissue-derived biomaterial (acellular porcine tissue implanted subcutaneously in a rat for 1 week). White arrows show inflammatory cells (neutrophils or macrophages) in close contact with the tissue-derived biomaterial. Scale bar 5 μm. (Adapted with permission from [14].)

behind the operation of this equipment were discussed in Chapter 7 and the same procedures are used for samples containing explanted materials. TEM allows the interface of the implant to be examined at the ultrastructural level (see Fig. 11.10). If used in conjunction with X-ray analysis (see Chapter 7), this method may also be used to determine what types of materials have leached from the sample and where they are located. At later time points, TEM can be employed to assess integration with the surrounding tissue. However, a major drawback to using this technique is the difficulty in obtaining the ultrathin sections required. Additionally, since samples must be imaged under vacuum, special care must be used to fix and dehydrate the specimens prior to sectioning to maintain tissue morphology.

SEM, which does not require sectioning of the sample, may be an alternative to provide topographical images of a tissue or implant-tissue interface (see Fig. 11.11 for an example of SEM of bone). As with TEM, soluble products that have leached away from the implant can be located via X-ray analysis associated with SEM. Also like TEM, because most SEM imaging is done *in vacuo*, proper fixation and dehydration protocols are very important to preserve the integrity of the sample. Development of environmental SEMs that allow imaging in the presence of water is a means to overcome this limitation.

**11.7.2.3 Biochemical Assays**   Biochemical assays can also help assess inflammation after biomaterial implantation. As described in Chapter 9, a number of techniques are used, including colorimetric assays for production of bioactive molecules, or immuno-based assays for identification of a specific protein. For example, using biochemical assays, it may be possible to assess amounts of inflammatory mediators in the tissue surrounding the implant. Major advantages of this method are that it is quantitative and a large number of samples can be examined at one time with the use of an automated plate reader. However, these assays do require knowledge of what biomolecules may be involved in the response to the implant.

**11.7.2.4 Mechanical Testing**   Mechanical testing of explanted specimens including the implant and surrounding tissue is often performed on a testing frame like

**Figure 11.11**
Scanning electron microscopy image of cancellous (woven) bone, showing the calcified trabecular structure, with bone marrow in the spaces within the trabeculae. Scale bar 100 µm. (Reprinted with permission from [15].)

that described in Chapter 4. Tensile, bending, or "push out" tests are particularly common. This method is useful to assess the longer-term response to implants, such as the time course of remodeling around the device, or how well the implant is integrated with the neighboring tissue. While this technique is quantitative, the results depend heavily on whether the samples are tested fresh, frozen, or after fixation. Thus, consistent sample handling is extremely important to allow for comparison of data between time points or between studies.

## EXAMPLE PROBLEM 11.3

A study was conducted to evaluate the inflammatory response to a novel degradable implant material. The material has been designed to degrade by a bulk process after six weeks. One group of mice (Group A) received implantation of discs of the material under the skin on their backs (dorsal subcutaneous implantation). Another group (Group B) of the study received dorsal subcutaneous injection of a volume of degradation products of the material equal to the volume of the disk implanted in Group A. In both cases, the tissue response to the material was evaluated after 24 hours of implantation via histology, immunohistochemistry, and biochemical assays. A profound inflammatory response was observed in Group B, while a minor inflammatory response was observed in Group A. Assuming that no difference exists in the inflammatory response due to surgical implantation versus injection in this case, what conclusions can be drawn regarding the compatibility of the material?

**Solution:** The minor inflammatory response observed in Group A indicates that the whole discs do not induce a significant inflammatory response after 24 hours. As the material was designed to degrade over the course of six weeks via a bulk degradation process, little to no degradation products would be expected to be present in or around the material after 24 hours of implantation. However, in the case of Group B, in which degradation products of the material were injected, a large inflammatory response was observed after 24 hours. This indicates that the degradation products of the implant material induce an inflammatory response. Thus, the implant material will likely induce a more pronounced inflammatory response as it degrades. However, it is difficult to project how severe the inflammatory response to the material would be after six weeks of implantation of the whole discs versus that observed in Group B, as not all degradation products will be presented at once when the actual material degrades *in vivo*. ∎

# Summary

- Granulation tissue generally develops several days after an injury. It is characterized histologically by a pebbly, granular appearance due to the sprouting of many vascular buds from existing blood vessels in a process called angiogenesis.

- The foreign body reaction to an implant involves the action of elements of granulation tissue and foreign body giant cells (multinucleated cells formed by the fusion of macrophages).

- Fibrous encapsulation is the final stage of healing in response to nondegradable implants. It involves the maturation of granulation tissue and formation of a fibrous capsule surrounding the implant. The degree of capsule formation can be influenced by the degree of original injury during implantation, the amount of subsequent cell death, the type of material implanted, and the location of the implant.

- Chronic inflammation has a less uniform histological appearance than acute inflammation/fibrous encapsulation, and it is characterized by the presence of lymphocytes, plasma cells, and, in some cases, granulomas.

- There are four primary types of resolution to the inflammatory and wound healing response following injury and/or implantation: extrusion, resorption, integration, and encapsulation. Extrusion involves the foreign material being forced out of the body. Resorbable implants disappear with time and may or may not involve the formation of a fibrous capsule. Integration involves the close approximation of the native tissue to the implant, with no intervening fibrous capsule. Encapsulation entails the fibrous encapsulation of the material, but does not include chronic inflammation. The intended application of the material determines if the generated response is a success or failure.

- Wound repair can be achieved through either tissue repair or tissue regeneration. In tissue repair, the defect is replaced by scar tissue, which may have different structure, biochemical composition, and/or mechanical properties from the native tissue. In tissue regeneration, the defect is replaced by tissue identical to that which was there prior to the wound. Normal repair or regeneration of wounds cannot be fully completed in the presence of a nondegradable implant material, as the capsule around the material remains and is not remodeled.

- Due to the complex interplay of cells and signaling molecules involved, the inflammatory response and biocompatibility associated with a biomaterial is often assessed through *in vivo* studies using appropriate animal models. Examination of the inflammatory response is only one of a number of tests required for determination of biocompatibility.

- Design of *in vivo* experiments should consider the type of animal, location of implant site, length of study, dose and administration of the biomaterial, inclusion of proper controls, and methods of assessment.

- The material can be assessed following explantation by a variety of means, including histology, immunohistochemistry, electron microscopy (TEM and/or SEM), biochemical assays, and mechanical testing.

# Problems

11.1 Following is an image that depicts fibrous encapsulation of an implanted biomaterial.

(a) Next to the numbers below, fill in the names of the cells involved in each stage depicted [6]. (Each different number represents a different cell type.)

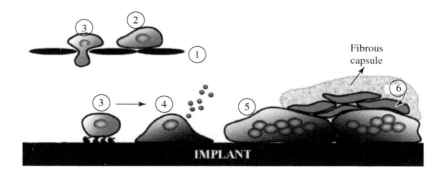

(b) What additional cells would be found in the diagram if the implant caused a chronic inflammatory response?

11.2 What type of resolution occurs with each of the following?

(a) Degradable drug delivery device
(b) In-dwelling vascular shunt for dialysis
(c) Splinter
(d) Degradable suture
(e) Cardiac pacemaker
(f) Titanium bone plate

11.3 You are testing a new tissue engineered skin substitute *in vivo*. What are the most important assays to include to determine if your approach results in repair or regeneration of the skin?

11.4 In experiments to evaluate tissue responses to a biomaterial, a control group is often included involving the complete surgical procedure but without implanting the biomaterial.

(a) Why is the surgery-only group an important control for these studies?
(b) List the differences in the tissue response at the wound site following implantation of a nondegradable biomaterial as compared to a simple lesion.

11.5 You have developed a novel nondegradable biomaterial for controlled drug release. *In vitro* experiments on a thin slab (20 mm × 10 mm × 2 mm) showed that your material has the release profile shown in the following image (solid line) with linear release over ~30 days. Following implantation *in vivo*, however, the release rate into the surrounding tissue was severely decreased within the first four days (dashed line) and zero release occurred after 12 days.

(a) What is the most likely explanation for the difference between the *in vitro* and *in vivo* release rates?

(b) Your company is investigating a degradable polymer as an alternative to the nondegradable material above. *In-vitro* release studies show the same results as the nondegradable polymer (solid line on the graph from part (a)). However, when implanted *in vivo*, it was observed that the polymer quickly (<3 days) formed particulates at the implantation site. Draw the expected drug release from the degradable polymer *in vivo* and explain why you drew the graph this way.

11.6 Make a list of advantages and disadvantages of all of the **in vivo** assessment techniques described in this chapter.

# References

1. J. M. Anderson and F. J. Schoen, "In vivo assessment of tissue compatibility," in *Biomaterials science: an introduction to materials and medicine*, 2nd ed., B. D. Ratner, A. S. Hoffman, F. J. Schoen, and J. E. Lemons, Eds. San Diego: Elsevier Academic Press, 2004, pp. 360–367.

2. Food and Drug Administration, *EPA Bluebook Memorandum #G95: Use of International Standard ISO-10993, Biological evaluation of medical devices Part I: evaluation and testing*. Washington, DC, 2000.

3. D. Williams, *Essential biomaterials science*. Cambridge, UK: Cambridge University Press, 2014.

4. M. Spector and P. A. Lalor, "In vivo assessment of tissue compatibility," in *Biomaterials science: an introduction to materials and medicine*, 1st ed., B. D. Ratner, A. S. Hoffman, F. J. Schoen, and J. E. Lemons, Eds. San Diego: Elsevier Academic Press, 1996, pp. 220–228.

5. J. M. Anderson and F. J. Schoen, "In vivo assessment of tissue compatibility," in *Biomaterials science: an introduction to materials and medicine*, 3rd ed. San Diego: Elsevier Academic Press, 2013, pp. 609–617.

6. A. W. Bridges and A. J. García, "Anti-inflammatory polymeric coatings for implantable biomaterials and devices," *Journal of Diabetes Science and Technology*, vol. 2, no. 6, pp. 984–994, 2008.

7. J. M. Anderson, "Mechanisms of inflammation and infection with implanted devices," in *Cardiovascular Pathology*, vol. 2, pp. 33–41, 1993.

8. D. L. Jeffery, D. P. Dressler, J. M. Anderson, and M. J. Gallagher, "Hemostatic and healing studies of sodium amylose succinate (IP760)," *Journal of Biomedical Materials Research*, vol. 16, no. 1, pp. 51–61, 1982.

9. L. J. Suggs, M. S. Shive, C. A. Garcia, J. M. Anderson, and A. G. Mikos, "In vitro cytotoxicity and in vivo biocompatibility of poly(propylene fumarate-co-ethylene glycol) hydrogels," *Journal of Biomedical Materials Research*, vol. 46, no. 1, pp. 22–32, 1999.

10. T. P. Schmalzried, M. Jasty, A. Rosenberg, and W. H. Harris, "Histologic identification of polyethylene wear debris using Oil Red O stain," *Journal of Applied Biomaterials*, vol. 4, no. 2, pp. 119–25, 1993.

11. D. M. Higgins, R. J. Basaraba, A. C. Hohnbaum, E. J. Lee, D. W. Grainger, and M. Gonzalez-Juarrero, "Localized immunosuppressive environment in the foreign body response to implanted biomaterials," *The American Journal of Pathology*, vol. 175, no. 1, pp. 161–170, 2009.

12. R. Marchant, A. Hiltner, C. Hamlin, A. Rabinovitch, R. Slobodkin, and J. M. Anderson, "In vivo biocompatibility studies. I. The cage implant system and a biodegradable hydrogel," *Journal of Biomedical Materials Research*, vol. 17, no. 2, pp. 301–25, 1983.

13. N. Peppas and R. Langer, "New challenges in biomaterials," *Science*, vol. 263, no. 5154, pp. 1715–1720, 1994.

14. R. Khorramirouz *et al.*, "A novel surgical technique for a rat subcutaneous implantation of a tissue engineered scaffold," *Acta Histochemica*, vol. 120, no. 3, pp. 282–291, 2018.

15. D. Prakash and J. Behari, "Synergistic role of hydroxyapatite nanoparticles and pulsed electromagnetic field therapy to prevent bone loss in rats following exposure to simulated microgravity," *International Journal of Nanomedicine*, vol. 4, pp. 133–144, 2009.

16. B. F. Ricciardi *et al.*, "Histopathological characterization of corrosion product associated adverse local tissue reaction in hip implants: a study of 285 cases," *BMC Clinical Pathology*, vol. 16, no. 3, 2016.

## Additional Reading

S. V. Bhat, Ed., *Biomaterials*, 2nd ed. Springer Netherlands, 2002.

J. Black, *Biological Performance of Materials: Fundamentals of Biocompatibility*, 4th ed. New York: CRC Press, 2005.

R. A. F. Clark and A. J. Singer, "Wound Repair: Basic Biology to Tissue Engineering," in *Principles of tissue engineering*, 2nd ed., R. P. Lanza, R. Langer, and J. Vacanti, Eds. Austin: Academic Press, 2000, pp. 857–878.

K. C. Dee, D. A. Puleo, and R. Bizios, *An introduction to tissue-biomaterial interactions*. Hoboken: Wiley-Liss, 2002.

S. C. Gad and S. Gad-McDonald, *Biomaterials, medical devices, and combination products: biocompatibility testing and safety assessment*. Boca Raton: CRC Press, 2015.

C. R. Jenney and J. M. Anderson, "Alkylsilane-modified surfaces: Inhibition of human macrophage adhesion and foreign body giant cell formation," *Journal of Biomedical Materials Research*, vol. 46, no. 1, pp. 11–21, 1999.

J. Kuby, *Immunology*, 3rd ed. New York: W. H. Freeman, 1997.

B. D. Matthews *et al.*, "Evaluation of adhesion formation and host tissue response to intra-abdominal polytetrafluoroethylene mesh and composite prosthetic mesh1," *Journal of Surgical Research*, vol. 123, no. 2, pp. 227–234, 2005.

F. H. Silver, *Biomaterials, medical devices and tissue engineering: an integrated approach*. New York: Chapman and Hall, 1994.

F. H. Silver and D. L. Christiansen, *Biomaterials science and biocompatibility*. New York: Springer Science & Business Media, 1999.

I. V. Yannas, "Synthesis of tissues and organs," *Chembiochem*, vol. 5, no. 1, pp. 26–39, 2004.

# 12

# Immune Response to Biomaterials

## Main Objective

To understand the steps involved in and the results of stimulation of the acquired immune response and the complement cascade after biomaterial implantation.

## Specific Objectives

1. To distinguish between humoral and cellular immunity.
2. To understand the process of antigen presentation in the immune response, including the roles of antigens, haptens, and adjuvants.
3. To understand the steps of lymphocyte maturation and of expansion of clonal populations.
4. To understand the characteristics and functions of antibodies.
5. To compare and contrast actions of stimulated B and T cells.
6. To distinguish between the roles of different types of T cells and natural killer cells.
7. To understand the steps involved in the complement cascade and potential interactions with the inflammatory and acquired immune responses.
8. To understand the effects of activation of the complement system and its regulation.
9. To distinguish among the four types of allergic responses and understand which are of major concern for biomaterials development.
10. To understand the concepts behind and possible limitations to the *in vitro* and *in vivo* techniques presented.

## 12.1 Introduction: Overview of Acquired Immunity

The previous few chapters have described the innate (nonspecific) response to an implanted material. However, it is also possible that the body could respond to specific portions of the biomaterial (or proteins adsorbed on the biomaterial). This is called **acquired immune response**, and it is mediated by lymphocytes circulating constantly in the blood and tissues.

In terms of the acquired immune response, of most concern to the biomaterialist is the issue of immunotoxicity. **Immunotoxicity** is a broad term that refers to adverse effects on the function of the immune system or other body systems as a result of alterations in immune system function [1]. For example, both allergies (immune system dysfunction) and autoimmune diseases (destruction of other tissues due to the immune system attacking "self" cells) have developed after biomaterial implantations. The acquired immune response to tissue-engineered products, which contain a mixture of materials and possibly foreign cells or proteins, is especially complex and should be a design criterion for these devices. In order to mitigate potentially immunotoxic responses to such products, we must first understand the basics of the structure of the acquired immune response, which is the focus of the first part of this chapter. Material hypersensitivity (allergy) is discussed later in the chapter.

The acquired immune response is adaptive and has four characteristics [2]:

1. Specificity
2. Diversity
3. Self/nonself recognition
4. Immunologic memory

There are two types of acquired immunity, humoral and cellular. **Humoral immunity** is based on the actions of antibodies, made by B cells, against foreign substances. It plays a large role in the response to foreign agents such as bacteria. In contrast, **cellular immunity** utilizes specialized T cells and its primary function is in the detection of altered self cells (such as from viral infections or cancer). A third type of lymphocyte, the natural killer (NK) cell, functions against altered self cells in a similar manner to T cells.

The specificity of acquired immunity comes from the fact that lymphocytes (B and T cells) involved in an immune reaction are activated in response to antigens. An **antigen** is a substance (usually foreign and having a molecular weight greater than 8,000 Da) that binds specifically to an **antibody** (an **immunoglobulin** glycoprotein) or **T cell receptor (TCR)** to initiate the acquired immune response. The specific site on the antigen recognized by the antibody is an **epitope** (or antigenic determinant). Antigens may have multiple epitopes that each bind the antibody or TCR.

Other substances frequently encountered when discussing acquired immunity, in particular with respect to the role of biomaterials in the immune response, are haptens and adjuvants. A **hapten** is a low molecular weight substance that combines with a larger molecule (such as a protein) to produce a much greater immune response than to either the hapten or carrier alone. Upon second exposure, some antibodies may react against the hapten even without the presence of the carrier molecule. This is important in the immune response to metallic implants, as discussed later in the chapter. An **adjuvant** is a substance that nonspecifically enhances the immune response to antigens, possibly by increasing their uptake by phagocytic cells or prolonging the time the antigen remains in the body. Nanoparticles of various biomaterials have been recently been explored as adjuvants, partially due to their small size, which may promote cellular targeting and uptake.

## 12.2  Antigen Presentation and Lymphocyte Maturation

### 12.2.1  Major Histocompatibility Complex (MHC) Molecules

The first step in the acquired immune response is recognition of the antigen. To be recognized, in many cases, the antigen must be displayed together with a **major histocompatibility complex (MHC)** *Class I* or *Class II* molecule. The MHC is a genetic complex with multiple genes that encode for Class I and II molecules. **Endogenous antigens,** or those resident within a host cell, such as viral proteins or proteins produced

**Figure 12.1**
Schematic of major histo-compatibility complex Class I molecule. Class I molecules are transmembrane glycoproteins that are found on almost all nucleated cells in conjunction with a smaller protein, $\beta$2-macroglobulin. A MHC Class I molecule is composed of two noncovalently associated chains ($\alpha$ and $\beta$). The cleft between the $\alpha_1$ and $\alpha_2$ portions interacts with the antigen, though this is not as specific as the binding sites for antibodies and T cell receptors. (Adapted with permission from [3].)

in cancerous cells, are processed and displayed on MHC Class I molecules. In contrast, **exogenous antigens,** or proteins that are produced outside the host cell and enter through phagocytosis, are presented on MHC Class II molecules.

**12.2.1.1 MHC Class I** As shown in Figure 12.1, **Class I** molecules are transmembrane glycoproteins that are found on almost all nucleated cells in conjunction with a smaller protein, $\beta$2-macroglobulin. An MHC Class I molecule is composed of two noncovalently associated chains ($\alpha$ and $\beta$). The distal end of the $\alpha$ chain forms a cleft to interact with the antigen, although it is not as specific as the binding sites for antibodies and T cell receptors. MHC Class I molecules are recognized by a subset of T cells (T cytotoxic or $T_c$ cells).

**12.2.1.2 MHC Class II** MHC **Class II** molecules are also transmembrane glycoproteins having $\alpha$ and $\beta$ chains (Fig. 12.2). In this case, the distal ends of both chains form the antigen-binding cleft, which has similar affinity for the antigen as MHC Class I molecules. As depicted in Figure 12.3, MHC Class II molecules are recognized by a different subset of T cells (T helper or $T_h$ cells) than Class I molecules. Also, in contrast to Class I molecules, Class II molecules are only found on **antigen-presenting cells (APCs).** APCs express MHC Class II molecules on their membranes and are able to deliver the co-stimulatory signal necessary for activation of $T_h$ cells (see Section 12.4 for a more in-depth discussion of T cell activation). They include macrophages (a major point of interaction between the innate and acquired immune system), B lymphocytes, and dendritic cells.

**12.2.1.3 MHC Molecule Variation and Tissue Typing** It has been found that genes in three regions (**loci**) code for MHC Class I molecules, and genes in three different loci code for MHC Class II molecules. Because an individual inherits genes from both parents for each locus, each person has multiple types of MHC molecules

**Figure 12.2**
Schematic of a major histocompatibility complex Class II molecule. Class II molecules are transmembrane glycoproteins having $\alpha$ and $\beta$ chains and are found only on antigen-presenting cells. The distal ends of both chains form the antigen-binding cleft, which has similar affinity for the antigen as MHC Class I molecules. (Adapted with permission from [3].)

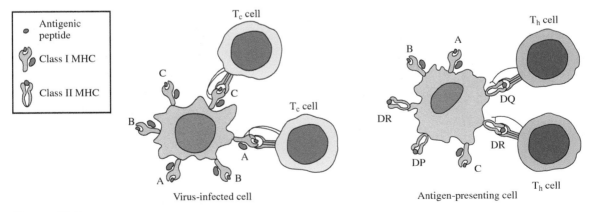

**Figure 12.3**
Recognition of MHC molecules by T cells. MHC Class I molecules are encoded by A, B, and C loci in humans and are recognized by T cytotoxic cells ($T_c$ cells). MHC Class II molecules are encoded by DP, DQ, and DR loci in humans and are recognized by a different subset of T cells ($T_h$ cells). Class II molecules are only found on antigen-presenting cells (APCs) [2].

present on the surface of their cells. However, MHC molecules not corresponding to any within the body (**nonself** molecules) are recognized and produce a primarily cell-based immune response. This is a main cause of organ rejection in transplant recipients. To counteract this, tissue typing is performed to determine how similar the MHC molecules are between the host and donor. The more similar the MHC molecules, the lower the chance of donor tissue rejection.

## EXAMPLE PROBLEM 12.1

A common treatment for bone defects is the introduction of bone grafts from either a donor site within the same patient (autograft) or a cadaver (allograft). In the case of an autograft, the bone is usually implanted with minimal processing following harvest. However, cadaver bone is generally subjected to stringent processing before implantation. One typical goal of the processing is to decellularize the bone graft. From an immunological point of view, why would removal of the cells from the allograft bone prior to implantation be important?

**Solution:** Rejection of grafts is generally mediated through a cellular immune response to MHC molecules present on the graft cells that are recognized as antigens by the host. Tissue typing should be performed to ensure similarity of MHC molecules between the donor and the recipient prior to implantation, if an allograft is to contain cells. Otherwise, dissimilar MHC molecules present on the cells of the graft may be recognized as foreign by the host immune cells and induce a cellular immune response that can lead to graft rejection and ultimate failure of the treatment. Thus, removing the resident cells would reduce the immune response to an allograft. ■

**12.2.1.4 Intracellular Complexation with MHC Molecules** Before extracellular presentation by MHC Class I or Class II molecules, antigens must first be processed intracellularly, where they complex with the appropriate MHC molecule, as depicted in Figure 12.4. Endogenous antigens, like viral proteins or proteins produced

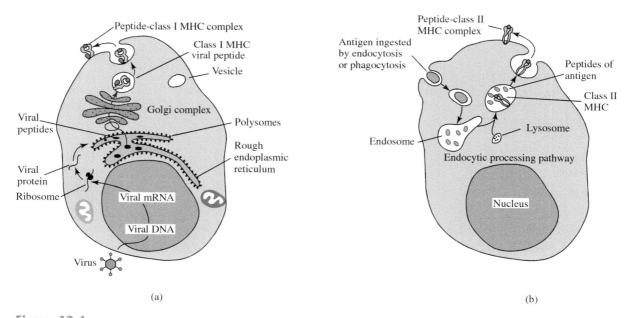

(a)                                                                                    (b)

**Figure 12.4**
Intracellular processing of antigens. (a) Endogenous antigens, such as proteins produced in cancerous cells or viral proteins, are first degraded into peptide fragments in the cytoplasm. At this point, they are free to bind to MHC Class I molecules in the rough endoplasmic reticulum. The antigen-MHC Class I complex is then transported to the cell membrane. (b) Exogenous antigens are produced outside the host cell and enter through phagocytosis. They are degraded during endocytosis and the fragments bind to MHC Class II molecules in the endocytotic vesicles. The antigen-MHC Class II complex is then transported to the cell membrane [2].

**TABLE** 12.1

| Key Properties of MHC Class I and II Molecules | | |
|---|---|---|
| Property | MHC Class I | MHC Class II |
| Chain characteristics | Distal end of α *chain* interacts with antigen | Distal end of *both chains* interacts with antigen |
| Type of antigen | Endogenous | Exogenous |
| On surface of | Almost all nucleated cells | Antigen-presenting cells |
| Recognized by | $T_c$ cells | $T_h$ cells |

in cancerous cells, are first degraded into peptide fragments in the cytoplasm. At this point, they are free to bind to MHC Class I molecules in the rough endoplasmic reticulum. The antigen-MHC Class I complex is then transported to the cell membrane.

In contrast, exogenous antigens enter the cell through phagocytosis (Fig. 12.4 (b)). They are degraded into peptide fragments during endocytosis and the fragments bind to MHC Class II molecules in the endocytotic vesicles. The antigen-MHC Class II complex is then transported to the cell membrane. Exogenous antigens are the type more commonly formed as a direct result of biomaterial implantation, whereas endogenous antigens may be produced after alteration of a native cell due to toxic or carcinogenic properties of the biomaterial (see Chapter 14 for a more complete discussion of malignant transformations). A summary of the differences between MHC Class I and II molecules is found in Table 12.1.

### 12.2.2 Maturation of Lymphocytes

There are two main types of lymphocytes that respond to antigens to produce the acquired immune response: B cells and T cells. B cells are mediators of humoral immunity and produce highly specific antibodies. T cells ( $T_c$ and $T_h$ ) are involved in cellular immunity and also produce proteins with high specificity, the T cell receptors (TCRs). Unlike antibodies, which can be released into the surrounding environment, TCRs remain bound to the cell membrane. A single lymphocyte possesses on the order of 10,000 antibodies/TCRs on its surface, all of which bind to the same antigen. However, each cell is reactive toward a different antigen, as determined by the rearrangement during cellular development of genes that encode for the antibody/TCR. The formation of antibodies and TCRs are examples of how the acquired immune system achieves its high specificity, while gene rearrangement in each cell provides immunologic diversity.

B cells are formed and processed in bone marrow, and further maturation occurs in the peripheral lymphoid tissues (lymph nodes and spleen). In contrast, T cells are formed in the bone marrow and mature in the thymus. After each cell expresses its specific antibody/TCR, it is exposed to "self" antigens during processing. Those cells that bind these antigens undergo apoptosis (up to 90% of cells generated), which prevents the production of cells that react against the body's own tissues. This process produces the self/nonself recognition that is critical to the proper function of the acquired immune system. After maturation, lymphocytes migrate to the lymphoid tissues, where they may remain for some time or directly enter the bloodstream to be circulated throughout the body.

### 12.2.3 Activation and Formation of Clonal Populations

Proper antigen presentation (with a MHC molecule) causes activation of T lymphocytes by promoting binding of the antigen to the TCR. As shown in Figure 12.5, cytokines released by $T_h$ cells aid in the activation of $T_c$ cells after antigen binding.

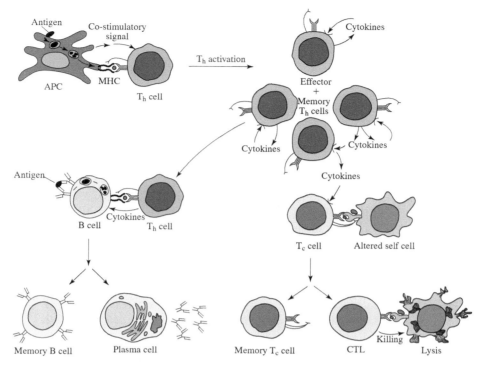

**Figure 12.5**

Interactions between $T_h$ and other cell types in development of the immune response. Proper antigen presentation (with a Class II MHC molecule) causes activation of $T_h$ lymphocytes by promoting binding of the antigen to the T cell receptor. $T_c$ cells and B cells can also bind to the antigen, depending on the properties of the antigen and how it is presented. Cytokines released by $T_h$ cells aid in the activation of $T_c$ cells after antigen binding. Similarly, co-stimulation by binding with and/or secreted products from $T_h$ cells is needed for full B cell activation after binding to the antigen. After activation, B and $T_c$ cells undergo rapid mitosis, forming a clonal population of cells all specific to that antigen. During this process, both effector cells (cytotoxic T lymphocytes (CTLs) or plasma cells) and memory cells are created [2].

Although antigen presentation by a MHC molecule is not required for B cells, costimulation by binding with and/or secreted products from $T_h$ cells is needed for full B cell activation. It should also be reiterated that interleukin-1 (IL-1) and interleukin-12 (IL-12) secreted by granulocytes can aid in activation of both B and T cells, thus promoting communication between the innate and acquired immune responses.

After activation, the lymphocyte undergoes rapid mitosis, forming a clonal population of cells that all are specific to that antigen. During this process, both **effector cells** and **memory cells** are created. Memory cells have longer lifetimes (up to years) than effector cells, but maintain their specificity for the given antigen. The existence of these cells causes a more rapid and heightened response if the body is exposed to the same antigen for a second time. It is through the production of both memory B and T cells that the acquired immune system's characteristic memory is achieved.

## 12.3 B Cells and Antibodies

### 12.3.1 Types of B Cells

As mentioned earlier, unlike T cells, B cells do not require antigen presentation by MHC molecules for activation. Once activated by both antigen binding and a stimulatory signal provided by $T_h$ cells, they proliferate to form memory B cells and effector cells called **plasma cells** (Fig. 12.5). Memory cells express membrane-bound antibodies, while plasma cells produce soluble antibodies. It is estimated that plasma cells can release up to 2,000 antibody molecules per second at maturity, and that this production rate can continue for several days to weeks.

## 12.3.2 Characteristics of Antibodies

### 12.3.2.1 Structure of Antibodies
As shown in Figure 12.6, the antibodies produced by the B cells are composed of four polypeptide chains. The two larger chains (**heavy chains**) have a molecular weight of 55–70 kDa and are joined by disulfide (S–S) bonds. The two smaller chains (**light chains**) have a molecular weight of 24 kDa. They are also linked via disulfide bonds, one to each heavy chain. The region at the end of each heavy/light chain combination is the cleft for antigen binding. This is called the **variable portion** or $F_{ab}$ (fragment antigen binding) and its specific structure (and thus antigen-binding capacity) is determined by the rearrangement of genes coding for amino acids in both the heavy and light chains. The rest of the molecule is termed the **constant portion** or $F_c$ (fragment crystallizable). This section is responsible for recognition of the antibody by receptors in phagocytic cells or by certain molecules of the complement complex (see Section 12.5 for further discussion of the complement cascade). The TCR has a similar variable portion, but the rest of the molecule is firmly anchored into the cell membrane.

### 12.3.2.2 Classes of Antibodies
Distinct amino acid sequences in the heavy-chain constant portions identify the **class** of the antibody. As depicted in Figure 12.7, there are five main classes of antibodies, each named with Ig to abbreviate "immunoglobulin" and then a capital letter indicating the class. IgG, IgD, and IgE all possess the

**Figure 12.6**
The structure of antibodies produced by B cells is composed of four polypeptide chains. The two larger chains (heavy chains) have a molecular weight of 55–70 kDa and are joined by disulfide (S–S) bonds. The two smaller chains (light chains) have a molecular weight of 24 kDa and are also linked via disulfide bonds, one to each heavy chain. The region at the end of each heavy/light chain combination is the cleft for antigen binding. This is called the variable portion and its specific structure (and thus antigen-binding capacity) is determined by the rearrangement of genes coding for amino acids in both the heavy and light chains. The rest of the molecule is termed the constant portion and is responsible for recognition of the antibody by receptors in phagocytic cells or by certain molecules of the complement complex [3].

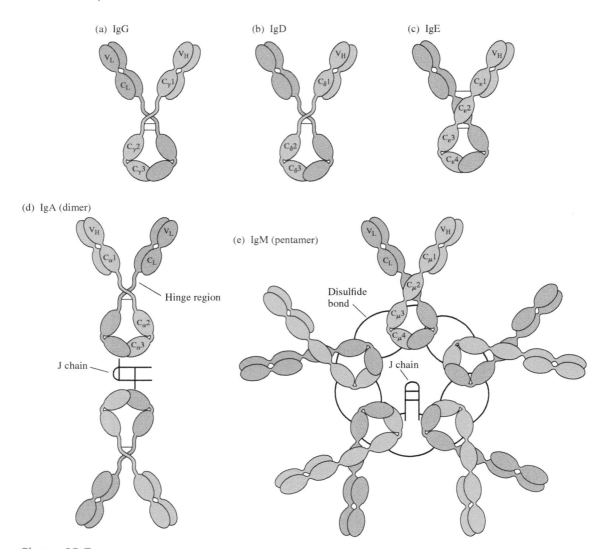

**Figure 12.7**
There are five main classes of antibodies, each named with Ig to signify "immunoglobulin" and then a capital letter indicating the class. (a–c) IgG, IgD, and IgE all possess the same general structure and have the capability to bind two antigen molecules simultaneously (one on each arm). (d) IgA has a similar structure to the other classes, but includes a J (joining) chain, which allows for dimerization. The dimer can then bind four antigen molecules at once. (e) IgM is characterized by the same general structure as the other antibody types, but its J chain allows for pentamerization, so it can bind up to 10 antigen molecules at once [2].

same general structure for a generic antibody as described previously and have the capability to bind two antigen molecules simultaneously (one on each arm). IgG is the most prevalent antibody class, and composes about 75% of the antibodies in humans. The fraction of antibodies of the IgE type is much lower, but this class plays an important role in the allergic reaction, as discussed later. IgA has a similar structure to the other classes, but includes a J (joining) chain, which allows for dimerization. The dimer can then bind four antigen molecules at once, which can be important in *agglutination* reactions, as described in the following section. IgM is characterized by the same general structure as the other antibody types, but its J chain allows for pentamerization, so it can bind up to 10 antigen molecules at once. Therefore, IgM is the most effective class for cell or bacterial agglutination.

### 12.3.2.3 Mechanisms of Antibody Action   Antibodies can act directly to aid in the removal of a pathogen via four means:

1. Agglutination
2. Precipitation
3. Neutralization
4. Lysis

**Agglutination** occurs when multiple large particles with antigens on their surfaces are bound into a clump by antibodies, so they cannot function properly. This can happen with bacteria, for example. For such a mechanism, IgA and IgM antibodies are the most effective since they can bind multiple antigens and thus facilitate three-dimensional linkage of the foreign molecules. **Precipitation** takes place when the complex of antibody and antigen becomes so large that it is no longer soluble. In many cases, the lack of solubility interferes with the function of the foreign substance. **Neutralization** occurs when antibodies bind and cover the active or toxic sites on a foreign substance. Certain antibodies are also capable of direct attack on the cell membrane of an invading organism, resulting in cell **lysis** and death.

In addition to these direct actions, antibodies also act indirectly to aid in the clearance of foreign substances. A number of receptors are present on phagocytic cells (granulocytes) for different classes of antibodies, so antibody binding increases the rate of phagocytosis of antigen-containing particles. Antigen–antibody binding is also a major means of complement system activation (discussed in Section 12.5), which provides yet another mechanism to rid the body of foreign invaders.

### EXAMPLE PROBLEM 12.2

A soldier in a battlefield sustained a critical injury and required a prompt blood transfusion. Although blood was in very short supply, the field surgeon found a unit of donor blood. However, the label indicating the blood type was missing. The surgeon decided to perform a quick serological cross-matching test by mixing red blood cells from the donor blood unit with a small sample of the injured soldier's serum. Through microscopic observation, the surgeon noted that small clumps of red blood cells were forming. Assuming that the clumping was not being caused by the clotting process, why might this clumping occur? Which antibody classes would most likely be involved? Should the donor blood unit be used in this patient, or should an alternate donor be found? Why or why not?

Solution:   The clumping could be the result of agglutination of the red blood cells from the donor. Such agglutination would indicate that the serum of the injured soldier contained antibodies against proteins present on the surfaces of the donor red blood cells. As IgA and IgM are capable of forming dimers and pentimers, respectively, they would be the most effective antibody classes for agglutination. The donor blood unit should not be used in this patient, as it appears that the patient possesses antibodies against the donor blood. In the event that the donor blood was used, an immune response would ensue that could be dangerous, or, at a minimum, would hinder the recovery of the patient.   ■

## 12.4   T Cells

### 12.4.1  T Cells and NK cells

There are three main types of T cell-like cells: the helper T cell ($T_h$), the cytotoxic T cell ($T_c$), and natural killer (NK) cells. $T_h$ cells usually possess the surface glycoprotein **CD 4** and recognize antigens presented on MHC Class II molecules. In contrast, $T_c$ cells generally possess the surface marker **CD 8** and interact with antigens presented on MHC Class I molecules. $T_h$ and $T_c$ cells require antigen presentation via a MHC complex to become activated. In contrast, NK cells do not require antigen presentation to be activated, but, like $T_c$ cells, are responsible for attacking altered-self cells.

## 12.4.2 Helper T Cells ($T_h$)

$T_h$ cells fulfill a key role in the acquired immune response—it is these cells that are destroyed in acquired immune deficiency syndrome (AIDS), with devastating effects. $T_h$ cells become activated in response to antigen-MHC Class II complexes in combination with a co-stimulatory signal supplied by an APC. This co-stimulatory signal is usually the presence of glycoproteins on the surface of the APC that can interact with specific receptors on the $T_h$ cell (Fig. 12.8).

Once activated, these cells form a clonal population including effector and memory $T_h$ cells (Fig. 12.5). Effector cells then secrete cytokines with a variety of actions. While a complete discussion of all of the cytokines involved in the acquired immune response is beyond the scope of this introductory text, their general actions include:

1. Stimulation of B cell growth and differentiation (result of interleukin (IL-4), among others).

2. Stimulation of $T_c$ cell proliferation (see Section 12.4.3) (result of IL-2, among others).

3. Further stimulation of $T_h$ cell activation (result of IL-2, among others).

4. Promotion of chemotaxis and activation of macrophages (result of Interferon $\gamma$, among others). This is another example of how the acquired and innate immune systems work together to rid the body of foreign substances.

Activated $T_h$ cells may also act directly by binding to B cells to stimulate the humoral response.

Recently, several subtypes of $T_h$ cells have been identified, including $T_{h1}$, $T_{h2}$, $T_{h17}$, and induced regulatory T cells ($T_{reg}$), which each play a different role in increasing or decreasing the acquired and, in some cases, innate immune response (see Fig. 12.9). While knowledge is still evolving in this field, a brief summary of the development and actions of some of the more fully characterized subtypes is provided here. For all subtypes, it is thought that specific polarizing cytokines produced

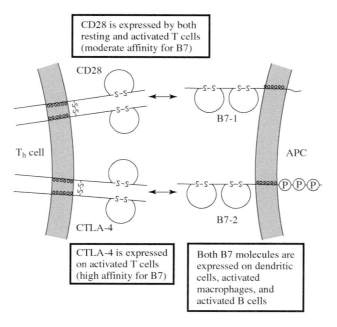

**Figure 12.8**
Activation of $T_h$ cells. These cells become activated in response to antigen-MHC Class II complexes in combination with a co-stimulatory signal supplied by an antigen-presenting cell (APC). This co-stimulatory signal is usually the presence of glycoproteins on the surface of the APC that can interact with specific receptors on the $T_h$ cell [2, 4].

CD28 is expressed by both resting and activated T cells (moderate affinity for B7)

CD28

$T_h$ cell

B7-1

APC

CTLA-4

B7-2

CTLA-4 is expressed on activated T cells (high affinity for B7)

Both B7 molecules are expressed on dendritic cells, activated macrophages, and activated B cells

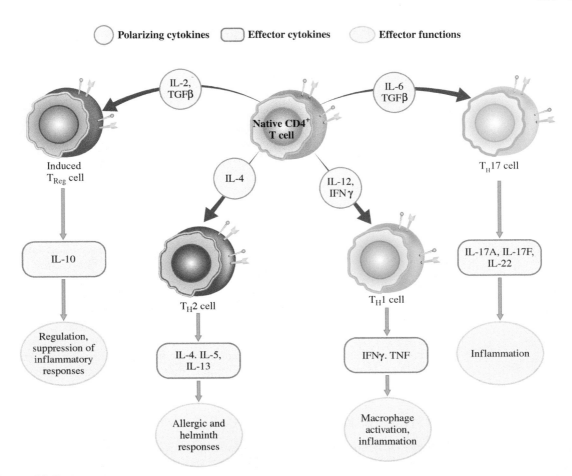

**Figure 12.9**
Subsets of $T_h$ cells with polarizing and effector cytokines depicted for each subtype.

by APCs and other cells in the local environment determine the subtype of T cell. During this differentiation process, a master gene regulator is activated, which causes production of effector cytokines specific to each subtype.

In particular, two "pairs" of subtypes have been characterized to date ($T_{h1}$/$T_{h2}$ and $T_{h17}$/$T_{reg}$; see Fig. 12.9). The most well-studied is $T_{h1}$/$T_{h2}$. $T_{h1}$ cells are associated with response to intracellular pathogens (i.e., endogenous antigens) and produce cytokines that activate cytotoxic T cells (see section 12.4.3) and induce B cells to produce antibodies that support phagocytosis by granulocytes, as described earlier. However, these cells are also implicated in some hypersensitivity reactions, such as the response to poison ivy (see section 12.6.2.4). In contrast, $T_{h2}$ cells respond to extracellular pathogens (i.e., exogenous antigens) and secrete cytokines that activate B cells and eosinophils. Because they generally cause the release of the IgE class of antibodies from B cells, $T_{h2}$ are also implicated in IgE-mediated hypersensitivity responses (see section 12.6.2.1). Interestingly, these subtypes cross-regulate each other, with the master genes and cytokines produced by one subtype acting to reduce differentiation toward the other subtype, although there is some plasticity between these two subtypes early in the differentiation process.

The other pair of subtypes ($T_{h17}/T_{reg}$) differentiate and cross-regulate using the same general principles as $T_{h1}/T_{h2}$, but respond to and secrete different cytokines, many of which communicate with the innate immune response. $T_{h17}$ cells, so named because the major effector cytokine secreted is interleukin-17 (IL-17), are pro-inflammatory, and are associated with chronic inflammatory diseases such as inflammatory bowel disease and multiple sclerosis. In contrast, induced $T_{reg}$ cells are responsive to and produce TGF-β, which downregulates inflammation.

### 12.4.3 Cytotoxic T Cells ($T_c$)

As mentioned earlier, cytokines from $T_h$ also act on $T_c$ cells to encourage their activation and expansion into clonal populations including $T_c$ memory cells and $T_c$ effector cells called **cytotoxic T lymphocytes (CTLs)**. CTLs secrete perforins, which can lyse cells by using mechanisms that are similar to the membrane attack complex of the complement system (discussed in the next section), as well as enzymes known as granzymes, which induce cellular apoptosis. Other CTLs secrete Fas ligand (FasL), which binds to the Fas receptor on the cell surface and induces apoptosis through a similar pathway to granzymes. Importantly, the receptors on the surface of a CTL can disengage the antigen on a cell that has been killed and move to another cell, so they are very efficient at removing "altered self" cells. They are important for prevention of viral infection and cancer, and are the main mediators of graft/transplant rejection if MHC molecules are not sufficiently similar between donor and host. However, $T_c$ cells generally play less of a role than $T_h$ cells in potential acquired immune responses to biomaterials.

### 12.4.4 Natural Killer Cells (NK Cells)

A third type of lymphocyte, the natural killer (NK) cell, is also responsible for attacking altered-self cells. NK cells possess fixed sets of receptors for foreign epitopes, rather than the wide range of receptors/antibodies possessed by $T_c$ and B cells. They also do not require antigen presentation for activation. Thus, they are considered nonspecific responders and are thought by some to be part of the innate immune response. They play a key role in both responses through secretion of cytokines to activate both arms of the immune system. Once activated, in addition to cytokine secretion, they can directly kill altered-self cells using the same mechanisms as described for CTLs.

## 12.5    The Complement System

The complement system is actually a part of innate immunity, but it is discussed in this chapter since it is highly interrelated with the acquired immune response. The **complement system** is composed of over 20 plasma proteins involved in a cascade that ultimately causes the elimination of foreign elements. Like the blood coagulation cascade discussed in the next chapter, there is much amplification in this process, resulting in a swift and decisive response. There are two means of complement activation, the **classical pathway** and **alternative pathway**, which converge to cause formation of the membrane attack complex to lyse foreign cells.

### 12.5.1 Classical Pathway

The main steps in complement activation via the **classical pathway** are depicted in Figure 12.10. Although many biomaterials activate the complement cascade via the alternative pathway (discussed in Section 12.5.2), there is evidence that, in some cases, the classical pathway may be involved.

**Figure 12.10**

Main steps in complement activation via the classical pathway. (a–f) The classical pathway begins with the binding of an antibody (IgG or IgM class) to an antigen on a suitable target (such as a bacterial cell or biomaterial) (a). The attachment of the antibody to the target induces a conformational change, which causes a cascade of chemical reactions starting with the cleavage of C4 (b) and resulting in the formation of the membrane attack complex (MAC), which form pores with diameters of 70–100Å in the membrane (f). These pores allow continuous leakage of ions and small molecules out of the cell, so osmotic stability is impossible to maintain and the cell lyses [2].

The classical pathway begins with the binding of an antibody (IgG or IgM class) to an antigen on a suitable target (such as a bacterial cell or biomaterial). The attachment of the antibody to the target induces a conformational change in the $F_c$ portion that exposes the binding site for the complement protein C1. This is one important example of how the complement system interacts with the acquired immune response.

C1 is actually a complex of C1q and two molecules each of C1r and C1s (Fig. 12.11). C1q is composed of 18 polypeptide chains forming six arms, each of which can bind to the $F_c$ portion of an antibody through its globular "heads." C1r and C1s are both enzymes (serine proteases). C1q must attach to at least two $F_c$ sites for a stable interaction, so IgM is more efficient in complement activation since its pentameric structure provides more binding sites in close proximity.

The binding of C1q to the antibodies causes a conformational change in the C1r that results in cleavage of C1r to form an active enzyme, **C1r**. (In the following sections, boldface type will indicate active enzymes.) **C1r** then cleaves C1s to activate it. **C1s** acts on C4, forming C4a (smaller fragment) and C4b (larger fragment).

C4b now has an exposed binding site, and can attach to the target surface near to **C1s** and act as a receptor for C2. C2 is then cleaved by **C1s** to form **C4b2a** (also called C3 convertase), while the smaller fragment, C2b, diffuses into the surroundings. **C4b2a** acts on C3 to produce C3a and C3b. The larger fragment, C3b, can bind to **C4b2a** to form **C4b2a3b** (C5 convertase). Alternatively, it may diffuse away and can act as an opsonin to promote phagocytosis of foreign materials (this is discussed later in the chapter). One molecule of **C4b2a** can cleave many C3 molecules, so a great deal of amplification occurs in this step of the cascade.

At this point, **C4b2a3b** acts on C5 to produce C5a and C5b. C5a diffuses away to become a soluble inflammatory mediator. C5a is a chemotactic agent for neutrophils and thus is an example of how the complement system aids in the actions of other arms of the innate immune response. The other product, C5b, remains bound to the target surface and initiates formation of the membrane attack complex (described later in this chapter.)

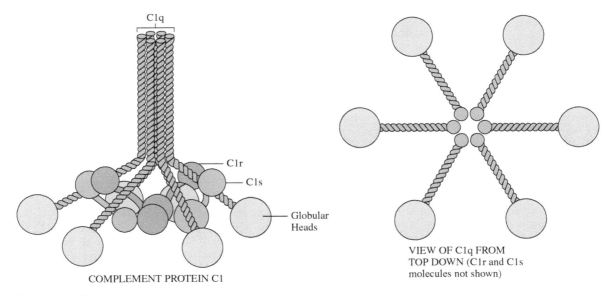

**Figure 12.11**
Structure of the complement protein C1. Schematic of C1, a complex of C1q and two molecules each of C1r and C1s. C1q is composed of 18 polypeptide chains forming six arms, each of which can bind to the $F_c$ portion of an antibody through its globular "heads." C1r and C1s are both enzymes (serine proteases).

## 12.5.2 Alternative Pathway

A second means of complement activation, the **alternative pathway**, is the main method of activation by biomaterials. This pathway does not require the presence of antibodies. Instead, the cascade results from binding of complement proteins on surfaces that possess characteristics different from those found on host cells.

As depicted in Figure 12.12, the origin of the alternative pathway is the serum protein C3, which undergoes slow spontaneous hydrolysis to form C3a and C3b. C3b can bind to a foreign surface or host cells. However, host cells possess cell-membrane-associated constituents that rapidly deactivate C3b (see the following

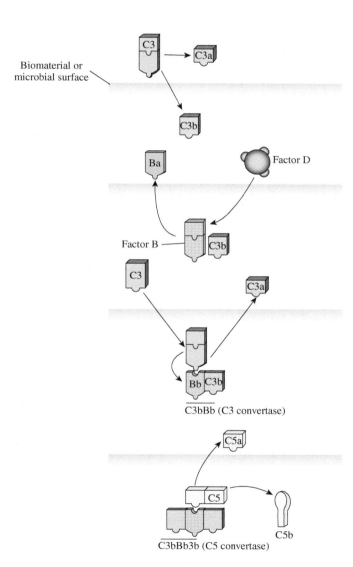

**Figure 12.12**
Complement activation via the alternative pathway. Serum protein C3 undergoes slow spontaneous hydrolysis to C3a and C3b, which commences a cascade that ends in the formation of **C3bBb3b. C3bBb3b** then cleaves C5 to form C5b as in the classical pathway, thus initiating the formation of the membrane attack complex (see Fig. 12.9).

text for further discussion of regulation of the complement system). When attached, C3b can then bind factor B, which exposes the binding site on this molecule for the enzyme **factor D**.[1]

After binding, **factor D** acts on factor B, producing Ba, which diffuses away, and the surface-bound **C3bBb**, also a C3 convertase. **C3bBb** then cleaves more C3 to C3b. As in the classical pathway, there is a great deal of amplification in this step of the cascade. Eventually, a C3b molecule binds to the **C3bBb** complex forming **C3bBb3b**, which is the C5 convertase of the alternative pathway. **C3bBb3b** then cleaves C5 to form C5b as in the classical pathway, thus initiating the formation of the membrane attack complex.

### 12.5.3 Membrane Attack Complex

Both the classical and alternative pathways result in the creation of C5b on the foreign surface. As depicted in Figure 12.10, C5b provides a binding site for C6. C7 then binds to C5b6 and the complex undergoes a conformational transition that exposes hydrophobic regions for interaction with the phospholipid bilayer on the target cell. After the further binding of C8, C5b678 inserts itself into the cell membrane, forming a small pore (diameter 10Å). The final step in the complement cascade is the binding and polymerization of C9 by C5b678. The C5b678 complex surrounded by the poly-C9 structure is termed the **membrane attack complex (MAC)** and it can form pores with diameters of 70–100Å. These pores allow continuous leakage of ions and small molecules out of the cell, so osmotic stability is impossible to maintain and the cell lyses.

### 12.5.4 Regulation of the Complement System

A plethora of molecules are involved in regulation of the complement cascade in order to confine its effects to a localized area and prevent host cells from being lysed by mechanisms intended to kill only foreign pathogens. A detailed discussion of each of these compounds is beyond the scope of this text. Instead, we will focus on different means by which regulation can occur.

An intrinsic means of control of the complement system is found in the short half-life of certain enzymes involved in the cascade. For example, the target-binding site on C3b is rendered unreactive by spontaneous hydrolysis by the time it has diffused 40 nm from the site where it was cleaved by either of the C3 convertases. This reduces binding of the molecule to, and eventual lysis of, nearby host cells.

Alternatively, regulatory proteins are present to limit the actions that occur at the various steps of the complement cascade. Of these, many function at either the stage of C3b or MAC formation. The creation of C3b is tightly regulated because this represents a step providing large amplification of the complement response, and accidental attachment of C3b to host cells can cause their lysis or phagocytosis. Similarly, the steps leading to MAC formation are limited because if the C5b67 complex cannot insert properly into the target (such as may occur when it attempts to insert into a biomaterial), it can be released, attach to bystander cells, and mediate their lysis.

Regulatory proteins can act via two major mechanisms: they can compete for key binding sites or encourage dissociation of molecular complexes. Examples in the classical pathway of proteins that mask binding sites include a number of **regulator of complement activation (RCA) proteins** that bind with C4b to block its attachment

---

[1]Interestingly, there is evidence that the (fully intact) C3 molecule adsorbed to a biomaterial surface can also bind factor B, thus providing another means of alternative pathway activation, which is less easily controlled by the regulatory proteins discussed in the following sections.

to C2a, thus preventing the formation of the C3 convertase. In the same vein, C3 convertase creation is limited in the alternative pathway by other RCA proteins that bind with C3b to prevent attachment to factor B. Other regulatory proteins act at the MAC stage to bind C8, eliminating the assembly of the poly-C9 complex. Examples of regulatory proteins that affect molecular complexes include RCA proteins such as **decay-accelerating factor** (**DAF**), which binds to C3 convertase in either the classical or alternative pathway and forces dissociation of the enzymatic component from the cell-bound component.

### 12.5.5 Effects of the Complement System

Complement system activation often amplifies the actions of antibodies. As discussed previously, these actions include agglutination, precipitation, neutralization, and cell lysis. Complement constituents, for example C3b, aid in the agglutination of foreign particles by promoting particle binding even with relatively low amounts of adsorbed antibodies. Neutralization is also enhanced when the combination of antibodies and complement proteins form a coating over the toxic sites of the foreign substance. In addition, as mentioned earlier, cell lysis is mediated via MAC formation as the final step in the complement cascade.

In addition to aiding the actions of antibodies, complement activation can stimulate another arm of innate immunity, the inflammatory response. In particular, C3a, C4a, and C5a bind to mast cells and basophils to induce the release of histamine and other agents from these cells (see the following section for further discussion). These molecules also cause smooth muscle cell contraction and an increase in vascular permeability, characteristic changes associated with inflammation (see Chapter 10). In addition, C3a, C5a, and the C5b67 complex promote chemotaxis of monocytes and neutrophils towards the site around the foreign agent. C3 has also been implicated in macrophage adhesion to poly(urethane) biomaterials.

Complement proteins also act in concert with the inflammatory response in additional ways to encourage phagocytosis, such as when C3b that is attached to the foreign surface binds to specific receptors on macrophages and neutrophils to facilitate uptake of a foreign particle. This is an example of the phenomenon called **opsonization**, in which a particular biomolecule coating causes an object to be more easily phagocytosed. In this case, the foreign object is said to be **opsonized**.

## 12.6   Undesired Immune Responses to Biomaterials

The previous sections of this chapter have explained the general response of the immune system to foreign surfaces derived either from nonself cells or proteins, or biomaterials. The acquired immune response is important to clear the body of pathogens; however, it can also have unwanted effects such as donor organ rejection, autoimmune disease, or allergies. Some of these undesired effects relating to biomaterials are discussed in this section.

### 12.6.1 Innate versus Acquired Responses to Biomaterials

It is important to note that biomaterials themselves are rarely "rejected" like donor tissue. Since this phenomenon occurs primarily in response to foreign MHC molecules on cell surfaces, unless the biomaterials are carriers for foreign cells (as may be the case for some tissue engineering strategies), complete activation of the acquired immune system resulting in destruction of the implant is unlikely. This pertains even to naturally derived materials, since such materials often undergo treatments like freezing or gluteraldehyde fixation to reduce their antigenic character prior to implantation. Although the natural material may still possess sufficient foreign epitopes to activate the acquired immune system to some extent, this usually does not cause immediate destruction or resorption of the material.

Rather, the "immunocompatibility" of a biomaterial, particularly a synthetic biomaterial, often has more to do with its interaction with the nonspecific (innate) branch of the immune system. For example, complement activation by a biomaterial can lead to a continuing accumulation of inflammatory cells around the implant. While this is not "rejection," it can represent device failure in that the presence of inflammatory cells and/ or a fibrous capsule may prevent integration of the implant with the surrounding tissue.

## 12.6.2 Hypersensitivity

However, sometimes another sort of undesired immune response mediated by the acquired immune system occurs, even with synthetic biomaterials. This is called the **hypersensitivity reaction** or **allergic reaction** and is defined as an unusual, excessive, or uncontrolled immune reaction. Allergies can be classified into four main groups (types I–IV), depending on the biological mechanism that causes the response.

### 12.6.2.1 Type I: IgE Mediated
Type I hypersensitivity is caused by plasma cells (effector B cells) that secrete IgE molecules specific for the allergen (Fig. 12.13). The IgE molecules then bind to receptors on basophils and mast cells, resulting in

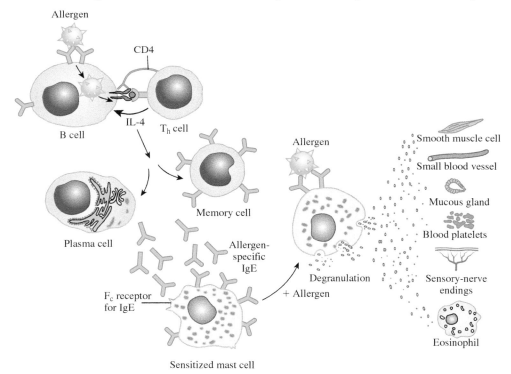

**Figure 12.13**

Type I hypersensitivity response. Type I hypersensitivity is caused by plasma cells (effector B cells) that secrete IgE molecules specific for the allergen. The IgE molecules bind to receptors on basophils and mast cells, resulting in sensitization of these cells. A second exposure to the antigen from the allergen causes crosslinking of these membrane-bound antibodies. This crosslinking provides a signal to induce degranulation of mast cells and the release of soluble mediators (e.g., histamine). These mediators cause a number of localized and systemic effects, including smooth muscle cell contraction and vasodilation.

sensitization of these cells. A second exposure to the antigen from the allergen causes crosslinking of these antibodies that are now membrane bound. This crosslinking provides a signal to induce degranulation of mast cells and the release of soluble mediators (e.g., histamine). These mediators then cause a number of localized and systemic effects, including vasodilation and smooth muscle cell contraction. Depending on its extent, this reaction can be fatal (e.g., allergy to peanuts or bee stings).

Type I reactions are the typical "allergic" response to environmental factors, such as ragweed pollen (known as "hay fever") and some antibiotics, such as penicillin. Documented cases of type I hypersensitivity to biomaterials are rare. However, it may be that an IgE-mediated response to metallic components could be generated if the patient was previously exposed to these compounds in the workplace, for example. Similarly, latex in latex examination gloves may produce a type I reaction in sensitized individuals.

### 12.6.2.2 Type II: Antibody Mediated

In type II reactions, generated antibodies work alone or in connection with the complement to destroy cells or platelets presenting a foreign antigen on their surface. A typical example of a type II reaction occurs when host cells respond to a mismatched blood type during blood transfusion. There are few documented cases of type II hypersensitivity to biomaterials.

### 12.6.2.3 Type III: Immune Complex Mediated

Symptoms of type III reactions may appear days to weeks after original exposure to the antigen because, in this type of hypersensitivity, both antigen and antibody must be present in the tissue or circulation at the same time. When this occurs, a large number of immune complexes (antigen–antibody complexes) are precipitated within a localized area, or, if the antigen is present in the blood, systemically in blood vessel walls. The binding of the antigen and antibody encourages activation of the complement system, with the subsequent migration of phagocytic cells to the area. Much of the tissue damage in type III reactions results from the release of enzymes and other active substances by the recruited inflammatory cells. Type III reactions are the mechanism of action of autoimmune diseases such as lupus. There have been some reports of type III reactions in response to gold, and this type of reaction may be a concern for biomaterial systems that are slowly degrading or involve slow drug release. However, in general, type III reactions are not a major cause of biomaterial hypersensitivity.

### 12.6.2.4 Type IV: T Cell Mediated

Like type I reactions, type IV hypersensitivity reactions usually involve more than one exposure to the allergen. This response is also called **delayed-type hypersensitivity** since the symptoms can appear 24–72 hours after the second contact with the allergen (antigen). This type of hypersensitivity is responsible for contact dermatitis, and can also cause the formation of granulomas, discussed in Chapter 11.

As depicted in Figure 12.14, unlike the previous types of hypersensitivity, antibodies are not involved in the type IV response. Instead, the action of specialized cells, $T_{DTH}$ cells (usually formed from $T_h$ cells), is the main cause of the reaction. Upon first exposure to the antigen presented on an APC, $T_h$ cells become sensitized and mature into $T_{DTH}$ cells. Further exposure causes the activation of the $T_{DTH}$ cells and secretion of cytokines to attract macrophages to the region. After their accumulation (1–3 days later), release of lytic agents by the inflammatory cells results in local tissue damage and clinical symptoms.

Reports of dermatitis or oral lesions after insertion of oral implants containing chromium, cobalt or nickel indicate that type IV reactions could be a concern for biomaterial use. Similarly, deep tissue reactions of this type have also been seen with metallic, silicone, and acrylic implants, indicating that this response is not confined to metallic biomaterials alone.

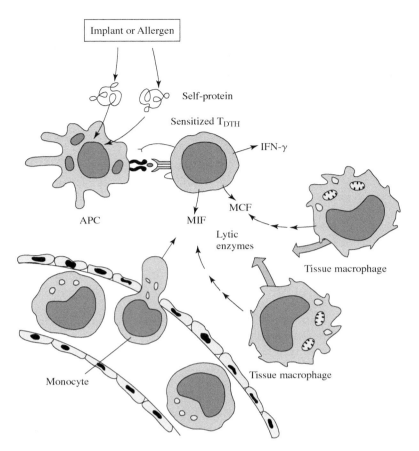

**Figure 12.14**
Diagram of a type IV hypersensitivity reaction. Specialized cells, $T_{DTH}$ cells, are the main cause of the reaction. Upon first exposure to the antigen presented on an APC, $T_h$ cells become sensitized and mature into $T_{DTH}$ cells. Further exposure causes the activation of the $T_{DTH}$ cells and secretion of cytokines to attract macrophages to the region. After their accumulation (one to three days later), release of lytic agents by the inflammatory cells results in local tissue damage and clinical symptoms.

**12.6.2.5 Hypersensitivity and the Classes of Biomaterials** Hypersensitivity reactions to biomaterials have been most extensively studied for metals. However, it is thought that released products must act as haptens, requiring complexation with a native protein before immune system activation, due to the low molecular weight of the ions involved.

Very little study of hypersensitivity to ceramic materials has been performed, and evidence of type IV responses to polymers remains controversial. Chemical additives used in the manufacture of latex gloves may cause this type of hypersensitive response. In addition, there is a continuing concern that the denaturation of native proteins through binding to biomaterial surfaces (see Chapter 8) may result in an undesired immune response since they are no longer recognized as "self."

Although the debate continues about how hypersensitive reactions to biomaterials develop, these responses can have serious consequences for hypersensitive individuals and can have profound business implications, as seen with the sale of silicone breast implants. In this case, due to litigation alleging that silicone breast implants caused autoimmune diseases (destruction of body tissues due to unchecked acquired immune response), many of the major makers of these implants decided to withdraw from the market in 1992. Subsequent settlements cost these companies billions of dollars and one manufacturer was forced into bankruptcy. (As an epilogue, after years of study that found no direct link between silicone breast implants and these diseases, in 2006 the U.S. Food and Drug Administration approved a new generation of these implants for use in cosmetic surgeries.)

## EXAMPLE PROBLEM 12.3

A retired employee of a company that manufactures bicycle frames from cobalt-chromium-molybdenum (Co-Cr-Mo) alloys was involved in an accident in which his knee was shattered. The orthopedic surgeon stated that the shattered knee must be replaced with an implanted prosthesis. The patient was allowed to decide between an implant composed of a titanium-aluminum-vanadium alloy and an implant composed of a Co-Cr-Mo alloy. Considering his history of cutting and grinding Co-Cr-Mo alloy frames in the bicycle factory, the patient enthusiastically chose the Co-Cr-Mo knee implant. Shortly after implantation, however, the patient exhibited symptoms consistent with a hypersensitivity reaction. How might this be explained?

**Solution:**   The hypersensitivity reaction was likely in response to the implantation of a Co-Cr-Mo knee prosthesis. The patient clearly had a history of exposure to Co-Cr-Mo alloys in his work producing bicycle frames in a factory. This exposure likely included tactile contact, as well as inhalation of Co-Cr-Mo particles. It is possible that his body responded to the Co-Cr-Mo material as an antigen. The primary exposure to the material during his factory work led to the production of memory cells and release of IgE molecules specific for the material. The IgE molecules bound to receptors on mast cells and basophils, thereby sensitizing these cells. Upon the secondary exposure presented by the implantation of the knee prosthesis, the membrane-bound IgE antibodies on sensitized cells crosslinked, resulting in the release of histamine and other soluble mediators. Thus, a hypersensitivity reaction was initiated.   ∎

# 12.7   Techniques: Assays for Immune Response

A wide variety of tests for immune response to materials have been developed, in part, due to the fact that biomaterials may either suppress the immune system by reducing lymphocytes' ability to respond to a stimulus, or can stimulate the lymphocytes to become reactive toward the implant (hypersensitivity) or the native tissues within body (autoimmune disease). Collectively, these are called **immunotoxic** responses to implanted materials. Because of the strong interaction between the immune and inflammatory response, many of the *in vitro* and *in vivo* techniques employed to determine possible immune responses to biomaterials are the same as those outlined in Chapters 10 and 11 for inflammation. In fact, given the interplay between the innate and acquired immune responses, it is prudent to include both inflammatory cells and lymphocytes in *in vitro* tests for a more complete screening of the biocompatibility of a new material. As for other assays, it is expected that *in vitro* activation of lymphocytes in response to a particular substance is a predictor that this material may be immunotoxic *in vivo*. A number of ISO and ASTM standards exist for immunotoxicity testing both *in vitro* (includes ISO10993-10 and ASTM F1905, F1906, F1984, F2065, F2567) and *in vivo* (includes ISO10993-10 and ASTM F719, F720, F2147, F2148).

## 12.7.1   *In Vitro* Assays

As with the inflammatory response, cells involved in the immune response can be isolated from the blood and then cultured in the presence of the biomaterial before determining their state of activation. In recent standards, ISO has recommended a two-tiered approach to assessing immunotoxicity. In the first tier, relatively simple assays are performed on cells representing humoral immunity (B cells), cellular immunity (T cells), and nonspecific immune reaction (NK cells). If positive responses are seen, more specific Tier II assays may be required.

Many Tier I assays are designed to monitor proliferation of lymphocytes in response to an appropriate stimulus that would normally lead to clonal expansion. These are often performed by radiolabeling or fluorescent-labeling cellular DNA and monitoring the change in its amount over time. A large increase in DNA synthesis

**Figure 12.15**

Data from an *in vitro* lymphocyte proliferation assay. In this study, T cells were cultured on several different materials and their proliferation tracked via a derivative of the MTT assay, which produces a purple salt in the presence of metabolically active cells (see Chapter 9). Here, it was found that direct co-culture with monocytes, or indirect co-culture with monocytes using a transwell culture system (see Chapter 9), promoted lymphocyte proliferation on all biomaterial surfaces at 3 days. Surfaces prepared for this study consisted of a poly(ethylene terephthalate) (PET) base coated with poly(benzyl N,N-diethyldithiocarbamate-co-styrene) (BDEDTC). Polyacrylamide (PAAm), sodium salt of poly(acrylic acid) (PAANa), or methiodide of poly(dimethylaminopropyl-acrylamide) (DMAPAAmMeI) were then polymerized on top of this base layer [5].

indicates that the lymphocytes are actively proliferating (see Fig. 12.15). Such experiments are done with both B cells and T cells, with the chemical stimuli specific for each, in the presence of the material or extracts to determine if the biomaterial suppresses or stimulates this component of the immune response. In other Tier I assays, since NK cells are known to attack tumor cells, a tumor cell line is placed with NK cells in the presence of the biomaterial or extracts, and amount of lysis of the tumor cells is monitored as a measure of the effectiveness of the NK cell response to stimuli (see Fig. 12.16). For additional examples of Tier I assays, see ISO 10993-20.

**Figure 12.16**

Data from a natural killer (NK) cell assay. In this case, NK cells were incubated with the K562 tumor cell line for 20 hours and stimulated with different concentrations of the growth factor transforming growth factor β(TGF-β) in order to determine the optimal concentration to stimulate NK cell lysis of the tumor cells. The assay was performed by pre-labeling the tumor cells with a radiolabel and then recording the amount of the label that was released when the cells were lysed. (Results shown as mean ± standard error of the mean for seven replicates [6].)

For Tier II assays, many of the recommended assays focus on cell migration, cytokine release, or cell surface marker expression. Cell migration assays were discussed in Chapters 9 and 10 and are also used for lymphocytes to determine if they will move toward a foreign antigen while on top of the biomaterial. In addition, while ELISAs and FACS sorting are employed to determine the type and amount of released cytokines and cell-surface markers, respectively (see Chapter 10 for detailed discussion of these methods), the exact cytokines and cell surface markers targeted are different for lymphocytes than those examined for granulocyte activation. For more detail about Tier II assays, please refer to ISO 10993-20.

### 12.7.2 *In Vivo* Assays

*In vivo*, an unresolved immune response has characteristics similar to chronic inflammation, but includes the presence of lymphocytes as well as inflammatory cells. Therefore, the techniques used to examine the *in vivo* immune response to implanted materials are very similar to those outlined in Chapter 11, and the experimental design must address concerns like those for *in vivo* inflammatory tests, such as the choice of animal, choice of implant site, length of study, dose and administration of biomaterial, and inclusion of proper controls. To date, the most common means of assessment after implantation in an animal model are histology/immunohistochemistry, with an emphasis on visualizing the amount of lymphocytes present around the material (see Fig. 12.17 for an example).

It is also possible to monitor the immune response relatively noninvasively over the course of implantation. Blood samples can be taken from the animal and tested for the presence of antibodies (usually IgG) against certain epitopes derived from the implanted biomaterial. The presence of such antibodies suggests that the material is immunogenic and may result eventually in deleterious effects to the device or patient. This procedure can also be used for human patients, particularly if it is believed that a hypersensitivity has developed to an implant. Blood samples can also be used to test for complement system proteins to determine the overall level of complement activation over the course of implantation.

**Figure 12.17**
*In vivo* histology of poly (trimethylene carbonate) films after 14 days of subcutaneous implantation in rats. Toluidine blue staining shows a number of types of cells, including lymphocytes, near the material (Scale bar 50 μm). (P) polymer, (fc) fibrous capsule, (g) giant cell, (arrow) macrophage, (L) lipid tissue, (V) blood vessel, (filled triangle) phagocytosed intracellular fragments, (open triangle) lymphocyte [8].

**Figure 12.18**
Data from patch testing for hypersensitivity to metals. Various metal extracts were injected into the skin on the back of the patient. Note the red welts near various types of metals, indicating hypersensitivity to that compound. (Adapted with permission from [7].)

In animals, hypersensitivity and irritation are often tested following similar procedures, usually by exposing the biomaterial or extracts to the animal by placing on or injecting in the skin. For irritation, signs of localized inflammation are examined within a few hours of exposure. For hypersensitivity (particularly delayed-type), often the animal will need to be exposed several times over 1–2 weeks, in order to first sensitize the animal, and then localized inflammation is monitored after the last exposure.

A common hypersensitivity test in humans is to place possible antigens from the biomaterial on/under the skin and look for localized inflammation (**skin patch testing**, see Fig. 12.18 for an example). If redness or swelling is apparent near the site of application of the antigen, then it is an indication that the patient may be hypersensitive to the implanted material. Similar procedures are used to determine allergic reactions to environmental factors (such as pollen and dander).

## EXAMPLE PROBLEM 12.4

Severe combined immunodeficiency (SCID) is a genetic disorder that results in a lack of B and T lymphocytes. People with SCID have severely compromised immune systems. Mice with SCID are capable of receiving transplanted tissue with a negligible risk of rejection. Consequently, they are useful as animal models for the evaluation of the biological activity of transplanted cells and/or tissues for therapeutic purposes. For instance, SCID mice can be used to evaluate the ability of marrow stromal cells to generate bone in an ectopic site *in vivo*. Would SCID mice be useful models for the evaluation of the immune response to a biomaterial? Why or why not?

Solution: SCID mice would not be a useful model for the evaluation of the immune response to an implanted biomaterial, as the immune system of SCID mice is severely compromised. The lack of an immune response to an implanted biomaterial in a SCID mouse would not be a reliable indicator of the potential immune response to this material in an individual with a fully functional immune system. ∎

# Summary

- The two types of acquired immunity are humoral, which is based on the actions of antibodies against foreign substances, and cellular, which utilizes specialized lymphocytes primarily to detect and neutralize altered cells of one's own body.

- A hapten is a low molecular weight substance that combines with a larger molecule to produce a much greater immune response than either entity would have alone. An adjuvant is a substance that nonspecifically enhances the immune response to antigens.

- The acquired immune response is activated by the binding of an antigen to an antibody or a T cell receptor (TCR), through specific recognition of an epitope on the antigen. Antigen recognition generally occurs through presentation of the antigen with an MHC Class I or Class II molecule. MHC Class I molecules are present on nearly all nucleated cells and are recognized by $T_c$ cells. MHC Class II molecules are only found on antigen-presenting cells (APCs) and are recognized by $T_h$ cells. Antigens must be processed within the cell, where they complex with the appropriate MHC molecule before extracellular presentation.

- The two primary types of lymphocytes that respond to antigens to produce the acquired immune response are B cells, which are mediators of humoral immunity that produce highly specific antibodies that can either be released into the environment or remain bound to the cell membrane, and T cells, which are involved in cellular immunity and produce high specificity TCRs that remain bound to the cell membrane.

- B cells are formed and processed in the bone marrow and are further matured in the peripheral lymphoid tissues, whereas T cells are processed in the thymus. After maturation, the B cells and T cells migrate to the lymphoid tissues, where they may either remain for some time or enter directly into the blood stream to be circulated throughout the body.

- Antibodies are composed of two heavy and two light polypeptide chains, linked through disulfide bonds. The region at the end of each heavy/light chain combination is the cleft for antigen binding, called the variable portion ($F_{ab}$). The remainder of the antigen is called the constant portion ($F_c$) and is responsible for recognition by the receptors in phagocytic cells or by certain molecules in the complement complex.

- Antibodies can assist in the removal of pathogens through agglutination (IgA and IgM are most effective at this), precipitation, neutralization, or lysis. Additionally, antibody binding can increase the rate of phagocytosis of antigen-containing particles and is a major mechanism for activating the complement system.

- Presentation of an antigen/MHC complex causes activation of T lymphocytes by promoting binding of the antigen to the TCR. Upon activation $T_h$ cells release cytokines that aid in the activation of $T_c$ cells. $T_h$ cells also bind with and release cytokines to fully activate B cells. Following activation, each lymphocyte undergoes rapid division to form a clonal population of cells specific for its respective antigen. Both effector and memory cells are produced in this process. Effector B cells are called plasma cells, and secrete soluble antibodies. Effector T cells are cytotoxic T lymphocytes (CTLs), which can secrete perforins to lyse cells.

- NK Cells are another type of lymphocyte, but do not require specific antigen presentation for activation. Instead, their fixed surface receptors are used for detecting "altered-self" cells. They can secrete cytokines to activate both innate and acquired immunity, as well as can directly kill altered-self cells using the same mechanisms as CTLs.

- Two means of complement activation (classical and alternative pathways) converge to result in the formation of the membrane attack complex to lyse foreign cells. The classical pathway is initiated with the binding of an antibody to an antigen on a suitable target. This results in a conformational change in the

$F_c$ region of the antibody that initiates a cascade of events that culminates in the production of C5b, which remains bound to the target surface and initiates formation of the membrane attack complex. The alternative pathway begins with the binding of a complement protein C3 to the foreign entity and ends ultimately in the formation of C5b. The membrane attack complex forms large pores in the membrane of the target cell, which result in its lysis.

- Regulation of the complement cascade occurs through a number of means, including the short half-life of many of the enzymes involved in the cascade and the action of regulatory proteins that occur at various stages of the cascade.

- Activation of the complement system allows for an amplification of the actions of antibodies. Additionally, complement activation can result in the stimulation of the inflammatory response through the action of C3a, C4a, and C5a. Factors in the complement cascade can act in concert with inflammatory cells to encourage phagocytosis of targeted entities.

- Allergic responses can be divided into four general categories. Type I responses are mediated by IgE antibodies produced by plasma cells against a particular allergen. Type II responses are generated when antibodies work alone or in connection with the complement to destroy cells presenting a foreign antigen. Type III responses occur when a large number of antigen-antibody complexes are precipitated within a localized area or if the antigen is present systemically in the blood, in which cases the complement is activated and results in the recruitment and action of inflammatory cells. Type IV reactions are delayed-type hypersensitivity responses that do not involve the action of antibodies, but instead involve the sensitization and activation of $T_{DTH}$ cells that recruit the action of macrophages.

- Techniques for determination of possible immune responses to biomaterials usually follow a two-tiered system, in which follow-on studies are only required if potential problems are identified in simpler initial tests. Immunotoxicity studies comprise a combination of *in vitro* and *in vivo* assays.

## Problems

12.1   Name the four major characteristics of acquired immunity and give a brief explanation of how each is achieved at a cellular/sub-cellular level.

12.2   Based on what was presented in this chapter, trace the fate of a virus protein that has infected a host cell, as well as the host cell. Include all major cell types and biomolecule types that would respond to this infection.

12.3   (a) Describe the role of $T_h$ cells in humoral and cellular immunity. What cells do $T_h$ cells interact with in each case and how do they interact?
       (b) Specifically, explain the role of $T_{h1}$ versus $T_{h2}$ cells in humoral and cellular immunity.

12.4   What are the four major actions of antibodies? Which one(s) is likely at play in the response to a bacterial infection? Justify your answer.

12.5   Stem cells have been proposed as therapies for many diseases. However, a problem with using stem cells from another person as a therapy is that they can be recognized as foreign and activate the complement system, leading to cell death.

       (a) What pathway is most likely involved in activation of the complement system in this case? Why?

(b) You have decided to engineer the surface of the stem cells to present an additional biological molecule to help reduce complement activation. What molecule would you put on the cell surface? Justify your answer by relating how this surface molecule interacts with the complement system to cause the desired result.

(c) Given all the assays so far described in this book, choose one assay to determine if your solution in b) was effective. Describe what outcome you would expect if your solution worked.

12.6 Based on your knowledge of both the innate and acquired immune response, if you wanted to prevent a type IV hypersensitivity reaction, which one cell type would be most important to block and why?

12.7 You are developing a new material as a part of a synthetic replacement heart valve.

(a) Describe the Tier I assays would you choose as a first-pass screen for immunotoxicity.

(b) What results would cause you to complete Tier II assays and which assay(s) would you choose? Justify your choice.

# References

1. J. M. Anderson and J. J. Langone, "Issues and perspectives on the biocompatibility and immunotoxicity evaluation of implanted controlled release systems," *Journal of Controlled Release*, vol. 57, no. 2, pp. 107–13, 1999.

2. J. Kuby, *Immunology*, 3rd ed. New York: W.H. Freeman, 1997.

3. F. H. Silver and D. L. Christiansen, *Biomaterials science and biocompatibility*. New York: Springer, 1999.

4. P S Linsley and J. A. Ledbetter, "The role of the CD28 receptor during T cell responses to antigen," *Annual Review of Immunology*, vol. 11, no. 1, pp. 191–212, 1993.

5. M. R. MacEwan, W. G. Brodbeck, T. Matsuda, and J. M. Anderson, "Monocyte/lymphocyte interactions and the foreign body response: in vitro effects of biomaterial surface chemistry," *Journal of Biomedical Materials Research Part A*, vol. 74A, no. 3, pp. 285–293, 2005.

6. A. H. Rook *et al.*, "Effects of transforming growth factor beta on the functions of natural killer cells: depressed cytolytic activity and blunting of interferon responsiveness," *Journal of Immunology*, vol. 136, no. 10, pp. 3916–3920, 1986.

7. M. Hosoki, K. Nishigawa, Y. Miyamoto, G. Ohe, and Y. Matsuka, "Allergic contact dermatitis caused by titanium screws and dental implants," *Journal of Prosthodontic Research*, vol. 60, no. 3, pp. 213–219, 2016.

8. B. Erhan *et al.*, "In vivo behavior of trimethylene carbonate and ε-caprolactone-based (co)polymer networks: Degradation and tissue response," *Journal of Biomedical Materials Research*, vol. 95, no. 3, pp. 940–949, 2010.

# Additional Reading

Center for Devices and Radiological Health, "Breast implants," *US Food & Drug Administration*. Available at https://www.fda.gov/MedicalDevices/ProductsandMedicalProcedures/ImplantsandProsthetics/BreastImplants/default.htm.

J. Black, *Biological performance of materials: Fundamentals of biocompatibility*, 4th ed. New York: CRC Press, 2005.

K. C. Dee, D. A. Puleo, and R. Bizios, *An introduction to tissue-biomaterial interactions*. Hoboken: Wiley-Liss, 2002.

S. C. Gad and S. Gad-McDonald, *Biomaterials, medical devices, and combination products: biocompatibility testing and safety assessment*. Boca Raton: CRC Press, 2015.

D. Granchi *et al.*, "Effects of bone cement extracts on the cell-mediated immune response," *Biomaterials*, vol. 23, no. 4, pp. 1033–1041, 2002.

T. Groth, K. Klosz, E. J. Campbell, R. R. New, B. Hall, and H. Goering, "Protein adsorption, lymphocyte adhesion and platelet adhesion/activation on polyurethane ureas is related to hard segment content and composition,"

*Journal of Biomaterials Science, Polymer Edition*, vol. 6, no. 6, pp. 497–510, 1994.

A. Guyton and J. Hall, *Textbook of medical physiology*, 11th ed. Philadelphia: W.B. Saunders Company, 2006.

N. Hallab, J. J. Jacobs, and J. Black, "Hypersensitivity to metallic biomaterials: a review of leukocyte migration inhibition assays," *Biomaterials*, vol. 21, no. 13, pp. 1301–1314, 2000.

N. J. Hallab, K. Mikecz, and J. J. Jacobs, "A triple assay technique for the evaluation of metal-induced, delayed-type hypersensitivity responses in patients with or receiving total joint arthroplasty," *Journal of Biomedical Materials Research*, vol. 53, no. 5, pp. 480–489, 2000.

G. Harris, "F.D.A. panel backs breast implants from one maker," *The New York Times*, 14 April 2005.

A. Hensten and N. Jacobsen, "Systemic toxicity and hypersensitivity," in *Biomaterials science: an introduction to materials and medicine*, 3rd ed., B. D. Ratner, A. S. Hoffman, F. J. Schoen, and J. E. Lemons, Eds. San Diego: Elsevier Academic Press, 2013, pp. 545–551.

R. J. Johnson, "Immunology and the complement system," in *Biomaterials science: an introduction to materials and medicine*, 3rd ed., B. D. Ratner, A. S. Hoffman, F. J. Schoen, and J. E. Lemons, Eds. San Diego: Elsevier Academic Press, 2013, pp. 533–545.

J. A. Owen, J. Punt, S. A. Stranford, and P. P. Jones, *Kuby immunology*, 7th ed. New York: W. H. Freeman, 2013.

M. M. Matzelle and J. E. Babensee, "Humoral immune responses to model antigen co-delivered with biomaterials used in tissue engineering," *Biomaterials*, vol. 25, no. 2, pp. 295–304, 2004.

J. P. Mayesh and M. F. Scranton, "Legal aspects of biomaterials," in *Biomaterials science: an introduction to materials and medicine*, 2nd ed., B. D. Ratner, A. S. Hoffman, F. J. Schoen, and J. E. Lemons, Eds. San Diego: Elsevier Academic Press, 2004, pp. 797–804.

A. K. McNally and J. M. Anderson, "Complement C3 participation in monocyte adhesion to different surfaces," *Proceedings of the National Academy of Sciences*, vol. 91, no. 21, pp. 10119–10123, 1994.

K. Merritt, "Systemic toxicity and hypersensitivity," in *Biomaterials science: an introduction to materials and medicine*, 1st ed., B. D. Ratner, A. S. Hoffman, F. J. Schoen, and J. E. Lemons, Eds. San Diego: Elsevier Academic Press, 1996, pp. 188–193.

R. N. Mitchell, "Innate and adaptive immunity: The immune response to foreign materials," in *Biomaterials science: an introduction to materials and medicine*, 3rd ed., B. D. Ratner, A. S. Hoffman, F. J. Schoen, and J. E. Lemons, Eds. San Diego: Academic Press, 2013, pp. 512–532.

E. M. Palmer, B. A. Beilfuss, T. Nagai, R. T. Semnani, S. F. Badylak, and G. A. van Seventer, "Human helper T cell activation and differentiation is suppressed by porcine small intestinal submucosa," *Tissue Engineering*, vol. 8, no. 5, pp. 893–900, 2002.

M. Rosales-Cortes, *et al.*, "Immunological study of a chitosan prosthesis in the sciatic nerve regeneration of the axotomized dog," *Journal of Biomaterials Applications*, vol. 18, no. 1, pp. 15–23, 2003.

P. Thomas, S. Barnstorf, B. Summer, G. Willmann, and B. Przybilla, "Immuno-allergological properties of aluminium oxide ($Al_2O_3$) ceramics and nickel sulfate in humans," *Biomaterials*, vol. 24, no. 6, pp. 959–966, 2003.

D. Williams, *Essential biomaterials science*. Cambridge, UK: Cambridge University Press, 2014.

# Biomaterials and Thrombosis

---

**Main Objective**

To understand the steps involved in, and results of, the blood coagulation cascade stimulated by biomaterial implantation.

**Specific Objectives**

1. To understand the functions of platelets, including how platelets are activated and the results of this activation.

2. To compare and contrast the intrinsic and extrinsic pathways for blood coagulation and understand how these interact with the inflammatory response.

3. To understand the steps of the final common blood coagulation pathway and fibrin polymerization.

4. To understand approaches to limiting clot formation.

5. To understand the pro- and anticoagulant properties of the vascular endothelium.

6. To understand the concepts behind and possible limitations to the *in vitro, in vivo*, and *ex vivo* tests presented.

---

## 13.1 Introduction: Overview of Hemostasis

Blood–biomaterials interactions are extremely important since almost all biomaterials are implanted in vascularized tissues and contact with blood occurs frequently, particularly during the implantation procedure. However, as reviewed in Chapters 7 and 8, it is important to remember that the body actually responds to the protein coat of the biomaterial in many cases, so controlling protein adsorption is a key method of altering blood coagulation caused by the implant.

After injury, **hemostatic** mechanisms in the body have been designed to arrest bleeding. These involve vascular constriction in the area of the insult, the formation of a platelet plug, and blood coagulation (**thrombosis**). The combination of these responses decreases regional blood flow and temporarily closes the hole in the vessel, thus preventing further blood loss from the area. Both proteinaceous and nonproteinaceous components of the blood (such as platelets), as well as the endothelial lining of the blood vessels, play a large role in hemostasis. We begin with a discussion of the importance of platelets in the coagulation process.

# 13.2 Role of Platelets

## 13.2.1 Platelet Characteristics and Functions

Platelets are nonnucleated fragments of megakaryocytes with a diameter of 3–4 μm. Because they do not possess nuclei, platelets cannot proliferate and have a half-life in the body of only 8–12 days. Platelets perform two main hemostatic functions: they initially reduce bleeding through the creation of a platelet plug and then further stabilize this plug through activation of the blood coagulation cascade.

Although they are only cell fragments, platelets contain mitochondria for energy production, as well as portions of the ER and Golgi apparatus for packaging of secretory products. These products are usually chemical mediators to be released upon platelet activation and are stored in intracellular granules before secretion.

Several types of platelet intracellular granules can be distinguished. The α **granules** contain platelet-specific proteins (platelet factors) and $\beta$-thromboglobulin as well as various plasma proteins including fibrinogen and the coagulation-cascade proteins Factor V and Factor XIII. **Dense granules** carry adenosine diphosphate (ADP), calcium ions, and serotonin, while **lysosomal granules** contain hydrolytic enzymes.

## 13.2.2 Platelet Activation

**13.2.2.1 Means of Activation** Platelets can become activated via a variety of stimuli, including exposure to soluble factors or interaction with ECM and/or cells of injured vessel walls. In particular, the ECM molecule collagen and the blood-borne soluble protein von Willebrand factor (vWF) are potent platelet activators, and platelets may respond to these and other proteins either from damaged tissue or adsorbed on biomaterial surfaces. In all cases, interaction of these extracellular stimuli with receptors on the cell membrane is the first step in platelet activation.

**13.2.2.2 Sequelae of Activation** Once stimulated, platelets undergo a number of changes. Briefly, while unactivated platelets have a disc-like morphology, activated platelets swell and take on an irregular form, extending pseudopodia in various directions. Also at this time, contraction of cytoskeletal proteins results in release of storage granule contents. As a result of these changes, platelets express several new functionalities. Activated platelets are observed to adhere to ECM proteins, aggregate, secrete various bioactive factors for further platelet stimulation, and exhibit coagulatory activity. Each of these characteristics is discussed in more detail in the rest of this section.

Platelet adhesion near the injured area (or onto a biomaterial) is mediated through interactions between appropriate ligands from collagen, vWF, fibrinogen, fibronectin, and glycoprotein or integrin receptors on the platelet surface. As the platelets begin to adhere to the target area, they release their granule contents, including large amounts of adenosine diphosphate (ADP). Release of **thrombin** (see Table 13.1) and thromboxane $A_2$ is also upregulated.

These soluble chemical mediators act on neighboring platelets to activate them and attract them to the growing aggregate. In particular, thrombin catalyzes the production of more thrombin and stimulates ADP and thromboxane $A_2$ release.

Also as a result of these soluble factors, platelets in the region of the aggregate begin to express the activated glycoprotein (GP) receptor **GP IIb/IIIa** on their surfaces. This receptor can then bind plasma proteins to increase platelet aggregation. Specifically, *fibrinogen* plays an important role in this process because it possesses two receptor binding sites, allowing for platelet–platelet bridging. Overall, these steps result in the formation of a platelet plug, although at this stage it is fairly fragile.

**TABLE 13.1**

| Different Actions of Thrombin | |
| --- | --- |
| Positive Effects on Coagulation | Negative Effects on Coagulation |
| Catalyzes production of more thrombin by platelets | |
| Stimulates release of granule contents by platelets (particularly ADP and thromboxane $A_2$) | Thrombomodulin–thrombin complex on endothelial cell membrane activates protein C, which can then inactivate Factors V and VIII |
| Cleaves fibrinogen to fibrin | |
| Activates Factor V | |
| Activates Factor XIII which crosslinks fibrin | |

In order to stabilize the plug, platelets also promote localized blood coagulation. In particular, when stimulated, alterations in the platelet phospholipid membrane allow the expression of certain receptors that accelerate Factor X activation (Factor X is a key protein in the blood coagulation cascade; see the next section). Platelet membranes also form a catalytic environment for conversion of prothrombin to thrombin (see later discussion).

# 13.3 Coagulation Cascade

Blood coagulation can occur via two main mechanisms, called the **intrinsic** and **extrinsic** pathways. Like complement activation, both cascades end in a common pathway, in this case causing the conversion of fibrinogen to fibrin, the main constituent of the blood clot. The proteins involved in these pathways are designated with the word "Factor" and a Roman numeral, although many of them have alternate names. A list of factors and their common names is found in Table 13.2. Except for the commencement of the intrinsic pathway, calcium is required for almost all reactions in the cascade, which is why substances that bind calcium (**calcium chelators**) are very effective anticoagulants.

## 13.3.1 Intrinsic Pathway

The intrinsic pathway is initiated by trauma to blood itself or exposure of blood to exposed ECM molecules in a damaged vessel wall. Clotting initiates in 1–6 minutes via this mechanism. Although in many classical hematology texts and much of the biomaterials literature, this pathway is treated as an equal alternative to the extrinsic pathway (described in section 13.3.2), recent texts have placed more emphasis on the extrinsic pathway as the main means of clot formation. The role of the intrinsic pathway remains unclear, particularly in the case of coagulation near biomaterials, where the blood interacts with a foreign surface. If the surface is negatively charged, a requirement for the initiation of this cascade, the intrinsic pathway may remain an important means of coagulation.

As mentioned earlier, the intrinsic pathway begins with adsorption of one of the coagulation **contact proteins**, Factor XII, to a negatively charged surface (Fig. 13.1). This surface can be naturally occurring, such as with glycosylated ECM molecules, or can be an anionic biomaterial. The act of adsorption causes conversion of Factor XII to the activated **XIIa** (as in Chapter 12, active enzymes in the cascade will be designated by boldface type.) **XIIa** converts *prekallikrein* to **kallikrein**

**TABLE 13.2**

| Coagulation Factors and Their Common Names | |
| --- | --- |
| Clotting Factor | Synonyms |
| Fibrinogen | Factor I |
| Prothrombin | Factor II |
| Tissue factor | Factor III, tissue thromboplastin |
| Calcium | Factor IV |
| Factor V | Proaccelerin, labile factor, Ac-globulin (Ac-G) |
| Factor VII | Serum prothrombin conversion accelerator (SPCA), proconvertin, stable factor |
| Factor VIII | Antihemophilic factor (AHF), antihemophilic globulin (AHG), antihemophilic factor A |
| Factor IX | Plasma thromboplastin component (PTC), Christmas factor, antihemophilic factor B |
| Factor X | Stuart factor, Stuart-Prower factor |
| Factor XI | Plasma thromboplastin antecedent (PTA), antihemophilic factor C |
| Factor XII | Hageman factor |
| Factor XIII | Fibrin-stabilizing factor |
| Prekallikrein | Fletcher factor |
| High-molecular weight kininogen | Fitzgerald factor, HMWK |

[1]

and Factor XI to **XIa.** This is accomplished because both prekallikrein and Factor XI bind to a cofactor, high molecular weight kininogen (HMWK), which anchors them to the charged surface and promotes interaction with Factor **XIIa.**

As an example of positive feedback within the cascade, the newly formed **kallikrein** converts Factor XII to more **XIIa. Kallikrein** also acts to cleave HMWK to release bradykinin, an inflammatory mediator (see Chapter 10). This provides an important point of crossover between thrombosis and the inflammatory response.

The coagulation pathway continues through the other major substrate of **XIIa,** Factor XI. As shown in Figure 13.1, after activation, **XIa** converts Factor IX to **IXa.** In the final step, the initiation of the common pathway (see section 13.3.3), Factor **IXa** and Factor VIII associate on a phospholipid (usually platelet) membrane to convert Factor X to **Xa.** The function of Factor VIII is to accelerate the activation of Factor X, which occurs very slowly without this cofactor or the presence of the phospholipid membrane.

### 13.3.2 Extrinsic Pathway

An alternative mechanism of blood coagulation, the extrinsic pathway, is initiated by the release of tissue factor (TF) (Fig. 13.1). Clotting can commence via this pathway within 15 seconds. TF is a membrane-associated protein composed of a single polypeptide chain that acts as a cofactor in the extrinsic pathway, similar to HMWK in the intrinsic pathway. TF synthesis by macrophages and endothelial cells can be induced by IL-1 and TNF-$\alpha$ (see Chapter 10); by this means, inflammatory mediators can stimulate coagulation.

**Figure 13.1**

Diagram of the intrinsic and extrinsic pathways of blood coagulation. The intrinsic pathway is initiated by trauma to blood itself or exposure of blood to exposed ECM molecules in a damaged vessel wall. The intrinsic pathway begins with adsorption of one of the coagulation contact proteins, Factor XII, to a negatively charged surface. The extrinsic pathway is initiated by the release of tissue factor (TF), which binds with Factor VII on the surface of a phospholipid membrane. Both cascades converge on the common pathway, which begins with the conversion of Factor X to **Xa**. Factor V and stimulated platelets then react with Factor **Xa**, and thrombin is formed. Thrombin is responsible for the polymerization of fibrin monomers, and the presence of Factor **XIIIa** helps stabilize and crosslink the fibrin to strengthen the thrombus [4].

After its release, TF binds with Factor VII on the surface of a phospholipid membrane. Factor VII can then become activated to **VIIa** through cleavage by a number of proteases found in the blood. In the final part of the cascade, the TF/**VIIa** complex on the cell membrane converts Factor X to **Xa**, initiating the common pathway (see the following section).

### 13.3.3 Common Pathway

Like other steps in the cascade, the common pathway depends on the actions of stimulated platelets. Activated platelets can secrete, as well as express receptors for Factor V. When attached to the platelet membrane, Factor V is a receptor for Factor **Xa**. This complex, along with calcium ions, is called the **prothrombin activator**. Of these components, it is actually Factor **Xa** that converts prothrombin to the active enzyme **thrombin**.

**Thrombin** is an extremely important substance in the coagulation cascade, with both pro- and anticoagulant activities (see Table 13.1). Its main procoagulant role is to cleave fibrinogen found in the platelet granules or from blood plasma. This cleavage results in the creation of fibrin monomer and fibrinopeptides A and B. The peptides are chemotactic for neutrophils and thus are another point at which thrombosis and the inflammatory response overlap.

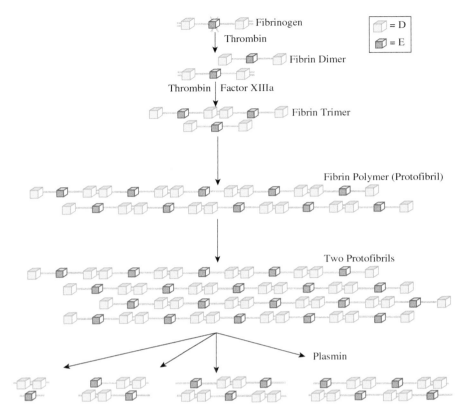

**Figure 13.2**
Process of fibrin polymerization. Crosslinking is initiated by the presence of Factor **XIIIa**, causing clot formation. After the wound has healed, activated plasmin then cleaves the fibrin to dissolve the thrombus.

The fibrin monomers can then polymerize to form long fibrin fibers[1] (Fig. 13.2). These fibers are the basis of the blood clot, but at this point, they are held together by hydrogen bonding, so the structure is fairly weak. However, **thrombin** has two additional substrates: Factors V and XIII. Factor V, when converted to **Va**, accelerates the conversion of prothrombin to thrombin in a positive feedback mechanism designed to speed clotting. The other substrate, Factor XIII (**XIIIa**) acts in the presence of calcium to covalently crosslink fibrin chains (Fig. 13.2), which provides mechanical integrity to the clot (**thrombus**). This meshwork of fibrin encasing platelets, adhesive proteins, and other bioactive factors is considered the mature thrombus. Within the clot, the fibrin acts to bridge plasma proteins and the platelet interior and prevents further bleeding by attaching to the blood vessel ECM though adhesive proteins such as fibronectin.

## EXAMPLE PROBLEM 13.1

A patient requires a replacement mitral heart valve. The cardiothoracic surgeon has determined that a tilting-disk pyrolytic carbon mechanical heart valve prosthesis will be the optimal choice for the patient. To reduce the risk of implant-related thrombosis, the patient will receive therapy with an anticoagulant drug for the lifetime of the implant. Describe a mechanism by which clot formation might be initiated by the implant.

**Solution:** Clot formation could be initiated by a number of mechanisms. For example, flow conditions or surface properties associated with the implant could contribute to the damage and rupture of cells, resulting in the release of tissue factor. The extrinsic pathway could then

---

[1]The combination of thrombin and fibrinogen has been explored as an injectable biomaterial. If they are taken from the patient into whom they will be reimplanted, there is no concern of an immune reaction.

be triggered with tissue factor binding Factor VII on the surface of a phospholipid membrane. The binding would initiate further steps that result in the conversion of Factor X to **Xa**, thereby beginning the common pathway. Alternatively, vWF may adsorb on the biomaterial surface and bind to receptors on the platelet surface. The binding of vWF to the receptors would result in the rapid influx of calcium ions into the platelet, thereby activating the platelet. The activated platelet can release various chemical modulators to encourage attachment and activation of surrounding platelets to form a platelet aggregate. Also, if proteins adsorbed to the surface of the pyrolytic carbon are negatively charged, the intrinsic pathway could be initiated through binding of one of the contact proteins, such as Factor XII, to the negatively charged surface. This binding can initiate a cascade of conversions resulting ultimately in the common pathway and clot formation. ■

## 13.4  Means of Limiting Clot Formation

Without a means to control thrombosis, clotting would be initiated readily throughout the body. Control mechanisms that are similar to those governing the complement cascade (see Chapter 12) prevent this from happening. These can generally be grouped into two means of coagulation control:

1. Physiological factors
2. Soluble and insoluble biochemical factors

The need for tight regulation of these pathways results in complex interrelations between pro- and anticoagulant factors, some of which are discussed in this section.

In addition to a number of biochemical inhibitors of thrombosis (discussed later in this section), several physiologic conditions also act to limit the coagulation cascade. The normal blood flow in the region can remove activated components or dilute them to an extent that they are not a concern in initiating systemic coagulation. Additionally, many reactions require or are catalyzed by a surface, such as the initial reactions of the intrinsic pathway, conversion of Factor X to **Xa** by either pathway, and cleavage of prothrombin to form thrombin. Without the presence of this membrane surface (usually supplied by activated platelets or platelet fragments), the cascade cannot proceed, thus limiting thrombosis to the traumatized region.

As an alternative means to control clotting, soluble agents may bind coagulation factors and inhibit their actions. An important example of this is the **heparin/anti-thrombin III (AT III) complex.** Heparin, a molecular cousin of the GAG heparan sulfate discussed in Chapter 9, is a highly negatively charged polysaccharide possessing anticoagulant properties that is secreted by basophils. It is found in small quantities in human blood and has been given to patients in soluble form as an anticoagulant since the 1930s. When heparin is conjugated with AT III, it increases AT III's effectiveness. AT III acts to inhibit thrombin by forming a tight complex and thus preventing the exposure of thrombin's catalytic site. AT III can also inhibit the actions of a number of other coagulation enzymes.

As discussed in Chapter 7, surface modification of cardiovascular biomaterials with heparin has been extensively explored due to the anticoagulant properties described earlier. Noncovalent modifications involving electrostatic interactions, as well as covalent coupling of the heparin to the material surface using methods like those described in Chapter 7, are possible. The advantage of covalent coupling is that it prevents protein exchange and thus allows the heparin to remain on the material for a longer period of time. Regardless of the method of immobilization, like with other biologically active molecules, heparin's native conformation must be maintained on the biomaterial surface in order to interact efficiently with AT III.

**Alpha$_2$-macroglobulin** is another soluble agent that acts as a secondary inhibitor for several important enzymes, including thrombin and plasmin (see the following text for discussion of the role of plasmin). The $\alpha_2$-macroglobulin molecule has a quaternary structure that is arranged to "entrap" the target enzyme in a cage. Once bound in this manner, it is much more difficult for the enzyme to form a complex with its substrate, and its actions are effectively inhibited.

Although it is not soluble, the protein **thrombomodulin**, found on the endothelial surface of the blood vessel walls, plays a large role in the control of coagulation. Thrombomodulin is attached to the endothelial cell membrane and can bind and sequester thrombin in this location, thus preventing further cleavage of fibrinogen to fibrin. The thrombomodulin–thrombin complex can then activate **protein C**, which, in turn, inactivates Factors V and VIII, thus providing further feedback to limit the extent of thrombosis.

After the thrombus has been formed and the damaged area repaired, clot dissolution is required to restore normal blood flow to the region. This process occurs primarily via **fibrinolysis**, or cleavage of the fibrin fibers in a controlled manner. During the coagulation process, **plasminogen**, a plasma protein, is trapped in the thrombus. At some point after clot maturation (the timing of this event is not well understood), endothelial cells begin to release **tissue plasminogen activator** (**TPA**), which converts plasminogen to **plasmin**. Activated plasmin then cleaves the fibrin to dissolve the thrombus, as shown in Figure 13.2. To balance this, another molecule found in the blood, $\alpha_2$ **plasmin inhibitor**, inhibits plasmin from acting on fibrin. Therefore, the relative amounts and locations of plasminogen, TPA, and $\alpha_2$-plasmin inhibitor determine the rate of thrombus dissolution.

## 13.5   Role of the Endothelium

As mentioned in Chapter 10, blood vessels are complex tissues with several layers (Fig. 13.3). The interior wall (**endothelium**) is a heterogeneous surface, formed and maintained by the endothelial cells. A number of molecules exist on the

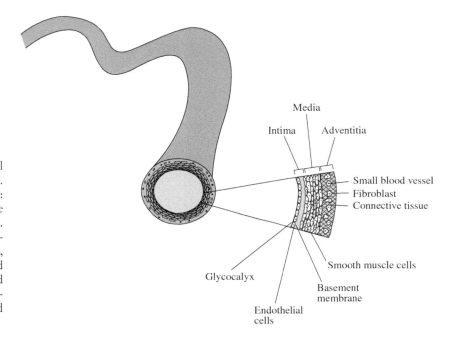

**Figure 13.3**
Structure of a blood vessel found in the human body. There are three main layers: the intima (endothelium), the media, and the adventitia. The innermost layer is composed of endothelial cells, the middle layer is populated by smooth muscle cells, and the outer layer has connective tissue and smaller blood vessels.

endothelial surface, including mucopolysaccharides/GAGs, such as heparan sulfate (see Chapter 9), that are adsorbed to the endothelial cells and interact with carbohydrate moieties already on the surface to form a **glycocalyx**. This coating imparts smoothness to the walls of the vessel, unlike the comparatively rough surface of many biomaterials. Integrins and other receptors for attachment of cells and adhesive proteins can also be found on the endothelial surface.

In its native state, the endothelium has a number of anticoagulative properties. The presence of heparan sulfate (like soluble heparin) may aid AT III in inhibiting thrombin. As discussed previously, thrombomodulin on the endothelial surface binds thrombin, and this complex then activates Protein C, which inhibits selected coagulation factors. Endothelial cells also secrete soluble chemical mediators, such as **prostaglandin** $I_2$ (**$PGI_2$**), which prevent platelet aggregation, and TPA, which activates plasmin to promote thrombus lysis.

However, the overall composition of the endothelium at a given time is very important to determining whether or not coagulation is likely to occur. After injury, the protective glycocalyx is compromised, and the exposure of endothelial ECM molecules to reactive plasma proteins is a main mechanism of coagulation initiation (via the intrinsic pathway). Additionally, in response to certain stimuli (including cytokines IL-1 and TNF-$\alpha$), the intact endothelial surface can become more coagulatory in nature. Because these cytokines are often products of granulocytes, this marks another means by which acute inflammation can promote coagulation. Examples of changes to the endothelium are a decrease in the amount of thrombomodulin at the surface and release of TF to promote coagulation through the extrinsic pathway. At this point, endothelial cells may also secrete vWF to mediate platelet aggregation.

# 13.6  Tests for Hemocompatibility

Another part of general biocompatibility testing is examination of hemocompatibility. Five categories of evaluation have been defined, including thrombosis, coagulation, platelets, hematology, and immunology (complement and leukocyte activation). Tests in some of all of these categories are required for FDA approval of different devices, depending on the length of time the device is predicted to be in contact with blood (e.g., short exposure during surgery vs. permanent implantation). *In vitro* and *in vivo* tests for immunological concerns were discussed in the previous chapter, so this section will focus on experiments to assess the other parameters.

## 13.6.1  General Testing Concerns

When designing hemocompatibility tests, one should consider both local and systemic effects. For example, localized blood clotting could negatively affect device function. Systemic results of device-mediated coagulation include thrombus **embolization**, in which pieces of the clot break off and are carried elsewhere in the circulatory system. In the most serious cases, this can lead to complications such as stroke if the thrombus becomes trapped in a location that blocks blood flow to the brain. Other systemic responses to coagulation involve the release of soluble products that stimulate the inflammatory response. Implantation of a coagulatory surface over long periods could deplete plasma clotting factors and platelets, thus reducing the patient's ability to respond to injury.

Also when considering experiments for hemocompatibility, it is important to keep in mind that both local and systemic effects from blood contacting devices can result from three factors:

1. Blood characteristics
2. Flow regime
3. Material surface characteristics

The following discussion, in which each of these factors is described in more detail, is based on that of Ratner and Horbett [2].

A number of factors can affect the study of coagulation. Blood chemistry differs greatly by species and can vary within a species, depending on age, diet, sex, or state of health. Additionally, the use of anticoagulants is often necessary in experimental procedures and this can affect the response to the test material. Similarly, the act of pumping blood over a material can cause damage of platelets or red blood cells, which can also impact coagulation properties. It is recommended that a large volume of the blood compared to area of the surface to be tested be used and interfaces with air be avoided within the experimental setup. All of these parameters can influence the overall "reactivity" of the blood to a test surface and thus should be kept consistent between samples.

Blood flow parameters are also important to hemocompatibility studies since they can provide a limiting step for the transport of platelets and plasma proteins to the surface of the material. In addition, it has been found that under low flow rates (such as those found in the veins), thrombus formation often occurs on polymeric materials since synthetic substrates do not release or possess attached anticoagulant factors like those found on the endothelium. Flow rate can also affect the composition of the thrombus *in vivo* (e.g., rich in platelets at higher flow rates vs. rich in red blood cells at lower flow rates), so it is important to test a new material at a flow rate that is similar to what is expected *in vivo*.

As discussed in previous chapters, a number of material surface characteristics affect plasma protein adsorption and thus hemocompatibility. Some of these are surface physicochemical properties, such as charge, hydrophobicity, and steric concerns. However, interaction with blood components depends not only on the material, but on how the material is used in the final device design. Therefore, surface topography and device geometry are important factors in determining the overall hemocompatibility of the implant. Direct correlations between material and device properties and hemocompatibility have thus far not been determined, due to the complex nature of the blood–device interactions. Thus the need for a complex set of evaluations when determining the overall blood compatibility of a device.

### 13.6.2 *In Vitro* Assessment

Like other types of biocompatibility testing, hemocompatibility can be assessed both *in vitro* and *in vivo*. For *in vitro* experiments, the interaction time is important: Short-term testing, such as examining platelet adhesion, may not be predictive of overall blood–material compatibility. However, the total length of *in vitro* experiments is often limited due to the fact that blood coagulation will occur over time, even in the presence of an anticoagulant.

Many materials are first tested for hemocompatibility using a **hemolysis** assay. If results are promising, further testing for thrombosis and coagulation will be conducted. In the direct contact version of the hemolysis test, whole blood is incubated in a tube with the test material for approximately 1 hour, and then the supernatant is assayed for hemoglobin, which is released when red blood cells lyse. Low lysis

**Figure 13.4**
Results from a test for partial thromboplastin time (PTT, a type of clotting time) for various biomaterial surfaces, using platelet poor plasma (PPP). Chitosan surfaces, or chitosan surfaces seeded with endothelial progenitor cells (Chitosan + EPC), demonstrated a similar clotting time to the negative control (PPP with no biomaterial), while the positive control (PPP with a pro-clotting agent) clotted significantly more quickly [6].

indicates that the material will not cause immediate negative effects on red blood cells, an important component of blood. Because the procedure is simple and the results can be easily quantified, this assay is often performed as an early screen for hemocompatibility of a new material.

*In vitro* thrombosis/coagulation testing can be either **static** or **dynamic**. In static coagulation experiments, the test material is exposed to freshly drawn whole blood (with or without an anticoagulant) and then the time for thrombus formation in reference to a control material (usually glass) is recorded (see Fig. 13.4). Dynamic tests measure similar parameters, but involve a variety of closed-loop flow systems with controlled flow regimes.

For these protocols, in addition to clotting time, it is also possible to measure further parameters to address other aspects of the ISO standards. Quantifiable parameters may include, but are not limited to the following:

1. Coagulation time
2. Amount of adhered platelets or amount of aggregated platelets
3. Mass of adherent thrombus

In addition, other, more sophisticated biochemical assays to determine the amount of platelet granule release or amount of coagulation proteins activated may be requested in some cases for regulatory approval. However, it is possible to misinterpret the results of any of these experiments. For example, if no adherent platelets are observed, this could mean that platelets did not aggregate on the surface, or that they did and were already "embolized" to another part of the system. Similarly, no apparent thrombus could mean that it has been sheared off the surface and transported to another area. If no soluble granule products are detected, it may be that the volume of the system was large enough to dilute them to undetectable concentrations. These alternatives must be considered when interpreting data from *in vitro* hemocompatibility experiments.

Several additional concerns with *in vitro* experimentation can complicate data analysis. A major limitation is that the use of anticoagulants affects the recorded coagulation time. Also, control materials must be tested at the same time and with the same blood as the experimental material, since (as discussed earlier) there can be significant differences in blood composition. Overall, it is thought that *in vitro* hemocompatibility experiments have limited value for prediction of *in vivo* responses, but data from such assessments are often required as first-pass screenings for safety of new blood-contacting materials/devices.

### 13.6.3 *In Vivo* Assessment

While *in vivo* assessment provides more information about hemocompatibility of materials than *in vitro* testing, it is still not completely predictive due to differences in the coagulation proteins between animal species and humans. In designing appropriate *in vivo* experiments, similar concerns exist as those discussed in previous chapters, including:

1. Choice of animal
2. Length of study and choice of time points
3. Inclusion of proper control materials
4. Deciding which assessment types are most appropriate

Sample assessment options are similar to that found *in vitro*, and may include histology at the end of the experiment to determine the extent of thrombus formation around the implant (see Fig. 13.5). Additionally, further information may be obtained if blood flow through the device is monitored using noninvasive imaging, or biochemical assays are performed on blood samples at various time points to examine the rate of depletion of key plasma coagulation factors.

However, in addition to differences in blood composition between animals and humans, other concerns about direct *in vivo* testing have been raised. One of these is that it is difficult to control or measure blood flow conditions in animal models. Also, variations in tissue trauma during implantation can affect the results of the experiments. In order to overcome some of these concerns, biomaterial testing using shunts has been developed.

In these experiments, which are usually considered *ex vivo* instead of *in vivo*, the material in tubular form is placed as an extension in a shunt that connects an artery to a vein or artery to an artery in a living animal (Fig. 13.6). The advantages to such a system are that the blood flow near the sample can be easily controlled and measured, native (nonanticoagulated) blood may be used, and the shunt can remain in place for up to several months, so long-term responses can be examined. However, a disadvantage to shunt-based systems is that this model does not

**Figure 13.5**

Histology results from an *in vivo* rat carotid artery model to test the effects of a poly(ethylene glycol)-poly(glutamic acid) carrier for an anti-thrombotic drug. Histology results show a thrombus filling the cross-section of the artery after damage (top), compared to an artery demonstrating less clotting after treatment with the biomaterial carrier + drug (bottom). (Adapted with permission from [7].)

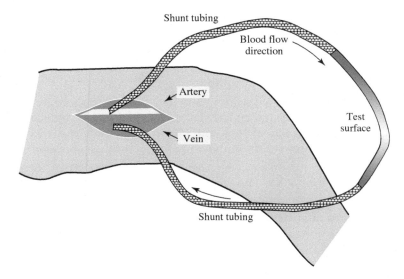

**Figure 13.6**
*Ex vivo* testing setup for a vascular material. The material (test surface) in tubular form is placed as an extension in a shunt that connects to the circulatory system of a living animal [2].

Shunt tubing

Blood flow direction

Artery

Vein

Test surface

Shunt tubing

replicate an implantation procedure, so the response from the trauma of surgery cannot be evaluated. In addition, the shunting procedure itself can be difficult to execute surgically, and there are ethical concerns with long-term shunting of large animals, particularly nonhuman primates.

### EXAMPLE PROBLEM 13.2

A researcher has developed a vascular graft from a novel polymeric material and plans to evaluate the hemocompatibility of the implant in a canine model over the course of six weeks. However, it is known in the scientific literature that canines endothelialize vascular grafts spontaneously, while humans do not [3]. Should the canine model be used to evaluate the graft implant, or should another model be sought? Would endothelialization of a vascular graft be beneficial? Why?

**Solution:**   The canine model should not be used in this case, as it does not appropriately approximate the human response to the vascular graft. The formation of an endothelial cell coating on the blood contacting surface of a vascular graft could result in the formation of a glycocalyx to impart smoothness to the walls of the graft. Further, endothelial cells present a number of anticoagulant properties that could reduce the risk of a thrombus formation response to the implant. Thus, endothelialization of the graft would be a substantial promoter of hemocompatibility. The spontaneous endothelialization of vascular grafts in canine models would result in more significant hemocompatibility of the graft than would be observed in humans, in which spontaneous endothelialization of vascular grafts does not occur.    ■

## Summary

- Platelets are nonnucleated fragments of megakaryocytes. They release soluble factors to initiate the formation of a platelet plug to stop bleeding and activate the blood coagulation cascade, which further stabilizes the plug.

- Platelets can become activated through a variety of means, including exposure to soluble factors or interaction with ECM components. Activated platelets transition to an irregular form and extend pseudopodia in various directions. Granule contents, including ADP and thrombin, are then released as a result of cytoskeletal protein contraction.

- The intrinsic blood coagulation pathway is initiated by trauma to the blood itself or to exposed ECM molecules in a damaged vessel wall. Factor XII can then adsorb to the negatively charged surface, resulting in a conversion to **XIIa**. The cascade continues until the common pathway is initiated with conversion of Factor X to **Xa**.

- The extrinsic pathway is initiated through the release of tissue factor from macrophages and endothelial cells, which can be induced through the inflammatory mediators IL-1 and TNF-$\alpha$. A cascade ensues, resulting ultimately in the initiation of the common pathway through conversion of Factor X to **Xa**.

- In the common pathway, Factor V attached to the platelet membrane serves as a receptor for **Xa**. This complex, along with calcium ions, is called the prothrombin activator and allows Factor **Xa** to cleave prothrombin to form thrombin.

- Thrombin cleaves fibrinogen to form fibrin monomers. These monomers can then polymerize to form long fibrin fibers that form the foundation of the blood clot. Also, thrombin activates Factor XIII, which works to covalently crosslink fibrin chains to stabilize the clot. Clot dissolution occurs primarily by fibrinolysis, a result of the action of plasmin.

- Control of coagulation can generally be achieved through physiological factors or soluble and insoluble biochemical factors. Blood flow can regionally remove and/or dilute activated components of the coagulation cascade to inhibit coagulation. Also, limitations in the presence of surfaces (such as activated platelet membranes) to catalyze several of the steps of the coagulation cascade can result in limitation of coagulation. Soluble agents can bind coagulation factors to inhibit their actions.

- The endothelium in its native state presents anticoagulative properties through the presence and action of entities such as heparin sulfate, PGI$_2$, and TPA. However, disruption of the glycocalyx by injury results in exposure of the endothelial ECM molecules to the reactive plasma proteins to initiate coagulation through the intrinsic pathway. Also, the stimuli provided by cytokines such as IL-1 and TNF-$\alpha$ released by cells of acute inflammation can result in the endothelium becoming increasingly pro-coagulatory in nature.

- The examination of the general biocompatibility of a material should, in many cases, include assessment of the hemocompatibility of the material. Both local and systemic effects from blood-contacting materials can result from three factors: blood characteristics, flow parameters, and material surface characteristics.

- *In vitro* testing can be either static or dynamic and can include quantification of parameters regarding red blood cell lysis, coagulation time, platelet adhesion, and/or thrombus formation.

- *In vivo* assessment of the hemocompatibility of materials provides more complete information than *in vitro* analyses. An alternative approach to assess hemocompatibility is *ex vivo* examination of a tubular material as a shunt.

## Problems

13.1 You are developing a polymeric material as a vascular graft. A method explored in the past to reduce blood coagulation is to pre-adsorb the graft with albumin, a noncoagulatory protein found in high concentrations in the blood.

(a) Based on your knowledge of protein adsorption, what is the rationale for using albumin to reduce blood coagulation?

(b) Below are images taken after exposing platelets to both albumin-coated and noncoated poly(styrene) (PS) surfaces. In addition to images, you want to perform a biochemical assay to determine the activation state of the platelets. What one assay would you choose? What would you expect the results to be on both surfaces? Does it appear that the albumin modification worked? Explain based on characteristics of activated platelets.

(c) If you put these two materials under dynamic flow, would you expect any changes in the results for either surface? Why or why not?

(d) Poly(styrene) is an uncharged, hydrophobic polymer. What is the most likely mechanism by which the coagulation cascade would be started for this material *in vivo*? Would it be the same mechanism for the albumin-coated material? Justify your answer.

13.2 Explain the role of each of the following molecules after injury to a blood vessel.

(a) Thrombin
(b) Plasminogen
(c) $\alpha_2$-macroglobulin
(d) Tissue factor
(e) Factor XIII

13.3 Why are calcium chelators (agents that bind calcium tightly) often used as anti-coagulants?

13.4 One approach to reduce blood clotting in vascular grafts is to attach heparin-mimetics to the interior surface? Give two potential reasons why this approach might be effective.

13.5 Describe the advantages and disadvantages of *in vivo* versus ex vivo testing for a biomaterial intended for use in a blood-contacting application.

# References

1. A. C. Guyton and J. E. Hall, *Textbook of medical physiology*, 9th ed. Philadelphia: W.B. Saunders, 1996.
2. S. R. Hanson and B. D. Ratner, "Evaluation of blood-materials interactions," in *Biomaterials science: an introduction to materials and medicine*, 2nd ed., B. D. Ratner, A. S. Hoffman, F. J. Schoen, and J. E. Lemons, Eds. San Diego: Elsevier Academic Press, 2004, pp. 367–379.
3. P. Dixit, D. Hern-Anderson, J. Ranieri, and C. E. Schmidt, "Vascular graft endothelialization: comparative analysis of canine and human endothelial cell migration on natural biomaterials," *Journal of Biomedical Materials Research*, vol. 56, no. 4, pp. 545–55, 2001.
4. S. R. Hanson, "Blood coagulation and blood-material interactions," in *Biomaterials science: an introduction to materials and medicine*, 2nd ed., B. D. Ratner, A. S. Hoffman, F. J. Schoen, and J. E. Lemons, Eds. San Diego: Elsevier Academic Pre, 2004, pp. 332–338.
5. R. W. Colman, J. Hirsh, V. J. Marder, A. W. Clowes, and J. N. George, *Hemostasis and thrombosis: basic principles and clinical practice*. Philadelphia: Lippincott, Williams, and Wilkins, 2001.
6. A. Aussel *et al.*, "Chitosan-based hydrogels for developing a small-diameter vascular graft: in vitro and in vivo evaluation," *Biomedical Materials*, vol. 12, no. 6, p. 065003, 2017.
7. Zhang S-F Zhang *et al.*, "Multiarm-polyethyleneglycol-polyglutamic acid peptide dendrimer: Design, synthesis, and dissolving thrombus," *Journal of Biomedical Materials Research Part A*, vol 106A, pp. 1687–1696, 2018.

# Additional Reading

J. M. Anderson and F. J. Schoen, "In vivo assessment of tissue compatility," in *Biomaterials science: an introduction to materials and medicine*, 2nd ed., B. D. Ratner, A. S. Hoffman, F. J. Schoen, and J. E. Lemons, Eds. San Diego: Elsevier Academic Press, 2004, pp. 360–367.

J. Black, *Biological performance of materials: fundamentals of biocompatibility*, 4th ed. New York: CRC Press, 2005.

S. D. Bruck, *Properties of biomaterials in the physiological environment*. Boca Raton: CRC Press, 1980.

K. C. Dee, D. A. Puleo, and R. Bizios, *An introduction to tissue-biomaterial interactions*. Hoboken: Wiley-Liss, 2002.

D. L. Dinwoodey and J. E. Ansell, "Heparins, low-molecular-weight heparins, and penta-saccharides: use in the older patient," *Cardiology Clinics*, vol. 26, no. 2, pp. 145–155, v, 2008.

S. C. Gad and S. Gad-McDonald, *Biomaterials, medical devices, and combination products: Biocompatibility testing and safety assessment*. Boca Raton: CRC Press, 2015.

M. B. Gorbet and M. V. Sefton, "Biomaterial-associated thrombosis: roles of coagulation factors, complement, platelets and leukocytes," *Biomaterials*, vol. 25, no. 26, pp. 5681–5703, 2004.

S. R. Hanson and B. D. Ratner, "Evaluation of blood-materials interactions," in *Biomaterials science: an introduction to materials and medicine*, 2nd ed., B. D. Ratner, A. S. Hoffman, F. J. Schoen, and J. E. Lemons, Eds. San Diego: Elsevier Academic Press, 2004, pp. 367–379.

T. A. Horbett, "Principles underlying the role of adsorbed plasma proteins in blood interactions with foreign materials," *Cardiovascular Pathology*, vol. 2, no. 3S, pp. 137S–148S, 1993.

M. A. Lafleur, M. M. Handsley, and D. R. Edwards, "Metalloproteinases and their inhibitors in angiogenesis," *Expert Reviews in Molecular Medicine*, vol. 5, 2003, pp. 1–39.

B. D. Ratner and T. A. Horbett, "Evaluation of blood-materials interactions," in *Biomaterials science: an introduction to materials and medicine*, 3rd ed., B. D. Ratner, A. S. Hoffman, F. J. Schoen, and J. E. Lemons, Eds. San Diego: Elsevier Academic Press, 2013, pp. 617–634.

M. V. Sefton, C. H. Gemmell, F. J. Schoen, and J. E. Lemons, "Nonthrombogenic treatments and strategies," in *Biomaterials science: an introduction to materials and medicine*, 2nd ed., B. D. Ratner, A. S. Hoffman, F. J. Schoen, and J. E. Lemons, Eds. San Diego: Elsevier Academic Press, 2004, pp. 456–470.

F. H. Silver and D. L. Christiansen, *Biomaterials science and biocompatibility*. New York: Springer, 1999.

# Infection, Tumorigenesis, and Calcification of Biomaterials

---

**Main Objective**

To understand the steps involved in, and results of, three potentially deleterious responses to implanted biomaterials: infection, tumorigenesis, and pathologic calcification.

**Specific Objectives**

1. To understand the characteristics of implant-associated infection and common pathogens, and the steps involved in these infections.
2. To understand how bacterial surface properties, biomaterial surface properties, and media type contribute to specific and nonspecific bacterial adhesion.
3. To distinguish among classes of carcinogens and explain the basic steps in tumor development.
4. To compare and contrast chemical and foreign body tumorigenesis.
5. To understand the mechanisms of pathologic calcification and how this can affect properties of biomaterials.
6. To understand the principles behind methods to reduce pathologic calcification.
7. To understand the concepts behind and possible limitations to the *in vitro* and *in vivo* models presented for examination of infection, tumorigenesis, and pathologic calcification.

---

## 14.1 Introduction: Overview of Other Potential Problems with Biomaterial Implantation

Previous chapters have described possible negative responses stemming from the innate and acquired immune responses or the coagulation pathways after biomaterials implantation. However, there are several other serious complications that can occur due to the presence of a biomaterial in the body. These include device-related *infection, tumorigenesis* by the implant, and *pathologic calcification*. In each of these pathological responses, the presence of the biomaterial affects normal body function and may necessitate removal of the implant. Therefore, preventing these reactions is the subject of much current biomaterials research.

# 14.2 Infection

Infection can occur on or surrounding any type of implant, including artificial organs, synthetic blood vessels, joint replacements, intravenous catheters, and urologic devices. Device infection is of increasing concern due to the spread of antibiotic-resistant bacterial strains in the past decade. A number of characteristics of implant-associated infection have been identified that distinguish it from other types of infection:

1. Presence of biomaterial and/or damaged underlying ECM
2. Bacterial colonization of tissue
3. Resistance to host defense mechanisms and antibiotic therapy
4. Presence of characteristic bacteria types (see the following section)
5. Transformation of relatively innocuous bacterial species into virulent organisms by the presence of a biomaterial
6. Presence of multiple bacteria species
7. Persistence of infection until removal of the substrate
8. Absence of integration of the biomaterial with the host
9. Presence of cell damage or necrosis

## 14.2.1 Common Pathogens and Categories of Infection

One characteristic of implant-associated infections is the relatively small number of pathogens usually present in the afflicted area. In addition, many of these are commonly found on or in the human body and do not produce infection prior to biomaterial implantation. The organisms most often responsible for biomaterial-related infection are the Gram-positive bacteria (see later sections of this chapter for explanation of this term) *Staphylococcus aureus* and *Staphylococcus epidermidis*, the Gram-negative bacteria *Enterobacteriaceae* and *Pseudomonas aeriginosa*, and fungi such as *Candida* spp.[1]

The presence of these pathogens can result in infection immediately upon implantation or at some later time. Thus, three categories of implant-associated infections have been defined, depending on the time of onset and the location in the body. A **superficial immediate infection** occurs if there is growth of microorganisms on the skin in association with an implant (e.g., growth under burn dressings). These infections, which develop soon after the implantation procedure, are usually caused by skin-dwelling bacteria such as *S. aureus* and *S. epidermidis*. A **deep immediate infection** is one in which there is the presence of an infection at the implant site soon after surgery. Like the previous type, this is often a result of the proliferation of skin-dwelling bacteria that were transported to the implant site during the procedure. In contrast, a **late infection** may occur months to years after the implantation surgery. The cause of this type of infection remains unclear, although it is thought to be a consequence of the seeding of bloodborne pathogens originating in another site (e.g., tooth infection).

---

[1]The designation spp. after a genus refers to more than one unnamed species.

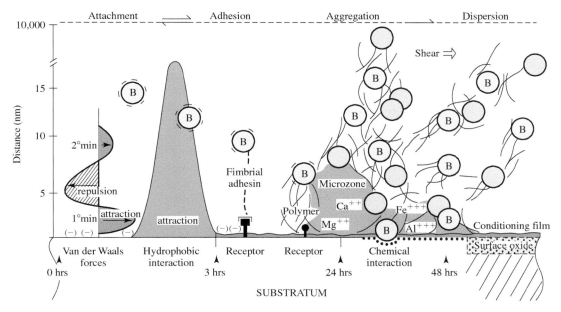

**Figure 14.1**

The four stages of infection. The first stage, bacterial (indicated by B) attachment to the surface, is reversible and is based on nonspecific interactions between the pathogen and the surface. In the second stage, adhesion, the microorganism becomes irreversibly bound to the biomaterial due to a combination of nonspecific and specific receptor–ligand interactions. The third stage, aggregation, occurs when the bacteria have firmly adhered to the substrate and begin to divide and form colonies. In the final stage, dispersion, shear forces from trauma, normal implant motion, or flowing blood may cause a portion of the bacterial colony to detach and move to other areas of the body. (Adapted with permission from [6].)

## 14.2.2  Steps to Infection

A number of steps must occur in order for bacterial attachment to a biomaterial to progress to a clinical infection. As summarized in Figure 14.1, four distinct stages have been identified.[2] First, **bacterial attachment** to the surface is *reversible* and is based on nonspecific interactions between the pathogen and the surface. Therefore, the surface characteristics of bacteria and the substrate play a large role in this step.

In the next stage, **adhesion,** the microorganism becomes irreversibly (permanently) bound to the biomaterial due to a combination of nonspecific and specific receptor–ligand interactions between the pathogen and the surface (discussed further in the following text). The strength of this interaction is time dependent and requires a matter of hours to develop.

After the bacteria have firmly adhered to the substrate, they begin to divide and form colonies. In this stage, termed **aggregation,** the pathogens often exude an extracellular polysaccharide slime (**biofilm**). This biofilm protects the microorganisms from phagocytosis by neutrophils or tissue macrophages and provides a favorable environment for bacterial growth. Biofilm formation may occur as early as one day after bacterial attachment.

In the final stage, **dispersion,** shear forces from normal implant motion, trauma, or flowing blood may carry a portion of the bacterial colony to other areas of the

---

[2]Although in this and subsequent sections we will focus on bacterial interactions with biomedical implants, the principles are similar for other microorganisms, such as fungi.

body. This can occur as soon as two days after initial bacterial attachment. The result is spreading of the infection locally, or, in some cases, a secondary infection at a disparate location.

Since it is increasingly difficult to control the infection after the formation of a biofilm layer, many of the approaches to reducing implant-related infections have focused on preventing bacteria from firmly adhering to biomaterials. After implantation of a device, the reactions that occur can be considered a "race for the surface" [6] between soluble proteins, surrounding cells, and potential pathogens. The outcome of this race determines whether or not infection develops and is highly affected by what proteins are initially adsorbed and how they interact with both mammalian cells and bacteria. For example, if a particular biomaterial surface supports attachment of cells that have mechanisms for preventing bacterial attachment to their membranes, infection may be reduced in these implants.

### 14.2.3 Characteristics of the Bacterial Surface, the Biomaterial Surface, and the Media

As mentioned earlier, the ideal biomaterial surface would be simultaneously bacteria resistant and cell friendly, both of which are directly related to the type of proteins that adsorb to the material. A wide variety of surface modification technologies have been employed in order to prepare biomaterial surfaces with the physicochemical properties to encourage cell adhesion while repelling bacteria. However, as with other protein adsorption processes described in Chapters 8–13, one must understand how the characteristics of the bacterial surface, the biomaterial surface, and the media interact in order to modify the biomaterial so it will discourage microbe binding in a biological milieu. All three aspects of bacterial adhesion are described in more detail in this section.

#### 14.2.3.1 Bacterial Surface Properties: Gram-Positive versus Gram-Negative Bacteria
Two major classes of bacteria can be distinguished: *Gram positive* and *Gram negative*. As illustrated in Figure 14.2, **Gram-positive** species have a single bilayered phospholipid membrane and a thick cell wall composed of peptidoglycan (the chemical structure of this molecule is shown in Figure 14.3). Several macromolecules are associated with this cell wall, including polysaccharides, teichoic and teichuronic acids, and proteins. Some of these may act as mediators for specific binding to the ECM or biomaterials.

In contrast, **Gram-negative** bacteria possess two phospholipid membranes: the cell membrane and an outer membrane. In these species, the peptidoglycan layer is thinner and located between the two membranes, as shown in Figure 14.2. Like Gram-positive bacteria, Gram-negative bacteria contain macromolecules that extend from their outer membranes to interact with the environment. In addition, they often demonstrate **fimbriae** or **pili** (surface appendages up to 1 μm long resembling small filaments). Gram-negative bacteria may also possess flagella, which are longer and used for locomotion. Any of these appendages may play an additional role in adhesion to tissue and biomaterial surfaces.

#### 14.2.3.2 Bacterial Surface Properties: Cell Capsule and Biofilm
Certain species of both Gram-positive and Gram-negative bacteria have an outer layer composed of polysaccharides called the **cell capsule**. These molecules are firmly attached to the cell wall and, thus, are distinguished from the slime that is also found near the exterior of many bacterial species. The polysaccharides produced as a part of the **slime** (or **biofilm**) coating are released into the surroundings, and therefore are not directly attached to the bacterial surface.

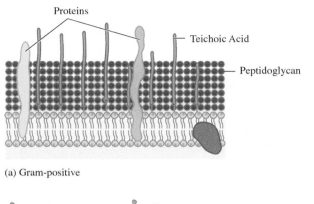

(a) Gram-positive

(b) Gram-negative

**Figure 14.2**
The two major classes of bacteria: Gram-positive (a) and Gram-negative (b) Gram-positive species have a single bilayered phospholipid membrane and a thick cell wall composed of peptidoglycan. Polysaccharides, teichoic and teichuronic acids, and proteins are among the macromolecules associated with this cell wall. Gram-negative bacteria possess two phospholipid membranes: the cell membrane and an outer membrane. In these species, the peptidoglycan layer is thinner and located between the two membranes. Like Gram-positive bacteria, Gram-negative bacteria contain macromolecules that extend from their outer membranes to interact with the environment [8].

**Figure 14.3**
Chemical structure of peptidoglycan. The dotted lines indicate that additional repeat units of the depicted polymer are attached at these points. X represents a peptide crosslinker in this figure, and AA represents a diamino acid, such as that participating in the crosslink at position 3 [9].

**Figure 14.4**
Schematic of a biofilm coating. Note that in a biofilm, the bacterial colonies (black spots) no longer remain attached to the surface, but are contained within the polysaccharide "slime." The arrow indicates the flow of water through open water channels in the biofilm. (Reprinted with permission from [10].)

As discussed earlier, exudation of slime allows for the formation of a specialized microenvironment (a microzone) that allows the bacteria to trap ions important to their survival and protects them from the body's natural defenses. Several types of bacteria can be housed under a single biofilm coating. As depicted in Figure 14.4, once encased in slime, bacterial colonies no longer remain attached to the surface, but are fixed to the biofilm, which can take on a mushroom-like appearance.

The production of slime reduces the body's ability to kill adherent bacteria for several reasons. The biofilm forms a physical barrier to phagocytic cells, and certain components are thought to inhibit T and B cell interaction, antibody production and bacterial opsonization, thus greatly decreasing the efficiency of both the innate and acquired immune responses. In addition, the presence of slime can impart antibiotic resistance. It has been found that the concentration of oral antibiotics required to kill biofilm bacteria is 100 times greater than the concentration needed to kill their planktonic counterparts. This may be partially due to the formation of a diffusional barrier for active agents. However, this effect may also be caused by the fact that bacteria within the biofilm can enter a dormant state. Moreover, phenotypic changes can render biofilm bacteria more resistant to oral antibiotics, many of which were developed to kill free-floating pathogens. In the same vein, the biofilm may protect or otherwise encourage slow growing "persister" bacteria that can impart long-term antibiotic resistance.

It should also be noted when designing experiments that bacterial surface properties may change depending on growth conditions. In fact, many laboratory-grown bacteria can have significantly different phenotypes than the wild strains from which they were derived. In fact, it is recommended that materials be tested *in vitro* both with common laboratory-grown reference bacterial strains, as well as bacteria isolated from clinical patients in order to best characterize the susceptibility of the biomaterial to infection. The bacterial surface properties of most importance in adhesion to biomaterials are surface hydrophobicity and charge, as well as the presence of any

**Figure 14.5**
Scanning electron micrograph depicting bacteria entrapped between fibers of woven Dacron™. (Reprinted with permission from [11].)

molecules that can promote specific interactions with the substrate. Means of bacterial surface characterization are discussed in the following techniques section.

### 14.2.3.3 Biomaterial Surface Properties

The same material surface properties that govern protein adsorption (see Chapter 7) also affect bacterial adhesion because components of the adsorbed protein layer may form specific interactions with bacterial cell membrane constituents. Important biomaterial properties include surface hydrophobicity and charge as well as physical properties such as steric concerns and surface roughness.

As with cell attachment, bacteria may be prevented from adhering to surfaces due to steric repulsion from bulky hydrophilic groups. In contrast, grooves or valleys may trap bacteria and encourage the formation of colonies on the substrate, as shown in Figure 14.5, which depicts bacteria entrapped between fibers of woven Dacron™. All of the surface characterization techniques described in Chapter 7 can be used to determine surface properties of biomaterials pertinent to bacterial adhesion. These include contact angle for hydrophobicity, ESCA, ATR-FTIR, and SIMS for chemical analysis, and SEM and AFM for topographical evaluation.

### 14.2.3.4 Media Properties

As mentioned earlier, the proteins deposited on the biomaterial surface can play a significant role in bacterial adhesion. In addition to biomaterial surface properties, the nature of this coating is affected by the type of proteins found in the media surrounding the material. Additionally, the media characteristics are important because both protein adsorption and bacterial adhesion are governed by thermodynamic parameters. For either event to occur spontaneously, the overall change in the Gibbs free energy ($\Delta G$) for the reaction must be negative. As discussed in Chapter 8, $\Delta G$ is partially dependent on the chemical properties of the media (solvent), such as the presence of ions that shield electrostatic repulsion between like-charged surfaces.

## 14.2.4 Specific and Nonspecific Interactions Involved in Bacterial Adhesion

Much like cell attachment, bacterial adhesion to biomedical implants can be caused by both nonspecific and specific interactions. As explained in Chapter 9, nonspecific binding can be modeled using DLVO theory (based on work from Derjaguin, Landau, Verway, and Overbeek). Figure 14.6 depicts the free energy of interaction, $G(z)$, between a particle (the bacterium) and the surface, as determined by DLVO theory,

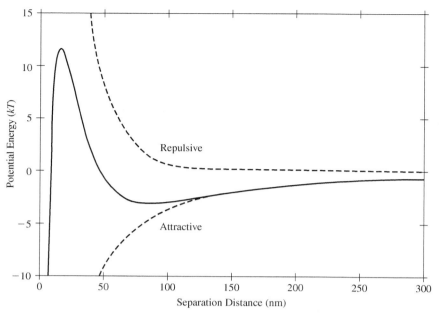

**Figure 14.6**

Dependence of the free energy of interaction between the bacterium and the biomaterial surface as a function of separation distance according to DLVO theory for bacterial adhesion. As the bacterium approaches the surface, there is a drop in potential energy (the secondary minimum), representing a balance between long-range electrostatic interactions (repulsive) and long-range van der Waals interactions (attractive). At this point, the bacterium is loosely (reversibly) bound to the surface. If the bacterium can overcome the potential energy barrier seen on the extreme left, it can reach the primary minimum (not shown) and become irreversibly bound. (Adapted with permission from [7].)

as a function of separation distance ($z$). As the bacterium approaches the surface, there is a drop in potential energy (the secondary minimum), representing a balance between long-range electrostatic interactions (repulsive) and long-range van der Waals interactions (attractive). If the random (Brownian) motion of the bacterium is sufficient to overcome the potential energy barrier and reach the primary minimum (not shown in the figure), the pathogen can become firmly adherent to the surface.

As discussed for cell attachment, DLVO theory is a highly idealized and simplified model. In reality, the complex nature of the bacterial cell membrane makes it probable that specific interactions between the membrane and the substrate also take place. In this case, receptors and ligands can extend into the media to promote binding and overcome the energy barrier depicted in the DLVO model. Many bacteria are known to have receptors for a variety of ECM components. These receptors are collectively called **microbial surface components recognizing adhesive matrix molecules (MSCRAMMs)**. For example, *S. aureus* employs MSCRAMMs to bind to the ECM molecules fibronectin, vitronectin, and von Willebrand factor.

## 14.2.5 Summary and Techniques to Reduce Implant-Associated Infections

Infections of biomedical implants are unique in that they are usually caused by transformation of relatively innocuous bacterial species into virulent organisms by the presence of a biomaterial. Several steps are required for this transformation, which is aided by the existence of the biomaterial and/or damaged underlying ECM as a surface for attachment of bacteria. The adherent bacteria then become resistant to host defense mechanisms and antibiotics for a number of reasons. The bacteria begin to form slime, which provides both a physical and a chemical barrier to the innate and acquired immune system and to the actions of antibiotics. In addition, the constant presence of the biomaterial may "exhaust" the granulocytes' ability to kill or phagocytose the pathogen.

For these reasons, the implanted biomaterial plays a compounding role in infection. Therefore, there is a great need for effective preimplantation sterilization, which can be achieved using a variety of methods, including those described in Chapter 6. In addition, further development of anti-infective materials is extremely important to reduce the occurrence of infections from pathogens that colonize the material after implantation (late infections). Key steps that could be targeted to prevent this type of infection include reduction of initial bacterial adhesion or arresting the conversion of adherent bacteria to a slime-forming phenotype. A number of approaches to creating infection-resistant biomaterials are currently being explored, particularly for indwelling catheters and orthopedic implants, including release of small molecule antibiotics or anti-microbial peptides to kill bacterial cells, as well as a number of surface coating techniques to reduce bacterial adhesion (similar to nonfouling surfaces to decrease protein adsorption/thrombosis).

## 14.3 Techniques for Infection Experiments

A main goal of many infection experiments is to understand how surface properties of biomaterials and/or bacteria affect the degree of bacterial adhesion or developed infection. Thus, a variety of techniques are required to relate measured parameters to overall infection potential. These include methods to characterize the biomaterial and bacterial surfaces and to quantify bacterial adhesion *in vitro* and the degree of infection *in vivo*. Biomaterial surface characterization was discussed in Chapter 7, and the other techniques are reviewed here.

### 14.3.1 Characterizing Bacterial Surfaces

As mentioned earlier, the bacterial surface properties of most importance to nonspecific binding are hydrophobicity and charge, and characterization methods for these parameters are discussed in this section. It may also be possible to use immunostaining or ELISA techniques (see Chapters 8 and 9) to examine bacteria for the presence of surface receptors that participate in specific binding to the substrate.

**14.3.1.1 Surface Hydrophobicity** As with biomaterial surfaces, bacterial hydrophobicity can be quantified using contact angle measurements as described in Chapter 7. Similar calculations can be completed to estimate the surface tension for a particular bacterial strain. In this case, the test surface is a material completely covered by bacteria. However, care must be taken in this procedure since contact angles can be difficult to measure and interactions between the test liquid (water) and the bacteria may change with time due to desorption of bacterial surface molecules into the water.

Another technique to assess bacterial hydrophobicity is called **microbial adherence to hydrocarbons (MATH)**. In this method, a test tube is filled with a mixture of two liquid phases: water and a hydrophobic hydrocarbon-based solvent. The bacteria are then added, and migration of bacteria from the water to the hydrocarbon phase is recorded. A more hydrophobic strain will show greater movement to the hydrocarbon phase because it is thermodynamically more stable for the bacteria to be suspended in a hydrophobic milieu. This is tracked by monitoring the turbidity (cloudiness) of the aqueous phase over time using optical density

**Figure 14.7**

Data from MATH (left axis, red) and electrophoretic mobility (right axis, blue) for a number of bacterial strains typically found in drinking water. Generally *V. cholerae* are more hydrophobic as they have more affinity to the hydrocarbon phase in MATH, while *E. coli* show the most electrophoretic mobility, indicating they are hydrophilic and highly charged [12].

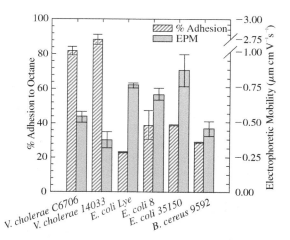

measurements (see Fig. 14.7). While this method is relatively simple and quick to perform, it is difficult to quantify and is therefore best suited to characterizing bacteria as generally "hydrophobic" or "hydrophilic."

A more quantitative assessment of the degree of bacterial hydrophobicity can be obtained through the use of **hydrophobic interaction chromatography (HIC)**. This is a type of affinity chromatography, as described in Chapter 8. In this case, the equipment may not be as extensive as that described for HPLC (see Chapter 2), but the technique is similar to any other reversed phase liquid chromatography. For HIC, bacteria suspended in an aqueous phase are passed through a column containing a hydrophobic packing material. The amount of bacteria remaining in the aqueous phase after exiting the column is measured, indicating the number of bacteria that were retained in the packing matrix. The fraction retained increases with greater strain hydrophobicity. As with other types of liquid chromatography, small changes in the chemistry of the packing material or composition of the aqueous phase reveal subtle differences in hydrophobicity between strains.

**14.3.1.2 Surface Charge** Another key bacterial surface characteristic, charge, can be assessed using variations on common techniques. For example, surface charge can be measured via an **electrophoretic mobility test** (see Fig. 14.7). In this method, microbes are introduced into an electrophoresis gel like that described in Chapter 8, using a buffer of known ionic strength. The velocity of migration in a known electric field is then determined and related to the surface charge through calculations based on the Helmholtz-Smoluchowski equation, the specifics of which are beyond the scope of this text.

Alternatively, bacterial surface charge may be quantified via **electrostatic interaction chromatography (EIC)**. EIC is actually a type of liquid chromatography known as ion exchange chromatography. This technique is generally similar to HIC, except that the packing material is either cationic or anionic. Depending on the type of packing material and the amount of bacteria retained in each case, both the degree and nature of the surface charge (positive or negative) can be determined.

### 14.3.2 *In Vitro* and *In Vivo* Models of Infection

Like other tests for biocompatibility, both *in vitro* and *in vivo* experiments to assess a biomaterial's proclivity to infection can be performed. *Ex vivo* assays using shunts, like those described in Chapter 13 for hemocompatibility testing, are also common.

In particular, testing for material anti-microbial activity is governed by a number of standards (ISO 22196, ASTM E2149, E2180 and E2315 among others). An overview of general testing techniques relating to device infection is provided in this section.

### 14.3.2.1 *In Vitro*: Bacterial Adhesion and Killing

*In vitro* infection testing focuses on quantification of (1) bacterial adhesion to biomaterials under static or well-defined flow conditions or (2) level of bacterial death from anti-microbial materials. The basic experimental design for bacterial adhesion is similar to that described in Chapter 9 for cell attachment assays and begins with the introduction of the bacteria in the media surrounding the test material. The microbes are allowed to attach over a set period of time and then a well-controlled washing step is performed. Adherent bacteria are usually quantified by microscopic visualization of the surface and manual counting of the number of bacteria per image (see Fig. 14.8). The microbes can be stained with colored or fluorescent dyes to aid in quantification. In some cases, image analysis software may be employed to automate the counting procedure.

Inclusion of control materials for the given application is important when using this method to evaluate bacterial adhesion to novel biomaterials. In this way, it can be determined whether or not a new biomaterial discourages bacterial adhesion when compared with a material currently used for the target device. Like all *in vitro* tests, this assay does not recapitulate the complex biochemical environment found *in vivo* that may mediate bacterial attachment, so these assays should only be used as first-pass screening techniques.

Although not officially part of the standards, a common method for determining the efficacy (bacterial killing potential) of an anti-microbial material is the **zone of inhibition assay**. This assay is performed much like the agar diffusion assay for cytotoxicity described in Chapter 9. In this case, a bacterial strain is inoculated on agar in a petri dish and the anti-microbial material is placed on top of the agar in the middle. If the material is effective, a ring showing a lack of bacteria will appear around the material after ~24 hours (zone of inhibition; see Fig. 14.9). The diameter of this zone is measured as an indicator of the efficacy of the anti-microbial treatment. However, drawbacks to this assay include that small molecules that are included within biomaterials may diffuse in the agar faster than larger ones, leading to a greater apparent

**Figure 14.8**
Fluorescent microscopy images of *S. epidermidis* adhesion to a poly(urethane) surface (top), and a poly(urethane) surface modified with the anti-adhesive polymer poly(ethylene glycol) (bottom). Less adherent bacteria are observed on the modified surface. (Image size: $226 \times 169$ mm$^2$). Adapted with permission from [13].)

**Figure 14.9**
Example of results from a zone of inhibition study in which the material (white discs) was soaked in an anti-microbial solution. Clear circles demonstrating lack of bacterial growth (zone of inhibition) can be seen around each disc [14].

efficacy (larger zone of inhibition) that may not be found *in vivo*. Thus, many standards include an alternative version of this assay where the material is incubated in a solution containing bacteria (rather than an agar plate) and the total number of remaining bacteria in solution at various timepoints are recorded.

## EXAMPLE PROBLEM 14.1

A biomaterials laboratory has had a persistent problem with a particular strain of bacteria adhering to an experimental biomaterial. The experimental material is inherently highly hydrophobic and uncharged. The researchers are considering chemical modification of the biomaterial surface through plasma treatment to form polar groups on the surface. The hydrophobicity of the bacteria in question was assessed with the microbial adherence to hydrocarbons (MATH) assay. It was found that the optical density of the hydrocarbon phase was significantly greater than that of the aqueous phase. Which *in vitro* assay is the most likely next step in determining if the chemical modification would work and what is the expected outcome?

**Solution:** The nonspecific binding of bacteria to a biomaterial surface is highly influenced by the charge and hydrophobicity of both the bacteria and the biomaterial surface. It is stated that the material is uncharged, so the nonspecific binding of bacteria to the biomaterial surface in this case will be dominated by hydrophobicity. It is given that the material is highly hydrophobic and that the researchers are considering surface modification through plasma treatment to add polar groups, which will increase the hydrophilicity of the biomaterial. The next likely *in vitro* step is a test of bacterial adhesion to the modified surface. (Since this is not meant as an anti-microbial material, a zone of inhibition study is not appropriate.)

*Expected results:* If the bacterial strain is hydrophobic, then the surface modification will discourage bacterial adhesion based on decreased hydrophobic interactions. However, if the bacterial strain is hydrophilic, then this modification could encourage bacterial adhesion based on increased hydrophilic interactions. The microbial adherence to hydrocarbons assay results show that the optical density of the hydrocarbon phase is greater than that of the aqueous phase. Thus, more bacteria migrated to the hydrocarbon phase than the aqueous phase, suggesting that the bacteria are hydrophobic. Consequently, plasma treatment of the biomaterial surface will likely decrease the adhesion of the bacterial strain.    ■

**14.3.2.2** *Ex Vivo* and *In Vivo* **Infection Models**    *Ex vivo* models of infection involve the use of shunts, much like those described for hemocompatibility testing (see Chapter 13). In this case, the pathogen of interest is inoculated near the biomaterial, and bacterial adhesion (and subsequent developments) in the presence of flowing blood is followed over the course of several hours. These assays are most useful for examining infections of blood-contacting devices. They provide the advantage that the flow environment is similar to that seen *in vivo*; however, the use of shunts is more expensive than *in vitro* testing and therefore may not be cost-effective if screening a large number of samples.

*In vivo* models of infection use both small animals (rodents) and larger animals. Rodents are most often employed to screen new biomaterials (e.g., novel anti-infectives) rather than to test entire devices. The cage implant system described in Chapter 11 for *in vivo* assessment of inflammation may also be used in infection testing to examine how an "infected material" responds to soluble antibiotic therapies. In contrast, a complete device may be implanted in larger animal models. In these experiments, bacteria may be introduced via direct placement at the implant site or through injection into the bloodstream to mimic different sources of infection. As discussed in Chapter 11, the type of animal and implantation location chosen depends on the final use for the device.

For both *ex vivo* or *in vivo* experiments, assessment methods are similar and usually include histology and SEM of explants at various time points, using techniques described in Chapter 11. In addition, in order to get quantitative data, the device can be explanted, washed, and the bacteria that are extracted from the surface can be counted. Additionally, the animal's blood may be tested over the course of the experiment for leukocyte and lymphocyte counts. As explained in earlier chapters, both of these cell types will be stimulated by the presence of certain molecules on the bacterial surface and, thus, a larger number of these cells would be expected if a severe infection is present.

Alternatively, the amount of bacterial cell wall antibodies found in the blood at different times may be quantified via ELISA techniques (see Chapter 8) to determine the extent of infection over time. In addition to antibody-based methods, the Limulus Amebocyte Lysate (LAL) assay, a colorimetric assay like that discussed in Chapter 8, has been developed to detect the presence of certain molecules (lipopolysaccharides, LPS) found in the outer membrane of Gram-negative bacteria. LPS molecules have the potential to bind with receptors found on monocytes/macrophages and neutrophils to stimulate the inflammatory response. Thus, this assay is particularly important because, even after bacterial death, the presence of these molecules around the material could negatively affect the biocompatibility of the implant. These nondestructive assays, along with imaging techniques to visualize small amounts of bacteria attached to an implant through X-ray (computed tomography) or magnetic resonance imaging are an important topic of current research, as they would enable monitoring of patients to promote early intervention before the implant becomes completely colonized with bacteria/biofilm.

# 14.4 Tumorigenesis

## 14.4.1 Definitions and Steps of Tumorigenesis

Another potential problem with biomaterial implantation having serious consequences is the formation of tumors (**tumorigenesis**). No solid correlation between biomedical implants and tumor formation has been found, but the complexity of the tumor formation process (see details in the text that follows) creates difficulties in directly correlating the presence of biomaterials with tumorigenesis. Moreover, concerns about tumorigenesis have been increasing due to the recent development of cell-containing therapies including or derived from pluripotent stem cells, which have a strong potential for tumor formation *in vivo*. Standards and regulatory guidelines for testing tumorigenic potential of these combination products are therefore still evolving (see section 14.5 on testing).

Before beginning a detailed discussion of this phenomenon, a number of terms should be defined. **Neoplasia** refers to excessive and uncontrolled cell proliferation. This cell division is not related to the physiologic requirements of tissue and is not arrested by removal of the stimulus that caused it, so it can be separated from all other types of normal cell proliferation during development or wound healing. This new growth is called a **neoplasm** or a **tumor** and is composed of proliferating neoplastic cells and surrounding connective tissue and blood vessels.

**Benign tumors** do not invade adjacent tissues or spread to distant sites. However, **malignant tumors** do invade surrounding tissues and gain entry into lymph and blood vessels, so they can be transported to distant sites (this is called tumor **metastasis**). Malignant tumors usually contain cells that are less differentiated than normal tissue cells. The degree to which the tumor maintains its normal cell phenotype is therefore referred to as the *grade* of the cancer, whereas the *stage* of the cancer describes how far it has metastasized within the body.

A **carcinogen** is a stimulus that causes malignant transformation, thought to occur due to mutations in the DNA of normal cells (**mutagenesis**). There have been several classes of carcinogens identified, including a number of chemical carcinogens. However, even in the presence of carcinogens, malignant transformation is often a result of an accumulation of genetic damage and is therefore a multistep process. Many of the mutations found in neoplasms target genes that regulate cell division, DNA replication, etc. The tumor that results is therefore usually derived from a single cell.

The complexity of the events leading to tumor formation and their timing provides a significant challenge in relating biomaterial properties to carcinogenic potential. Three basic stages of tumorigenesis have been identified:

1. Initiation
2. Latency
3. Promotion

The primary cellular transformation occurs in the **initiation** phase. This can be followed by a **latency** period whose length varies by species. For humans, this may be on the order of 15–20 years. No tumor formation is visible during this period. At some point (the exact timing is not understood), the **promotion** stage is entered. This is the phase where obvious tumor development and growth can be observed.

## 14.4.2 Chemical versus Foreign Body Carcinogenesis

Two main routes of malignant transformation can be encountered: chemical carcinogenesis and foreign body carcinogenesis. **Chemical carcinogenesis** is possible near biomaterials since tumors may be caused by substances that have leached from the implant. Similarly, transformations in organs distant from the device may occur if the carcinogen is transported away from the implant site. Known chemical carcinogens are usually hydrocarbon-based molecules.

The concept of **foreign body carcinogenesis** was developed based on data from implantation of various materials in rodents. In many experiments, a solid material with no chemical carcinogenic activity was observed to cause tumor formation, and the ability of the material to induce malignant transformation increased with the size of the implant. Materials exhibiting a resolved inflammatory response (fibrous encapsulation) were usually more able to cause tumorigenesis. The exact cause of foreign body carcinogenesis remains unclear, but chemical and electrical conditions near the tissue–implant interface differ from those found in regular tissue, so alterations in the local environment may be one factor (see the following text for further discussion).

## 14.4.3 Timeline for Foreign Body Tumorigenesis

**14.4.3.1 Foreign Body Tumorigenesis with Large Implants**   Like other types of tumor formation, foreign body tumorigenesis involves several steps. The process begins during the foreign body reaction to an implanted material, which is described in more detail in Chapter 11. During this time, cellular proliferation associated with creation of a fibrous capsule is common. Preneoplastic cells may be present at this point, but transformation has not yet occurred.

After the fibrous capsule is fully generated, the inflammatory response becomes quiescent. However, there is continued contact of the preneoplastic cells with the implanted material. During this phase, malignant transformation may occur, followed by a latent period. At a later time, there is final maturation of preneoplastic cells, resulting in tumor growth.

Certain aspects relating to the mechanism of foreign body tumorigenesis have been observed in *in vivo* experiments. It is thought that the transformation event occurs early in implantation and is not directly caused by the foreign body (material). Additionally, the final steps leading to tumor growth can only occur if the malignant cells are in a relatively protected, quiet environment such as the fibrous capsule. This is not permitted in implants with continued macrophage activity (unresolved inflammation). Among the possible causes of foreign body carcinogenesis are the following [1]:

1. Bulk chemical properties of the implant
2. Physicochemical surface properties of the implant
3. Viral contamination of the implant
4. Interruption of cellular communication due to the presence of the implant
5. Local tissue damage leading to insufficient nutrient exchange
6. Disturbed cellular growth around the implant

**14.4.3.2 Foreign Body Tumorigenesis with Nanomaterials**   The previous discussion of foreign body tumorigenesis has focused on implants where the material was much larger than the size of a cell. However, it should be noted that small fibers (less than 1 μm in diameter and more than 8 μm in length) have been implicated in certain cancers, regardless of chemical composition. This was first discovered in humans who had inhaled asbestos fibers and subsequently developed a type of cancer known as mesothelioma. There are several reasons why malignant transformation may occur in these cases, including an overexpression of reactive oxygen species and pro-inflammatory cytokines by granulocytes interacting with these particles, or that the small fibers can penetrate the cell membrane and directly cause genetic alterations in the cell.

The observations from asbestos fibers have led to questions about toxicity of nanoscale particles in general. Because of their size, they can interact with specific proteins on the cell surface and thus behave differently than larger particles or bulk materials. They also are relatively easily endocytosed compared to larger particles. Once in the cell, a number of interactions can occur with intracellular proteins and organelles, which depend on the surface chemistry of the material as well as the composition of the proteins adsorbed to the surface (the *protein corona*).

Some nanoparticles can (or are designed to) enter the nucleus, where they can cause a number of effects that might lead to tumor formation. For example, they may cause intranuclear protein aggregation that alters DNA replication, or decrease expression of DNA repair genes. They can also cause secondary effects, such as promoting the cell to increase reactive oxygen species, which can then diffuse into the nucleus and damage DNA. A number of common types of nanoparticles, including gold and titanium dioxide, have exhibited some of these negative effects on cells, although material presence has not been directly correlated with tumor formation. Thus, there is continuing debate about the best way to assess long-term exposure risk for these nanomaterials.

## 14.4.4 Summary of Biomaterial-Related Tumorigenesis

Tumorigenesis results from a complex series of events, most likely involving genetic mutation, that are not at present fully understood (Fig. 14.10). Tumor formation can be caused by the presence of a biomedical implant, which may lead to disruption of cell–cell communication or physical damage to surrounding cells, or by chemicals leached from the device. There is a relatively low incidence of implant-related tumorigenesis in humans. This may be because the solubility of many implant materials (like metals) is low in physiologic fluids, so the concentration may stay below threshold values for initiation of malignant transformation in humans.

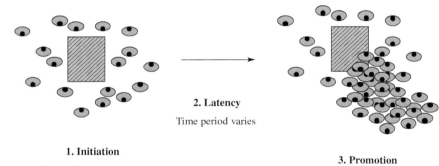

**2. Latency**

Time period varies

**1. Initiation**

Implantation of biomaterial = malignant transformation of DNA

*Due to:*

Chemical carcinogenesis (chemicals leached from implant)

**OR**

Foreign-body carcinogenesis (mechanism unknown, may be related to surface or bulk properties of the implant or alterations in local environment)

**3. Promotion**

Obvious tumor growth around implant

**Figure 14.10**
Steps of tumorigenesis, which results from a complex series of events, most likely involving genetic mutation, that are not at present fully understood. Tumor formation can be initiated by the presence of a biomedical implant, which may lead to disruption of cell–cell communication or physical damage to surrounding cells, or by chemicals leached from the device. It also remains unclear what controls the timeline of tumor formation and the length of the latent phase between initiation and promotion (tumor growth). No solid correlation between biomedical implants and tumor formation has been found, but the latent period creates difficulties in directly correlating the presence of biomaterials with tumorigenesis.

If malignant transformation does occur, it also remains unclear what controls the time line of tumor formation and the length of the latent phase between mutagenesis and tumor growth. No strong correlation between biomedical implants and tumor formation has been found, but the latent period creates difficulties in directly correlating the presence of biomaterials with tumorigenesis.

# 14.5 Techniques for Tumorigenesis Experiments

Of the implant-associated pathologies described in this chapter, tumorigenesis testing is the best regulated by organizations such as ISO and ASTM. ISO standards require assays for carcinogenesis, although they may be combined with tests for other long-term sequelae, such as chronic toxicity. ISO regulations are most concerned with *in vivo* testing, but, due to the generally low incidence of implant-related tumors in humans, this is only necessary when other sources (initial trials or *in vitro* testing) indicate a potential for tumor formation. The following discussion focuses primarily on biomedical devices, for which regulation is more established. More extensive tumorigenesis testing is generally required for combination products, particularly those involving cells, although the exact tests needed would depend on the cell type used and the intended application.

## 14.5.1 *In Vitro* Models

ISO standards require at least three *in vitro* tests, two of which should be in mammalian cells, for determining negative effects on the genome (**genotoxicity**), and they must address the three major types of genetic damage: DNA destruction, gene mutations, and chromosomal aberrations. DNA damage can be assessed through the unscheduled DNA synthesis test (see Fig. 14.11). In this case, the DNA synthesis rate of cells in the presence of the biomaterial or extracts is assessed through the cells' incorporation of radio-labeled nucleotides over a particular time, compared to control cells without the biomaterial. The rationale for this assay is that if the biomaterial causes DNA damage, the cell would repair this through synthesizing more, new DNA, so synthesis rates similar to (rather than higher than) control samples are desired.

A commonly used method of predicting gene mutagenic potential is the Ames test. This technique employs a mutant bacteria line that requires the amino acid histidine for growth. The bacteria are cultured with the sample material and an enzyme preparation in histidine-free media, so only the bacteria able to mutate to a non-histidine-dependent phenotype will be able to survive and proliferate. The number

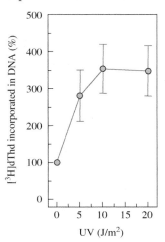

**Figure 14.11**
Example of results from an unscheduled DNA synthesis test. B cell chronic lymphocytic leukemia (B-CLL) lymphocytes showed increased radiolabel incorporation (indicative of greater DNA synthesis) with increased UV light exposure, up to a dose of 15 J/M$^2$ [15].

**Figure 14.12**
Example of results from the Ames test showing the response of a weak (ethylmethane sulfonate) moderate (BaP: benzo[a]pyrene) and strong mutagen (MNNG: N-methyl-N'-nitro-N-nitrosoguanidine). The more potent the mutagen, the more colonies are visible on the plate [16].

of surviving colonies is then quantified to provide an indicator of the mutagenic potential of the sample (see Fig. 14.12). Although this method is quick and inexpensive, it may have limited sensitivity to mutagenic agents, particularly when they are administered at low concentrations. Therefore, the Ames test should be conducted using proper positive and negative controls and should be considered only as a preliminary screening mechanism.

**Figure 14.13**
Example of results from a chromosome aberration test. (A) Images of chromosomes from Chinese hamster ovary (CHO) cells (a) untreated, (b) treated with a known mutagen (positive control), (c) treated with 6.2 mg/mL gold nanoparticles (AuNPs), (d) treated with 12.5 mg/mL gold nanoparticles, (e) treated with 25 mg/mL gold nanoparticles and (f) treated with 50 mg/mL gold nanoparticles (chromatid break aberration indicated by arrow). (B) Quantification of the aberrant breaks seen in (A), showing that the gold nanoparticles do not demonstrate genotoxicity (results similar to untreated). (Reprinted with permission from [17].)

To assess chromosomal aberrations, cells are cultured with the biomaterial or extracts, and, at specified time points, are treated with a drug to arrest cells in metaphase. Cells are then examined under a microscope to visually determine if chromosomes appear altered, compared to control cells that were cultured without the biomaterial (see Fig. 14.13). While image analysis software can be employed to help in examining the images, this technique is relatively qualitative.

### 14.5.2 *In Vivo* Models

*In vivo* carcinogenesis assessment is generally undertaken as a part of general biocompatibility testing, as suggested by ISO and ASTM guidelines. In this case, the experimental material is usually fabricated in the form of the final device. In addition, controls of the same shape made from a noncarcinogenic material should be implanted to distinguish responses observed only because of foreign body tumorigenesis (foreign body–based tumors should occur in response to both control and experimental materials). This is particularly important in rodents, since they have a high propensity for foreign body carcinogenesis, regardless of the material. Thus, the goal of these experiments is to determine if a novel material exhibits a higher tendency for chemical and/or foreign body carcinogenesis than the control.

As discussed previously, the exact animal type and implantation location for these procedures depend on the final intended device function. Regardless of the animal model or duration of the study, at various time points during the experiment, the tissue around the implant should be excised and evaluated using general histological techniques and/or SEM (see Chapter 11) to detect tumor growth.

### EXAMPLE PROBLEM 14.2

A research lab has developed a dental implant composed exclusively of a well-known and characterized biomaterial. The biomaterial has been studied extensively in various *in vitro* models to evaluate the genotoxicity of the material, with no negative results. To the surprise of the research lab, however, it was found during the *in vivo* evaluation of the dental implants that tumors were forming in the mandibles of the recipient animals. Is this dental implant most likely an example of a chemical or a foreign body carcinogen? Would nondental implants composed of this material be expected to form a tumor?

**Solution:** The dental implant is likely an example of a foreign body carcinogen, as the *in vitro* assays (cells only) did not show any genotoxic effects, yet tumor formation occurred in the dental implant application. The size and shape of the implant, the implantation site, and the procedure could influence the tumorigenicity of the implant. Thus, although the implant resulted in tumor formation in the dental site, other implants of different sizes and shapes composed of this material might not necessarily result in tumor formation in other implantation sites. ∎

## 14.6 Pathologic Calcification

### 14.6.1 Introduction to Pathologic Calcification

In addition to infection or tumor formation around a biomedical implant, an additional pathology that may occur to disrupt device function is pathologic calcification. **Pathologic calcification,** or undesired formation of nodules of calcium phosphate within or on the surface of an implanted material, has affected the operation of such devices as cardiac valves, cardiac assist devices (blood pumps), vascular grafts, soft contact lenses, intrauterine contraceptive devices, and urinary prostheses. Often ECM-derived materials are associated with this pathology, but calcification (or

**TABLE 14.1**

| Clinical Consequences of Biomaterials Calcification | | |
|---|---|---|
| Configuration | Biomaterial | Clinical Consequence |
| Cardiac valve prostheses | Glutaraldehyde-pretreated porcine aortic valve or bovine pericardium, and allograft aortic/pulmonary valves | Valve obstruction or incompetency |
| Cardiac ventricular assist bladders | Poly(urethane) | Dysfunction by stiffening or cracking |
| Vascular grafts | Dacron™ grafts and aortic allografts | Graft obstruction or stiffening |
| Soft contact lenses | Hydrogels | Opacification |
| Intrauterine contraceptive devices | Silicone rubber, Poly(urethane), or copper | Birth control failure by dysfunction or expulsion |
| Urinary prostheses | Silicone rubber or Poly(urethane) | Incontinence and/or infection |

(Adapted with permission from [2].)

mineralization) of synthetic polymers is also a large concern. Although calcification can be desired in conjunction with some biomaterials applications, such as in bone tissue engineering to produce mineralized bone matrix, calcification can be undesirable in other applications, such as in artificial heart valves, which require flexibility for function. In this text, the term mineralization will denote the deposition of inorganic material in a tissue, whereas calcification will denote a subset of mineralization in which calcium is the major specific inorganic material deposited in the tissue.

The presence of mineral deposits can be considered deleterious to device function in some applications because they can have a large impact on the mechanical properties of biomaterials. As discussed in Chapter 4, ceramics, like the calcium phosphate materials that are deposited in pathologic calcification, are quite brittle. Therefore, pathologic calcification of natural or synthetic polymers can lead to premature fracture, particularly in devices that perform continued movement, such as pumps or heart valves. Details about how calcification leads to device failure for a number of applications are provided in Table 14.1. In general, calcification can occur within the transplanted tissue (such as for transplanted heart valves, called *intrinsic calcification*), at the surface of the implant (*extrinsic calcification*), or inside the fibrous capsule surrounding the implant.

Pathologic calcification of devices shares many characteristics with native pathologies demonstrating undesired mineralization in the body, such as arteriosclerosis, including that the amount can vary greatly between patients. The extent of pathologic calcification in a given system is dependent on the structure and chemistry of the biomaterial, as expected, but also on host metabolic factors and on the mechanical environment of the implant. The role of mechanical factors has not been fully elucidated, but the state of mineral metabolism in the host has a large effect on calcium deposition. For example, pathologic calcification occurs more quickly in younger patients, possibly because the metabolism of children with rapidly growing bones favors mineralization.

## 14.6.2 Mechanism of Pathologic Calcification

Pathologic calcification is found with either synthetic or naturally based materials, but natural materials treated with gluteraldehyde or formaldehyde are extremely susceptible. In many cases, these natural materials are not composed of individual

ECM components, such as collagen, but are those in which the entire ECM is intact, and the material has been exposed to the agents listed earlier to preserve them and render them less immunogenic. A common example of an implant that often undergoes calcification in humans is the porcine heart valve.

Initiation of calcium deposits on these pretreated natural materials is thought to occur on dead cells or cell membrane fragments. As mentioned in Chapter 9, cell membranes contain proteins with attached phosphate groups that may act as nucleation sites to form calcium phosphate crystals. In addition, the enzyme alkaline phosphatase is linked to the membrane and is thought to have a role in promoting calcification in bone. Nonviable cells also do not possess the transport mechanisms (such as cell membrane pumps) to control the intracellular calcium concentration, leading to a potential increase in calcium ions near the phosphorous-containing proteins on the cell membrane. Fixing agents, such as gluteraldehyde, may promote these interactions by crosslinking and stabilizing the cell-surface proteins. Localized mechanical forces can increase the probability of calcification in an area, possibly due to an increase in regional cell death.

Later in the process, collagen, a major component of most natural biomaterials, can act as a template for the growth of mineral crystals, similar to what occurs in normal bone formation. As with calcification in bone, there are also a number of noncollagenous proteins that are associated with pathologic calcification and may act to direct or regulate crystal formation.

### 14.6.3 Summary and Techniques to Reduce Pathologic Calcification

Pathologic calcification of biomedical implants depends on the host metabolism, surface and bulk properties of the biomaterial chosen, and the mechanical environment of the device. In many cases, calcium phosphate deposition occurs first near cell membrane fragments and later in the collagen-rich ECM of naturally derived implants. It is thought that crystal formation in pathologic calcification follows a similar mechanism as that observed for normal bone formation.

Several means to reduce unwanted calcification have been explored. Some of these approaches have included either systemic or local delivery of anti-calcification agents after device implantation, such as bisphosphonates (calcium chelators used to reduce bone resorption in osteoporosis). Alternatively, others have focused on alterations to the biomaterial to either release a calcification inhibitor or reduce the contents of the substrate that promote calcification. Examples of the latter approach include decellularizing porcine tissue prior to implantation to decrease the amount of cell membrane fragments that are known to encourage calcium deposits, or replacing gluteraldehyde with another fixative.

## 14.7 Techniques for Pathologic Calcification Experiments

Both *in vitro* and *in vivo* models of pathologic calcification have been developed, although *in vivo* studies provide more information and, thus, are more commonly used. A review of various experimental systems is provided in this section.

### 14.7.1 *In Vitro* Models of Calcification

In *in vitro* studies of calcium deposition, materials or entire devices can be placed in a bath containing media approximating the chemical composition of a particular *in vivo* location (e.g., urine or blood). In alternate experimental configurations, the liquid may be either static or continuously circulating, and the implant may be in motion (such as flexion) or remain immobile during the course of the experiment. At appropriate time points, the sample is removed and analyzed for degree of calcification using the techniques described in subsequent sections. While these methods do not completely re-create the *in vivo* environment, like other *in vitro* experiments, they can be useful for initial screening of new biomaterials.

### 14.7.2 *In Vivo* Models of Calcification

Two types of *in vivo* experiments can be performed to assess the pathologic calcification of a biomaterial: subcutaneous implantation and insertion of the final device directly at the target location. In **subcutaneous** experiments, the material to be tested is placed under the skin, usually in mice or rats, although rabbit models are sometimes used. The advantage of such a procedure is that a smaller animal can be used and an extensive surgery is not required for implantation. In addition, similar types of calcium deposits are seen as those that would normally be found at the device site, but mineralization occurs at a more rapid rate, thus decreasing the overall time needed for the study. While subcutaneous assays may be used for preliminary or secondary testing of new biomaterials, it should be noted that this model does not fully recreate the dynamic environment found at the site of device function.

Another option for *in vivo* experiments is the placement of a prototype of the final device at the site where it would be found in human patients. This usually requires a large animal model such as a cow or sheep, particularly with cardiovascular implants. Other disadvantages include that the implantation procedure can be lengthy and complex (involving cardiopulmonary bypass) and thus operative costs may be high. However, this model is often used as a final test of a new device design or material because it best represents the environment that such a device would encounter in human patients.

### 14.7.3 Sample Assessment

Specimens from both *in vitro* and *in vivo* experiments can be evaluated for degree of calcium deposition in a similar manner. In terms of destructive assays (those that require damaging the sample in order to extract information), entire samples may be subjected to biochemical assays to determine calcium content via color change after reaction with the appropriate reagent (see Fig. 14.14 for example of one of these reagents). As described in more detail in Chapter 8, the color change is quantified

**Figure 14.14**
Staining for ectopic calcification. Alazirin Red stain shows calcium deposits (red) in the wall of the aorta in this mouse model of a genetic disease, generalized arterial calcification of infancy (GACI), that causes ectopic calcification in cardiovascular tissues. The stain can be released from the sample and the color quantified, using methods described in Chapter 2, to produce data on the amount of calcium deposited in each sample [18].

on a microplate reader equipped with a spectrophotometer and compared with a standard curve to determine the amount of calcium present in the sample.

Alternatively, the sample may be sectioned as per standard histological techniques (see Chapters 9 and 11) and stained for calcium content to examine the location of the calcification (see example of calcium staining in Fig. 14.14). Explants can also be analyzed via SEM or TEM to visualize the specimen, as well as to quantify Ca and P content using the EDXA X-ray attachment described in Chapter 7. X-ray diffraction experiments (see Chapter 2) on a ground portion of the sample may provide additional useful information about the structure of the crystals formed.

For assessment that does not require explantation of *in vivo* specimens, radiographs (traditional X-rays) can be used to monitor calcification within samples from both *in vitro* and *in vivo* experiments (Fig. 14.15). Radiography is a nondestructive technique that can be used with living animals and is based on principles similar to those of X-ray diffraction. However, in radiographic imaging, elements with high atomic numbers (such as calcium phosphates) in essence absorb the X-rays as they travel through the sample and do not allow them to reach the detector, usually a radiographic film. This leaves a white area on the film directly under the calcified material. The size and location of these white (radiopaque) areas can reveal changes in calcification over time within the same sample. However, conventional radiography only yields two-dimensional representations of three-dimensional samples and often presents limited spatial resolution.

Microcomputed tomography ($\mu$CT) is an alternative nondestructive method to evaluate calcification in a sample using X-rays (Fig. 14.16). In this case, a fine-beam X-ray source exposes the sample to X-rays. The X-rays projecting through the sample are detected by a two-dimensional detector array. The sample is then rotated and another projection is rendered, and the process is repeated until two-dimensional projections have been collected for the entire specimen. A computer processes these projections into images of two-dimensional cross sections of the sample, which can

**Figure 14.15**
Radiographic imaging of a healing defect in the radius (long bone in forearm) of a rabbit. A tissue engineering scaffold was placed in the defect, and radiographs were used to determine the extent of bone formation that occurred at the defect site. The bone from the rabbit in (a) exhibits some degree of repair whereas the bone from a different rabbit in (b) shows minimal repair. Although in this case calcified matrix deposition was desired, similar methods can also be used to determine the extent of pathologic calcification in a tissue. Scale bar 10 mm. (Reprinted with permission from [19].)

(b)     (c)

**Figure 14.16**

Microcomputed tomography imaging. (a) is a diagram depicting how rotating the sample can result in a series of 2D radiographs that can be reconstructed into a 3D image. (b) and (c) are resulting images of engineered bone tissue following the implantation of a scaffold in a bone defect in the radius of a rabbit. (b) shows an exterior view and (c) shows a cross section of the repaired region. Because this imaging modality creates a three-dimensional image, it can be used for quantification of calcified matrix production in a certain volume. ((b) and (c) reprinted with permission from [19].)

be combined to reconstruct the three-dimensional internal and external architecture of the sample. The spatial resolution of this technique is of the order of micrometers. While μCT equipment can be expensive, the advantage of producing three-dimensional images makes this technique popular among biomaterials researchers. It is also important to note that a suitable difference must exist in the X-ray attenuation coefficient between the calcified material and the other materials (such as surrounding soft tissue and/or implant material) in order to differentiate them by this and other radiographic techniques.

## EXAMPLE PROBLEM 14.3

A company plans to evaluate a new heart valve prosthesis fabricated with crosslinked porcine pericardium in an *in vitro* model. The company is specifically interested in assessing whether the tissue in the heart valve prosthesis will calcify with time. The researcher in charge of the project has decided to place the prosthesis in a pulsatile flow circuit with porcine blood being perfused through the system to simulate physiologic conditions. However, to prevent coagulation of the blood in the system, the researcher wants to supplement the porcine blood with large amounts of ethylenediaminetetraacetic acid (EDTA), a chelating agent for calcium ions. How might EDTA serve to inhibit coagulation? Could the EDTA affect the validity of the calcification study? How? Should the EDTA be used in this system? What is a good technique to assess amount of calcification in this system and why?

**Solution:**   Recalling from Chapter 13 that calcium ions play a crucial role in the coagulation cascade, EDTA will work to inhibit coagulation by sequestering the calcium ions in the blood, limiting their availability to promote coagulation. Additionally, as the EDTA sequesters the calcium in solution, it could reduce the concentration of calcium present during the *in vitro* assays to levels significantly below the values that would normally be found in blood *in vivo*. Thus, if calcification is found not to occur in this *in vitro* analysis, it could be an artifact of the chelation of calcium and might not reflect what would normally happen *in vivo*. It follows that the EDTA should not be used in this system. It would be more suitable to use an anticoagulant that does not sequester calcium as an alternative to EDTA.

In terms of assessment, since this is a first-pass screen on a flat (2D) sample, either histology including a stain for mineralization, or a bioassay to quantitatively measure the amount of calcification would be appropriate. X-ray and other techniques could be used, but the assays listed are generally cheaper and more accessible to most laboratories for screening purposes. ■

# Summary

- Implant-associated infections have a number of related characteristics. The pathogens most commonly connected with implant-associated infection are the Gram-positive bacteria *S. aureus* and *S. epidermidis*, the Gram-negative bacteria *Enterobacteriaceae* and *P. aeriginosa*, and fungi such as *Candida*. These pathogens can result in different categories of infections, including superficial immediate infection, deep immediate infection, and late infection.

- Four distinct stages are involved in the development of implant-associated infection. First, preliminary reversible bacterial attachment to the surface occurs through nonspecific interactions (attachment). Second, the preliminary attachment becomes permanent as specific receptor-ligand interactions develop and nonspecific interactions remain (adhesion). Third, the bacteria divide after firmly attaching to the surface, causing the development of a biofilm (aggregation). Fourth, the bacteria travel from the colony to other areas of the body (dispersion).

- The biofilm produced by bacteria assists in trapping ions important to bacterial survival, offers protection against the natural defenses of the body, and can impart antibiotic resistance.

- The two major classes of bacteria are Gram-positive and Gram-negative species. Gram-positive species have a single bilayered phospholipid membrane and a thick cell wall composed of peptidoglycan. Gram-negative species have two phospholipid membranes (cell membrane and outer membrane), with the peptidoglycan layer between them.

- Bacterial adhesion to a biomaterial can be strongly influenced by the layer of proteins adsorbed to the material surface; thus, material properties can influence protein adsorption and bacterial attachment. Further, the protein and/or ion content of the media can affect the composition of the protein layer adsorbed to a material and consequently the attachment of bacteria.

- The bacterial surface properties of most importance to adhesion to biomaterial surfaces are surface hydrophobicity and charge. The surface hydrophobicity of bacteria can be assessed by contact angle measurements, the microbial adherence to hydrocarbons (MATH) technique, or through hydrophobic interaction chromatography (HIC). Bacterial surface charge can be assessed through electrophoretic mobility tests or electrostatic interaction chromatography (EIC).

- *In vitro* assays having to do with device infection include those for bacterial attachment and bacterial cell death on biomaterial surfaces. Biomaterials can also be assessed *in vivo*, often through co-implantation of the material with bacteria to recreate what occurs in implant-related infection.

- A carcinogen is a stimulus that results in malignant transformation of cells. It is thought to occur due to mutations in the DNA of normal cells, a process called mutagenesis. There have been several classes of carcinogens identified, including a number of chemical carcinogens.

- The three basic stages of tumorigenesis are initiation, latency, and promotion. The initiation phase involves the primary cellular transformation. It is followed by a period of no visible tumor formation called latency. The point at which tumor development and growth can be observed marks the onset of the promotion phase.

- There are two primary routes of malignant transformation: chemical carcinogenesis and foreign body carcinogenesis. Chemical carcinogenesis involves exposure to chemicals that are known to be carcinogens. Foreign body carcinogenesis occurs when materials with no known chemical carcinogenic activity are observed to cause tumor development.

- Possible contributing factors to foreign body carcinogenesis include bulk chemical properties of the implant, physicochemical surface properties of the implant, viral contamination of the implant, interruption of cellular communication due to the presence of the implant, local tissue damage leading to insufficient nutrient exchange, and disturbed cellular growth around the implant.

- Potential tumorigenecity of nanoscale materials remains under investigation. Because of their size, they can interact with specific proteins on the cell surface, and are more easily endocytosed, and thus behave differently than larger particles or bulk materials.

- *In vitro* assays for genotoxicity must address the three major types of genetic damage: DNA destruction, gene mutations, and chromosomal aberrations. *In vivo* assays to assess tumor formation, where the device is fabricated in its final form and then implanted in an appropriate animal model at the final intended location, should also be conducted.

- Undesired calcification is termed pathologic calcification, and it can be deleterious to device function as it imparts stiffness and brittleness to the material. Pathologic calcification of biomedical implants depends on the host metabolism, surface and bulk properties of the biomaterial chosen, and the mechanical environment of the device.

- Naturally based ECM materials are especially susceptible to pathologic calcification, since it is thought that initiation of calcium deposits may occur on dead cells or cell membrane fragments, with crystal growth templated by the remaining ECM molecules.

- The potential for a material to be calcified can be assessed preliminarily through *in vitro* studies employing media that approximate the physiological environment that the device would face in its intended application. *In vivo* models of calcification generally provide more complete information and can be conducted either subcutaneously or at the site of intended final application. In both cases, sample assessment methods include biochemical assays, histology, or X-ray analysis.

# Problems

14.1 What are the major steps in implant infection? Which one would you target in order to reduce device-related infections and why?

14.2 Your company is developing a new material for a urinary catheter that includes sustained release of antibiotics to reduce infection. Your colleague has performed a zone of inhibition study with several samples (three formulations, each releasing different antibiotics and one control polymer with no antibiotic), but mixed up the labels on the samples. The results of the study are as follows.

(a) Which sample is likely the control and why?
(b) Of the remaining samples, which of the formulations worked the best and why?

| Bacteria | Material | Inhibition Zone (mm) Mean ± SD |
|----------|----------|-------------------|
| *E. coli* | MR | $1.0 \pm 2.8$ |
| | NF | $3.1 \pm 6.1$ |
| | SN | $9.3 \pm 10.0$ |
| | PS | $0.0 \pm 0.0$ |

[3].

14.3 You are developing a textured titanium-based material to potentially reduce orthopaedic implant-related infection. You first characterize the width of the grooves produced on the surface of each sample type using atomic force microscopy (shown as "peak to peak distance" on the graph here). You then perform a static bacterial adhesion assay on each of these samples over 24 hours. The results are found in the graph below [4]. (Notes: Bacteria are generally 1–2 μm in diameter; fraction of attached bacteria refers to the ratio of amount attached/amount introduced into the system at time = 0.)

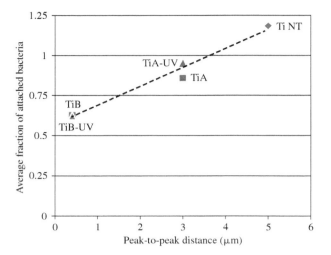

(a) Explain the effects of groove size on bacterial adhesion. In particular, what may be occurring at groove widths of 0.5 μm and 5 μm to produce the data shown here?

(b) Which size of grooves would you choose to try *in vivo*? Design an *in vivo* experiment (including proper controls and outcome measures) to test the ability of this surface to reduce implant infection.

14.4 (a) What is the main difference between chemical and foreign body carcinogenesis?

(b) Would an *in vitro* assay to detect chromosomal aberrations usually detect chemical, foreign-body or both types of carcinogenesis? Justify based on how this assay works and how that relates to changes that occur in both types of carcinogenesis.

14.5 List three proposed mechanisms of how nanoscale materials may cause malignant transformation of a cell.

14.6 You are developing a new titanium dioxide ($TiO_2$) sunscreen. It is known that this type of sunscreen provides protection by scattering UV rays, so that fewer rays penetrate the skin, where they can potentially cause mutagenesis. You are developing a new carrier for the $TiO_2$ to further improve scattering properties and you want to determine if this provides additional protection to underlying skin cells.

(a) You will be using an Ames test. Explain the principles behind this assay and how you would set up the assay to test your material, including proper control groups.

(b) You find the following results:

| Sample | Number of viable colonies |
|---|---|
| Control (UV only) | 3,000 |
| $TiO_2$ + UV | 1,300 |
| $TiO_2$ + carrier + UV | 500 |

Based on the results above, did your new carrier work?

14.7 Which part of pathologic calcification is most likely to occur faster in younger patients? Justify your answer.

14.8 You are investigating two hydrolytically degradable polymers as potential scaffolds for bioresorbable vascular grafts. You implant grafts made from a slow degrading (SD) and fast degrading (FD) polymer in mice. After eight weeks, you retrieve the samples and complete histology on cross sections of the blood vessels using von Kossa stain, which stains mineralized matrix black. (Note: In the images given here, arrows indicate the inner and outer layers of the blood vessel.)

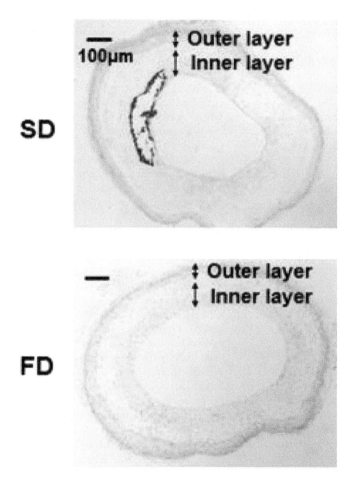

Scale bar is 100 μm. (Reprinted with permission from [5].)

(a) Based on the images given here, which polymer would you recommend to use? Justify your answer based on the final application for this material.
(b) Matrix Gla protein (MGP) is a known natural inhibitor of calcification, which is thought to act, in part, by binding to the ions and thus preventing deposition of calcium phosphate mineral in tissues. What would you expect if you implanted both of these materials in an individual with a genetic mutation that prevented production of MGP?

14.9 Make a list of the advantages and disadvantages of the assessment methods described in this chapter for assays of pathologic calcification.

# References

1. J. Black, *Biological performance of materials: fundamentals of biocompatibility*, 4th ed. New York: CRC Press, 2005.

2. F. J. Schoen and R. J. Levy, "Pathological calcification of biomaterials," in *Biomaterials science: An introduction to materials and medicine*, 3rd ed., B. D. Ratner, A. S. Hoffman, F. J. Schoen, and J. E. Lemons, Eds. San Diego: Elsevier Academic Press, 2013, pp. 739–754.

3. A. Salvarci, M. Koroglu, and B. Erayman, "Investigation of antibacterial activity and biofilm formation of silicones coated with minocycline-rifampicin, silver nitrate, and nitrofurantoin for short-term utilization in in vitro urinary system models," *Urology*, vol. 88, pp. 66–75, 2016.

4. M. Lorenzetti *et al.*, "The influence of surface modification on bacterial adhesion to titanium-based substrates," *ACS Applied Materials & Interfaces*, vol. 7, no. 3, pp. 1644–1651, 2015.

5. T. Sugiura *et al.*, "Fast-degrading bioresorbable arterial vascular graft with high cellular infiltration inhibits calcification of the graft," *Journal of Vascular Surgery*, vol. 66, no. 1, pp. 243–250, 2017.

6. A. G. Gristina, "Biomaterial-centered infection: microbial adhesion versus tissue integration," *Science*, vol. 237, no. 4822, pp. 1588–1595, 1987.

7. R. B. Dickinson, A. G. Ruta, and S. E. Truesdail, "Physiochemical basis of bacterial adhesion to biomaterial surfaces," in *Antimicrobial/anti-infective materials: principles, applications, and devices*, S. P. Sawan and G. Manivannan, Eds. Lancaster: Technomic Publishing, 2000, pp. 67–93.

8. M. T. Madigan, J. M. Martinko, T. D. Brock, and J. Parker, *Brock biology of microorganisms*, 9th ed. Upper Saddle River: Prentice Hall, 2000.

9. I. Hancock and I. Poxton, *Bacterial cell surface techniques*. New York: John Wiley and Sons, 1988.

10. B. Costerton, G. Cook, M. Shirtliff, P. Stoodley, and M. Pasmore, "Biofilms, biomaterials, and device-related infections," in *Biomaterials science: an introduction to materials and medicine*, 2nd ed., B. D. Ratner, A. S. Hoffman, F. J. Schoen, and J. E. Lemons, Eds. San Diego: Elsevier Academic Press, 2004, pp. 345–354.

11. I. W. Wang, J. M. Anderson, M. R. Jacobs, and R. E. Marchant, "Adhesion of *Staphylococcus epidermidis* to biomedical polymers: contributions of surface thermodynamics and hemodynamic shear conditions," *Journal of Biomedical Materials Research*, vol. 29, no. 4, pp. 485–93, 1995.

12. J. Popovici, C. P. White, J. Hoelle, B. K. Kinkle, and D. A. Lytle, "Characterization of the cell surface properties of drinking water pathogens by microbial adhesion to hydrocarbon and electrophoretic mobility measurements," *Colloids and Surfaces B: Biointerfaces*, vol. 118, pp. 126–132, 2014.

13. P. P. Modiya, C. N. Patel, "Synthesis and screening of antibacterial and antifungal activity of 5-chloro-1,3-benzoxazol-2(3 h)-one derivatives," *"https://orgmedchemlett.springeropen.com/" Organic and Medicinal Chemistry Letters*, vol. 2, no. 1, p 29, Aug, 2012.

14. P. R. Modiya and C. N. Patel, "Synthesis and screening of antibacterial and antifungal activity of 5-chloro-1,3-benzoxazol-2(3 h)-one derivatives," *Organic and Medicinal Chemistry Letters*, vol. 2, no. 1, pp. 29–29, 2012.

15. E. Van Den Neste *et al.*, "2-Chloro-2"-deoxyadenosine inhibits DNA repair synthesis and potentiates UVC cytotoxicity in chronic lymphocytic leukemia B lymphocytes," *Leukemia*, vol. 16, no. 1, pp. 36–43, 2002.

16. R. Devoret, "Bacterial tests for potential carcinogens," *Scientific American*, vol. 241, no. 2, pp. 40–49, 1979.

17. J. M. George, M. Magogotya, M. A. Vetten, A. V. Buys, and M. Gulumian, "An investigation of the genotoxicity and interference of gold nanoparticles in commonly used in vitro mutagenicity and genotoxicity assays," *Toxicological Sciences*, vol. 156, no. 1, pp. 149–166, 2017.

18. Q. Li *et al.*, "Spontaneous asj-2J mutant mouse as a model for generalized arterial calcification of infancy: a large deletion/insertion mutation in the Enpp1 gene," *PloS One*, vol. 9, no. 12, pp. e113542–e113542, 2014.

19. E. L. Hedberg *et al.*, "Methods: a comparative analysis of radiography, microcomputed tomography, and histology for bone tissue engineering," *Tissue Engineering*, vol. 11, no. 9–10, pp. 1356–67, 2005.

# Additional Reading

J. M. Anderson, "Mechanisms of inflammation and infection with implanted devices," *Cardiovascular Pathology*, vol. 2, 1993, pp. 33–41.

J. M. Anderson and F. J. Schoen, "In vivo assessment of tissue compatibility," in *Biomaterials science: an introduction to materials and medicine*, 3rd ed., B. D. Ratner, A. S. Hoffman, F. J. Schoen, and J. E. Lemons, Eds. San Diego: Elsevier Academic Press, 2013, pp. 609–617.

B. Appelmelk and W. Lynn, "Chapter 2: the cause of sepsis: bacterial cell components that trigger the cytokine cascade," in *Septic shock*, J. F. Dhainaut, L. Thijs, and G. Park, Eds. London: W.B. Saunders, 2000.

A. Assmann *et al.*, "The degeneration of biological cardiovascular prostheses under pro-calcific metabolic conditions in a small animal model," *Biomaterials*, vol. 35, no. 26, pp. 7416–7428, 2014.

A. L. Barry, M. B. Coyle, C. Thornsberry, E. H. Gerlach, and R. W. Hawkinson, "Methods of measuring zones of inhibition with the Bauer-Kirby disk susceptibility test," *Journal of Clinical Microbiology*, vol. 10, no. 6, pp. 885–889, 1979.

S. C. Gad and S. Gad-McDonald, *Biomaterials, medical devices, and combination products: biocompatibility testing and safety assessment*. Boca Raton: CRC Press, 2015.

A. G. Gristina and P. T. Naylor, "Implant-associated infection," in *Biomaterials science: an introduction to materials and medicine*, 1st ed., B. D. Ratner, A. S. Hoffman, F. J. Schoen, and J. E. Lemons, Eds. San Diego: Elsevier Academic Press, 1996, pp. 205–214.

R. Giardino, F. J. Schoen, and N. N. Aldini, "Infection and Sterilization," in *Integrated biomaterials science*, R. Barbucci, Ed. New York: Kluwer, 2002, pp. 815–832.

R. J. Levy *et al.*, "Cardiovascular implant calcification: a survey and update," *Biomaterials*, vol. 12, no. 8, pp. 707–714, 1991.

B. D. Ratner, "Characterization of biomaterial surfaces," *Cardiovascular Pathology*, vol. 2, no. 3S, pp. 87S-100S, 1993.

S. Runa, M. Hussey, and C. K. Payne, "Nanoparticle–cell interactions: relevance for public health," *The Journal of Physical Chemistry B*, vol. 122, no. 3, pp. 1009–1016, 2018.

F. J. Schoen, "Tumors associated with biomaterials and implants," in *Biomaterials science: an introduction to materials and medicine*, 3rd ed., B. D. Ratner, A. S. Hoffman, F. J. Schoen, and J. E. Lemons, Eds. San Diego: Elsevier Academic Press, 2013, pp. 558–565.

F. J. Schoen and R. J. Levy, "Pathological Calcification of Biomaterials," in *Biomaterials Science: an introduction to materials and medicine*, 3rd ed., B. D. Ratner, A. S. Hoffman, F. J. Schoen, and J. E. Lemons, Eds. San Diego: Elsevier Academic Press, 2013, pp. 739–754.

A. W. Smith, "Biofilms and antibiotic therapy: is there a role for combating bacterial resistance by the use of novel drug delivery systems?," *Advanced Drug Delivery Reviews*, vol. 57, no. 10, pp. 1539–1550, 2005.

P. Stoodley *et al.*, "Biofilms, biomaterials, and device-related infections," in *Biomaterials science: an introduction to materials and medicine*, 3rd ed., B. D. Ratner, A. S. Hoffman, F. J. Schoen, and J. E. Lemons, Eds. San Diego: Elsevier Academic Press, 2013, pp. 565–583.

A. F. Von Recum, *Handbook of biomaterials evaluation: scientific, technical, and clinical testing of implant materials*. Philadelphia: Taylor and Francis, 1999.

D. Williams, *Essential biomaterials science*. Cambridge, UK: Cambridge University Press, 2014.

US Food & Drug Administration, "IV.C.1.b in vitro mammalian chromosomal aberration test," *Redbook 2000*. Available at: https://www.fda.gov/Food/GuidanceRegulation/GuidanceDocumentsRegulatoryInformation/IngredientsAdditivesGRASPackaging/ucm078332.htm.

Y. Yu *et al.*, "Evaluation of inherent toxicology and biocompatibility of magnesium phosphate bone cement," *Colloids and Surfaces B: Biointerfaces*, vol. 76, no. 2, pp. 496–504, 2010.

X. Zhang, "Anti-infective coatings reduce device-related infections," in *Antimicrobial/anti-infective materials: principles, applications, and devices*, S. P. Sawan and G. Manivannan, Eds. Lancaster: Technomic Publishing, 2000, pp. 149–180.

# APPENDIX

# List of Abbreviations and Symbols

## List of Abbreviations (alphabetical)

| | |
|---|---|
| 3DP | Three-dimensional printing |
| A | Adenine |
| ADP | Adenosine diphosphate |
| AFM | Atomic force microscopy |
| AIDS | Acquired immune deficiency syndrome |
| APC | Antigen-presenting cell |
| APF | Atomic packing factor |
| ASTM | American Society for Testing and Materials |
| AT III | Antithrombin III |
| ATP | Adenosine triphosphate |
| ATR-FTIR | Attenuated total internal reflectance-Fourier transform infrared |
| BCC | Body-centered cubic |
| BDEDTC | Benzyl N,N-diethyldithiocarbamate-co-styrene |
| BMP-2 | Bone morphogenetic protein-2 |
| C | Cytosine |
| CAD | Computer-aided design |
| CAM | Cell adhesion molecule |
| CBER | Center for Biologics Evaluation and Research |
| CDER | Center for Drug Evaluation and Research |
| cDNA | Complementary DNA |
| CDRH | Center for Devices and Radiological Health |
| ChiP | Chromatin immunoprecipitation |
| CHO | Chinese hamster ovary |
| CS | Chondroitin sulfate |
| CTL | Cytotoxic T lymphocyte |
| CVD | Chemical vapor deposition |
| DAF | Decay-accelerating factor |
| DAPI | Dye (4′,6-diamidino-2-phenylindole) |
| DLVO | Derjaguin, Landau, Verway, and Overbeek |
| DMA | Dynamic mechanical analysis |
| DMAPA AmMeI | Poly(dimethylaminopropyl-acrylamide) |
| DNA | Deoxyribonucleic acid |
| dNTP | Deoxyribonucleotide triphosphates |
| DS | Dermatan sulfate |
| DSC | Differential scanning calorimetry |
| dsDNA | Double-stranded DNA |
| ECM | Extracellular matrix |
| EDS | Energy dispersive X-ray spectroscopy |
| EDTA | Ethylenediaminetetraacetic acid |
| EDXA | Energy-dispersive X-ray analysis |
| EIC | Electrostatic interaction chromatography |
| ELISA | Enzyme-linked immunosorbent assay |
| emf | Electromotive force |
| EPC | Endothelial progenitor cell |
| ER | Endoplasmic reticulum |
| ESCA | Electron spectroscopy for chemical analysis |
| ESC | Embryonic stem cell |
| EtO | Ethylene oxide |
| $F_{ab}$ | Fragment antigen-binding |
| FasL | Fas ligand |
| FACS | Fluorescence-activated cell sorter |
| FBGC | Foreign body giant cell |
| $F_c$ | Fragment crystallizable |
| FCC | Face-centered cubic |
| FDA | Food and Drug Administration |
| FGF | Fibroblast growth factor |
| FTIR | Fourier transform infrared |
| G | Guanine |
| GACI | Generalized arterial calcification of infancy |
| GAG | Glycosaminoglycan |
| GFC | Gel filtration chromatography |
| GP | Glycoprotein |
| GPC | Gel permeation chromatography |
| HA | Hyaluronic acid |
| HCP | Hexagonal close-packed |
| HIC | Hydrophobic interaction chromatography |
| HIP | Hot isostatic pressing |
| HMWK | High molecular weight kininogen |
| HPLC | High-performance liquid chromatography |
| HS | Heparin sulfate |
| Ig | Immunoglobulin |
| IL-1 | Interleukin-1 |
| IL-1ra | IL-1 receptor agonist |
| IL-6 | Interleukin-6 |

| IL-8 | Interleukin-8 |
|---|---|
| IL-12 | Interleukin-12 |
| IND | Investigational New Drug |
| iPSC | Induced pluripotent stem cell |
| IR | Infrared |
| ISO | International Organization for Standardization |
| KS | Keratan sulfate |
| LAL | Limulus Amebocyte Lysate |
| LB-film | Langmuir-Blodgett film |
| LbL | Layer-by-layer |
| LCSM | Laser confocal scanning microscopy |
| LPS | Lipopolysaccharide |
| MAC | Membrane attack complex |
| MATH | Microbial adherence to hydrocarbons |
| MHC | Major histocompatibility complex |
| MIP-1b | Macrophage inflammatory protein-1b |
| MMP | Matrix metalloproteinase |
| mRNA | Messenger RNA |
| MSC | Mesenchymal stem cell |
| MSCRAMM | Microbial surface components recognizing adhesive matrix molecules |
| MTT | 3-(4,5-dimethylthiazolyl-2)-2,5-diphenyltetrazolium bromide) |
| MWNT | Multi-walled nanotube |
| NDA | New Drug Application |
| NK | Natural killer |
| NMR | Nuclear magnetic resonance |
| P/M | Powder metallurgy |
| PAAm | Poly(acrylamide) |
| PAF | Platelet activating factor |
| PAMP | Pathogen-associated molecular pattern |
| PCR | Polymerase chain reaction |
| PDMS | Poly(dimethylsiloxane) |
| PE | Poly(ethylene) |
| PEG | Poly(ethylene glycol) |
| PET | Poly(ethylene terephthalate) |
| PFP | Powder fusion printing |
| PGA | Poly(glycolic acid) |
| $PGI_2$ | Prostaglandin $I_2$ |
| PHEMA | Poly(2-hydroxyethyl methacrylate) |
| PI | Polydispersity index |
| PLA | Poly(lactic acid) |
| PLGA | Poly(lactic-co-glycolic acid) |
| PMA | Premarket Approval |
| PMMA | Poly(methyl methacrylate) |
| PPF | Poly(propylene fumarate) |
| PPP | Platelet poor plasma |
| PS | Poly(styrene) |
| PTFE | Poly(tetrafluoroethylene) |
| PTT | Partial thromboplastin time |
| PVD | Physical vapor deposition |
| RCA | Regulator of complement activation |
| RNA | Ribonucleic acid |
| rRNA | Ribosomal RNA |
| RT-PCR | Reverse transcription-polymerase chain reaction |
| SAL | Sterility assurance level |

| SAM | Self-assembled monolayer |
|---|---|
| SCID | Severe combined immunodeficiency |
| SDS | Sodium dodecyl sulfate |
| SDS-PAGE | SDS-poly(acrylamide) gel electrophoresis |
| SEC | Size exclusion chromatography |
| SEM | Scanning electron microscopy |
| SFF | Solid freeform fabrication |
| SIMS | Secondary ion mass spectrometry |
| SLS | Selective laser sintering |
| SMA | Surface-modifying additive |
| SPM | Scanning probe microscopy |
| ssDNA | Single-stranded DNA |
| SWNT | Single-walled nanotube |
| T | Thymine |
| $T_c$ | Cytotoxic T cell |
| TCP | Tricalcium phosphate |
| TCR | T cell receptor |
| $T_{DTH}$ | Delayed-type hypersensitivity T cell |
| TEM | Transmission electron microscopy |
| TF | Tissue factor |
| TGA | Thermogravimetric analysis |
| TGF-$\beta$ | Transforming growth factor-$\beta$ |
| $T_h$ | Helper T cell |
| TIM | Triosephosphate isomerase |
| TIMP | Tissue inhibitor of metalloproteinase |
| TMS | Tetramethylsilane |
| TNF-$\alpha$ | Tumor necrosis factor-$\alpha$ |
| TPA | Tissue plasminogen activator |
| $T_{reg}$ | Regulatory T cell |
| tRNA | Transfer RNA |
| U | Uracil |
| UHMWPE | Ultra-high molecular weight poly(ethylene) |
| UHV | Ultra-high vacuum |
| UV-VIS | Ultraviolet and visible light spectroscopy |
| vWF | Von Willebrand factor |
| WDS | Wavelength dispersive X-ray spectroscopy |
| WGS | Whole genome sequencing |
| XPS | X-ray photoelectron spectroscopy |
| YAP | Yes-associated protein |
| $\mu$CT | Microcomputed tomography |

## List of Symbols (alphabetical)

| Symbol | Definition | Chapter |
|---|---|---|
| $A$ | Absorbance | 2 |
| $A$ | Amplitude | 2 |
| $A$ | Cross-sectional area | 2 |
| $a$ | Length of a crack on the surface or half the length of an internal crack | 4 |
| $A_0$ | Original cross-sectional area | 4 |
| $A_f$ | Cross-sectional area at fracture | 4 |
| $A_{in}$ | Instantaneous area | 4 |
| $a, b, c$ | Unit cell edge lengths | 2 |
| **b** | Burger's vector | 3 |
| $b, d$ | Specimen dimensions | 4 |

| Symbol | Definition | Chapter |
|---|---|---|
| $C$ | Molar concentration of a compound | 2 |
| $C$ | Concentration of a protein | 8 |
| $C$ | Concentration of a chemical signal | 9 |
| $C$ | Coulombs | 1 |
| $C$ | Concentration of a receptor–ligand complex | 9 |
| $D$ | Diffusivity | 2, 8 |
| $d_{hkl}$ | Interplanar spacing | 2 |
| $E$ | Energy | 1 |
| $E$ | Modulus of elasticity (Young's modulus) | 4 |
| $E_1^0$, $E_2^0$ | Measured potential of materials 1 and 2 | 5 |
| $E_A$ | Attractive energy | 1 |
| $E_b$ | Binding energy | 7 |
| $E_k$ | Kinetic energy | 7 |
| $E_R$ | Repulsive energy | 1 |
| $E_{total}$ | Total energy | 1 |
| $F$ | Force | 1, 4 |
| $F$ | Faraday's constant | 5 |
| $F_A$ | Attractive force between two atoms | 1 |
| $F_C$ | Coulombic force | 1 |
| $F_f$ | Load at fracture | 4 |
| $F_R$ | Repulsive force between two atoms | 1 |
| $F_{total}$ | Total force between two atoms | 1 |
| $G$ | Shear modulus | 4 |
| $G$ | Gibbs free energy | 8, 14 |
| $h$ | Planck's constant | 2, 7 |
| $h$ | Distance between plates | 9 |
| $H$ | Enthalpy | 8 |
| $J$ | Diffusion flux | 2 |
| $k$ | Boltzmann's constant | 2 |
| $k$ | Kinetic rate constant of crystal growth | 3 |
| $k_0$ | Proportionality constant | 1 |
| $k_f$ | Kinetic rate constant of complex formation | 9 |
| $k_r$ | Kinetic rate constant of complex dissociation | 9 |
| $l$ | Thickness of a sample through which light is passed | 2 |
| $L$ | Distance between supports | 4 |
| $L$ | Concentration of a free ligand | 9 |
| $l_0$ | Length of sample before loading (gauge length) | 4 |
| $l_f$ | Length at fracture | 4 |
| $l_i$ | Sample length at any point during a testing procedure (instantaneous length) | 4 |
| $M$ | Mass (or number of atoms) | 2 |
| $M$ | Molecule | 2 |
| $M$ | Flux of cells | 9 |

| Symbol | Definition | Chapter |
|---|---|---|
| $M^*$ | Molecule excited to a new state | 2 |
| $M_c$ | Molecular weight between crosslinks | 2 |
| $M_i$ | Average molecular weight for a chosen molecular weight range | 2 |
| $\bar{M}_n$ | Number-average molecular weight | 2 |
| $\bar{M}_w$ | Weight-average molecular weight | 2 |
| $N$ | Total number of atomic sites | 2 |
| $N$ | Cell number | 9 |
| $n$ | Number characteristic of the mechanism of crystal nucleation and growth | 3 |
| $N_f$ | Fatigue life | 4 |
| $N_i$ | Number of chains with molecular weight $M_i$ | 2 |
| $N_i$ | Number of cycles required for crack initiation | 4 |
| $N_{in}$ | Number of interstitials | 2 |
| $N_p$ | Number of cycles for propagation of a crack to critical size for failure | 4 |
| $N_v$ | Number of vacancies | 2 |
| $N_{v,an}$ | Number of anion vacancies | 2 |
| $N_{v,cat}$ | Number of cation vacancies | 2 |
| $O$ | Origin | 2 |
| $p$ | Persistence time | 9 |
| $q$ | Charge of a single electron | 1 |
| $Q$ | Activation energy for diffusion | 2 |
| $Q$ | Volumetric flow rate | 8, 9 |
| $Q_v$ | Activation energy for formation of a vacancy | 2 |
| $Q_{vi}$ | Activation energy for formation of a vacancy and an interstitial | 2 |
| $Q_{vp}$ | Activation energy for formation of a cation/anion vacancy pair | 2 |
| $r$ | Separation distance between ions 1 and 2 | 1 |
| $r$ | Atomic radius | 2 |
| $r$ | Distance coordinate | 8 |
| $R$ | Gas constant | 2, 5 |
| $R$ | Radius of cylinder | 8 |
| $R$ | Concentration of the free receptor | 9 |
| $r_0$ | Separation distance between two atoms where equilibrium is reached | 1 |
| $r_a$ | Radius of an anion | 2 |
| $r_c$ | Radius of a cation | 2 |
| $s$ | Translocation speed | 9 |
| $S$ | Entropy | 8 |
| $t$ | Time | 2 |
| $T$ | Absolute temperature | 2, 5, 8 |
| $T$ | Torque | 4 |
| $T_c$ | Crystallization temperature | 3 |
| $T_g$ | Glass transition temperature | 3, 4 |
| $T_m$ | Melting temperature | 3, 4 |

| Symbol | Definition | Chapter |
|--------|------------|---------|
| $t_r$ | Time to rupture | 4 |
| $V$ | Velocity | 8 |
| $w$ | Width | 9 |
| $x$ | Distance coordinate | 9 |
| $X(t)$ | Degree of crystallinity of a polymer at time $t$ | 3 |
| $y$ | Distance coordinate | 8 |
| $Z$ | Atomic number | 1 |
| $Z_1, Z_2$ | Valance of ions 1 and 2 | 1 |
| $\%EL$ | % elongation | 4 |
| $\%AR$ | % area reduction | 4 |
| $\alpha, \beta, \gamma$ | Angles between axes of unit cell | 2 |
| $\gamma$ | Shear strain | 4 |
| $\gamma$ | Surface tension (surface free energy) | 7 |
| $\dot{\gamma}$ | Rate of applied (shear) strain, or rate of deformation | 3, 4 |
| $\gamma_c$ | Critical surface tension | 7 |
| $\gamma_{LV}$ | Liquid-vapor surface tension | 7 |
| $\gamma_{SL}$ | Solid-liquid surface tension | 7 |
| $\gamma_{SV}$ | Solid-vapor surface tension | 7 |
| $\Delta E^0$ | Electrochemical potential | 5 |
| $\Delta G$ | Gibbs free energy change | 14 |
| $\Delta G_{ads}$ | Change in $G$ for the entire adsorption process | 8 |
| $\Delta G_{prot}$ | Change in $G$ for a protein during an adsorption process | 8 |
| $\Delta G_{sol}$ | Change in $G$ for a solvent during an adsorption process | 8 |
| $\Delta G_{surf}$ | Change in $G$ for a surface during an adsorption process | 8 |
| $\varepsilon$ | Molar absorption coefficient for a compound at a given wavelength | 2 |
| $\varepsilon$ | Engineering strain | 4 |
| $\dot{\varepsilon}$ | Creep rate | 4 |
| $\varepsilon_a$ | Strain along loading axis | 4 |

| Symbol | Definition | Chapter |
|--------|------------|---------|
| $\varepsilon_t$ | Transverse strain | 4 |
| $\varepsilon_t$ | True strain | 4 |
| $\varepsilon_{yp}$ | Yield point strain | 4 |
| $\eta$ | Viscosity | 3, 4 |
| $\theta$ | Contact angle | 7 |
| $\lambda$ | Wavelength | 2 |
| $\lambda$ | Angle between slip direction and direction of applied force | 4 |
| $\mu$ | Viscosity | 8, 9 |
| $\nu$ | Poisson's ratio | 4 |
| $\nu$ | Frequency | 2, 7 |
| $\rho_a$ | Density of polymer in amorphous form | 3 |
| $\rho_c$ | Density of polymer in crystalline form | 3 |
| $\rho_s$ | Density of polymer sample | 3 |
| $\rho_t$ | Radius of curvature of a crack tip | 4 |
| $\sigma$ | Engineering stress | 4 |
| $\sigma$ | Random motility coefficient | 9 |
| $\sigma_0$ | Overall applied stress | 4 |
| $\sigma_f$ | Fracture strength | 4 |
| $\sigma_m$ | Maximum stress at a crack tip | 4 |
| $\sigma_{mr}$ | Modulus of rupture | 4 |
| $\sigma_t$ | True stress | 4 |
| $\sigma_{uts}$ | Ultimate tensile strength | 4 |
| $\sigma_y$ | Yield strength | 4 |
| $\tau$ | Shear stress | 3, 4, 9 |
| $\tau_{crss}$ | Critical resolved shear stress | 4 |
| $\tau_r$ | Resolved shear stress | 4 |
| $\phi$ | Angle between normal to the slip plane and direction of force | 4 |
| $\chi$ | Chemotactic coefficient | 9 |
| $\perp$ | Edge dislocation | 3 |
| $\circlearrowright$ | Screw dislocation | 3 |

# Index

## A

Abbreviations, 504–505
Acquired immune deficiency
    syndrome (AIDS), 438
Acquired immune response, 391,
    404, 428–429, 438
    adaptivity of, 429
    antibodies, 435–437
    antigen presentation, 429–433
    assays for, 449–452
        *in vitro* assays, 449–451
        *in vivo* assays, 451–452
    B cells, 434–435
        types of, 434–435
    hypersensitivity, 446–449
        and classes of biomaterials,
            448–449
        innate immune responses *vs.*,
            445–446
    lymphocyte maturation,
        433–434
    major histocompatibility
        complex (MHC) molecules
        class I, 430
        class II, 430, 431
        intracellular complexation,
            432–433
        variation and tissue typing,
            430, 432
    specificity of, 429
    T cells, 437–440
        cytotoxic T cells (T$_c$), 440
        helper T cells (T$_h$), 438–440
        natural killer (NK) cells,
            437–438, 440
        types of, 429
    undesired immune responses to,
        445–449
Activation, of neutrophils, 394
Active site, 345
Acute inflammation, 393
    termination of, 400–401
Acute toxicity, 419
Addition polymerization, 67–68,
    101
    termination, 67–68
Adenine, 330
Adenosine diphosphate (ADP), 328
Adenosine triphosphate (ATP), 328
Adhesion models
    cell migration, 360–364
    cell spreading, 360
    DLVO theory, 358–360
        limitations of, 359–360
        other models, 360
Adhesion/spreading assays, 367–368
Adjuvant, 429
Adsorption chromatography
    basic principles, 310
    defined, 310

information provided by,
    310–311
instrumentation, 310
Adsorption, of proteins, 235, 280
Adult stem cells, 351
Advancing contact angle, 262
Affinity chromatography, 96,
    310–314
    basic principles, 310
    information provided by,
        310–311
    instrumentation, 310
Agar diffusion assay, 366
Agglutination, 436, 437, 445
Aggregation, 475, 497
AIDS, *See* Acquired immune
    deficiency syndrome
    (AIDS); Acquired immune
    response
Alginate, 11–12
Allergic reaction, 446
Allergies
    antibody mediated (type II),
        447
    classification of, 446
    IgE mediated (type I), 446–447
    immune complex mediated
        (type III), 447
    T cell mediated (type IV),
        447–448
Alloying, 210–211
Alloys, 45, 100
Alpha$_2$-macroglobulin, 464
α-chains, 338
α-helix, 298, 320
α$_2$-plasmin inhibitor, 464
Alternating copolymers, 69
Alternative pathway, 440, 443–444
    complement system, 440,
        443–444
Aluminum oxides, 10
Ames test, 490
Amino acids, 320, 339
    properties of, 293
    and protein structure, 293
    standard, 293, 294
Amorphous ceramics (glasses), 132
    causes of plastic deformation in,
        150–151
    thermal transitions, 123
Amorphous materials, 34
Amorphous polymers, 117
Amphipathic molecule, 318
Amphiphilic self-assembling
    molecules, 242–243
Amplification, 378
$A_mX_p$ crystals, 52–53
Anaphase, 350
Anatomic barriers, innate
    immunity, 392

Angiogenesis, 408, 409
Anion, 24
Anisotropy, 15
Annealing, 211–212
Annealing twin, 115
Anode, 183
Anodization, 249
Antibodies, 435–437
    agglutination, 437
    classes of, 435–436
    Ig, defined, 435–436
    IgA, 436, 437, 453
    IgD, 435–436
    IgE, 435–436, 449, 454
        mediated, 446–447
    IgG, 435–436, 441, 442, 451
    IgM, 436, 437, 441, 442, 453
    lysis, 437
    mechanisms of antibody action,
        437
    neutralization, 437
    precipitation, 437
    structure of, 435
Antibody, 429
Antibonding molecular orbitals, 27
Anticodon, 355
Antigen-antibody binding, 437
Antigen-presenting cells (APCs),
    399, 430
Antiparallel β-pleated sheet, 295
APCs, *See* Antigen-presenting cells
    (APCs)
Apoptosis, 347
"Armchair" tubes, 54
Arrest and adhesion, of neutrophils,
    394
Artificial joint replacements, 5
ASTM International (ASTM),
    8, 365
ASTM standards, 136, 417, 449
    F86 standard, 194
Atactic configuration, 65
Atom percent composition, 45
Atomic excitation, 20
Atomic force microscopy (AFM),
    255, 276–280
    basic principles, 276–277
    information provided by,
        279–280
    instrumentation, 277–278
Atomic hard-sphere model, 35
Atomic mass, 16
Atomic models, 16–18
Atomic orbitals, 18–20
Atomic packing factor (APF), 35
Atomic subshells (orbitals)
    order of, and Aufbau principle,
        18–20
    shapes of, 18
Atomic weights, 16fn2

Attenuated total internal
    reflectance-Fourier
    transform infrared
    spectroscopy (ATR-FTIR),
    268–270, 281, 309
    basic principles, 268–269
    information provided, 270
    instrumentation, 269–270
Aufbau principle, 30
    defined, 19
    and order of subshells, 18–20
Auger electron spectroscopy, 265
Autoclaving, 229
Avrami equation, 126–127, 213
AX crystals, 50–52

## B

B cells, 434–435
    types of, 434–435
B cells, and antibodies, 435–437
β-pleated sheet, 294, 295, 299, 320
Bacterial attack, 475
Bacterial surface characterization
    surface charge, 482
    surface hydrophobicity, 290,
        481–482
Bacterial surface properties, 476
    cell capsule and biofilm,
        476–479
    gram-positive *vs.* gram-negative
        bacteria, 476, 477
Basophils, 392, 400
Beer-Lambert's law, 83, 315, 317
Belt desmosomes, 335
Bending properties, 155–157
Benign tumors, 486
Bioactive biomaterials, 6
Bioactive glasses, 10, 249
Biochemical assays, 422
Biocompatibility, 417
    defined, 2
    fixation of natural materials,
        230
    processing to improve,
        228–230
    and protein adsorption, 235
    sterilization, 228–230
Biocompatibility assessment, 417
Biodegradable materials, 199–205
    ceramics, 200–201
    and fatigue fracture, 173
    and implants, 166–167
    polymers, 201–205
Biodegradation, defined, 200
Bioerosion, 200
Biofilm, 475, 497
    coating, schematic of, 478
    formation, 475
Biological environment, contribution
    to corrosion, 193

Biological surface modification techniques, 250–254
  covalent biological coatings, 251–253
  immobilized enzymes, 253–254
  non-covalent biological coatings, 253
Biology, 234–237
Biomaterial processing, 13, 30, 209–232
  biocompatibility, 228–230
  ceramics, 213, 219–222
  importance of, 209
  to improve bulk properties, 209–214
  metals, 214–219
  polymers, 213–214, 223–228
Biomaterial-related tumorigenesis, 488–489
Biomaterialist, role of, 2, 9
Biomaterials
  bioactive, 6
  biological response to, 7–8, 30
  bonding, 34
  bulk properties of, 15
  categories of, 9–12, 30
  cell interactions with, 324–387
  ceramics, 10
    structure of, 49–57
  characterization techniques, 15–16
  chemical composition of, 15
  chemical structure of, 34–104
  combination product, 9
  defined, 1–2
  degradation, 13–14, 166–167, 181–207
  degradative properties of, 13–14
  development of field, 3
  device regulation, 9
  drug/biologics regulation, 9
  ECM molecules as, 346–347
  history/current status of the field, 2–3, 30
  immune response to, 428–455
  implantation, and acute inflammation, 390–406
  inert, 6
  infection of, 474–485
  market size, 3
  material characterization, 74–100
  mechanical assessment, 15
  mechanical properties of, 15, 135–180
  metals, 10
    structure of, 35–49
  pathologic calcification, 491–497
  and phagocytosis, 398
  physical properties of, 106–134
    defined, 106–107
  polymers, 10–12
    structure of, 57–73
  processing, 13, 30, 209–232
  product testing and regulatory approval, 8–9
  protein interactions with, 288–323
  qualitative characterization, 15–16
  quantitative characterization, 15–16
  surface characterization of, 258–280
  surface properties of, 14, 234–285
  and thrombosis, 457–472
  tumorigenesis of, 486–491
  undesired immune responses to, 445–449
  in the U.S. healthcare market, 4
  wound healing and, 408–426
Biomaterials science, 2, 30
  future directions, 6–7
Block copolymers, 69
Blood coagulation, 461
  common pathway, 461–462, 470
  extrinsic pathway, 460–461, 470
  intrinsic pathway, 459–460, 470
Blow molding, polymers, 226
Blowing operations, glass, 219
Bohr atomic model, 17–18
Boltzmann's constant, 43, 56
Bond length, 23
Bonding and force-distance curves, 22–23
Bonding energy, 23
Bonding molecular orbitals, 27
Boyden chamber assay, 369–370
Bradykinin, 460
Bragg's law, 77
Branched polymers, 65
Brittle fracture, 167–168, 178
Brittle materials, 143
Bulk, 14
Bulk degradation, 203, 207
Bulk physical properties, 15
Bulk polymerization, 70
Burger's vector, 108–112, 132
  defined, 108

**C**
C1, 442
C1q, 442
C1r, 442
C1s, 442
C3 convertase, 442, 444
C3a, 445
C3b, 443–445
C3bBb, 444
C4b, 444
C4b2a, 442
C4b2a3b, 442
C5 convertase, 442, 444
C5a, 445
C5b, 444
C5b6, 444
C5b67 complex, 444, 445
C5b678 complex, 444
C6, 444
C7, 444
C8, 445
Cadherins, 336–337
Calcium, 459, 460
Calcium chelators, 459
Calcium phosphates, 10
CAM–integrin binding, 338

*Candida* spp., 474
Capillary tube test, 368
Carbon-based materials, 53–54, 100
Carcinogen, 486, 498
Cardinal signs, of inflammation, 393
Cardiovascular area, replacement heart valves, 3
Carrier proteins, 326
Casting, 216
  ceramics, 220
  polymers, 225–226
Cathode, 183
Cation, 24
Cationic polymerization, 67
Cell adhesion molecules (CAMs), 338, 394
Cell adhesion, quantification of, 367
Cell capsule, 476–479
Cell contacts, 335–336
Cell cycle
  interphase, 348
  mitosis, 348–350
Cell differentiation, 350–352
Cell interactions, with biomaterials, 324–387
Cell lysis, 437, 445
Cell-material interactions
  assays determining effects of, 364–380
    adhesion/spreading assays, 367–368
    cytotoxicity assays, 365–367
    DNA and RNA assays, 370–377
    laser confocal scanning microscopy (LCSM), 378–380
    migration assays, 368–370
    protein production assays, 377–378
Cell membrane, 325–327
Cell proliferation, 347–350
Cell-surface interactions, 324–325
Cell survival, 347
Cellular functions, 324–325
  cell–environment interactions affecting, 347–358
Cellular immunity, 429
Cellular structure, 325–338
  cell contacts, 335–336
  cell membrane, 325–327
  cytoskeleton, 327–328
  differentiated (committed) cells, 325
  endoplasmic reticulum (ER), 334
  membrane receptors, 335–338
  mitochondria, 328
  non-differentiated (progenitor) cells, 325
  nucleus, 328–334
  vesicles, 334–335
Center for Biologics Evaluation and Research (CBER), 8, 9, 30
Center for Devices and Radiological Health (CDRH), 8, 30
Center for Drug Evaluation and Research (CDER), 8, 9, 30
Ceramics, 10
  biodegradable, 200–201
  corrosion of, 182–194

crystal structures, 49–54, 100
  $A_mX_p$ crystals, 52–53
  AX crystals, 50–52
  defects in, 55–57
  impurities, 56–57
  point defects, 55–56
  degradation of, 194, 206
  processing, 219–222
    casting, 220
    firing, 220–221
    glass forming techniques, 219–220
    powder processing, 221
    rapid manufacturing of, 221–222
      cold-plotting process, 221, 222
      extrusion printing, 221
      powder fusion printing (PFP), 221
  structure of, 49–57
  thermal transitions, 122
Cesium chloride structure, 52
Chain flexibility, 125
Chain-folded model of crystallinity, 119–120, 132
Chain scission, 195–198
  by hydrolysis, 195
  by oxidation, 195–198
Channel proteins, 326
Charge, and protein adsorption, 291–292
Charpy and Izod impact tests, 168, 169
Chemical carcinogenesis, 486–487, 498
Chemical composition, of biomaterials, 15
Chemical principles, 16–29
  atomic mass units (amu), 16
  atomic models, 16–18
  atomic number (Z), 16
  atomic orbitals, 18–21
  atomic structure, 16, 17
  Bohr atomic model, 17, 18
  covalent bonding, 24–28
  ionic bonding, 22–24
  metallic bonding, 28–29
  periodic table, 20, 22
  secondary forces, 29
  valence electrons, 20, 22
  wave-mechanical model, 17–18
Chemical vapor deposition (CVD), 241
Chemoattractants, 405
"Chiral" tubes, 54
Chitosan, 11, 12
Chondroitin/dermatan sulfate (CS/DS), 341
Chromatids, 350
Chromatin immunoprecipitation (ChIP), 375–376, 382
Chromatography, 15, 75, 101
  adsorption
    basic principles, 310
    defined, 310
    information provided by, 310–311
    instrumentation, 310

affinity, 96, 310–314
    basic principles, 310
    information provided by,
        310–311
    instrumentation, 310
    high-performance liquid (HPLC),
        96–100, 310–314
    basic principles, 96–97
    information provided by,
        99–100
    instrumentation, 97–99
    hydrophobic interaction (HIC),
        482, 498
    ion exchange, 310
    liquid, 310
    normal-phase, 310
    reversed-phase, 310
    size-exclusion (SEC), 96–100
    basic principles, 96–97
    information provided by,
        99–100
    instrumentation, 97–99
Chromophore, 377
Chromosome aberration test, 490
Chronic inflammation, 393,
    412–413, 424
Chronic toxicity, 419
Cis structure, 65
Classical pathway, 440–442
    complement system, 440–442
Clonal populations, activation and
    formation of, 433–434
Closed-shell configuration, 20
Clot dissolution, 464, 470
Coagulation factors, common names
    of, 460 (table)
Cobalt-chromium alloys, 10, 45,
    216, 218
Coble creep, 159
Cold-plotting process, 221, 222
Cold working, 211
Collagen, 11, 12, 338–340
    accumulation in scar tissue, 415
    synthesis
        transcription, 352–353
        translation and post-
            translational modification,
            353–358
Colony-forming assays, 366
Colorimetric assays, 309, 314–316,
    320
Complement system, 440
    alternative pathway, 440,
        443–444
    classical pathway, 440–442
    effects of, 445
    membrane attack complex, 444
    regulation of, 444–445
Composites, 12
Compression molding, polymers,
    225–226
Compression testing, 138
Concentration gradient, 47
Concentration profile, 47
Condensation polymerization,
    68, 101
Constant portion ($F_c$), 435
Contact angle analysis, 259–262
    basic principles, 259–261
    information provided, 262

instrumentation, 261–262
Contact angle hysteresis, 262
Controlled degradation, 181, 206
Conversion coatings, 249
Coordination number, 35
Copolymers, 69–70
    alternating, 69
    block, 69
    graft, 70
    random, 69
Corrosion
    biological environment,
        contribution of, 193
    characterization and prediction
        of, 182
    corrosion control, means of, 194
    crevice, 190–192, 206
    defined, 182
    as electrochemical process, 183
    fatigue, 193
    fretting, 193, 206
    fundamentals of, 183–188
    galvanic, 188, 192, 194
    half-cell potentials, 184–185
    intergranular, 191–192, 206
    mechanical environment,
        contribution of, 192–193
    of metals and ceramics, 182–194
    Nernst equation, 185–188, 206
    oxidation-reduction reactions,
        183–184
    pitting, 191, 206
    processing parameters,
        contribution of, 190–192
Corrosion fatigue, 173
Coulombic force, 24
Covalent biological coatings,
    251–253
Covalent bonds, 101
    atomic orbitals and
        hybridization, 24–27
    defined, 24
    mixed bonds, 27–28
    molecular orbitals, 27
Covalent surface coatings, 237–244,
    281
    chemical vapor deposition
        (CVD), 241
    physical vapor deposition (PVD),
        241–242
    plasma treatment, 239–240
    radiation grafting/photografting,
        242–243
    self-assembled monolayers
        (SAMs), 243–244
Crazing, polymers, 168–169
Creep, 157–159, 177
    Coble, 159
    creep curves, 158–159
    dislocation, 159
    mathematical models of,
        161–162
    Maxwell model, schematic of,
        162–163, 177
    molecular causes of
        ceramics, 159–160
        polymers, 160
    Nabarro-Herring, 159
    and stress relaxation, 160–161
    viscoelastic behavior

mathematical models of,
    161–162
    Maxwell model, schematic
        of, 162–163
    Voigt model, 163–165
    Voigt model, 163–165, 178
Crevice corrosion, 190–192, 206
Critical area, 246
Critical resolved shear stress, 149
Crosslinked polymers, 65
Crystal structures
    ceramics, 49–54
        $A_mX_p$ crystals, 52–53
        AX crystals, 50–52
        defects in, 55–57
        impurities, 56–57
        point defects, 55–56
    defects in, 43–45
    impurities, 44–45
    metals, 35–38
        body-centered cubic (BCC)
            structure, 37–38
        defects in, 43–45
        face-centered cubic (FCC)
            structure, 35–37
        hexagonal close-packed
            (HCP) unit cells, 38
        solid state diffusion, 45–49
    planes in, 39
    point defects, 43–44
    polymers, 72
Crystal systems, 38–43
    lattice parameters/angles, 38
Crystalline materials, 34
Crystallinity, 15
    chain-folded model of, 119–120,
        132
    characteristics of dislocations,
        110
    deformation, 110–113
    edge dislocations, 107–108
    and linear defects, 107–113, 132
    mixed dislocations, 108–110
    and planar defects, 113–116, 132
        external surface, 113–114
        grain boundaries, 114–116,
            132
    polymer crystals
        linear defects, 120–122
        planar and volume defects,
            122
    and polymeric materials,
        117–122
    chain-folded model of
        crystallinity, 119–120
    defects in, 120–122
    linear defects, 120–122
    percent crystallinity,
        117–119, 133
    planar and volume defects,
        122
    screw dislocations, 108–110
    thermal analysis, 128–132
    thermal transitions, 122–128
        amorphous ceramics
            (glasses), 123
        metals and crystalline
            ceramics, 122
        polymers, 123–126
        viscous flow, 122

and volume defects, 116–117, 132
Crystallization temperature,
    125–126
Cubic system, 39, 40, 100
Cysteine, 293
Cytokines, 396, 398, 405, 451, 470
    actions of, 396
    $T_h$ cells, 439, 440
Cytokinesis, 350
Cytoplasm, 327
Cytosine, 330
Cytoskeleton, 327–328
Cytotoxic T cells ($T_c$), 440
Cytotoxic T lymphocytes (CTLs),
    440
Cytotoxicity, 364, 411
Cytotoxicity assays
    agar diffusion, 366
    colony-forming, 367
    direct contact, 365–366
    elution (extract), 366–367
    indirect contact, 366

**D**

Dashpot, 162, 164
Decay-accelerating factor (DAF), 445
Deformation, 110–113
    of polycrystalline materials, 149
Deformation twin, 115
Degradation, 13–14, 166–167,
    181–207
    assays for extent of, 205
    of biodegradable materials,
        199–205
    in the biological environment,
        181–182
    bulk, 203, 207
    of ceramics, 194
    environmental stress cracking,
        198–199
    enzyme-catalyzed, 199
    factors influencing rate of,
        204–205
    hydrolytic, 201, 204
    influence on mechanical
        properties, 166–167, 178
    mechanisms, 204
    of metals, 182–194
    of polymers, 194–199
    porosity, 199
    quantification of, 205
    surface, 203
Dehydration, and protein
    adsorption, 291
Dentin, 365
Deoxyribose sugar, in DNA, 330
Dermal layer, skin, 414
Deshielded nucleus, 90
Desmosomes, 335
Destructive interference, 75
Diapedesis, 394
Differential scanning calorimeter,
    components of, 128–130
Differential scanning calorimetry
    (DSC), 128–133
    basic principles, 128
    heat-flux, 128, 129
    information provided by,
        130–132
    instrumentation, 128–130

Differential scanning calorimetry
(DSC) (*continued*)
power-compensated, 128, 129
types of, 129
Differentiated (committed) cells, 325
Diffractometer, 78
Diffusion, 101
defined, 45
interstitial, 46
mechanisms, 46
modeling of, 46–48
solid state, 45–49
steady-state, 47–48
vacancy, 46
Diffusion flux (*J*), 47
Diffusivity, 48
Dip-pen nanolithography, 255
Direct contact assay, 365–366
Direct-write photolithography, 255
Disintegration, 347
Dislocation creep, 159
Dislocation glide, 111, 112
Dislocations
characteristics of, 110
edge, 107–108
mixed, 108–110
screw, 108–110
Dispersion, 475–476, 497
Disproportionation, 67
DLVO theory, 358–360, 479
limitations of, 359–360
other models, 360
DNA assays, 370–377
DNA (deoxyribonucleic acid)
base–base interactions in, 331
codons, 329
defined, 330
encoding, of protein polymer, 69
microarrays, 373
purines, 330
pyrimidines, 330
RNA sequencing, 373–375
structure of, 328–332
sugar backbone of, 331
synthesis test, 489
DNA polymerases, 353
Drawing
glass, 220
metals, 215–216
Drug/biologics regulation, 9
Drug-eluting cardiovascular stent, 8
Ductile failure, 167–168, 178
Ductile-to-brittle transition
temperature, 168
Ductility, 143
Dunn chamber, 369
Dynamic contact angle
measurements, 262

**E**

E-beam lithography, 255, 274
Edge dislocations, 107–108
Effector cells, 434, 438
Elastic deformation, 139, 177
molecular causes of, 141
and stress-strain curves, 139–141
Elastic fibers, 340
Elasticity, 148
Elastin, 11, 154–155, 338, 340
Elastomers, 11, 148, 154–155

Electrochemical cell, 183
Electrochemical testing, 205
Electromotive force (emf) series,
184–185
Electron configuration, of atom, 19
Electron microscopy, 272–276,
421–422, 424
Electron spectroscopy for chemical
analysis (ESCA), 75,
265–268, 281
basic principles, 265–266
information provided, 268
instrumentation, 266–267
Electron spin resonance, 74
Electronegative elements, 20
Electrophoretic mobility test, 482
Electropositive elements, 20
Electrospinning, 224
Electrostatic interaction
chromatography (EIC),
482, 498
ELISA, *See* Enzyme-linked
immunosorbent assay
(ELISA)
Elongation phase, protein assembly,
355–356
Elution (extract) assays, 366–367
Elution time, fractionation, 311
Embryonic stem cells, 350
Emulsion polymerization, 71
Encapsulation, 413, 424
Endocytosis, 335
Endogenous antigens, 429, 439
Endoplasmic reticulum (ER), 334
Endothelial cells, 469
Endothelium, 464–465, 470
Endurance limit, 173
Energy-dispersive X-ray analysis
(EDXA), 275
Energy dispersive X-ray spectroscopy
(EDS), 75
Engineering strain, 137
Engineering stress and strain, 144
*Enterobacteriaceae*, 474
Enthalpy, 289
Entropy, 289
Environmental stress cracking,
198–199
Enzyme-catalyzed degradation, 199
Enzyme factor D, 444
Enzyme-linked immunosorbent
assay (ELISA), 309, 310,
317–318, 320, 377, 451
Enzymes, 345–346
Eosinophils, 392, 400
Epidermal layer, skin, 414
Epitheloid cells, 412
Epitope, 429
ER, *See* Endoplasmic reticulum (ER)
Ethylene oxide sterilization, 229
Evanescent wave, 269
Excitation, 74
Excited state, 20
Exocytosis, 334
Exogenous antigens, 432, 433, 439
Extensometer, 176
Extracellular environment, 338–347
collagen, 338–340
elastin, 340
glycoproteins, 341–343

matrix remodeling, 345–346
molecules, as biomaterials, 346
proteoglycans, 341–343
Extracellular matrix (ECM)
interactions, 335
Extract assays, 366–367
Extravasation, 394
Extrusion, 413, 424
metals, 215
polymers, 223–224
printing methods, ceramics,
221, 222

**F**

Factor V, 460, 462
Factor VII, 460, 461, 463
Factor VIII, 460
Factor IX, 460
Factor X, 460, 461
Factor Xa, 460, 461
Factor XI, 460
Factor XIa, 460
Factor XII, 459–461
Factor XIIa, 459–460
Factor XIII, 460, 462
Factor XIIIa, 461, 462
Fatigue corrosion, 193
Fatigue, defined, 170
Fatigue failure, stages of, 170–171
Fatigue fracture, 170
Fatigue life, 171, 172
factors affecting, 172–173
Fatigue limit, 171
Fatigue strength, 171–172
Fatigue testing, 171–172
FDA device categories, biological
testing, 418
Fiber spinning, polymers, 224–225
Fibers, 340
Fibrils, 340
Fibrin, 11, 12, 462
Fibrin monomers, 461, 462, 470
Fibrinogen, 394, 458–461
Fibrinolysis, 464
Fibroblasts, 409, 415
Fibronectin, 341, 344
Fibrous encapsulation, 411–412,
424
Fick's first law of diffusion, 48
Fillers, 173
Filter diffusion test, 366
Fimbriae, 476
Firing ceramics, 220–221
Flexural strength, 155
Flow cytometry, 402, 405
Fluorescent assays, 309, 316–317,
320
basic principles, 316
information provided by, 317
instrumentation, 316–317
Fluorophore, 316
Focal adhesions, 335
Food and Drug Administration
(FDA), 8, 9, 448
Foreign body carcinogenesis, 487,
498
Foreign body giant cells (FBGCs),
410–411
Foreign body reaction, 410–411,
424

Foreign body tumorigenesis
with large implants, 487
with nanomaterials, 487–488
timeline for, 487–488
Forging, 215
Forming, polymers, 223–225
Fractionation, 311
Fracture strength, 143
Frenkel defect, 56, 101
Fretting corrosion, 193, 206

**G**

Galvanic cell, 183
Galvanic corrosion, 188
and stress, 192
Galvanic series, 185
in seawater, 186 (table)
Gamma counter, 318
Gamma-ray emission, 74
Gap junctions, 335
Gaseous polymerization, 72
Gaseous porogens, 117
Gel filtration chromatography
(GFC), 97, 101
Gel permeation chromatography
(GPC), 97–99, 101
Gene expressions, alterations to, 347
Generalized arterial calcification of
infancy (GACI), 494
Genotoxicity, 489, 498
Glass-ceramics, 221
Glass forming techniques, 219–220
Glass transition temperature, 123,
132
Glasses, 10
Glycocalyx, 327, 465, 470
Glycoproteins, 341–343
fibronectin, 341, 344
laminin, 341, 344
Glycosaminoglycans (GAGs), 11,
341
Gold, 10
Golgi apparatus, 334
GP IIb/IIIa, 458
Graft copolymers, 70
Grain boundaries, 114–116, 132
Grain size refinement, 211
Gram-positive bacteria, 474, 497
gram-negative bacteria *vs.*, 476,
477
Granular tissue, formation of,
408–410
Granulation tissue, 408, 424
Granulocytes, 392, 394, 400, 404
Granulomas, 412
Graphite, 53
Ground state, 20
Guanine, 330

**H**

Half-cell, 183
Half-cell potentials, 184–185
Hapten, 429
Heart-lung machines, 5
Heat extraction, 212
Heat-flux differential scanning
calorimetry (DSC), 128,
129
Helmholtz-Smoluchowski equation,
482

Helper T cells (T_h), 438–440
Hematopoietic stem cells, 351
Hemidesmosomes, 335
Hemocompatibility, 465–469, 470
    general testing concerns,
        465–466
    *in vitro* assessment, 466–467,
        470
        dynamic coagulation
            experiments, 467
        static coagulation
            experiments, 467
    *in vivo* assessment, 468–469
Hemoglobin, schematic of the
    structures of, 296
Hemostasis, 457
    coagulation cascade, 459–463
    coagulation factors, common
        names of, 460 (table)
    endothelium, 464–465
    hemocompatibility, tests for,
        465–469
    and platelets, 457–459
Hemostatic mechanisms, 457
Heparan sulfate (HS), 341, 465, 470
    interaction of fibroblast growth
        factor (FGF) with, 345
Heparin, 463
Heparin/antithrombin III (AT III)
    complex, 463
Heterodimers, 338
Heterophilic binding, 336
Hexagonal system, 39, 40, 100
High-angle grain boundaries,
    114
High-molecular weight kininogen
    (HMWK), 460
High-performance liquid
    chromatography (HPLC),
    96–100, 310–314
    basic principles, 96–97
    information provided by,
        99–100
    instrumentation, 97–99
Histamines, 447
Homeostasis, 390
Homophilic binding, 336
Homopolymers, 69–70
Hooke's law, 139, 155, 162, 164,
    176
Hot isostatic pressing (HIP), 217
Hot working, defined, 214
Hume-Rothery rules, 44
Humoral immunity, 429
Hund's rule, 19, 30
Hyaluronic acid (HA), 11, 12, 341
Hybrid orbitals, 24–25
Hybridization, 24–26
Hydrogels, 12, 72–73, 101
Hydrogen bond, 29
Hydrolytic degradation, 201, 204
Hydrophilic materials, 14
Hydrophilic, use of term, 235
Hydrophobic interaction
        chromatography (HIC),
        482, 498
Hydrophobic materials, 14
Hydrophobic, use of term, 235
Hydrophobicity, 14, 30, 235–236,
    291

Hypersensitivity, 446–449
    antibody mediated (type II), 447
    and classes of biomaterials,
        448
    delayed-type, 447
    IgE mediated (type I), 446–447
    immune complex mediated (type
        III), 447
    T cell mediated (type IV),
        447–448
Hypersensitivity reaction, 446
Hysteresis, 262

**I**

IgM, 436, 437, 441, 442
IL-8, 393, 395
Immobilized enzymes, 253–254
Immunoglobulin glycoprotein, 429
Immunohistochemistry, 377–378,
    421
Immunostaining, 377–378
    indirect method of, 378
Immunotoxicity, 428–429
Implant-associated infection,
    480–481
Implantation of plastics (synthetic
    polymers) in humans, 3
Impurities, 44–45
Impurity diffusion, 45
*In vitro* assays, 401, 405
    for acquired immune response,
        449–451
    leukocyte assays, 401–402
    response of endothelial cells,
        tests for, 402
    tissue-engineered constructs to
        examine inflammatory
        response, 402
*In vitro* experiments, 7
*In vivo* assays, 416–423
    for acquired immune response,
        451–452
    animal models development,
        417, 424
        biomaterial dose and
            administration, 419–420
        choice of animal, 417
        choice of implant site,
            418–419
        inclusion of proper controls,
            420
        length of study, 419
*In vivo* tissue compatibility
    evaluation, 416
Indirect contact assays, 366
Indirect method, of immunostaining,
    378
Induced pluripotent stem cell (iPSC),
    350, 381
Inert biomaterials, 6
Infection
    bacterial adhesion, interactions
        involved in, 479–480
    bacterial surface characterization
        surface charge, 482
        surface hydrophobicity,
            481–482
    bacterial surface properties, 476
        cell capsule and biofilm,
            476–479

biomaterial surface properties,
        479
    categories of, 474
    common pathogens, 474
    *ex vivo* infection models, 485
    experiments, techniques for,
        481–485
    implant-associated, 480–481
    media properties, 479
    stages of, 475
    steps to, 475–476
    *in vitro* bacterial adhesion and
        killing, 483–484
    *in vivo* infection models, 485
Inflammasome, 398
Inflammation, 393
    acute, 393
        termination of, 400–401
    chronic, 393, 412–413, 424
    clinical signs of, 393–394,
        404–405
    *in vitro* assays, 401
        leukocyte assays, 401–402
        response of endothelial cells,
            tests for, 402
        tissue-engineered constructs
            to examine inflammatory
            response, 402
    *in vivo* assays, 416–423
Inflammatory effects, mediators
    of, 393
Infrared absorption, 74
Infrared (IR) spectroscopy, 83–89
    basic principles, 83–85
    Fourier-transform techniques
        (FTIR), 86, 87
    information provided by, 86–89
    instrumentation, 85–86
    IR frequencies absorbed by
        chemical groups, 85
Initiation, addition polymerization,
    67
Initiation phase, tumorigenesis, 486,
    498
Initiation stage, protein assembly,
    355
Injection molding, polymers, 226
Ink-jet printing, 228, 255–256
Innate (nonspecific) immunity,
    390–391
    sources of, 392–393
Inner membrane, 328
"Inside-out" signaling, 335
Integration, 413, 424
Integrins, 337, 338, 465
Interdiffusion, 45
Intergranular corrosion, 191–192, 206
Intermediate filaments, 327
Internal standard, 91
International Organization for
    Standardization (ISO), 8,
    365, 419, 449, 489
Interpenetrating network hydrogels,
    73
Interstitial diffusion, 46
Interstitial space, 393, 404
Intrinsic angular momentum (spin),
    19
Investigational New Drug (IND)
    application, 9

Investment casting, 216
Ion beam implantation, 247–249
Ion beam lithography, 255
Ion exchange chromatography, 310
Ionic bonding, 22–24
    characteristics of the ionic bond,
        23–24
Isoelectric point, defined, 291
Isotactic configuration, 65
Isotopes, 16fn2

**K**

Kallikrein, 459
Kelvin model, *See* Voigt model
Keratan sulfate (KS), 341
Kinins, 394, 405

**L**

Laminin, 341, 344
Langmuir-Blodgett film (LB film),
    245–246, 281
Langmuir trough, 245
Laser-assisted bioprinting, 227–228
Laser confocal scanning microscopy
        (LCSM)
    basic principles, 378–379
    information provided by, 380
    instrumentation, 379–380
Lasers, and surface modification,
    249–250
Latency period, tumorigenesis, 486,
    498
Lateral interactions, 305
Lattice parameters, 38, 100
Lattice points, 38
Lattice strain, 44
Lattice structures, 38
Layer-by-layer coatings, 246
Leukocytes, 391
    formation of, 392
    life span of, 392
    macrophages, 397–400
    monocytes, 397
    types of, 392
Ligands, 336–338
Light microscopy, 262–265, 281
    basic principles, 262–263
    information provided, 265
    instrumentation, 263–264
Limiting clot formation, means of,
    463–464
Limulus Amebocyte Lysate (LAL)
    assay, 485
Linear defects, and crystallinity,
    107–113, 132
Linear polymers, 65
Liquid chromatography, 310
Load cell, 176
Lost-wax casting, 216
Lumen, 334
Lymphocytes, 391, 392, 404
Lysis, 437, 445
Lysosomes, 335
Lysyl oxidase, 340

**M**

Machining, 219
Macrophages, 397, 405, 408, 470
    actions of, 397–399
        chemical mediator secretion,
            398–399

Macrophages (*continued*)
  phagocytosis, 398
  role as antigen-presenting
    cell (APC), 399
  subtypes, 399–400
Major histocompatibility complex
    (MHC) molecules
  class I, 430
  class II, 430, 431
  intracellular complexation,
    432–433
  variation and tissue typing, 430,
    432
Malignant transformation, routes
    of, 498
Malignant tumors, 486
Mass per mole, 16
Mass spectrometer, schematic of, 95
Mass spectrometry, 92–96
  basic principles, 92–94
  information provided by, 95–96
  instrumentation, 94–95
  secondary ion mass spectrometry
    (SIMS), 96, 270–272, 281
Material characterization, 74–100
  high-performance liquid
    chromatography (HPLC),
    96–100
  infrared (IR) spectroscopy,
    83–89
  mass spectrometry, 92–96
  nuclear magnetic resonance
    spectroscopy (NMR),
    89–92
  ultraviolet and visible (UV-VIS)
    light spectroscopy, 79–83
  X-ray diffraction, 75–79
Matrix metalloproteinases (MMPs),
    346
Matrix remodeling, 345–346
Matrix space, 328
Maxwell model, schematic of,
    162–163, 177
Mechanical analysis, 175–176
Mechanical environment, and
    corrosion, 192–193
  fatigue corrosion, 193
  fretting corrosion, 193, 206
  stress and galvanic corrosion, 192
  stress corrosion cracking,
    192–193
Mechanical properties
  of biomaterials, 15, 135–180
  influence of porosity and
    degradation on, 166–167
  methods to improve, 173–174
Mechanical testing, 422–423
  basic principles, 175
  bending properties, 155–157
  compression testing, 138
  destructive, 175
  fatigue and fatigue testing,
    170–173
  fracture and failure, 167–170
  information provided by, 176
  instrumentation, 175–176
  methods of, 136–167
  methods to improve, 173–175
  plastic deformation, 141–155, 176
  shear testing, 139

tensile testing, 137–138
  time-dependent properties,
    157–165, 177
  types of properties, 135–136
Mechanical testing frame, 136
Megakaryocytes, 392, 469
Melting point, 122, 132
Membrane attack complex (MAC),
    444
Membrane receptors, 335–338
  cell contacts, 335–336
  types of, 336–338
Memory cells, 434
Mesenchymal stem cells (MSCs),
    351, 352
Mesothelioma, 487
Messenger RNA (mRNA), 332,
    352–356
Metal-catalyzed oxidation, 197
Metallic bonds, 28–29
  attractive force, 29
  and electron sharing, 28
Metals, 10
  casting, 216
  corrosion of, 182–194
  crystal structures, 35–38, 100
    body-centered cubic (BCC)
      structure, 37–38
    defects in, 43–45
    face-centered cubic (FCC)
      structure, 35–37
    hexagonal close-packed
      (HCP) unit cells, 38
    solid state diffusion, 45–49
  crystal systems, 38–43
  degradation of, 182–194
  drawing, 215–216
  extrusion of, 215
  forging, 215
  forming, 214–216
  investment casting, 216
  machining, 219
  powder processing, 216–218
  processing, 210–219
    alloying, 210–211
    annealing, 211–213
    grain size refinement, 211
    precipitation hardening, 213
    strain hardening, 211
  rapid manufacturing of, 218
  rolling, 215
  sand casting, 216
  structure of, 35–49
  thermal transitions, 122
  welding, 218–219
Metaphase, 350
MHC molecules, *See* Major
    histocompatibility complex
    (MHC) molecules
Microbial adherence to
    hydrocarbons (MATH),
    481, 498
Microbial surface components
    recognizing adhesive
    matrix molecules
    (MSCRAMMs), 480
Microcomputed tomography (μCT),
    495–496
Microcontact printing, 256, 257
Microfluidics, 257–258

Microtubules, 327
Microwave absorption, 74
Migration, of neutrophils, 394–395
Miller indices, 38–41, 75, 100
Mineral crystals, 343
MIP-1b, 395
Mitochondria, 328
Mitotic spindle, 350
Mixed bonds, 27–28
Mixed dislocations, 108–110
Modulus of elasticity, 139
Modulus of rupture, 155
Mole, 16
Molecular dipole, 29
Molecular orbitals, 27
Monoclinic system, 39, 40, 100
Monocytes, 392, 397
Monomers, 301
Morphology, 351
Mucins, 338
Mucin–selectin interactions, 338
Multipotent stem cells, 350
Multi-walled nanotubes (MWNTs),
    54
Mutagenesis, 486
Mutual irradiation, 242
Myofibroblasts, 409

**N**

Nabarro-Herring creep, 159
Nanocomposite hydrogel, 73
Natural killer (NK) cells, 437–438,
    440, 450
Naturally derived polymers, 11
Necrosis, 347
Neoplasia, 486
Neoplasm, 486
Neovascularization, 408
Nernst equation, 185–188, 206
Network polymers, 65
Neutralization, 437, 445
Neutrophils, 392, 394, 400, 405,
    461
  actions of, 395–397
    phagocytosis, 396
    respiratory burn, 396
    secretion of chemical
      mediators, 396–397
  activated, 397
  migration of, 394–395
New Drug Application (NDA), 9
Next-generation sequencing,
    373–375
Non-covalent biological coatings,
    253
Non-covalent surface coatings,
    244–249, 281
  bioactive glasses, 249
  conversion coatings, 249
  ion beam implantation, 247–249
  Langmuir-Blodgett film (LB
    film), 245–246
  layer-by-layer coatings, 246
  plasma treatment, 249
  solution coatings, 245
  surface-modifying additives
    (SMAs), 247
Non-differentiated (progenitor)
    cells, 325
Nonself molecules, 432

Normal-phase chromatography, 310
Nuclear magnetic resonance
    spectroscopy (NMR), 74,
    89–92
  basic principles, 89–90
  information provided by, 92
  instrumentation, 90–92
Nucleic acid, 329
Nucleolus, 328
Nucleus, 328–334
  chromatin, 328
  DNA, structure of, 328–332
  nuclear envelope, 328
  RNA, structure of, 332–334
  structure and function of, 328
Nylon 6,6, glass transition
    temperature of, 125

**O**

Open-shell configuration, 20
Opsonin, 442
Opsonization, 445
Opsonized particle, 445
Orbitals, *See* Atomic subshells
    (orbitals)
Organelle, 325
Organ-on-a-chip, 402
Orthopedic hip implant, 5
Orthorhombic system, 39, 40, 100
Outer membrane, 328
"Outside-in" signaling, 335
Oxidation, 183
  defined, 183
  metal-catalyzed, 197
Oxidation-reduction reactions,
    183–184

**P**

Parallel β-pleated sheet, 294
Parison, 219
Pascals (Pa), 137
Passivation, 188
  and Pourbaix diagrams,
    188–190, 206
Pathogen-associated molecular
    patterns (PAMPs), 396,
    405
Pathologic calcification, 491–497
  biomaterials, clinical
    consequences of, 492
  defined, 491
  experiments, 493–497
  extrinsic, 492
  intrinsic, 492
  mechanism of, 492–493
  reduction of, 493
  sample assessment, 494–496
  *in vitro* models, 493–494
  *in vivo* models, 494
Pauli exclusion principle, 19, 20, 30
Peptide bonds, 293
Peptidoglycan, 476, 477
  chemical structure of, 477
Percent crystallinity, 117–119, 133
Periodic table, 20, 22
Phagocytic cells, innate immunity,
    393
Phenotype, 351
Phospholipids, 325
Photografting, 242–243
Photolithography, 256

Physical properties, 15
Physical vapor deposition (PVD), 241–242
Physicochemical surface modification methods, 237–250, 281
    covalent interactions, 237–244, 281
        chemical vapor deposition (CVD), 241
        physical vapor deposition (PVD), 241–242
        plasma treatment, 239–240
        radiation grafting/photografting, 242–243
        self-assembled monolayers (SAMs), 243–244
    laser methods, 249–250
    non-covalent interactions, 244–249, 281
        bioactive glasses, 249
        conversion coatings, 249
        ion beam implantation, 247–249
        Langmuir-Blodgett film (LB film), 245–246, 281
        layer-by-layer coatings, 246
        plasma treatment, 249
        solution coatings, 245
        surface-modifying additives (SMAs), 247
Physiologic barriers, innate immunity, 392
Piezoelectric printing, 228
Pili, 476
Pitting corrosion, 191, 206
Planar defects
    and crystallinity, 113–116, 132
        external surface, 113–114
        grain boundaries, 114–116
Planck's constant, 79
Plasma-assisted chemical vapor deposition, 241
Plasma-assisted PVD techniques, 241
Plasma cells, 392, 434–435
Plasma, defined, 239
Plasma discharge, 239–240
    treatments
        advantages/disadvantages of, 240
        schematic of, 240
Plasma environment, 239
Plasma polymerization, 72
Plasma spray coatings, 240
Plasma torch, 240
Plasma treatment, 239–240, 249
Plasminogen, 464
Plastic deformation, 141–145, 176
    causes of
        amorphous polymers and ceramics (glasses), 150–151
        metals and crystalline ceramics, 148–150
        polymers, 151–152
        semi-crystalline polymers and elastomers, 152–155
    defined, 141
    molecular causes of, 148
    and stress-strain curves, 141–145

Platelets, 469
    activation, 458–459
        means of, 458
        sequelae of, 458–459
    adhesion, 458
    characteristics and functions, 458
    and hemostasis, 457–459
    platelet–platelet bridging, 458
Platinum, 10
Pluripotent cells, 350
Point defects, 43–44
Poisson's ratio, 140
Polar molecules, 29
Poly(2-hydroxyethyl methacrylate) (PHEMA), 11, 72, 73
Poly(anhydride), 202, 203
Polycrystalline ceramics, 220–221
Poly(cyanoacrylate), 202
Poly(dimethylsiloxane) (PDMS), 11, 256–258
Poly(dioxanone), 202
Poly(ε-caprolactone), 11, 202
Poly(ethylene), 11, 67, 117
    glass transition temperature, 125
Poly(ethylene glycol), 11, 68
Poly(ethylene terephthalate), 11
    glass transition temperature, 125
Poly(ethyleneglycol) (PEG), 73, 236
Poly(hydroxybutyrate), 202
Poly(hydroxyvalerate), 202
Poly(glycolic acid), 202
Poly(isoprene), 11
Poly(lactic acid), 202
Poly(lactic-co-glycolic acid) (PLGA), 11, 202, 204–205
Polymer production via genetic engineering, 68–69
Polymer spherulites, 121
Polymerase chain reaction (PCR), 370–372
Polymerization, 67–68, 101
    addition, 67–68, 101
    bulk, 70
    cationic, 67
    condensation, 68, 101
    degree of, 59
    emulsion, 71
    gaseous, 72
    methods of, 70–72
    plasma, 72
    solid-state, 72
    solution, 70
    suspension, 71
Polymers, 10–12, 30
    addition polymerization, 67–68
    amorphous, 117
    biodegradable, 201–205
    branched, 65
    causes of plastic deformation in, 151
    composites, 12
    condensation polymerization, 68
    configuration, 63
    conformations, 63–65
        defined, 63
    crazing, 168–169
    creep curves for, 158–159
    crosslinked, 65
    crystal structures, 72

    degradation of, 194–199, 206
        chain scission, 195–198
            primary means, 195
    degree of polymerization, 59
    elastomers, 11–12
    fiber spinning, 224–225
    forming, 223–225
    hydrogels, 12
    impurities, 72
    linear, 65
    molecular weight determination, 59
    naturally derived, 11
        synthetic vs., 11–13, 30
    network, 65
    number-average molecular weight, 61
    point defects, 72
    polydispersity index (PI), 61
    polymer production via genetic engineering, 68–69
    processing, 223–228
        blow molding, 226
        casting, 225–226
        compression molding, 225–226
        extrusion, 223–224
        fiber spinning, 224–225
        forming, 223–225
        injection molding, 226
        rapid manufacturing of, 226–228
        thermoplasts vs. thermosets, 223
    repeat units, 57–59
    resonance stabilization of radicals, 197
    structure of, 57–73
    synthesis of, 67–69
    synthetic, 11, 30
    thermal transitions, 123–126
    thermoplastic, 223
    thermosetting, 223
    weight-average molecular weight, 61
Poly(methyl methacrylate), 11, 68
Poly(orthoester), 202
Polypeptides, 293
Poly(phosphazene), 202
Poly(propylene), 11, 67
    glass transition temperature, 125
Poly(propylene fumarate), 202
Poly(styrene), 67, 117
Poly(tetrafluoroethylene), 11
    glass transition temperature, 125
Poly(trimethylene carbonate), 202
Poly(vinyl chloride), 67
Porogens, 116–117
Porosity, 199
    influence on mechanical properties, 166–167
Post-translational processing, 356
Pourbaix diagrams, and passivation, 188–190, 206
Powder fusion printing (PFP), 221
Powder metallurgy (P/M), 216–218
Powder processing
    ceramics, 221
    metals, 216–218

Powder X-ray diffractometer, schematic of, 78
Power-compensated differential scanning calorimetry (DSC), 128, 129
Precipitation, 437, 445
Precipitation hardening, 213
Prekallikrein, 459–460
Premarket Approval (PMA) process, 9
Premarket Notification 510(k) procedure, 9
Preneoplastic cells, 487
Pressing, 219
Primary antibody, 317
Primary bonds, 22
Primary creep, 158
Procollagen, 339–340, 356
Product testing and regulatory approval, 8–9
Proline, 293
Prometaphase, 350
Promotion phase, tumorigenesis, 486, 498
Propagation, addition polymerization, 67
Prophase, 350
Prostaglandin $I_2$ ($PGI_2$), 465
Protein adsorption, 235, 272, 280, 320
    and biocompatibility, 235
    desorption and exchange, 306–308
    Gibbs free energy ($G$) and, 289–290
    kinetics, 304–305
    protein transport, 302–305
    reversibility of, 305–309
    reversible and irreversible binding, 305–306, 320
    surface properties governing, 235–237
    system properties governing, 290–293
    thermodynamics of, 288–293
Protein corona, 488
Protein desorption, 305–309
Protein stability, 293
Protein structure, 293–302
    amino acid chemistry, 293, 294
    primary structure, 293, 320
    quaternary structure, 301–302, 320
    secondary structure, 293–300, 320
    tertiary structure, 300–301, 320
Protein synthesis, 352–358
Proteins, 314–315
    assays for, 309–320
        colorimetric assays, 309, 314–316
        enzyme-linked immunosorbent assay (ELISA), 309, 310, 317–318
        fluorescent assays, 316–317
        Western blotting, 309, 318–320
    carrier, 326
    channel, 326
    transmembrane, 325–326

Proteoglycan receptors, 338
Proteoglycans, 338, 341–343, 409
Proteomics, 377, 383
Prothrombin, 460–462, 470
Prothrombin activator, 461
*Pseudomonas aeriginosa*, 474
Pseudopodia, 328
PTFE (GORE-TEX™) vascular
    grafts, 224
Pyrolysis, 241
Pyrolytic carbon, 53
    coatings, 241

**Q**

Quanta, 74
Quantum mechanics, 16
Quantum numbers, 18
Quenching, 212

**R**

Radiation detector, 318
Radiation grafting, 242–243
Radiation sterilization, 229–230
Radiography, 495–496
Raman scattering, 74
Random copolymers, 69
Rapid manufacturing
    ceramics, 221–222
    metals, 218
    polymers, 226–228
Rapid prototyping, 218, 222
Real-time RT-PCR, 372, 382
Redox reactions, defined, 183
Reepithelialization, 415
Regulator of complement activation
    (RCA) proteins, 444–445
Renal dialysis, 6
Replacement heart valves, 3
Resolution, 424
Resolved shear stress, 149
Resonance, 89, 90
Resonance frequency, 89, 90
Resorption, 413, 424
Reverse-transcription polymerase
    chain reaction (RT-PCR),
    370–372
Reversed-phase chromatography, 310
Rhombohedral system, 39, 40, 100
Ribosomal RNA (rRNA), 332
Ribosomes, 334
RNA assays, 370–377
RNA polymerases, 352
RNA (ribonucleic acid)
    purpose of, 332
    structure of, 332–334
    types of, 332
Rolling, 215
    of neutrophils, 394
Rough ER, 334
Rough topography, 14

**S**

S-N curves, 171, 172
Salt bridge, 183
Sand casting, 216
Sandwich ELISA, 317, 318
Scanning electron microscopy
    (SEM), 272–276, 421–422
    basic principles, 272–275
    information provided by,
    275–276

instrumentation, 275
Scanning probe microscopy (SPM),
    276–280
    basic principles, 276–277
    information provided by,
    279–280
    instrumentation, 277–278
Schottky defect, 55, 101
Scratch tests, 369
Screw dislocations, 108–110
SDS polyacrylamide-gel
    electrophoresis
    (SDS-PAGE), 318
Secondary antibody, 317
Secondary bonds, 22, 29
Secondary creep, 157, 158
Secondary forces, 29
Secondary ion mass spectrometry
    (SIMS), 96, 270–272, 281
Secondary messengers, 347
Selectins, 336
Selective laser sintering (SLS), 218
Self-assembled monolayers (SAMs),
    243–244
Self-diffusion, 45
Self-interstitial, 43
Semi-crystalline polymers and
    elastomers, causes of
    plastic deformation in,
    152–155
Shear modulus, 140
Shear testing, 139
Shielded nucleus, 90
Side groups, 117
Sigma (σ) bonds, 25
Silly Putty®, 161
Silver-tin-copper alloys, 10
Single-cell analysis, 376
Single-walled nanotubes (SWNTs),
    54, 173
Sintering, 217
    selective laser sintering (SLS),
    218
Size-exclusion chromatography
    (SEC), 96–100
    basic principles, 96–97
    information provided by,
    99–100
    instrumentation, 97–99
Skin
    collagen accumulation in scar
    tissue, 415
    composition of, 414
    scar formation (remodeling), 415
Skin regeneration, 415–416
Skin repair, 414–415
Slip, 111, 148–149, 173
Slip plane, 111, 113, 148
Slip system, 111, 113
Small-angle grain boundary, 114
Smooth ER, 334
Sodium chloride structure, 50
Softening point, glass, 219
Solid freeform fabrication (SFF), 218
Solid solutions, 44–45
Solid-state polymerization, 72
Solute, 44
Solution coatings, 245
Solution polymerization, 70
Spectroscopy, 15, 74, 101

spectrum of energies employed
    in, 74
Spherulites, 120, 132
    composition of, 121
Spot desmosomes, 335
Spring, 162
Sputter deposition, 241
Stainless steel, 10
Standard conditions, 184
Standard hydrogen electrode, 184
Standard linear solid model, 165
Standard reduction potentials, 184
*Staphylococcus aureus*, 474, 480,
    497
*Staphylococcus epidermidis*, 474,
    483, 497
Start codon, 355
Steady state creep rate, 158
Steady-state diffusion, 47–48
Steam sterilization, 229
Stem cells, 350–351
Stereolithography, 227
Steric repulsion, 236
Sterility assurance level (SAL), 229
Sterilization, 228–230
    ethylene oxide, 229
    radiation, 229–230
    steam, 229
Strain hardening, 170, 211
Stress amplitude, 171
Stress, and galvanic corrosion, 192
Stress concentrators/stress raisers,
    169–170
Stress corrosion cracking, 192–193
Stress relaxation, 177
    and creep, 160–161
    experiments, 161
    molecular causes for, 161
Stress-strain curves, 176
    and elastic deformation,
    139–141
    and plastic deformation,
    141–148
    producing from bending data,
    156
Stress-strain diagram, 144
Subacute toxicity, 419
Subchronic toxicity, 419
Subshells, *See* Atomic subshells
    (orbitals)
Substitutional solution, 44
Substrate patterning, 254–258
Surface characterization
    atomic force microscopy (AFM),
    276–280
    basic principles, 276–277
    information provided by,
    279–280
    instrumentation, 277–278
    attenuated total internal
    reflectance-Fourier
    transform infrared
    spectroscopy (ATR-FTIR),
    268–270
    basic principles, 268–269
    information provided, 270
    instrumentation, 269–270
    of biomaterials, 258–280
    contact angle analysis, 259–262
    basic principles, 259–261

information provided, 262
    instrumentation, 261–262
    electron microscopy, 272–276
    electron spectroscopy for
    chemical analysis (ESCA),
    265–268
    basic principles, 265–266
    information provided, 268
    instrumentation, 266–267
    light microscopy, 262–265
    methods, summary of, 259
    scanning electron microscopy
    (SEM), 272–276
    basic principles, 272–275
    information provided by,
    275–276
    instrumentation, 275
    scanning probe microscopy
    (SPM), 276–280
    basic principles, 276–277
    information provided by,
    279–280
    instrumentation, 277–278
    secondary ion mass spectrometry
    (SIMS), 270–272, 281
    transmission electron microscopy
    (TEM), 272–276
    basic principles, 272–275
    information provided by,
    275–276
    instrumentation, 275
    X-ray photoelectron
    spectroscopy (XPS),
    265–268
    basic principles, 265–266
    information provided, 268
    instrumentation, 266–267
Surface charge, 235, 236, 290, 482
Surface chemistry, 234–237
Surface degradation, 203
Surface erosion, 203
Surface free energy, 113
Surface hydrophobicity, 290,
    481–482
Surface interactions, protein
    properties affecting, 291
    (table)
Surface modification techniques,
    physicochemical, 237–250
Surface-modifying additives (SMAs),
    247
Surface patterning, 254–258, 281
    categories, 254–255
    dip-pen nanolithography, 255
    direct-write photolithography,
    255
    e-beam lithography, 255
    ink-jet printing, 255–256
    ion beam lithography, 255
    microcontact printing, 256, 257
    microfluidics, 257–258
    photolithography, 256
    size of biological molecules/
    cells, 254
Surface properties
    affecting interactions with
    proteins, 292 (table)
    and degradation, 254
Surface roughness, 14
Surface tension, 113, 235

Surface treatments, 254
Suspension polymerization, 71
Symbols, 505–507
Syndiotactic configuration, 64, 65
Synthetic polymers, 11, 30

**T**

T cell receptors (TCRs), 429, 433
T cells, 437–440
    cytotoxic T cells ($T_c$), 440
    helper T cells ($T_h$), 438–440
    natural killer (NK) cells,
        437–438, 440
$T_{DTH}$ cells, 447
Telophase, 350
Tensile strength, 143
Tensile testing, 137–138
Termination, addition
        polymerization, 67–68
Tertiary creep, 158
Tetragonal system, 39, 40, 100
Thermal analysis, 128–132
    differential scanning calorimeter,
        components of, 128–130
    differential scanning calorimetry
        (DSC), 128–133
        basic principles, 128
        heat-flux, 128, 129
        information provided by,
            130–132
        instrumentation, 128–130
        power-compensated, 128,
            129
        types of, 129
    dynamic mechanical analysis
        (DMA), 128
    thermogravimetric analysis
        (TGA), 128
Thermal transitions, 122–128
    amorphous ceramics (glasses),
        123
    metals and crystalline ceramics,
        122
    polymers, 123–126
Thermoplastic polymers, 223
Thermoplasts *vs.* thermosets, 223
Thermosetting polymers, 223
Three-dimensional printing (3DP),
    221
Thrombin, 458, 459, 461, 462, 469
    actions of, 459 (table)
    combination of fibrinogen and,
        462fn1

Thrombomodulin, 464
Thrombomodulin–thrombin
    complex, 464
Thrombosis
    and biomaterials, 457–472
    defined, 457
    limiting clot formation, means
        of, 463–464
Thrombus, 462
Thymine, 330
Tight junctions, 335
Tilt boundary, 114, 115
TIM-barrel fold, 300
Time-dependent properties,
        157–165, 177
    creep, 157–159
Tissue factor (TF), 460–461
Tissue inhibitors of metalloproteinases
    (TIMPs), 346
Tissue plasminogen activator (TPA),
    464
Titanium alloys, 10
Torsion forces, 139
Totipotent stem cells, 350
Trans configuration, 65
Transcription, 352–353
Transcriptomics, 374
Transendothelial migration, 394
Transfer RNA (tRNA), 332, 353,
    355–357
Translation, 356
    process, 357
Transmembrane proteins, 325–326
Transmission electron microscopy
    (TEM), 272–276,
    421–422
    basic principles, 272–275
    information provided by,
        275–276
    instrumentation, 275
Triclinic system, 39, 40, 100
Triosephosphate isomerase (TIM),
    300
True stress and strain, 144–145
Tumor metastasis, 486
Tumorigenesis, 486–491
    biomaterial-related, 488–489
    chemical *vs.* foreign body
        carcinogenesis, 486–487
    defined, 486
    experiments, techniques for,
        489–491

    *in vitro* models, 489–490
    *in vivo* models, 491
    foreign body
        with large implants, 487
        with nanomaterials,
            487–488
        timeline for, 487–488
    stages of, 486, 488, 498
Tumors, 486
Twin boundary, 115
Twin, defined, 115
Twist boundary, 114

**U**

Ultimate tensile strength, 143
Ultra-high molecular weight
        poly(ethylene)
        (UHMWPE), 197, 230,
        411
Ultraviolet and visible (UV-VIS) light
        spectroscopy, 79
    basic principles, 79–81
    chromophores/characteristic
        UV-VIS absorption
        wavelengths, 80 (table)
    information provided by, 82–83
    instrumentation, 81–82
    UV-VIS spectrophotometer, 315
Ultraviolet visible absorption,
        emission, and fluorescence,
        74
Uncontrolled degradation, 181, 206
Unipotent stem cells, 350
Unit cell, 35
Uracil, 332

**V**

Vacancy, 43
Vacancy diffusion, 46
Vacuum ultraviolet absorption, 74
Valence electrons, 20
Van der Waals bonds, 29
Variable portion ($F_{ab}$), 435
Vasculogenesis, 409–410
Vasodilation, 393–394
Vesicles, 334–335
Viscous flow, 122, 132
Vitrification, 221
Voigt model, 163–165, 178
Voltmeter, 183
Volume defects, and crystallinity,
    116–117, 132
Vroman effect, 306

**W**

Wave-mechanical model, 17–18
Wavelength dispersive X-ray
        spectroscopy
        (WDS), 75
Weight percent composition, 45
Welding, 218–219
Western blotting, 309, 318–320, 377
Whole genome sequencing (WGS),
    373, 382
Working point, 123, 219
Wound healing, 424
    assessment method, 420–423
        biochemical assays, 422
        electron microscopy,
            421–422
        histology/
            immunohistochemistry,
            377–378, 421
        mechanical testing, 422–423
    biomaterials and, 408–426
    chronic inflammation, 412–413
    fibrous encapsulation, 411–412
    foreign body reaction, 410–411
    granular tissue, formation of,
        408–410
    *in vivo* assays for inflammatory
        response, 416–423
    resolution, types of, 413
    skin regeneration, 415–416
    skin repair, 414–415

**X**

X-ray diffraction, 75–79, 265, 495
    basic principles, 75–77
    information provided by, 79
    instrumentation, 77–79
X-ray fluorescence, 75, 265
X-ray photoelectron spectroscopy
        (XPS),
        265–268
    basic principles, 265–266
    information provided, 268
    instrumentation, 266–267

**Y**

Yield point strain, 143
Young's modulus, 139, 176

**Z**

Zigmond chamber, 369
"Zigzag" tubes, 54
Zone of inhibition assay, 483–484